List of Applications

BUSINESS AND ECONOMICS

(continued)

List of Applications (*continued*)

SOCIAL SCIENCES

LIFE SCIENCES

GENERAL INTEREST

Introduction to Probability

University of Maryland, College Park

10e

Soo T. Tan

CENGAGE
Learning·

Australia • Brazil • Japan • Korea • Mexico • Singapore • Spain • United Kingdom • United States

CENGAGE
Learning·

Introduction to Probability
University of Maryland, College Park
10e

Executive Editors:
 Maureen Staudt
 Michael Stranz

Senior Project Development Manager:
 Linda deStefano

Marketing Specialist:
 Courtney Sheldon

Senior Production/Manufacturing Manager:
 Donna M. Brown

Production Editorial Manager:
 Kim Frv

Sr. Rights Acquisition Account Manager:
 Todd Osborne

Finite Mathematics for the Managerial, Life, and Social Sciences,
Tenth Edition
Soo T. Tan

© 2012, 2009 Brooks/Cole, Cengage Learning. All rights reserved.

Library of Congress Control Number: 2010935414

For product information and technology assistance, contact us at
Cengage Learning Customer & Sales Support, 1-800-354-9706

For permission to use material from this text or product,
submit all requests online at **cengage.com/permissions**
Further permissions questions can be emailed to
permissionrequest@cengage.com

This book contains select works from existing Cengage Learning resources and
was produced by Cengage Learning Custom Solutions for collegiate use. As such,
those adopting and/or contributing to this work are responsible for editorial
content accuracy, continuity and completeness.

Compilation © 2012 Cengage Learning
ISBN-13: 978-1-285-10566-6

ISBN-10: 1-285-10566-4

Cengage Learning
5191 Natorp Boulevard
Mason, Ohio 45040
USA
Cengage Learning is a leading provider of customized learning solutions with
office locations around the globe, including Singapore, the United Kingdom,
Australia, Mexico, Brazil, and Japan. Locate your local office at:
international.cengage.com/region.

Cengage Learning products are represented in Canada by Nelson Education, Ltd.
For your lifelong learning solutions, visit **www.cengage.com/custom.**
Visit our corporate website at **www.cengage.com.**

Printed in the United States of America

Brief Contents

STUDY SKILLS FOR MATHEMATICS

"Make up your mind. First you tell me 3 plus 3
is six, and now you say 4 plus 2 is six!"

6

SETS AND COUNTING

WE OFTEN DEAL with well-defined collections of objects called *sets*. In this chapter, we see how sets can be combined algebraically to yield other sets. We also look at some techniques for determining the number of elements in a set and for determining the number of ways in which the elements of a set can be arranged or combined. These techniques enable us to solve many practical problems, as you will see throughout the chapter.

In how many ways can the Futurists (a rock group) plan their concert tour to San Francisco, Los Angeles, San Diego, Denver, and Las Vegas if the three performances in California must be given consecutively? In Example 13, page 353, we will show how to determine the number of possible different itineraries.

6.1   Sets and Set Operations

Set Terminology and Notation

We often deal with collections of different kinds of objects. For example, in conducting a study of the distribution of the weights of newborn infants, we might consider the collection of all infants born in Massachusetts General Hospital during 2011. In a study of the fuel consumption of compact cars, we might be interested in the collection of compact cars manufactured by General Motors in the 2011 model year. Such collections are examples of sets. More specifically, a **set** is a well-defined collection of objects. Thus, a set is not just any collection of objects; a set must be well defined in the sense that if we are given an object, then we should be able to determine whether or not it belongs to the collection.

The objects of a set are called the **elements,** or *members*, **of a set** and are usually denoted by lowercase letters $a, b, c, \ldots$; the sets themselves are usually denoted by uppercase letters $A, B, C, \ldots$. The elements of a set can be displayed by listing all the elements between braces. For example, in **roster notation**, the set A consisting of the first three letters of the English alphabet is written

$$A = \{a, b, c\}$$

The set B of all letters of the alphabet can be written

$$B = \{a, b, c, \ldots, z\}$$

Another notation that is commonly used is **set-builder notation.** Here, a rule is given that describes the definite property or properties an object x must satisfy to qualify for membership in the set. In this notation, the set B is written as

$$B = \{x \mid x \text{ is a letter of the English alphabet}\}$$

and is read "B is the set of all elements x such that x is a letter of the English alphabet."

If a is an element of a set A, we write $a \in A$ and read "a belongs to A" or "a is an element of A." If the element a does not belong to the set A, however, then we write $a \notin A$ and read "a does not belong to A." For example, if $A = \{1, 2, 3, 4, 5\}$, then $3 \in A$ but $6 \notin A$.

Explore & Discuss

1. Let A denote the collection of all the days in August 2011 in which the average daily temperature at the San Francisco International Airport was approximately 75°F. Is A a set? Explain your answer.

2. Let B denote the collection of all the days in August 2011 in which the average daily temperature at the San Francisco International Airport was between 73.5°F and 81.2°F, inclusive. Is B a set? Explain your answer.

Set Equality

Two sets A and B are **equal,** written $A = B$, if and only if they have exactly the same elements.

EXAMPLE 1 Let A, B, and C be the sets

$$A = \{a, e, i, o, u\}$$
$$B = \{a, i, o, e, u\}$$
$$C = \{a, e, i, o\}$$

Then $A = B$, since they both contain exactly the same elements. Note that the order in which the elements are displayed is immaterial. Also, $A \neq C$, since $u \in A$ but $u \notin C$. Similarly, we conclude that $B \neq C$.   ∎

> **Subset**
>
> If every element of a set A is also an element of a set B, then we say that A is a **subset** of B and write $A \subseteq B$.

By this definition, two sets A and B are equal if and only if (1) $A \subseteq B$, and (2) $B \subseteq A$. You can verify this (see Exercise 66).

EXAMPLE 2 Referring to Example 1, we find that $C \subseteq B$, since every element of C is also an element of B. Also, if D is the set

$$D = \{a, e, i, o, x\}$$

then D is not a subset of A, written $D \nsubseteq A$, since $x \in D$ but $x \notin A$. Observe that $A \nsubseteq D$ as well, since $u \in A$ but $u \notin D$.   ∎

If A and B are sets such that $A \subseteq B$ but $A \neq B$, then we say that A is a **proper subset** of B. In other words, a set A is a proper subset of a set B, written $A \subset B$, if (1) $A \subseteq B$ and (2) there exists at least one element in B that is not in A. The second condition states that the set A is properly "smaller" than the set B.

EXAMPLE 3 Let $A = \{1, 2, 3, 4, 5, 6\}$ and $B = \{2, 4, 6\}$. Then B is a proper subset of A because (1) $B \subseteq A$, which is easily verified, and (2) there exists at least one element in A that is not in B—for example, the element 1.   ∎

 When we refer to sets and subsets, we use the symbols $\subset$, $\subseteq$, $\supset$, and $\supseteq$ to express the idea of "containment." However, when we wish to show that an element is contained in a set, we use the symbol $\in$ to express the idea of "membership." Thus, in Example 3, we would write $1 \in A$ and *not* $\{1\} \in A$.

> **Empty Set**
>
> The set that contains no elements is called the **empty set** and is denoted by $\varnothing$.

The empty set, $\varnothing$, is a subset of every set. To see this, observe that $\varnothing$ has no elements and therefore contains no element that is not also in any set A.

[VIDEO] **EXAMPLE 4** List all subsets of the set $A = \{a, b, c\}$.

Solution There is one subset consisting of no elements, namely, the empty set $\varnothing$. Next, observe that there are three subsets consisting of one element,

$$\{a\}, \{b\}, \{c\}$$

three subsets consisting of two elements,

$$\{a, b\}, \{a, c\}, \{b, c\}$$

and one subset consisting of three elements, the set A itself. Therefore, the subsets of A are

$$\varnothing, \{a\}, \{b\}, \{c\}, \{a, b\}, \{a, c\}, \{b, c\}, \{a, b, c\}$$ ∎

In contrast with the empty set, we have, at the other extreme, the notion of a largest, or universal, set. A **universal set** is the set of all elements of interest in a particular discussion. It is the largest in the sense that all sets considered in the discussion of the problem are subsets of the universal set. Of course, different universal sets are associated with different problems, as shown in Example 5.

EXAMPLE 5

a. If the problem at hand is to determine the ratio of female to male students in a college, then a logical choice of a universal set is the set consisting of the whole student body of the college.

b. If the problem is to determine the ratio of female to male students in the business department of the college in part (a), then the set of all students in the business department can be chosen as the universal set. ■

A visual representation of sets is realized through the use of **Venn diagrams,** which are of considerable help in understanding the concepts introduced earlier as well as in solving problems involving sets. The universal set U is represented by a rectangle, and subsets of U are represented by regions lying inside the rectangle.

EXAMPLE 6 Use Venn diagrams to illustrate the following statements:

a. The sets A and B are equal.
b. The set A is a proper subset of the set B.
c. The sets A and B are not subsets of each other.

Solution   The respective Venn diagrams are shown in Figure 1a–c.

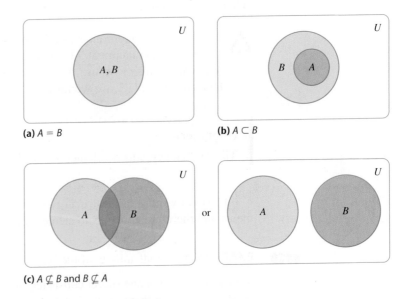

(a) $A = B$

(b) $A \subset B$

(c) $A \nsubseteq B$ and $B \nsubseteq A$

FIGURE **1**

Set Operations

Having introduced the concept of a set, our next task is to consider operations on sets—that is, to consider ways in which sets can be combined to yield other sets. These operations enable us to combine sets in much the same way that the operations of addition and multiplication enable us to combine numbers to obtain other numbers. In what follows, all sets are assumed to be subsets of a given universal set U.

> ### Set Union
>
> Let A and B be sets. The **union** of A and B, written $A \cup B$, is the set of all elements that belong to either A or B or both.
>
> $$A \cup B = \{x \mid x \in A \text{ or } x \in B \text{ or both}\}$$

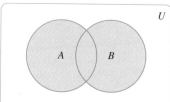

FIGURE 2
Set union $A \cup B$

The shaded portion of the Venn diagram (Figure 2) depicts the set $A \cup B$.

EXAMPLE 7 If $A = \{a, b, c\}$ and $B = \{a, c, d\}$, then $A \cup B = \{a, b, c, d\}$. ■

> ### Set Intersection
>
> Let A and B be sets. The set of elements common to the sets A and B, written $A \cap B$, is called the **intersection** of A and B.
>
> $$A \cap B = \{x \mid x \in A \text{ and } x \in B\}$$

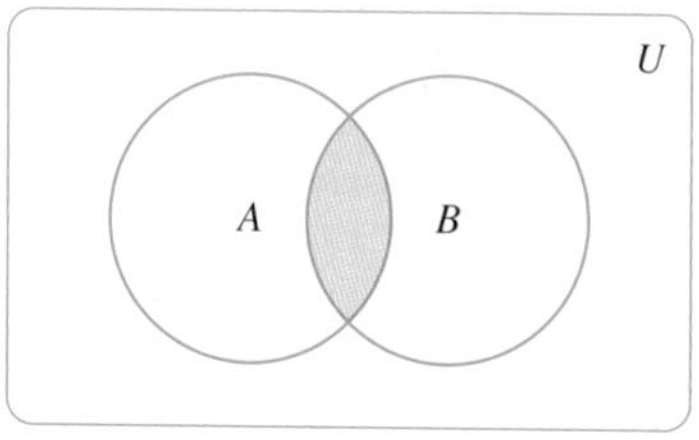

FIGURE 3
Set intersection $A \cap B$

The shaded portion of the Venn diagram (Figure 3) depicts the set $A \cap B$.

EXAMPLE 8 Let $A = \{a, b, c\}$, and let $B = \{a, c, d\}$. Then $A \cap B = \{a, c\}$. (Compare this result with Example 7.) ■

EXAMPLE 9 Let $A = \{1, 3, 5, 7, 9\}$, and let $B = \{2, 4, 6, 8, 10\}$. Then $A \cap B = \varnothing$. ■

The two sets of Example 9 have empty, or null, intersection. In general, the sets A and B are said to be **disjoint** if they have no elements in common—that is, if $A \cap B = \varnothing$.

EXAMPLE 10 Let U be the set of all students in the classroom. If $M = \{x \in U \mid x \text{ is male}\}$ and $F = \{x \in U \mid x \text{ is female}\}$, then $F \cap M = \varnothing$, so F and M are disjoint. ■

> ### Complement of a Set
>
> If U is a universal set and A is a subset of U, then the set of all elements in U that are not in A is called the **complement** of A and is denoted A^c.
>
> $$A^c = \{x \mid x \in U \text{ and } x \notin A\}$$

The shaded portion of the Venn diagram (Figure 4) shows the set A^c.

EXAMPLE 11 Let $U = \{1, 2, 3, 4, 5, 6, 7, 8, 9, 10\}$, and let $A = \{2, 4, 6, 8, 10\}$. Then $A^c = \{1, 3, 5, 7, 9\}$. ■

FIGURE 4
Set complementation

Explore & Discuss

Let A, B, and C be nonempty subsets of a set U.

1. Suppose $A \cap B \neq \varnothing$, $A \cap C \neq \varnothing$, and $B \cap C \neq \varnothing$. Can you conclude that $A \cap B \cap C \neq \varnothing$? Explain your answer with an example.

2. Suppose $A \cap B \cap C \neq \varnothing$. Can you conclude that $A \cap B \neq \varnothing$, $A \cap C \neq \varnothing$, and $B \cap C \neq \varnothing$? Explain your answer.

The following rules hold for the operation of **complementation.** See whether you can verify them.

Set Complementation

If U is a universal set and A is a subset of U, then

a. $U^c = \emptyset$ **b.** $\emptyset^c = U$ **c.** $(A^c)^c = A$

d. $A \cup A^c = U$ **e.** $A \cap A^c = \emptyset$

The operations on sets satisfy the following properties.

Properties of Set Operations

Let U be a universal set. If A, B, and C are arbitrary subsets of U, then

$$A \cup B = B \cup A \qquad \text{Commutative law for union}$$

$$A \cap B = B \cap A \qquad \text{Commutative law for intersection}$$

$$A \cup (B \cup C) = (A \cup B) \cup C \qquad \text{Associative law for union}$$

$$A \cap (B \cap C) = (A \cap B) \cap C \qquad \text{Associative law for intersection}$$

$$A \cup (B \cap C)$$
$$= (A \cup B) \cap (A \cup C) \qquad \text{Distributive law for union}$$

$$A \cap (B \cup C)$$
$$= (A \cap B) \cup (A \cap C) \qquad \text{Distributive law for intersection}$$

Two additional properties, referred to as De Morgan's Laws, hold for the operations on sets.

De Morgan's Laws

Let A and B be sets. Then

$$(A \cup B)^c = A^c \cap B^c \qquad \textbf{(1)}$$

$$(A \cap B)^c = A^c \cup B^c \qquad \textbf{(2)}$$

Equation (1) states that the complement of the union of two sets is equal to the intersection of their complements. Equation (2) states that the complement of the intersection of two sets is equal to the union of their complements.

We will not prove De Morgan's Laws here, but we will demonstrate the validity of Equation (2) in the following example.

EXAMPLE 12 Using Venn diagrams, show that

$$(A \cap B)^c = A^c \cup B^c$$

Solution $(A \cap B)^c$ is the set of elements in U but not in $A \cap B$ and is therefore the shaded region shown in Figure 5. Next, A^c and B^c are shown in Figure 6a–b. Their union, $A^c \cup B^c$, is easily seen to be equal to $(A \cap B)^c$ by referring once again to Figure 5.

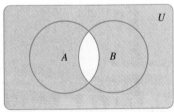

FIGURE 5
$(A \cap B)^c$

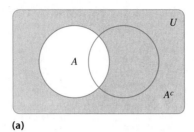 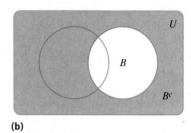

FIGURE **6**
$A^c \cup B^c$ is the set obtained by joining (a)
and (b).

(a)   **(b)**

EXAMPLE 13 Let $U = \{1, 2, 3, 4, 5, 6, 7, 8, 9, 10\}$, $A = \{1, 2, 4, 8, 9\}$, and $B = \{3, 4, 5, 6, 8\}$. Verify by direct computation that $(A \cup B)^c = A^c \cap B^c$.

Solution $A \cup B = \{1, 2, 3, 4, 5, 6, 8, 9\}$, so $(A \cup B)^c = \{7, 10\}$. Moreover, $A^c = \{3, 5, 6, 7, 10\}$ and $B^c = \{1, 2, 7, 9, 10\}$, so $A^c \cap B^c = \{7, 10\}$. The required result follows.

APPLIED EXAMPLE 14 Automobile Options Let U denote the set of all cars in a dealer's lot, and let

$$A = \{x \in U \,|\, x \text{ is equipped with Sirius XM Radio}\}$$
$$B = \{x \in U \,|\, x \text{ is equipped with a moonroof}\}$$
$$C = \{x \in U \,|\, x \text{ is equipped with side air bags}\}$$

Find an expression in terms of A, B, and C for each of the following sets:

a. The set of cars with at least one of the given options
b. The set of cars with exactly one of the given options
c. The set of cars with Sirius XM Radio and side air bags but no moonroof.

Solution

a. The set of cars with at least one of the given options is $A \cup B \cup C$ (Figure 7a).
b. The set of cars with Sirius XM Radio only is given by $A \cap B^c \cap C^c$. Similarly, we find that the set of cars with a moonroof only is given by $B \cap C^c \cap A^c$, while the set of cars with side air bags only is given by $C \cap A^c \cap B^c$. Thus, the set of cars with exactly one of the given options is $(A \cap B^c \cap C^c) \cup (B \cap C^c \cap A^c) \cup (C \cap A^c \cap B^c)$ (Figure 7b).
c. The set of cars with Sirius XM Radio and side air bags but no moonroof is given by $A \cap C \cap B^c$ (Figure 7c).

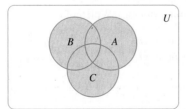 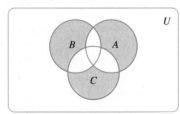 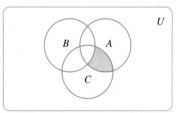

(a) The set of cars with at least one option

(b) The set of cars with exactly one option

(c) The set of cars with Sirius XM Radio and side air bags but no moonroof

FIGURE **7**

6.1 Self-Check Exercises

1. Let $U = \{1, 2, 3, 4, 5, 6, 7\}$, $A = \{1, 2, 3\}$, $B = \{3, 4, 5, 6\}$, and $C = \{2, 3, 4\}$. Find the following sets:
   a. A^c **b.** $A \cup B$ **c.** $B \cap C$
   d. $(A \cup B) \cap C$ **e.** $(A \cap B) \cup C$ **f.** $A^c \cap (B \cup C)^c$

2. Let U denote the set of all members of the House of Representatives. Let

$$D = \{x \in U \mid x \text{ is a Democrat}\}$$
$$R = \{x \in U \mid x \text{ is a Republican}\}$$

$$F = \{x \in U \mid x \text{ is a female}\}$$
$$L = \{x \in U \mid x \text{ is a lawyer by training}\}$$

Describe each of the following sets in words.
   a. $D \cap F$ **b.** $F^c \cap R$ **c.** $D \cap F \cap L^c$

Solutions to Self-Check Exercises 6.1 can be found on page 333.

6.1 Concept Questions

1. **a.** What is a set? Give an example.
   b. When are two sets equal? Give an example of two equal sets.
   c. What is the empty set?

2. What can you say about two sets A and B such that
   a. $A \cup B \subseteq A$ **b.** $A \cup B = \varnothing$
   c. $A \cap B = B$ **d.** $A \cap B = \varnothing$

3. **a.** If $A \subset B$, what can you say about the relationship between A^c and B^c?
   b. If $A^c = \varnothing$, what can you say about A?

6.1 Exercises

In Exercises 1–4, write the set in set-builder notation.

1. The set of gold medalists in the 2010 Winter Olympic Games

2. The set of football teams in the NFL

3. $\{3, 4, 5, 6, 7\}$

4. $\{1, 3, 5, 7, 9, 11, \ldots, 39\}$

In Exercises 5–8, list the elements of the set in roster notation.

5. $\{x \mid x \text{ is a digit in the number } 352{,}646\}$

6. $\{x \mid x \text{ is a letter in the word } HIPPOPOTAMUS\}$

7. $\{x \mid 2 - x = 4 \text{ and } x \text{ is an integer}\}$

8. $\{x \mid 2 - x = 4 \text{ and } x \text{ is a fraction}\}$

In Exercises 9–14, state whether the statements are true or false.

9. **a.** $\{a, b, c\} = \{c, a, b\}$ **b.** $A \in A$

10. **a.** $\varnothing \in A$ **b.** $A \subset A$

11. **a.** $0 \in \varnothing$ **b.** $0 = \varnothing$

12. **a.** $\{\varnothing\} = \varnothing$ **b.** $\{a, b\} \in \{a, b, c\}$

13. $\{$Chevrolet, Cadillac, Buick$\} \subset \{x \mid x \text{ is a division of General Motors}\}$

14. $\{x \mid x \text{ is a silver medalist in the 2010 Winter Olympic Games}\} = \varnothing$

In Exercises 15 and 16, let $A = \{1, 2, 3, 4, 5\}$. Determine whether the statements are true or false.

15. **a.** $2 \in A$ **b.** $A \subseteq \{2, 4, 6\}$

16. **a.** $0 \in A$ **b.** $\{1, 3, 5\} \in A$

17. Let $A = \{1, 2, 3\}$. Which of the following sets are equal to A?
    a. $\{2, 1, 3\}$ **b.** $\{3, 2, 1\}$
    c. $\{0, 1, 2, 3\}$

18. Let $A = \{a, e, l, t, r\}$. Which of the following sets are equal to A?
    a. $\{x \mid x \text{ is a letter of the word } later\}$
    b. $\{x \mid x \text{ is a letter of the word } latter\}$
    c. $\{x \mid x \text{ is a letter of the word } relate\}$

19. List all subsets of the following sets:
    a. $\{1, 2\}$ **b.** $\{1, 2, 3\}$ **c.** $\{1, 2, 3, 4\}$

20. List all subsets of the set $A = \{$IBM, U.S. Steel, Union Carbide, Boeing$\}$. Which of these are proper subsets of A?

In Exercises 21–24, find the smallest possible set (i.e., the set with the least number of elements) that contains the given sets as subsets.

21. $\{1, 2\}, \{1, 3, 4\}, \{4, 6, 8, 10\}$

22. $\{1, 2, 4\}, \{a, b\}$

23. $\{$Jill, John, Jack$\}, \{$Susan, Sharon$\}$

24. $\{$GM, Ford, Chrysler$\}, \{$Daimler-Benz, Volkswagen$\}, \{$Toyota, Nissan$\}$

25. Use Venn diagrams to represent the following relationships:
   a. $A \subset B$ and $B \subset C$
   b. $A \subset U$ and $B \subset U$, where A and B have no elements in common
   c. The sets A, B, and C are equal.

26. Let U denote the set of all students who applied for admission to the freshman class at Faber College for the upcoming academic year, and let

$$A = \{x \in U \mid x \text{ is a successful applicant}\}$$
$$B = \{x \in U \mid x \text{ is a female student who enrolled in the freshman class}\}$$
$$C = \{x \in U \mid x \text{ is a male student who enrolled in the freshman class}\}$$

   a. Use Venn diagrams to represent the sets U, A, B, and C.
   b. Determine whether the following statements are true or false.
   i. $A \subseteq B$ **ii.** $B \subset A$ **iii.** $C \subset B$

In Exercises 27 and 28, shade the portion of the accompanying figure that represents each set.

27. a. $A \cap B^c$
   b. $A^c \cap B$

28. a. $A^c \cap B^c$
   b. $(A \cup B)^c$

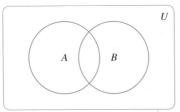

In Exercises 29–32, shade the portion of the accompanying figure that represents each set.

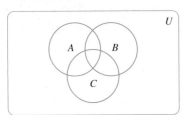

29. a. $A \cup B \cup C$ **b.** $A \cap B \cap C$

30. a. $A \cap B \cap C^c$ **b.** $A^c \cap B \cap C$

31. a. $A^c \cap B^c \cap C^c$ **b.** $(A \cup B)^c \cap C$

32. a. $A \cup (B \cap C)^c$ **b.** $(A \cup B \cup C)^c$

In Exercises 33–36, let $U = \{1, 2, 3, 4, 5, 6, 7, 8, 9, 10\}$, $A = \{1, 3, 5, 7, 9\}$, $B = \{2, 4, 6, 8, 10\}$, and $C = \{1, 2, 4, 5, 8, 9\}$. List the elements of each set.

33. a. A^c **b.** $B \cup C$ **c.** $C \cup C^c$

34. a. $C \cap C^c$ **b.** $(A \cap C)^c$ **c.** $A \cup (B \cap C)$

35. a. $(A \cap B) \cup C$ **b.** $(A \cup B \cup C)^c$
    c. $(A \cap B \cap C)^c$

36. a. $A^c \cap (B \cap C^c)$ **b.** $(A \cup B^c) \cup (B \cap C^c)$
    c. $(A \cup B)^c \cap C^c$

In Exercises 37 and 38, determine whether the pairs of sets are disjoint.

37. a. $\{1, 2, 3, 4\}, \{4, 5, 6, 7\}$
    b. $\{a, c, e, g\}, \{b, d, f\}$

38. a. $\varnothing, \{1, 3, 5\}$
    b. $\{0, 1, 3, 4\}, \{0, 2, 5, 7\}$

In Exercises 39–42, let U denote the set of all employees at Universal Life Insurance Company, and let

$$T = \{x \in U \mid x \text{ drinks tea}\}$$
$$C = \{x \in U \mid x \text{ drinks coffee}\}$$

Describe each set in words.

39. a. T^c **b.** C^c

40. a. $T \cup C$ **b.** $T \cap C$

41. a. $T \cap C^c$ **b.** $T^c \cap C$

42. a. $T^c \cap C^c$ **b.** $(T \cup C)^c$

In Exercises 43–46, let U denote the set of all employees in a hospital. Let

$$N = \{x \in U \mid x \text{ is a nurse}\}$$
$$D = \{x \in U \mid x \text{ is a doctor}\}$$
$$A = \{x \in U \mid x \text{ is an administrator}\}$$
$$M = \{x \in U \mid x \text{ is a male}\}$$
$$F = \{x \in U \mid x \text{ is a female}\}$$

Describe each set in words.

43. a. D^c **b.** N^c

44. a. $N \cup D$ **b.** $N \cap M$

45. a. $D \cap M^c$ **b.** $D \cap A$

46. a. $N \cap F$ **b.** $(D \cup N)^c$

In Exercises 47 and 48, let U denote the set of all senators in Congress and let

$$D = \{x \in U \mid x \text{ is a Democrat}\}$$
$$R = \{x \in U \mid x \text{ is a Republican}\}$$
$$F = \{x \in U \mid x \text{ is a female}\}$$
$$L = \{x \in U \mid x \text{ is a lawyer}\}$$

Write the set that represents each statement.

47. a. The set of all Democrats who are female
    b. The set of all Republicans who are male and are not lawyers

48. a. The set of all Democrats who are female or are lawyers
    b. The set of all senators who are not Democrats or are lawyers

In Exercises 49 and 50, let U denote the set of all students in the business college of a certain university. Let

$A = \{x \in U \mid x$ had taken a course in accounting$\}$

$B = \{x \in U \mid x$ had taken a course in economics$\}$

$C = \{x \in U \mid x$ had taken a course in marketing$\}$

Write the set that represents each statement.

49. a. The set of students who have not had a course in economics
b. The set of students who have had courses in accounting and economics
c. The set of students who have had courses in accounting and economics but not marketing

50. a. The set of students who have had courses in economics but not courses in accounting or marketing
b. The set of students who have had at least one of the three courses
c. The set of students who have had all three courses

In Exercises 51 and 52, refer to the following diagram, where U is the set of all tourists surveyed over a 1-week period in London and where

$A = \{x \in U \mid x$ has taken the underground [subway]$\}$

$B = \{x \in U \mid x$ has taken a cab$\}$

$C = \{x \in U \mid x$ has taken a bus$\}$

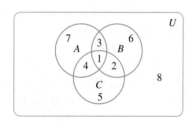

Express the indicated regions in set notation and in words.

51. a. Region 1
b. Regions 1 and 4 together
c. Regions 4, 5, 7, and 8 together

52. a. Region 3
b. Regions 4 and 6 together
c. Regions 5, 6, and 7 together

In Exercises 53–58, use Venn diagrams to illustrate each statement.

53. $A \subseteq A \cup B$; $B \subseteq A \cup B$ **54.** $A \cap B \subseteq A$; $A \cap B \subseteq B$

55. $A \cup (B \cup C) = (A \cup B) \cup C$

56. $A \cap (B \cap C) = (A \cap B) \cap C$

57. $A \cap (B \cup C) = (A \cap B) \cup (A \cap C)$

58. $(A \cup B)^c = A^c \cap B^c$

In Exercises 59 and 60, let

$$U = \{1, 2, 3, 4, 5, 6, 7, 8, 9, 10\}$$
$$A = \{1, 3, 5, 7, 9\}$$
$$B = \{1, 2, 4, 7, 8\}$$
$$C = \{2, 4, 6, 8\}$$

Verify each equation by direct computation.

59. a. $A \cup (B \cup C) = (A \cup B) \cup C$
b. $A \cap (B \cap C) = (A \cap B) \cap C$

60. a. $A \cap (B \cup C) = (A \cap B) \cup (A \cap C)$
b. $(A \cup B)^c = A^c \cap B^c$

In Exercises 61–64, refer to the accompanying figure, and list the points that belong to each set.

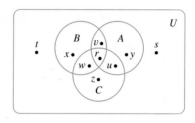

61. a. $A \cup B$ **b.** $A \cap B$

62. a. $A \cap (B \cup C)$ **b.** $(B \cap C)^c$

63. a. $(B \cup C)^c$ **b.** A^c

64. a. $(A \cap B) \cap C^c$ **b.** $(A \cup B \cup C)^c$

65. Suppose $A \subset B$ and $B \subset C$, where A and B are any two sets. What conclusion can be drawn regarding the sets A and C?

66. Verify the assertion that two sets A and B are equal if and only if (1) $A \subseteq B$ and (2) $B \subseteq A$.

In Exercises 67–76, determine whether the statement is true or false. If it is true, explain why it is true. If it is false, give an example to show why it is false.

67. A set is never a subset of itself.

68. A proper subset of a set is itself a subset of the set but not necessarily vice versa.

69. If $A \cup B = \varnothing$, then $A = \varnothing$ and $B = \varnothing$.

70. If $A \cap B = \varnothing$, then either $A = \varnothing$ or $B = \varnothing$.

71. $(A \cup A^c)^c = \varnothing$

72. If $A \subseteq B$, then $A \cap B = A$.

73. If $A \subseteq B$, then $A \cup B = B$.

74. If $A \cup B = A$, then $A \subseteq B$.

75. If $A \subset B$, then $A^c \supset B^c$.

76. $A \cap \varnothing = \varnothing$

Solutions to Self-Check Exercises

1. a. A^c is the set of all elements in U but not in A. Therefore,

$$A^c = \{4, 5, 6, 7\}$$

b. $A \cup B$ consists of all elements in A and/or B. Hence,

$$A \cup B = \{1, 2, 3, 4, 5, 6\}$$

c. $B \cap C$ is the set of all elements in both B and C. Therefore,

$$B \cap C = \{3, 4\}$$

d. Using the result from part (b), we find

$$(A \cup B) \cap C = \{1, 2, 3, 4, 5, 6\} \cap \{2, 3, 4\}$$
$$= \{2, 3, 4\}$$

e. First, we compute

$$A \cap B = \{3\}$$

Next, since $(A \cap B) \cup C$ is the set of all elements in $(A \cap B)$ and/or C, we conclude that

$$(A \cap B) \cup C = \{3\} \cup \{2, 3, 4\}$$
$$= \{2, 3, 4\}$$

f. From part (a), we have $A^c = \{4, 5, 6, 7\}$. Next, we compute

$$B \cup C = \{3, 4, 5, 6\} \cup \{2, 3, 4\}$$
$$= \{2, 3, 4, 5, 6\}$$

from which we deduce that

$$(B \cup C)^c = \{1, 7\} \quad \text{The set of elements in } U \text{ but not in } B \cup C$$

Finally, using these results, we obtain

$$A^c \cap (B \cup C)^c = \{4, 5, 6, 7\} \cap \{1, 7\} = \{7\}$$

2. a. $D \cap F$ denotes the set of all elements in both D and F. Since an element in D is a Democrat and an element in F is a female representative, we see that $D \cap F$ is the set of all female Democrats in the House of Representatives.

b. Since F^c is the set of male representatives and R is the set of Republicans, it follows that $F^c \cap R$ is the set of male Republicans in the House of Representatives.

c. L^c is the set of representatives who are not lawyers by training. Therefore, $D \cap F \cap L^c$ is the set of female Democratic representatives who are not lawyers by training.

The Number of Elements in a Finite Set

Counting the Elements in a Set

The solution to some problems in mathematics calls for finding the number of elements in a set. Such problems are called **counting problems** and constitute a field of study known as **combinatorics.** Our study of combinatorics is restricted to the results that will be required for our work in probability later on.

The number of elements in a finite set is determined by simply counting the elements in the set. If A is a set, then $n(A)$ denotes the number of elements in A. For example, if

$$A = \{1, 2, 3, \ldots, 20\} \qquad B = \{a, b\} \qquad C = \{8\}$$

then $n(A) = 20$, $n(B) = 2$, and $n(C) = 1$.

The empty set has no elements in it, so $n(\varnothing) = 0$. Another result that is easily seen to be true is the following: If A and B are disjoint sets, then

$$n(A \cup B) = n(A) + n(B) \tag{3}$$

EXAMPLE 1 If $A = \{a, c, d\}$ and $B = \{b, e, f, g\}$, then $n(A) = 3$ and $n(B) = 4$, so $n(A) + n(B) = 7$. Moreover, $A \cup B = \{a, b, c, d, e, f, g\}$ and $n(A \cup B) = 7$. Thus, Equation (3) holds true in this case. Note that $A \cap B = \varnothing$. ∎

In the general case, A and B need not be disjoint, which leads us to the formula

$$n(A \cup B) = n(A) + n(B) - n(A \cap B) \tag{4}$$

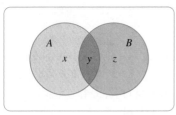

FIGURE 8
$n(A \cup B) = x + y + z$

To see this, we observe that the set $A \cup B$ may be viewed as the union of three mutually disjoint sets with x, y, and z elements, respectively (Figure 8). This figure shows that

$$n(A \cup B) = x + y + z$$

Also,

$$n(A) = x + y \quad \text{and} \quad n(B) = y + z$$

so

$$
\begin{aligned}
n(A) + n(B) &= (x + y) + (y + z) \\
&= (x + y + z) + y \\
&= n(A \cup B) + n(A \cap B) \qquad {\scriptstyle n(A \cap B) = y}
\end{aligned}
$$

Solving for $n(A \cup B)$, we obtain

$$n(A \cup B) = n(A) + n(B) - n(A \cap B)$$

which is the desired result.

EXAMPLE 2 Let $A = \{a, b, c, d, e\}$, and let $B = \{b, d, f, h\}$. Verify Equation (4) directly.

Solution

$$
\begin{aligned}
A \cup B &= \{a, b, c, d, e, f, h\} \quad \text{so} \quad n(A \cup B) = 7 \\
A \cap B &= \{b, d\} \quad \text{so} \quad n(A \cap B) = 2
\end{aligned}
$$

Furthermore,

$$n(A) = 5 \quad \text{and} \quad n(B) = 4$$

so

$$n(A) + n(B) - n(A \cap B) = 5 + 4 - 2 = 7 = n(A \cup B)$$

∎

VIDEO   **APPLIED EXAMPLE 3** Consumer Surveys In a survey of 100 coffee drinkers, it was found that 70 take sugar, 60 take cream, and 50 take both sugar and cream with their coffee. How many coffee drinkers take sugar or cream with their coffee?

Solution Let U denote the set of 100 coffee drinkers surveyed, and let

$$
\begin{aligned}
A &= \{x \in U \mid x \text{ takes sugar}\} \\
B &= \{x \in U \mid x \text{ takes cream}\}
\end{aligned}
$$

Then $n(A) = 70$, $n(B) = 60$, and $n(A \cap B) = 50$. The set of coffee drinkers who take sugar or cream with their coffee is given by $A \cup B$. Using Equation (4), we find

$$
\begin{aligned}
n(A \cup B) &= n(A) + n(B) - n(A \cap B) \\
&= 70 + 60 - 50 = 80
\end{aligned}
$$

Thus, 80 out of the 100 coffee drinkers surveyed take cream or sugar with their coffee.

∎

Explore & Discuss

Prove Equation (5), using an argument similar to that used to prove Equation (4). Another proof is outlined in Exercise 45 on page 339.

An equation similar to Equation (4) can be derived for the case that involves any finite number of finite sets. For example, a relationship involving the number of elements in the sets A, B, and C is given by

$$
\begin{aligned}
n(A \cup B \cup C) = {}& n(A) + n(B) + n(C) - n(A \cap B) \\
& - n(A \cap C) - n(B \cap C) + n(A \cap B \cap C)
\end{aligned}
\tag{5}
$$

As useful as equations such as Equation (5) are, in practice it is often easier to attack a problem directly with the aid of Venn diagrams, as shown by the following example.

APPLIED EXAMPLE 4 Marketing Surveys A leading cosmetics manufacturer advertises its products in three magazines: *Allure, Cosmopolitan*, and the *Ladies Home Journal*. A survey of 500 customers by the manufacturer reveals the following information:

180 learned of its products from *Allure*.

200 learned of its products from *Cosmopolitan*.

192 learned of its products from the *Ladies Home Journal*.

84 learned of its products from *Allure* and *Cosmopolitan*.

52 learned of its products from *Allure* and the *Ladies Home Journal*.

64 learned of its products from *Cosmopolitan* and the *Ladies Home Journal*.

38 learned of its products from all three magazines.

How many of the customers saw the manufacturer's advertisement in
a. At least one magazine?
b. Exactly one magazine?

Solution Let U denote the set of all customers surveyed, and let

$$A = \{x \in U \,|\, x \text{ learned of the products from } \textit{Allure}\}$$
$$C = \{x \in U \,|\, x \text{ learned of the products from } \textit{Cosmopolitan}\}$$
$$L = \{x \in U \,|\, x \text{ learned of the products from the } \textit{Ladies Home Journal}\}$$

The result that 38 customers learned of the products from all three magazines translates into $n(A \cap C \cap L) = 38$ (Figure 9a). Next, the result that 64 learned of the products from *Cosmopolitan* and the *Ladies Home Journal* translates into $n(C \cap L) = 64$. This leaves

$$64 - 38 = 26$$

who learned of the products from only *Cosmopolitan* and the *Ladies Home Journal* (Figure 9b). Similarly, $n(A \cap L) = 52$, so

$$52 - 38 = 14$$

learned of the products from only *Allure* and the *Ladies Home Journal*, and $n(A \cap C) = 84$, so

$$84 - 38 = 46$$

learned of the products from only *Allure* and *Cosmopolitan*. These numbers appear in the appropriate regions in Figure 9b.

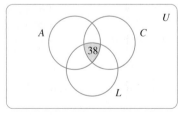

(a) All three magazines

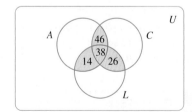

(b) Two or more magazines

FIGURE 9

Continuing, we have $n(L) = 192$, so the number who learned of the products from the *Ladies Home Journal* only is given by

$$192 - 14 - 38 - 26 = 114$$

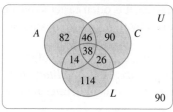

FIGURE 10
The completed Venn diagram

(Figure 10). Similarly, $n(C) = 200$, so

$$200 - 46 - 38 - 26 = 90$$

learned of the products from only *Cosmopolitan*, and $n(A) = 180$, so

$$180 - 14 - 38 - 46 = 82$$

learned of the products from only *Allure*. Finally,

$$500 - (90 + 26 + 114 + 14 + 82 + 46 + 38) = 90$$

learned of the products from other sources.

We are now in a position to answer questions (a) and (b).

a. Referring to Figure 10, we see that the number of customers who learned of the products from at least one magazine is given by

$$n(A \cup C \cup L) = 500 - 90 = 410$$

b. The number of customers who learned of the products from exactly one magazine (Figure 11) is given by

$$n(L \cap A^c \cap C^c) + n(C \cap A^c \cap L^c) + n(A \cap L^c \cap C^c) = 114 + 90 + 82 = 286$$

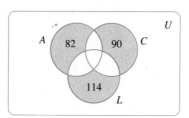

FIGURE 11
Exactly one magazine

6.2 Self-Check Exercises

1. Let A and B be subsets of a universal set U, and suppose that $n(U) = 100$, $n(A) = 60$, $n(B) = 40$, and $n(A \cap B) = 20$. Compute:
   a. $n(A \cup B)$ **b.** $n(A \cap B^c)$ **c.** $n(A^c \cap B)$

2. In a survey of 1000 readers of *Video Magazine*, it was found that 166 own at least one HD player in the HD-DVD format, 161 own at least one HD player in the Blu-ray format, and 22 own HD players in both formats. How many of the readers surveyed own HD players in the HD-DVD format only? How many of the readers surveyed do not own an HD-player in either format?

Solutions to Self-Check Exercises 6.2 can be found on page 339.

6.2 Concept Questions

1. **a.** If A and B are sets with $A \cap B = \emptyset$, what can you say about $n(A) + n(B)$? Explain.
   b. If A and B are sets satisfying $n(A \cup B) \neq n(A) + n(B)$, what can you say about $A \cap B$? Explain.

2. Let A and B be subsets of U, the universal set, and suppose that $A \cap B = \emptyset$. Is it true that $n(A) - n(B) = n(B^c) - n(A^c)$? Explain.

6.2 Exercises

In Exercises 1 and 2, verify the equation

$$n(A \cup B) = n(A) + n(B)$$

for the given disjoint sets.

1. $A = \{a, e, i, o, u\}$ and $B = \{g, h, k, l, m\}$

2. $A = \{x \mid x \text{ is a whole number between } 0 \text{ and } 4\}$
   $B = \{x \mid x \text{ is a negative integer greater than } -4\}$

3. Let $A = \{2, 4, 6, 8\}$ and $B = \{6, 7, 8, 9, 10\}$. Compute:
   a. $n(A)$ **b.** $n(B)$
   c. $n(A \cup B)$ **d.** $n(A \cap B)$

4. Let $U = \{1, 2, 3, 4, 5, 6, 7, a, b, c, d, e\}$. If $A = \{1, 2, a, e\}$ and $B = \{1, 2, 3, 4, a, b, c\}$, find:
   a. $n(A^c)$ b. $n(A \cap B^c)$
   c. $n(A \cup B^c)$ d. $n(A^c \cap B^c)$

5. Verify directly that $n(A \cup B) = n(A) + n(B) - n(A \cap B)$ for the sets in Exercise 3.

6. Let $A = \{a, e, i, o, u\}$ and $B = \{b, d, e, o, u\}$. Verify by direct computation that $n(A \cup B) = n(A) + n(B) - n(A \cap B)$.

7. If $n(A) = 15$, $n(A \cap B) = 5$, and $n(A \cup B) = 30$, then what is $n(B)$?

8. If $n(A) = 10$, $n(A \cup B) = 15$, and $n(B) = 8$, then what is $n(A \cap B)$?

In Exercises 9 and 10, refer to the following Venn diagram.

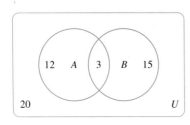

9. Find:
   a. $n(A)$ b. $n(A \cup B)$ c. $n(A^c \cap B)$
   d. $n(A \cap B^c)$ e. $n(U)$ f. $n[(A \cup B)^c]$

10. Find:
    a. $n(A \cap B)$ b. $n(A^c \cap B^c)$ c. $n[(A \cap B)^c]$
    d. $n(A^c \cup B^c)$ e. $n[(A \cap B^c) \cup (A^c \cap B)]$ f. $n(U^c)$

In Exercises 11 and 12, let A and B be subsets of a universal set U and suppose $n(U) = 200$, $n(A) = 100$, $n(B) = 80$, and $n(A \cap B) = 40$. Compute:

11. a. $n(A \cup B)$ b. $n(A^c)$ c. $n(A \cap B^c)$

12. a. $n(A^c \cap B)$ b. $n(B^c)$ c. $n(A^c \cap B^c)$

13. Find $n(A \cup B)$ given that $n(A) = 6$, $n(B) = 10$, and $n(A \cap B) = 3$.

14. If $n(B) = 6$, $n(A \cup B) = 14$, and $n(A \cap B) = 3$, find $n(A)$.

15. If $n(A) = 4$, $n(B) = 5$, and $n(A \cup B) = 9$, find $n(A \cap B)$.

16. If $n(A) = 16$, $n(B) = 16$, $n(C) = 14$, $n(A \cap B) = 6$, $n(A \cap C) = 5$, $n(B \cap C) = 6$, and $n(A \cup B \cup C) = 31$, find $n(A \cap B \cap C)$.

17. If $n(A) = 12$, $n(B) = 12$, $n(A \cap B) = 5$, $n(A \cap C) = 5$, $n(B \cap C) = 4$, $n(A \cap B \cap C) = 2$, and $n(A \cup B \cup C) = 25$, find $n(C)$.

18. A survey of 1000 subscribers to the *Los Angeles Times* revealed that 900 people subscribe to the daily morning edition and 500 subscribe to both the daily morning and the Sunday editions. How many subscribe to the Sunday edition? How many subscribe to the Sunday edition only?

19. On a certain day, the Wilton County Jail held 190 prisoners accused of a crime (felony and/or misdemeanor). Of these, 130 were accused of felonies and 121 were accused of misdemeanors. How many prisoners were accused of both a felony and a misdemeanor?

20. Of 100 clock radios with digital tuners and/or CD players sold recently in a department store, 70 had digital tuners and 90 had CD players. How many radios had both digital tuners and CD players?

21. **CONSUMER SURVEYS** In a survey of 120 consumers conducted in a shopping mall, 80 consumers indicated that they buy Brand A of a certain product, 68 buy Brand B, and 42 buy both brands. How many consumers participating in the survey buy
    a. At least one of these brands?
    b. Exactly one of these brands?
    c. Only Brand A?
    d. Neither of these brands?

22. **CONSUMER SURVEYS** In a survey of 200 members of a local sports club, 100 members indicated that they plan to attend the next Summer Olympic Games, 60 indicated that they plan to attend the next Winter Olympic Games, and 40 indicated that they plan to attend both games. How many members of the club plan to attend
    a. At least one of the two games?
    b. Exactly one of the games?
    c. The Summer Olympic Games only?
    d. None of the games?

23. **INVESTING** In a poll conducted among 200 active investors, it was found that 120 use discount brokers, 126 use full-service brokers, and 64 use both discount and full-service brokers. How many investors
    a. Use at least one kind of broker?
    b. Use exactly one kind of broker?
    c. Use only discount brokers?
    d. Don't use a broker?

24. **COMMUTER TRENDS** Of 50 employees of a store located in downtown Boston, 18 people take the subway to work, 12 take the bus, and 7 take both the subway and the bus. How many employees
    a. Take the subway or the bus to work?
    b. Take only the bus to work?
    c. Take either the bus or the subway to work?
    d. Get to work by some other means?

25. **CONSUMER SURVEYS** In a survey of 200 households regarding the ownership of desktop and laptop computers, the following information was obtained:

    120 households own only desktop computers.

    10 households own only laptop computers.

    40 households own neither desktop nor laptop computers.

    How many households own both desktop and laptop computers?

26. **CONSUMER SURVEYS** In a survey of 400 households regarding the ownership of HDTVs and DVD players, the following data were obtained:

    360 households own one or more HDTVs.

    170 households own one or more HDTVs and one or more DVD players.

    19 households do not own a HDTV or a DVD player.

    How many households own only one or more DVD players?

In Exercises 27 and 28, refer to the following Venn diagram.

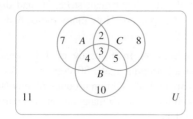

27. Find:
  a. $n(A)$ **b.** $n(A \cup B)$ **c.** $n(A \cap B \cap C^c)$
  d. $n[(A \cup B) \cap C^c)]$ **e.** $n[(A \cup B \cup C)^c]$

28. Find:
  a. $n(A \cup B^c)$ **b.** $n[(A \cap (B \cup C)^c]$ **c.** $n(A^c)$
  d. $n[(A \cap B \cap C)^c]$ **e.** $n(A^c \cup B^c \cup C^c)$

In Exercises 29–32, let A, B, and C be subsets of a universal set U and suppose $n(U) = 100$, $n(A) = 28$, $n(B) = 30$, $n(C) = 34$, $n(A \cap B) = 8$, $n(A \cap C) = 10$, $n(B \cap C) = 15$, and $n(A \cap B \cap C) = 5$. Compute:

29. a. $n(A \cup B \cup C)$ **b.** $n(A^c \cap B \cap C)$

30. a. $n[A \cap (B \cup C)]$ **b.** $n[A \cap (B \cup C)^c]$

31. a. $n(A^c \cap B^c \cap C^c)$ **b.** $n[A^c \cap (B \cup C)]$

32. a. $n[A \cup (B \cap C)]$ **b.** $n[(A^c \cap B^c \cap C^c)^c]$

33. Economic Surveys A survey of the opinions of ten leading economists in a certain country showed that, because oil prices were expected to drop in that country over the next 12 months,

Seven had lowered their estimate of the consumer inflation rate.

Eight had raised their estimate of the gross national product (GNP) growth rate.

Two had lowered their estimate of the consumer inflation rate but had not raised their estimate of the GNP growth rate.

How many economists had both lowered their estimate of the consumer inflation rate and raised their estimate of the GNP growth rate for that period?

34. Student Dropout Rate Data released by the Department of Education regarding the rate (percentage) of ninth-grade students who don't graduate showed that, out of 50 states,

12 states had an increase in the dropout rate during the past 2 years.

15 states had a dropout rate of at least 30% during the past 2 years.

21 states had an increase in the dropout rate and/or a dropout rate of at least 30% during the past 2 years.

a. How many states had both a dropout rate of at least 30% and an increase in the dropout rate over the 2-year period?

b. How many states had a dropout rate that was less than 30% but that had increased over the 2-year period?

35. Student Reading Habits A survey of 100 college students who frequent the reading lounge of a university revealed the following results:

40 read *Time*.

30 read *Newsweek*.

25 read *U.S. News & World Report*.

15 read *Time* and *Newsweek*.

12 read *Time* and *U.S. News & World Report*.

10 read *Newsweek* and *U.S. News & World Report*.

 4 read all three magazines.

How many of the students surveyed read:
  a. At least one of these magazines?
  b. Exactly one of these magazines?
  c. Exactly two of these magazines?
  d. None of these magazines?

36. SAT Scores Results of a Department of Education survey of SAT test scores in 22 states showed that

10 states had an average composite SAT score of at least 1000 during the past 3 years.

15 states had an increase of at least 10 points in the average composite SAT score during the past 3 years.

 8 states had both an average composite SAT score of at least 1000 and an increase in the average composite SAT score of at least 10 points during the past 3 years.

a. How many of the 22 states had composite SAT scores of less than 1000 and showed an increase of at least 10 points over the 3-year period?
b. How many of the 22 states had composite SAT scores of at least 1000 and did not show an increase of at least 10 points over the 3-year period?

37. Consumer Surveys The 120 consumers of Exercise 19 were also asked about their buying preferences concerning another product that is sold in the market under three labels. The results were as follows:

12 buy only those sold under Label *A*.

25 buy only those sold under Label *B*.

26 buy only those sold under Label *C*.

15 buy only those sold under Labels *A* and *B*.

10 buy only those sold under Labels *A* and *C*.

12 buy only those sold under Labels *B* and *C*.

 8 buy the product sold under all three labels.

How many of the consumers surveyed buy the product sold under:
  a. At least one of the three labels?
  b. Labels *A* and *B* but not *C*?
  c. Label *A*?
  d. None of these labels?

38. Student Surveys To help plan the number of meals (breakfast, lunch, and dinner) to be prepared in a college cafeteria, a survey was conducted and the following data were obtained:

130 students ate breakfast.

180 students ate lunch.

275 students ate dinner.

68 students ate breakfast and lunch.

112 students ate breakfast and dinner.

90 students ate lunch and dinner.

58 students ate all three meals.

How many of the students ate:
a. At least one meal in the cafeteria?
b. Exactly one meal in the cafeteria?
c. Only dinner in the cafeteria?
d. Exactly two meals in the cafeteria?

39. **INVESTMENTS** In a survey of 200 employees of a company regarding their 401(k) investments, the following data were obtained:

141 had investments in stock funds.

91 had investments in bond funds.

60 had investments in money market funds.

47 had investments in stock funds and bond funds.

36 had investments in stock funds and money market funds.

36 had investments in bond funds and money market funds.

5 had investments only in some other vehicle.

a. How many of the employees surveyed had investments in all three types of funds?
b. How many of the employees had investments in stock funds only?

40. **NEWSPAPER SUBSCRIPTIONS** In a survey of 300 individual investors regarding subscriptions to the *New York Times* (*NYT*), *Wall Street Journal* (*WSJ*), and *USA Today* (*UST*), the following data were obtained:

122 subscribe to the *NYT*.

150 subscribe to the *WSJ*.

62 subscribe to the *UST*.

38 subscribe to the *NYT* and *WSJ*.

20 subscribe to the *NYT* and *UST*.

28 subscribe to the *WSJ* and *UST*.

36 do not subscribe to any of these newspapers.

a. How many of the individual investors surveyed subscribe to all three newspapers?
b. How many subscribe to only one of these newspapers?

In Exercises 41–44, determine whether the statement is true or false. If it is true, explain why it is true. If it is false, give an example to show why it is false.

41. If $A \cap B \neq \varnothing$, then $n(A \cup B) \neq n(A) + n(B)$.

42. If $A \subseteq B$, then $n(B) = n(A) + n(A^c \cap B)$.

43. If $n(A \cup B) = n(A) + n(B)$, then $A \cap B = \varnothing$.

44. If $n(A \cup B) = 0$ and $n(A \cap B) = 0$, then $A = \varnothing$.

45. Derive Equation (5).
Hint: Equation (4) can be written as $n(D \cup E) = n(D) + n(E) - n(D \cap E)$. Now, put $D = A \cup B$ and $E = C$. Use Equation (4) again if necessary.

46. Find conditions on the sets A, B, and C so that $n(A \cup B \cup C) = n(A) + n(B) + n(C)$.

6.2 Solutions to Self-Check Exercises

1. Use the given information to construct the following Venn diagram:

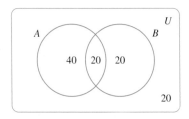

Using this diagram, we see that
a. $n(A \cup B) = 40 + 20 + 20 = 80$
b. $n(A \cap B^c) = 40$
c. $n(A^c \cap B) = 20$

2. Let U denote the set of all readers surveyed, and let

$A = \{x \in U \mid x$ owns at least one HD player in the HD-DVD format$\}$

$B = \{x \in U \mid x$ owns at least one HD player in the Blu-ray format$\}$

The fact that 22 of the readers own HD players in both formats means that $n(A \cap B) = 22$. Also, $n(A) = 166$ and $n(B) = 161$. Using this information, we obtain the following Venn diagram:

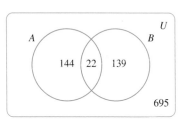

From the Venn diagram, we see that the number of readers who own HD players in the Blu-ray format only is given by

$$n(A \cap B^c) = 144$$

The number of readers who do not own an HD player in either format is given by

$$n(A^c \cap B^c) = 695$$

6.3 The Multiplication Principle

The Fundamental Principle of Counting

The solution of certain problems requires more sophisticated counting techniques than those developed in the previous section. We look at some such techniques in this and the following section. We begin by stating a fundamental principle of counting called the **multiplication principle.**

> The Multiplication Principle
>
> Suppose there are m ways of performing a task T_1 and n ways of performing a task T_2. Then there are mn ways of performing the task T_1 followed by the task T_2.

EXAMPLE 1 Three trunk roads connect Town A and Town B, and two trunk roads connect Town B and Town C.

a. Use the multiplication principle to find the number of ways in which a journey from Town A to Town C via Town B can be completed.
b. Verify part (a) directly by exhibiting all possible routes.

Solution

a. Since there are three ways of performing the first task (going from Town A to Town B) followed by two ways of performing the second task (going from Town B to Town C), the multiplication principle says that there are $3 \cdot 2$, or 6, ways to complete a journey from Town A to Town C via Town B.
b. Label the trunk roads connecting Town A and Town B with the Roman numerals I, II, and III, and label the trunk roads connecting Town B and Town C with the lowercase letters a and b. A schematic of this is shown in Figure 12. Then the routes from Town A to Town C via Town B can be exhibited with the aid of a **tree diagram** (Figure 13).

FIGURE 12
Roads from Town A to Town C

If we follow all of the branches from the initial point A to the right-hand edge of the tree, we obtain the six routes represented by six ordered pairs:

$$(\text{I}, a), (\text{I}, b), (\text{II}, a), (\text{II}, b), (\text{III}, a), (\text{III}, b)$$

where (I, a) means that the journey from Town A to Town B is made on Trunk Road I with the rest of the journey, from Town B to Town C, completed on Trunk Road a, and so forth.

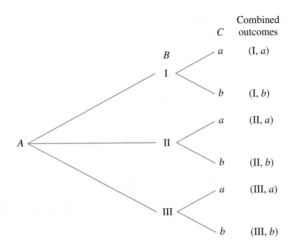

FIGURE 13
Tree diagram displaying the possible routes from Town *A* to Town *C*

Explore & Discuss

One way of gauging the performance of an airline is to track the arrival times of its flights. Suppose we denote by *E*, *O*, and *L* a flight that arrives early, on time, or late, respectively.

1. Use a tree diagram to exhibit the possible outcomes when you track two successive flights of the airline. How many outcomes are there?

2. How many outcomes are there if you track three successive flights? Justify your answer.

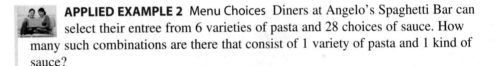

APPLIED EXAMPLE 2 Menu Choices Diners at Angelo's Spaghetti Bar can select their entree from 6 varieties of pasta and 28 choices of sauce. How many such combinations are there that consist of 1 variety of pasta and 1 kind of sauce?

Solution   There are 6 ways of choosing a pasta followed by 28 ways of choosing a sauce, so by the multiplication principle, there are 6 · 28, or 168, combinations of this pasta dish.

The multiplication principle can be easily extended, which leads to the **generalized multiplication principle**.

Generalized Multiplication Principle

Suppose a task T_1 can be performed in N_1 ways, a task T_2 can be performed in N_2 ways, . . . , and, finally, a task T_m can be performed in N_m ways. Then, the number of ways of performing the tasks $T_1, T_2, \ldots, T_m$ in succession is given by the product

$$N_1 N_2 \cdots N_m$$

We now illustrate the application of the generalized multiplication principle to several diverse situations.

EXAMPLE 3 A coin is tossed three times, and the sequence of heads and tails is recorded.

a. Use the generalized multiplication principle to determine the number of possible outcomes of this activity.
b. Exhibit all the sequences by means of a tree diagram.

Solution

a. The coin may land in two ways. Therefore, in three tosses, the number of outcomes (sequences) is given by $2 \cdot 2 \cdot 2$, or 8.
b. Let H and T denote the outcomes "a head" and "a tail," respectively. Then the required sequences may be obtained as shown in Figure 14, giving the sequence as HHH, HHT, HTH, HTT, THH, THT, TTH, and TTT.

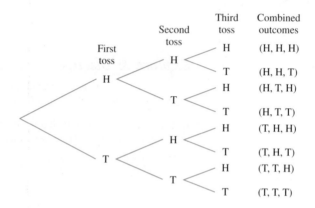

FIGURE 14
Tree diagram displaying possible outcomes of three consecutive coin tosses

APPLIED EXAMPLE 4 Combination Locks A combination lock is unlocked by dialing a sequence of numbers: first to the left, then to the right, and to the left again. If there are ten digits on the dial, determine the number of possible combinations.

Solution   There are ten choices for the first number, followed by ten for the second and ten for the third, so by the generalized multiplication principle there are $10 \cdot 10 \cdot 10$, or 1000, possible combinations.

APPLIED EXAMPLE 5 Investment Options An investor has decided to purchase shares in the stock of three companies: one engaged in aerospace activities, one involved in energy development, and one involved in electronics. After some research, the account executive of a brokerage firm has recommended that the investor consider stock from five aerospace companies, three energy development companies, and four electronics companies. In how many ways can the investor select the group of three companies from the executive's list?

Solution   The investor has five choices for selecting an aerospace company, three choices for selecting an energy development company, and four choices for selecting an electronics company. Therefore, by the generalized multiplication principle, there are $5 \cdot 3 \cdot 4$, or 60, ways in which she can select a group of three companies, one from each industry group.

APPLIED EXAMPLE 6 Travel Options Tom is planning to leave for New York City from Washington, D.C., on Monday morning and has decided that he will either fly or take the train. There are five flights and two trains departing for New York City from Washington that morning. When he returns on

Sunday afternoon, Tom plans to either fly or hitch a ride with a friend. There are two flights departing from New York City to Washington that afternoon. In how many ways can Tom complete this round trip?

Solution   There are seven ways in which Tom can go from Washington, D.C., to New York City (five by plane and two by train). On the return trip, Tom can travel in three ways (two by plane and one by car). Therefore, by the multiplication principle, Tom can complete the round trip in 7 · 3, or 21, ways.   ■

6.3   Self-Check Exercises

1. Encore Travel offers a "Theater Week in London" package originating from New York City. There is a choice of eight flights departing from New York City each week, a choice of five hotel accommodations, and a choice of one complimentary ticket to one of eight shows. How many such travel packages can a tourist choose from?

2. The Café Napoleon offers a dinner special on Wednesdays consisting of a choice of two entrées (beef bourguignon

and chicken basquaise); one dinner salad; one French roll; a choice of three vegetables; a choice of a carafe of burgundy, rosé, or chablis wine; a choice of coffee or tea; and a choice of six french pastries for dessert. How many combinations of dinner specials are there?

Solutions to Self-Check Exercises 6.3 can be found on page 345.

6.3   Concept Questions

1. Explain the multiplication principle, and illustrate it with a diagram.

2. Given the following tree diagram for an activity, what are the possible outcomes?

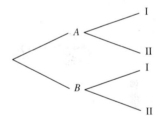

6.3   Exercises

1. **RENTAL RATES** Lynbrook West, an apartment complex financed by the State Housing Finance Agency, consists of one-, two-, three-, and four-bedroom units. The rental rate for each type of unit—low, moderate, or market—is determined by the income of the tenant. How many different rates are there?

2. **COMMUTER PASSES** Five different types of monthly commuter passes are offered by a city's local transit authority for each of three different groups of passengers: youths, adults, and senior citizens. How many different kinds of passes must be printed each month?

3. **BLACKJACK** In the game of blackjack, a 2-card hand consisting of an ace and either a face card or a 10 is called a "blackjack." If a standard 52-card deck is used, determine how many blackjack hands can be dealt. (A "face card" is a jack, queen, or king.)

4. **COIN TOSSES** A coin is tossed four times, and the sequence of heads and tails is recorded.
   a. Use the generalized multiplication principle to determine the number of outcomes of this activity.
   b. Exhibit all the sequences by means of a tree diagram.

5. **WARDROBE SELECTION** A female executive selecting her wardrobe purchased two blazers, four blouses, and three skirts in coordinating colors. How many ensembles consisting of a blazer, a blouse, and a skirt can she create from this collection?

6. **COMMUTER OPTIONS** Four commuter trains and three express buses depart from City *A* to City *B* in the morning, and three commuter trains and three express buses operate on the return trip in the evening. In how many ways can a commuter from City *A* to City *B* complete a daily round trip via bus and/or train?

7. **PSYCHOLOGY EXPERIMENTS** A psychologist has constructed the following maze for use in an experiment. The maze is constructed so that a rat must pass through a series of one-way doors. How many different paths are there from start to finish?

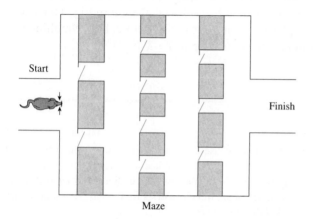

Maze

8. **UNION BARGAINING ISSUES** In a survey conducted by a union, members were asked to rate the importance of the following issues: (1) job security, (2) increased fringe benefits, and (3) improved working conditions. Five different responses were allowed for each issue. Among completed surveys, how many different responses to this survey were possible?

9. **HEALTH-CARE PLAN OPTIONS** A new state employee is offered a choice of ten basic health plans, three dental plans, and two vision care plans. How many different health-care plans are there to choose from if one plan is selected from each category?

10. **CODE WORDS** How many three-letter code words can be constructed from the first ten letters of the Greek alphabet if no repetitions are allowed?

11. **SOCIAL SECURITY NUMBERS** A Social Security number has nine digits. How many Social Security numbers are possible?

12. **MENU CHOICES** The New Shanghai Restaurant offers a choice of 3 appetizers, 2 choices of soups, and 10 choices of entrees for its lunch special. How many different complete lunches can be ordered from the restaurant's lunch special menu?

13. **MENU CHOICES** Maria's Trattoria offers mushrooms, onions, green pepper, pepperoni, Italian sausage, and anchovies as toppings for the plain cheese base of its pizzas. How many different pizzas can be made?

14. **SERIAL NUMBERS** Computers manufactured by a certain company have a serial number consisting of a letter of the alphabet followed by a four-digit number. If all the serial numbers of this type have been used, how many sets have already been manufactured?

15. **COMPUTER DATING** A computer dating service uses the results of its compatibility survey for arranging dates. The survey consists of 50 questions, each having five possible answers. How many different responses are possible if every question is answered?

16. **AUTOMOBILE COLORS** The 2010 BMW 335i Coupe is offered with a choice of 13 exterior colors (10 metallic and 3 standard), 6 interior colors, and 4 trims. How many combinations involving color and trim are available for the model?
Source: BMW.

17. **AUTOMOBILE COLORS** The 2011 Toyota Camry comes with 5 grades of models, 2 sizes of engines, 4 choices of transmissions, 5 exterior colors, and 2 interior colors. How many choices of the Camry are available for a prospective buyer?
Source: Toyota.

18. **TELEVISION-VIEWING POLLS** An opinion poll is to be conducted among cable TV viewers. Six multiple-choice questions, each with four possible answers, will be asked. In how many different ways can a viewer complete the poll if exactly one response is given to each question?

19. **ATM CARDS** To gain access to his account, a customer using an automatic teller machine (ATM) must enter a four-digit code. If repetition of the same four digits is not allowed (for example, 5555), how many possible combinations are there?

20. **POLITICAL POLLS** An opinion poll was conducted by the Morris Polling Group. Respondents were classified according to their sex (M or F), political affiliation (D, I, R), and the region of the country in which they reside (NW, W, C, S, E, NE).
   a. Use the generalized multiplication principle to determine the number of possible classifications.
   b. Construct a tree diagram to exhibit all possible classifications of females.

21. **LICENSE PLATE NUMBERS** Over the years, the state of California has used different combinations of letters of the alphabet and digits on its automobile license plates.
   a. At one time, license plates were issued that consisted of three letters followed by three digits. How many different license plates can be issued under this arrangement?
   b. Later on, license plates were issued that consisted of three digits followed by three letters. How many different license plates can be issued under this arrangement?

22. **LICENSE PLATE NUMBERS** In recent years, the state of California issued license plates using a combination of one letter of the alphabet followed by three digits, followed by another three letters of the alphabet. How many different license plates can be issued using this configuration?

23. **EXAMS** An exam consists of ten true-or-false questions. Assuming that every question is answered, in how many different ways can a student complete the exam? In how many ways can the exam be completed if a student can leave some questions unanswered because a penalty is assessed for each incorrect answer?

24. **WARRANTY NUMBERS** A warranty identification number for a certain product consists of a letter of the alphabet followed by a five-digit number. How many possible identification numbers are there if the first digit of the five-digit number must be nonzero?

25. LOTTERIES In a state lottery, there are 15 finalists who are eligible for the Big Money Draw. In how many ways can the first, second, and third prizes be awarded if no ticket holder can win more than one prize?

26. TELEPHONE NUMBERS
a. How many seven-digit telephone numbers are possible if the first digit must be nonzero?
b. How many direct-dialing numbers for calls within the United States and Canada are possible if each number consists of a 1 plus a three-digit area code (the first digit of which must be nonzero) and a number of the type described in part (a)?

27. SLOT MACHINES A "lucky dollar" is one of the nine symbols printed on each reel of a slot machine with three reels. A player receives one of various payouts whenever one or more "lucky dollars" appear in the window of the machine. Find the number of winning combinations for which the machine gives a payoff.
Hint: (a) Compute the number of ways in which the nine symbols on the first, second, and third wheels can appear in the window slot and (b) compute the number of ways in which the eight symbols other than the "lucky dollar" can appear in the window slot. The difference $(a - b)$ is the number of ways in which the "lucky dollar" can appear in the window slot. Why?

28. STAFFING Student Painters, which specializes in painting the exterior of residential buildings, has five people available to be organized into two-person and three-person teams.
a. In how many ways can a two-person team be formed?
b. In how many ways can a three-person team be formed?
c. In how many ways can the company organize the available people into either two-person teams or three-person teams?

In Exercises 29 and 30, determine whether the statement is true or false. If it is true, explain why it is true. If it is false, give an example to show why it is false.

29. There are 32 three-digit odd numbers that can be formed from the digits 1, 2, 3, and 4.

30. If there are six toppings available, then the number of different pizzas that can be made is 2^5, or 32, pizzas.

6.3 Solutions to Self-Check Exercises

1. A tourist has a choice of eight flights, five hotel accommodations, and eight tickets. By the generalized multiplication principle, there are $8 \cdot 5 \cdot 8$, or 320, travel packages.

2. There is a choice of two entrées, one dinner salad, one French roll, three vegetables, three wines, two nonalcoholic beverages, and six pastries. Therefore, by the generalized multiplication principle, there are $2 \cdot 1 \cdot 1 \cdot 3 \cdot 3 \cdot 2 \cdot 6$, or 216, combinations of dinner specials.

6.4 Permutations and Combinations

Permutations

In this section, we apply the generalized multiplication principle to the solution of two types of counting problems. Both types involve determining the number of ways the elements of a set can be arranged, and both play an important role in the solution of problems in probability.

We begin by considering the permutations of a set. Specifically, given a set of distinct objects, a **permutation** of the set is an arrangement of these objects in a *definite order*. To see why the order in which objects are arranged is important in certain practical situations, suppose the winning number for the first prize in a raffle is 9237. Then the number 2973, although it contains the same digits as the winning number, cannot be the first-prize winner (Figure 15). Here, the four objects—the digits 9, 2, 3, and 7—are arranged in a different order; one arrangement is associated with the winning number for the first prize, and the other is not.

FIGURE 15
The same digits appear on each ticket, but the order of the digits is different.

VIDEO   **EXAMPLE 1** Let $A = \{a, b, c\}$.

a. Find the number of permutations of A.

b. List all the permutations of A with the aid of a tree diagram.

Solution

a. Each permutation of A consists of a sequence of the three letters a, b, c. There-fore, we may think of such a sequence as being constructed by filling in each of the three blanks

$$\underline{\quad} \quad \underline{\quad} \quad \underline{\quad}$$

with one of the three letters. Now, there are three ways in which we can fill the first blank—we can choose a, b, or c. Having selected a letter for the first blank, there are two letters left for the second blank. Finally, there is but one way left to fill the third blank. Schematically, we have

$$\underline{3} \quad \underline{2} \quad \underline{1}$$

Invoking the generalized multiplication principle, we conclude that there are $3 \cdot 2 \cdot 1$, or 6, permutations of the set A.

b. The tree diagram associated with this problem appears in Figure 16, and the six permutations of A are abc, acb, bac, bca, cab, and cba.

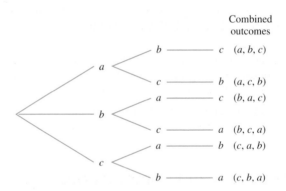

FIGURE 16
Permutations of three objects

Note   Notice that when the possible outcomes are listed in the tree diagram in Example 1, order is taken into account. Thus, (a, b, c) and (a, c, b) are two different arrangements.

EXAMPLE 2 Find the number of ways in which a baseball team consisting of nine people can arrange themselves in a line for a group picture.

Solution   We want to determine the number of permutations of the nine members of the baseball team. Each permutation in this situation consists of an arrangement of the nine team members in a line. The nine positions can be represented by nine blanks. Thus,

Position $\underline{1}$ $\underline{2}$ $\underline{3}$ $\underline{4}$ $\underline{5}$ $\underline{6}$ $\underline{7}$ $\underline{8}$ $\underline{9}$

There are nine ways to choose from among the nine players to fill the first position. When that position is filled, eight players are left, which gives us eight ways to fill the second position. Proceeding in a similar manner, we find that there are seven ways to fill the third position, and so on. Schematically, we have

Number of ways to $\underline{9}$ $\underline{8}$ $\underline{7}$ $\underline{6}$ $\underline{5}$ $\underline{4}$ $\underline{3}$ $\underline{2}$ $\underline{1}$
fill each position

Invoking the generalized multiplication principle, we conclude that there are $9 \cdot 8 \cdot 7 \cdot 6 \cdot 5 \cdot 4 \cdot 3 \cdot 2 \cdot 1$, or 362,880, ways in which the baseball team can be arranged for the picture.

Whenever we are asked to determine the number of ways in which the objects of a set can be arranged in a line, order is important. For example, if we take a picture of two baseball players, A and B, then the two players can line up for the picture in two ways, AB or BA, and the two pictures will be different.

Pursuing the same line of argument used in solving the problems in the last two examples, we can derive an expression for the number of ways of permuting a set A of n distinct objects taken n at a time. In fact, each permutation may be viewed as being obtained by filling each of n blanks with one and only one element from the set. There are n ways of filling the first blank, followed by $(n-1)$ ways of filling the second blank, and so on. Thus, by the generalized multiplication principle, there are

$$n(n-1)(n-2)\cdots 3\cdot 2\cdot 1$$

ways of permuting the elements of the set A.

Before stating this result formally, let's introduce a notation that will enable us to write in a compact form many of the expressions that follow. We use the symbol $n!$ (read "**n-factorial**") to denote the product of the first n positive integers.

---

n-Factorial

For any natural number n,

$$n! = n(n-1)(n-2)\cdots 3\cdot 2\cdot 1$$
$$0! = 1$$

For example,

$$1! = 1$$
$$2! = 2\cdot 1 = 2$$
$$3! = 3\cdot 2\cdot 1 = 6$$
$$4! = 4\cdot 3\cdot 2\cdot 1 = 24$$
$$5! = 5\cdot 4\cdot 3\cdot 2\cdot 1 = 120$$
$$\vdots$$
$$10! = 10\cdot 9\cdot 8\cdot 7\cdot 6\cdot 5\cdot 4\cdot 3\cdot 2\cdot 1 = 3,628,800$$

Using this notation, we can express *the number of permutations of n distinct objects taken n at a time, denoted by $P(n, n)$, as*

$$P(n, n) = n!$$

In many situations, we are interested in determining the number of ways of permuting n distinct objects taken r at a time, where $r \le n$. To derive a formula for computing the number of ways of permuting a set consisting of n distinct objects taken r at a time, we observe that each such permutation may be viewed as being obtained by filling each of r blanks with precisely one element from the set. Now there are n ways of filling the first blank, followed by $(n-1)$ ways of filling the second blank, and so on. Finally, there are $(n-r+1)$ ways of filling the rth blank. We can represent this argument schematically:

Number of ways	n	$n-1$	$n-2$	$\cdots$	$n-r+1$
Position	1st	2nd	3rd		rth

Using the generalized multiplication principle, we conclude that *the number of ways of permuting n distinct objects taken r at a time, denoted by $P(n, r)$, is given by*

$$P(n, r) = \underbrace{n(n-1)(n-2)\cdots(n-r+1)}_{r \text{ factors}}$$

Since

$$n(n - 1)(n - 2) \cdots (n - r + 1)$$

$$= [n(n - 1)(n - 2) \cdots (n - r + 1)] \cdot \frac{(n - r)(n - r - 1) \cdot \cdots \cdot 3 \cdot 2 \cdot 1}{(n - r)(n - r - 1) \cdot \cdots \cdot 3 \cdot 2 \cdot 1}$$

$$\underbrace{}_{\text{Here we are multiplying by 1.}}$$

$$= \frac{[n(n - 1)(n - 2) \cdots (n - r + 1)][(n - r)(n - r - 1) \cdot \cdots \cdot 3 \cdot 2 \cdot 1]}{(n - r)(n - r - 1) \cdot \cdots \cdot 3 \cdot 2 \cdot 1}$$

$$= \frac{n!}{(n - r)!}$$

we have the following formula.

> **Permutations of n Distinct Objects**
>
> The number of *permutations* of n distinct objects taken r at a time is
>
> $$P(n, r) = \frac{n!}{(n - r)!} \qquad (6)$$

Note When $r = n$, Equation (6) reduces to

$$P(n, n) = \frac{n!}{0!} = \frac{n!}{1} = n! \qquad \text{Note that } 0! = 1.$$

In other words, the number of permutations of a set of n distinct objects, taken all together, is $n!$. ■

EXAMPLE 3 Compute (a) $P(4, 4)$ and (b) $P(4, 2)$, and interpret your results.

Solution

a. $P(4, 4) = \dfrac{4!}{(4 - 4)!} = \dfrac{4!}{0!} = \dfrac{4!}{1} = \dfrac{4 \cdot 3 \cdot 2 \cdot 1}{1} = 24$ Note that $0! = 1.$

This gives the number of permutations of four objects taken four at a time.

b. $P(4, 2) = \dfrac{4!}{(4 - 2)!} = \dfrac{4!}{2!} = \dfrac{4 \cdot 3 \cdot 2 \cdot 1}{2 \cdot 1} = 4 \cdot 3 = 12$

This is the number of permutations of four objects taken two at a time. ■

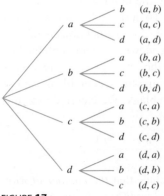

Combined outcomes

b (a, b)
a c (a, c)
  d (a, d)
a (b, a)
b c (b, c)
  d (b, d)
a (c, a)
c b (c, b)
  d (c, d)
a (d, a)
d b (d, b)
  c (d, c)

FIGURE 17
Permutations of four objects taken two at a time

EXAMPLE 4 Let $A = \{a, b, c, d\}$.

a. Use Equation (6) to compute the number of permutations of the set A taken two at a time.

b. Display the permutations of part (a) with the aid of a tree diagram.

Solution

a. Here, $n = 4$ and $r = 2$, so the required number of permutations is given by

$$P(4, 2) = \frac{4!}{(4 - 2)!} = \frac{4!}{2!} = \frac{4 \cdot 3 \cdot 2 \cdot 1}{2 \cdot 1} = 4 \cdot 3$$

$$= 12$$

b. The tree diagram associated with the problem is shown in Figure 17, and the permutations of A taken two at a time are

$$ab, \, ac, \, ad, \, ba, \, bc, \, bd, \, ca, \, cb, \, cd, \, da, \, db, \, dc$$

■

VIDEO **EXAMPLE 5** Find the number of ways in which a chairman, a vice-chairman, a secretary, and a treasurer can be chosen from a committee of eight members.

Solution The problem is equivalent to finding the number of permutations of eight distinct objects taken four at a time. Therefore, there are

$$P(8, 4) = \frac{8!}{(8-4)!} = \frac{8!}{4!} = 8 \cdot 7 \cdot 6 \cdot 5 = 1680$$

ways of choosing the four officials from the committee of eight members. ∎

The permutations considered thus far have been those involving sets of *distinct* objects. In many situations, we are interested in finding the number of permutations of a set of objects in which not all of the objects are distinct.

Permutations of n Objects, Not All Distinct

Given a set of n objects in which n_1 objects are alike and of one kind, n_2 objects are alike and of another kind, . . . , and n_m objects are alike and of yet another kind, so that

$$n_1 + n_2 + \cdots + n_m = n$$

then the number of permutations of these n objects taken n at a time is given by

$$\frac{n!}{n_1!\, n_2! \cdots n_m!} \tag{7}$$

To establish Formula (7), let's denote the number of such permutations by x. Now, if we *think* of the n_1 objects as being distinct, then they can be permuted in $n_1!$ ways. Similarly, if we *think* of the n_2 objects as being distinct, then they can be permuted in $n_2!$ ways, and so on. Therefore, if we *think* of the n objects as being distinct, then, by the generalized multiplication principle, there are $x \cdot n_1! \cdot n_2! \cdot \cdots \cdot n_m!$ permutations of these objects. But the number of permutations of a set of n distinct objects taken n at a time is just equal to $n!$. Therefore, we have

$$x(n_1! \cdot n_2! \cdot \cdots \cdot n_m!) = n!$$

from which we deduce that

$$x = \frac{n!}{n_1! \, n_2! \cdots n_m!}$$

EXAMPLE 6 Find the number of permutations that can be formed from all the letters in the word *ATLANTA*.

Solution There are seven objects (letters) involved, so $n = 7$. However, three of them are alike and of one kind (the three As), while two of them are alike and of another kind (the two Ts); hence, in this case, we have $n_1 = 3$, $n_2 = 2$, $n_3 = 1$ (the one L), and $n_4 = 1$ (the one N). Therefore, by Formula (7), there are

$$\frac{7!}{3! \, 2! \, 1! \, 1!} = \frac{7 \cdot 6 \cdot 5 \cdot 4 \cdot 3 \cdot 2 \cdot 1}{3 \cdot 2 \cdot 1 \cdot 2 \cdot 1 \cdot 1 \cdot 1} = 420$$

permutations.

APPLIED EXAMPLE 7 Management Decisions Weaver and Kline, a stock brokerage firm, has received nine inquiries regarding new accounts. In how many ways can these inquiries be directed to any three of the firm's account executives if each account executive is to handle three inquiries?

Solution If we think of the nine inquiries as being slots arranged in a row with inquiry 1 on the left and inquiry 9 on the right, then the problem can be thought of as one of filling each slot with a business card from an account executive. Then nine business cards would be used, of which three are alike and of one kind, three are alike and of another kind, and three are alike and of yet another kind. Thus, by using Formula (7) with $n = 9$ and $n_1 = n_2 = n_3 = 3$, there are

$$\frac{9!}{3! \, 3! \, 3!} = \frac{9 \cdot 8 \cdot 7 \cdot 6 \cdot 5 \cdot 4 \cdot 3 \cdot 2 \cdot 1}{3 \cdot 2 \cdot 1 \cdot 3 \cdot 2 \cdot 1 \cdot 3 \cdot 2 \cdot 1} = 1680$$

ways of assigning the inquiries.

Combinations

Until now, we have dealt with permutations of a set—that is, with arrangements of the objects of the set in which the *order* of the elements is taken into consideration. In many situations, one is interested in determining the number of ways of selecting r objects from a set of n objects without any regard to the order in which the objects are selected. Such a subset is called a **combination**.

For example, if one is interested in knowing the number of 5-card poker hands that can be dealt from a standard deck of 52 cards, then the order in which the poker hand is dealt is unimportant (Figure 18). In this situation, we are interested in determining the number of combinations of 5 cards (objects) selected from a deck (set) of 52 cards (objects). (We will solve this problem in Example 10.)

 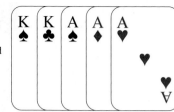

is considered
the same
hand as

FIGURE **18**

To derive a formula for determining the number of combinations of n objects taken r at a time, written

$$C(n, r) \quad \text{or} \quad \binom{n}{r}$$

we observe that each of the $C(n, r)$ combinations of r objects can be permuted in $r!$ ways (Figure 19).

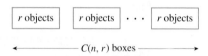

FIGURE **19**

Thus, by the multiplication principle, the product $r!\, C(n, r)$ gives the number of permutations of n objects taken r at a time; that is,

$$r!\, C(n, r) = P(n, r)$$

from which we find

$$C(n, r) = \frac{P(n, r)}{r!}$$

or, using Equation (6),

$$C(n, r) = \frac{n!}{r!\,(n - r)!}$$

> **Combinations of n Objects**
> The number of combinations of n distinct objects taken r at a time is given by
> $$C(n, r) = \frac{n!}{r!\,(n - r)!} \qquad \text{(where } r \leq n\text{)} \tag{8}$$

EXAMPLE 8 Compute and interpret the results of (a) $C(4, 4)$ and (b) $C(4, 2)$.

Solution

a. $C(4, 4) = \dfrac{4!}{4!\,(4 - 4)!} = \dfrac{4!}{4!\,0!} = 1$ Recall that $0! = 1$.

This gives 1 as the number of combinations of four distinct objects taken four at a time.

b. $C(4, 2) = \dfrac{4!}{2!\,(4 - 2)!} = \dfrac{4!}{2!\,2!} = \dfrac{4 \cdot 3 \cdot 2 \cdot 1}{2 \cdot 2} = 6$

This gives 6 as the number of combinations of four distinct objects taken two at a time.

APPLIED EXAMPLE 9 Committee Selection A Senate investigation sub-committee of four members is to be selected from a Senate committee of ten members. Determine the number of ways in which this can be done.

Solution The order in which the members of the subcommittee are selected is unimportant, so the number of ways of choosing the subcommittee is given by $C(10, 4)$, the number of combinations of ten objects taken four at a time. Hence, there are

$$C(10, 4) = \frac{10!}{4!\,(10 - 4)!} = \frac{10!}{4!\,6!} = \frac{10 \cdot 9 \cdot 8 \cdot 7}{4 \cdot 3 \cdot 2 \cdot 1} = 210$$

ways of choosing such a subcommittee. ■

Note Remember, a combination is a selection of objects *without* regard to order. Thus, in Example 9, we used a combination formula rather than a permutation formula to solve the problem because the order of selection was not important; that is, it did not matter whether a member of the subcommittee was selected first, second, third, or fourth. ■

 APPLIED EXAMPLE 10 Poker How many poker hands of 5 cards can be dealt from a standard deck of 52 cards?

Solution The order in which the 5 cards are dealt is not important. The number of ways of dealing a poker hand of 5 cards from a standard deck of 52 cards is given by $C(52, 5)$, the number of combinations of 52 objects taken five at a time. Thus, there are

$$\begin{aligned} C(52, 5) &= \frac{52!}{5!\,(52 - 5)!} = \frac{52!}{5!\,47!} \\ &= \frac{52 \cdot 51 \cdot 50 \cdot 49 \cdot 48}{5 \cdot 4 \cdot 3 \cdot 2 \cdot 1} \\ &= 2{,}598{,}960 \end{aligned}$$

ways of dealing such a poker hand. ■

The next several examples show that solving a counting problem often involves the repeated application of Equation (6) and/or (8), possibly in conjunction with the multiplication principle.

 APPLIED EXAMPLE 11 Selecting Members of a Group The members of a string quartet consisting of two violinists, a violist, and a cellist are to be selected from a group of six violinists, three violists, and two cellists.

a. In how many ways can the string quartet be formed?
b. In how many ways can the string quartet be formed if one of the violinists is to be designated as the first violinist and the other is to be designated as the second violinist?

Solution

a. Since the order in which each musician is selected is not important, we use combinations. The violinists can be selected in $C(6, 2)$, or 15, ways; the violist can be selected in $C(3, 1)$, or 3, ways; and the cellist can be selected in $C(2, 1)$, or 2, ways. By the multiplication principle, there are $15 \cdot 3 \cdot 2$, or 90, ways of forming the string quartet.
b. The order in which the violinists are selected is important here. Consequently, the number of ways of selecting the violinists is given by $P(6, 2)$, or 30, ways.

The number of ways of selecting the violist and the cellist remain, of course, 3 and 2, respectively. Therefore, the number of ways in which the string quartet can be formed is given by 30 · 3 · 2, or 180, ways. ■

Note   The solution of Example 11 involves both a permutation and a combination. When we select two violinists from six violinists, order is not important, and we use a combination formula to solve the problem. However, when one of the violinists is designated as a first violinist, order is important, and we use a permutation formula to solve the problem. ■

APPLIED EXAMPLE 12 Investment Options Refer to Example 5, page 342. Suppose the investor has decided to purchase shares in the stocks of two aerospace companies, two energy development companies, and two electronics companies. In how many ways can the investor select the group of six companies for the investment from the recommended list of five aerospace companies, three energy development companies, and four electronics companies?

Solution   There are $C(5, 2)$ ways in which the investor can select the aerospace companies, $C(3, 2)$ ways in which she can select the companies involved in energy development, and $C(4, 2)$ ways in which she can select the electronics companies as investments. By the generalized multiplication principle, there are

$$C(5, 2)C(3, 2)C(4, 2) = \frac{5!}{2! \, 3!} \cdot \frac{3!}{2! \, 1!} \cdot \frac{4!}{2! \, 2!}$$

$$= \frac{5 \cdot 4}{2} \cdot 3 \cdot \frac{4 \cdot 3}{2} = 180$$

ways of selecting the group of six companies for her investment. ■

APPLIED EXAMPLE 13 Scheduling Performances The Futurists, a rock group, are planning a concert tour with performances to be given in five cities: San Francisco, Los Angeles, San Diego, Denver, and Las Vegas. In how many ways can they arrange their itinerary if

a. There are no restrictions?
b. The three performances in California must be given consecutively?

Solution

a. The order is important here, and we see that there are

$$P(5, 5) = 5! = 120$$

ways of arranging their itinerary.
b. First, note that there are $P(3, 3)$ ways of choosing between performing in California and in the two cities outside that state. Next, there are $P(3, 3)$ ways of arranging their itinerary in the three cities in California. Therefore, by the multiplication principle, there are

$$P(3, 3)P(3, 3) = \frac{3!}{(3-3)!} \cdot \frac{3!}{(3-3)!} = 6 \cdot 6 = 36$$

ways of arranging their itinerary. ■

APPLIED EXAMPLE 14 U.N. Security Council Voting The United Nations Security Council consists of 5 permanent members and 10 nonpermanent members. Decisions made by the council require 9 votes for passage. However, any permanent member may veto a measure and thus block its passage. Assuming that there are no abstentions, in how many ways can a measure be passed if all 15 members of the Council vote?

Solution   If a measure is to be passed, then all 5 permanent members must vote for passage of that measure. This can be done in $C(5, 5)$, or 1, way.

Next, observe that since 9 votes are required for passage of a measure, *at least* 4 of the 10 nonpermanent members must also vote for its passage. To determine the number of ways in which this can be done, notice that there are $C(10, 4)$ ways in which exactly 4 of the nonpermanent members can vote for passage of a measure, $C(10, 5)$ ways in which exactly 5 of them can vote for passage of a measure, and so on. Finally, there are $C(10, 10)$ ways in which all 10 nonpermanent members can vote for passage of a measure. Hence, there are

$$C(10, 4) + C(10, 5) + \cdots + C(10, 10)$$

ways in which at least 4 of the 10 nonpermanent members can vote for a measure. So by the multiplication principle, there are

$$C(5, 5)[C(10, 4) + C(10, 5) + \cdots + C(10, 10)]$$
$$= (1)\left[\frac{10!}{4! \, 6!} + \frac{10!}{5! \, 5!} + \cdots + \frac{10!}{10! \, 0!}\right]$$
$$= (1)(210 + 252 + 210 + 120 + 45 + 10 + 1) = 848$$

ways in which a measure can be passed.   ■

6.4 Self-Check Exercises

1. Evaluate:
   a. $5!$ **b.** $C(7, 4)$ **c.** $P(6, 2)$

2. A space shuttle crew consists of a shuttle commander, a pilot, three engineers, a scientist, and a civilian. The shuttle commander and pilot are to be chosen from 8 candidates, the three engineers from 12 candidates, the scientist from 5 candidates, and the civilian from 2 candidates. How many such space shuttle crews can be formed?

Solutions to Self-Check Exercises 6.4 can be found on page 358.

6.4 Concept Questions

1. **a.** What is a permutation of a set of distinct objects?
   b. How many permutations of a set of five distinct objects taken three at a time are there?

2. Given a set of ten objects in which three are alike and of one kind, three are alike and of another kind, and four are alike and of yet another kind, what is the formula for computing the permutation of these ten objects taken ten at a time?

3. **a.** What is a combination of a set of n distinct objects taken r at a time?
   b. How many combinations are there of six distinct objects taken three at a time?

6.4 Exercises

In Exercises 1–22, evaluate the given expression.

1. $3 \cdot 5!$ **2.** $2 \cdot 7!$ **3.** $\dfrac{5!}{2! \, 3!}$

4. $\dfrac{6!}{4! \, 2!}$ **5.** $P(5, 5)$ **6.** $P(6, 6)$

7. $P(5, 2)$ **8.** $P(5, 3)$ **9.** $P(n, 1)$

10. $P(k, 2)$ **11.** $C(6, 6)$ **12.** $C(8, 8)$

13. $C(7, 4)$ **14.** $C(9, 3)$ **15.** $C(5, 0)$

16. $C(6, 5)$ **17.** $C(9, 6)$ **18.** $C(10, 3)$

19. $C(n, 2)$ **20.** $C(7, r)$ **21.** $P(n, n - 2)$

22. $C(n, n - 2)$

In Exercises 23–30, classify each problem according to whether it involves a permutation or a combination.

23. In how many ways can the letters of the word *GLACIER* be arranged?

24. A 4-member executive committee is to be formed from a 12-member board of directors. In how many ways can it be formed?

25. As part of a quality-control program, 3 cell phones are selected at random for testing from 100 cell phones produced by the manufacturer. In how many ways can this test batch be chosen?

26. How many three-digit numbers can be formed by using the numerals in the set {3, 2, 7, 9} if repetition is not allowed?

27. In how many ways can nine different books be arranged on a shelf?

28. A member of a book club wishes to purchase two books from a selection of eight books recommended for a certain month. In how many ways can she choose them?

29. How many five-card poker hands can be dealt consisting of three queens and a pair?

30. In how many ways can a six-letter security password be formed from letters of the alphabet if no letter is repeated?

31. How many four-letter permutations can be formed from the first four letters of the alphabet?

32. How many three-letter permutations can be formed from the first five letters of the alphabet?

33. In how many ways can four students be seated in a row of four seats?

34. In how many ways can five people line up at a checkout counter in a supermarket?

35. How many different batting orders can be formed for a nine-member baseball team?

36. In how many ways can the names of six candidates for political office be listed on a ballot?

37. In how many ways can a member of a hiring committee select 3 of 12 job applicants for further consideration?

38. In how many ways can an investor select four mutual funds for his investment portfolio from a recommended list of eight mutual funds?

39. Find the number of distinguishable permutations that can be formed from the letters of the word *ANTARCTICA*.

40. Find the number of distinguishable permutations that can be formed from the letters of the word *PHILIPPINES*.

41. In how many ways can the letters of the Website *MySpace* be arranged if all of the letters are used and the vowels *a* and *e* must always stay in the order *ae*?

42. In how many ways can five people boarding a bus be seated if the bus has eight vacant seats?

43. How many distinct five-digit numbers can be made using the digits 1, 2, 2, 2, 7?

44. How many different signals can be made by hoisting two yellow flags, four green flags, and three red flags on a ship's mast at the same time?

45. **MANAGEMENT DECISIONS** In how many ways can a supermarket chain select 3 out of 12 possible sites for the construction of new supermarkets?

46. **BOOK SELECTIONS** A student is given a reading list of ten books from which he must select two for an outside reading requirement. In how many ways can he make his selections?

47. **QUALITY CONTROL** In how many ways can a quality-control engineer select a sample of 3 microprocessors for testing from a batch of 100 microprocessors?

48. **STUDY GROUPS** A group of five students studying for a bar exam has formed a study group. Each member of the group will be responsible for preparing a study outline for one of five courses. In how many different ways can the five courses be assigned to the members of the group?

49. **TELEVISION PROGRAMMING** In how many ways can a television-programming director schedule six different commercials in the six time slots allocated to commercials during a 1-hour program?

50. **WAITING LINES** Seven people arrive at the ticket counter of Starlite Cinema at the same time. In how many ways can they line up to purchase their tickets?

51. **MANAGEMENT DECISIONS** Weaver and Kline, a stock brokerage firm, has received six inquiries regarding new accounts. In how many ways can these inquiries be directed to its 12 account executives if each executive handles no more than one inquiry?

52. **CAR POOLS** A company car that has a seating capacity of six is to be used by six employees who have formed a car pool. If only four of these employees can drive, how many possible seating arrangements are there for the group?

53. **BOOK DISPLAYS** At a college library exhibition of faculty publications, three mathematics books, four social science books, and three biology books will be displayed on a shelf. (Assume that none of the books is alike.)
    a. In how many ways can the ten books be arranged on the shelf?
    b. In how many ways can the ten books be arranged on the shelf if books on the same subject matter are placed together?

54. **SEATING** In how many ways can four married couples attending a concert be seated in a row of eight seats if:
    a. There are no restrictions?
    b. Each married couple is seated together?
    c. The members of each sex are seated together?

55. NEWSPAPER ADVERTISEMENTS Four items from five different departments of Metro Department Store will be featured in a one-page newspaper advertisement, as shown in the following diagram:

Advertisement

1	2	3	4
5	6	7	8
9	10	11	12
13	14	15	16
17	18	19	20

  a. In how many different ways can the 20 featured items be arranged on the page?
  b. If items from the same department must be in the same row, how many arrangements are possible?

56. MANAGEMENT DECISIONS C & J Realty has received 12 inquiries from prospective home buyers. In how many ways can the inquiries be directed to any four of the firm's real estate agents if each agent handles three inquiries?

57. SPORTS A Little League baseball team has 12 players available for a 9-member team (no designated team positions).
  a. How many different 9-person batting orders are possible?
  b. How many different 9-member teams are possible?
  c. How many different 9-member teams and 2 alternates are possible?

58. SPORTS In the men's tennis tournament at Wimbledon, two finalists, A and B, are competing for the title, which will be awarded to the first player to win three sets. In how many different ways can the match be completed?

59. SPORTS In the women's tennis tournament at Wimbledon, two finalists, A and B, are competing for the title, which will be awarded to the first player to win two sets. In how many different ways can the match be completed?

60. JURY SELECTION In how many different ways can a panel of 12 jurors and 2 alternate jurors be chosen from a group of 30 prospective jurors?

61. U.N. VOTING Refer to Example 14. In how many ways can a measure be passed if two particular permanent and two particular nonpermanent members of the Security Council abstain from voting?

62. EXAMS A student taking an examination is required to answer exactly 10 out of 15 questions.
  a. In how many ways can the 10 questions be selected?
  b. In how many ways can the 10 questions be selected if exactly 2 of the first 3 questions must be answered?

63. TEACHING ASSISTANTSHIPS Twelve graduate students have applied for three available teaching assistantships. In how many ways can the assistantships be awarded among these applicants if:
  a. No preference is given to any student?
  b. One particular student must be awarded an assistantship?
  c. The group of applicants includes seven men and five women and it is stipulated that at least one woman must be awarded an assistantship?

64. SENATE COMMITTEES In how many ways can a subcommittee of four be chosen from a Senate committee of five Democrats and four Republicans if:
  a. All members are eligible?
  b. The subcommittee must consist of two Republicans and two Democrats?

65. CONTRACT BIDDING UBS Television Company is considering bids submitted by seven different firms for each of three different contracts. In how many ways can the contracts be awarded among these firms if no firm is to receive more than two contracts?

66. PERSONNEL SELECTION JCL Computers has five vacancies in its executive trainee program. In how many ways can the company select five trainees from a group of ten female and ten male applicants if the vacancies
  a. Can be filled by any combination of men and women?
  b. Must be filled by two men and three women?

67. COURSE SELECTION A student planning her curriculum for the upcoming year must select one of five business courses, one of three mathematics courses, two of six elective courses, and either one of four history courses or one of three social science courses. How many different curricula are available for her consideration?

68. DRIVERS' TESTS A state Motor Vehicle Department requires learners to pass a written test on the motor vehicle laws of the state. The exam consists of ten true-or-false questions, of which eight must be answered correctly to qualify for a permit. In how many different ways can a learner who answers all the questions on the exam qualify for a permit?

A list of poker hands ranked in order from the highest to the lowest is shown in the following table, along with a description and example of each hand. Use the table to answer Exercises 69–74.

Hand	Description	Example
Straight flush	5 cards in sequence in the same suit	A♥ 2♥ 3♥ 4♥ 5♥
Four of a kind	4 cards of the same rank and any other card	K♥ K♦ K♠ K♣ 2♥
Full house	3 of a kind and a pair	3♥ 3♦ 3♣ 7♥ 7♦
Flush	5 cards of the same suit that are not all in sequence	5♥ 6♥ 9♥ J♥ K♥
Straight	5 cards in sequence but not all of the same suit	10♥ J♦ Q♣ K♠ A♥
Three of a kind	3 cards of the same rank and 2 unmatched cards	K♥ K♦ K♠ 2♥ 4♦
Two pair	2 cards of the same rank and 2 cards of any other rank with an unmatched card	K♥ K♦ 2♥ 2♠ 4♣
One pair	2 cards of the same rank and 3 unmatched cards	K♥ K♦ 5♥ 2♠ 4♥

If a 5-card poker hand is dealt from a well-shuffled deck of 52 cards, how many different hands consist of the following:

69. A straight flush? (Note that an ace may be played as either a high or a low card in a straight sequence—that is, A, 2, 3, 4, 5 or 10, J, Q, K, A. Hence, there are ten possible sequences for a straight in one suit.)

70. A straight (but not a straight flush)?

71. A flush (but not a straight flush)?

72. Four of a kind?

73. A full house?

74. Two pair?

75. **Bus Routing** The following is a schematic diagram of a city's street system between the points A and B. The City Transit Authority is in the process of selecting a route from A to B along which to provide bus service. If the company's intention is to keep the route as short as possible, how many routes must be considered?

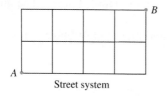

Street system

76. **Sports** In the World Series, one National League team and one American League team compete for the title, which is awarded to the first team to win four games. In how many different ways can the series be completed?

77. **Voting Quorums** A quorum (minimum) of 6 voting members is required at all meetings of the Curtis Townhomes Owners Association. If there is a total of 12 voting members in the group, find the number of ways this quorum can be formed.

78. **Circular Permutations** Suppose n distinct objects are arranged in a circle. Show that the number of (different) circular arrangements of the n objects is $(n - 1)!$.
Hint: Consider the arrangement of the five letters A, B, C, D, and E in the accompanying figure. The permutations ABCDE, BCDEA, CDEAB, DEABC, and EABCD are not distinguishable. Generalize this observation to the case of n objects.

79. Refer to Exercise 78. In how many ways can five TV commentators be seated at a round table for a discussion?

80. Refer to Exercise 78. In how many ways can four men and four women be seated at a round table at a dinner party if each guest is seated between members of the opposite sex?

81. At the end of Section 3.3, we mentioned that solving a linear programming problem in three variables and five constraints by the methods of corners requires that we solve 56 3×3 systems of linear equations. Verify this assertion.

82. Refer to Exercise 81. Show that, in order to solve a linear programming problem in five variables and ten constraints, we must solve 3003 5×5 systems of linear equations. This assertion was also made at the end of Section 3.3.

In Exercises 83–86, determine whether the statement is true or false. If it is true, explain why it is true. If it is false, give an example to show why it is false.

83. The number of permutations of n distinct objects taken all together is $n!$.

84. $P(n, r) = r! \, C(n, r)$

85. The number of combinations of n objects taken $n - r$ at a time is the same as the number taken r at a time.

86. If a set of n objects consists of r elements of one kind and $n - r$ elements of another kind, then the number of permutations of the n objects taken all together is $P(n, r)$.

6.4 Solutions to Self-Check Exercises

1. a. $5! = 5 \cdot 4 \cdot 3 \cdot 2 \cdot 1 = 120$

   b. $C(7, 4) = \dfrac{7!}{4! \, 3!} = \dfrac{7 \cdot 6 \cdot 5}{3 \cdot 2 \cdot 1} = 35$

   c. $P(6, 2) = \dfrac{6!}{4!} = 6 \cdot 5 = 30$

2. There are $P(8, 2)$ ways of picking the shuttle commander and pilot (the order *is* important here), $C(12, 3)$ ways of picking the engineers (the order is not important here), $C(5, 1)$ ways of picking the scientist, and $C(2, 1)$ ways of picking the civilian. By the multiplication principle, there are

$$P(8, 2) \cdot C(12, 3) \cdot C(5, 1) \cdot C(2,1)$$

$$= \frac{8!}{6!} \cdot \frac{12!}{9! \, 3!} \cdot \frac{5!}{4! \, 1!} \cdot \frac{2!}{1! \, 1!}$$

$$= \frac{8 \cdot 7 \cdot 12 \cdot 11 \cdot 10 \cdot 5 \cdot 2}{3 \cdot 2}$$

$$= 123{,}200$$

ways in which a crew can be selected.

USING TECHNOLOGY

Evaluating $n!$, $P(n, r)$, and $C(n, r)$

Graphing Utility

A graphing utility can be used to calculate factorials, permutations, and combinations with relative ease. A graphing utility is therefore an indispensable tool in solving counting problems involving large numbers of objects. Here, we use the **nPr** (permutation) and **nCr** (combination) functions of a graphing utility.

EXAMPLE 1 Use a graphing utility to find (a) 12!, (b) $P(52, 5)$, and (c) $C(38, 10)$.

Solution

a. Using the factorial function, we find that $12! = 479{,}001{,}600$.

b. Using the **nPr** function, we have

$$P(52, 5) = 52 \text{ } \mathbf{nPr} \text{ } 5 = 311{,}875{,}200$$

c. Using the **nCr** function, we obtain

$$C(38, 10) = 38 \text{ } \mathbf{nCr} \text{ } 10 = 472{,}733{,}756$$

Excel

Excel has built-in functions for calculating factorials, permutations, and combinations.

EXAMPLE 2 Use Excel to calculate

a. 12!

b. $P(52, 5)$

c. $C(38, 10)$

Solution

a. In cell A1, enter =FACT(12) and press . The number 479001600 will appear.

b. In cell A2, enter =PERMUT(52,5) and press **Shift-Enter**. The number 311875200 will appear.

c. In cell A3, enter =COMBIN(38,10) and press **Shift-Enter**. The number 472733756 will appear.

Note: Boldfaced words/characters enclosed in a box (for example, **Enter**) indicate that an action (click, select, or press) is required. Words/characters printed blue (for example, Chart sub-type:) indicate words/characters that appear on the screen. Words/characters printed in a monospace font (for example, =(−2/3)*A2+2)) indicate words/characters that need to be typed and entered.

TECHNOLOGY EXERCISES

In Exercises 1–10, evaluate the expression.

1. $15!$

2. $20!$

3. $4(18!)$

4. $\dfrac{30!}{18!}$

5. $P(52, 7)$

6. $P(24, 8)$

7. $C(52, 7)$

8. $C(26, 8)$

9. $P(10, 4)C(12, 6)$

10. $P(20, 5)C(9, 3)C(8, 4)$

11. A mathematics professor uses a computerized test bank to prepare her final exam. If 25 different problems are available for the first three exam questions, 40 different problems are available for the next five questions, and 30 different problems are available for the last two questions, how many different ten-question exams can she prepare? (Assume that the order of the questions within each group is not important.)

12. S & S Brokerage has received 100 inquiries from prospective clients. In how many ways can the inquiries be directed to any five of the firm's brokers if each broker handles 20 inquiries?

CHAPTER 6 Summary of Principal Formulas and Terms

FORMULAS

1. Commutative laws	$A \cup B = B \cup A$ $A \cap B = B \cap A$
2. Associative laws	$A \cup (B \cup C) = (A \cup B) \cup C$ $A \cap (B \cap C) = (A \cap B) \cap C$
3. Distributive laws	$A \cup (B \cap C) = (A \cup B) \cap (A \cup C)$ $A \cap (B \cup C) = (A \cap B) \cup (A \cap C)$
4. De Morgan's laws	$(A \cup B)^c = A^c \cap B^c$ $(A \cap B)^c = A^c \cup B^c$
5. Number of elements in the union of two finite sets	$n(A \cup B) = n(A) + n(B) - n(A \cap B)$
6. Permutation of n distinct objects, taken r at a time	$P(n, r) = \dfrac{n!}{(n - r)!}$
7. Permutation of n objects, not all distinct, taken n at a time	$\dfrac{n!}{n_1! \, n_2! \cdots n_m!}$
8. Combination of n distinct objects, taken r at a time	$C(n, r) = \dfrac{n!}{r! \, (n - r)!}$

TERMS

set (324)	empty set (325)	set complementation (328)
element of a set (324)	universal set (326)	multiplication principle (340)
roster notation (324)	Venn diagram (326)	generalized multiplication principle (341)
set-builder notation (324)	set union (327)	permutation (345)
set equality (324)	set intersection (327)	n-factorial (347)
subset (325)	complement of a set (327)	combination (350)

CHAPTER 6 | Concept Review Questions

Fill in the blanks.

1. A well-defined collection of objects is called a/an _____. These objects are called _____ of the _____.

2. Two sets having exactly the same elements are said to be _____.

3. If every element of a set A is also an element of a set B, then A is a/an _____ of B.

4. **a.** The empty set $\varnothing$ is the set containing _____ elements.
   b. The universal set is the set containing _____ elements.

5. **a.** The set of all elements in A and/or B is called the _____ of A and B.
   b. The set of all elements in both A and B is called the _____ of A and B.

6. The set of all elements in U that are not in A is called the _____ of A.

7. Applying De Morgan's Laws, we can write $(A \cup B \cup C)^c =$ _____.

8. An arrangement of a set of distinct objects in a definite order is called a/an _____; an arrangement in which the order is not important is a/an _____.

CHAPTER 6 | Review Exercises

In Exercises 1–4, list the elements of each set in roster notation.

1. $\{x \mid 3x - 2 = 7 \text{ and } x \text{ is an integer}\}$

2. $\{x \mid x \text{ is a letter of the word } TALLAHASSEE\}$

3. The set whose elements are the even numbers between 3 and 11

4. $\{x \mid (x - 3)(x + 4) = 0 \text{ and } x \text{ is a negative integer}\}$

Let $A = \{a, c, e, r\}$. In Exercises 5–8, determine whether the set is equal to A.

5. $\{r, e, c, a\}$

6. $\{x \mid x \text{ is a letter of the word } career\}$

7. $\{x \mid x \text{ is a letter of the word } racer\}$

8. $\{x \mid x \text{ is a letter of the word } cares\}$

In Exercises 9–12, shade the portion of the accompanying figure that represents the given set.

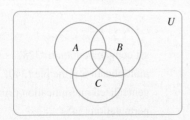

9. $A \cup (B \cap C)$

10. $(A \cap B \cap C)^c$

11. $A^c \cap B^c \cap C^c$

12. $A^c \cap (B^c \cup C^c)$

Let $U = \{a, b, c, d, e\}$, $A = \{a, b\}$, $B = \{b, c, d\}$, and $C = \{a, d, e\}$. In Exercises 13–16, verify the equation by direct computation.

13. $A \cup (B \cup C) = (A \cup B) \cup C$

14. $A \cap (B \cap C) = (A \cap B) \cap C$

15. $A \cap (B \cup C) = (A \cap B) \cup (A \cap C)$

16. $A \cup (B \cap C) = (A \cup B) \cap (A \cup C)$

Let $U = \{$all participants in a consumer-behavior survey conducted by a national polling group$\}$

$A = \{$consumers who avoided buying a product because it is not recyclable$\}$

$B = \{$consumers who used cloth rather than disposable diapers$\}$

$C = \{$consumers who boycotted a company's products because of its record on the environment$\}$

$D = \{$consumers who voluntarily recycled their garbage$\}$

In Exercises 17–20, describe each set in words.

17. $A \cap C$

18. $A \cup D$

19. $B^c \cap D$

20. $C^c \cup D^c$

Let A and B be subsets of a universal set U and suppose $n(U) = 350$, $n(A) = 120$, $n(B) = 80$, and $n(A \cap B) = 50$. In Exercises 21–26, find the number of elements in each set.

21. $n(A \cup B)$

22. $n(A^c)$

23. $n(B^c)$

24. $n(A^c \cap B)$

25. $n(A \cap B^c)$

26. $n(A^c \cap B^c)$

In Exercises 27–30, evaluate each quantity.

27. $C(20, 18)$

28. $P(9, 7)$

29. $C(5, 3) \cdot P(4, 2)$

30. $4 \cdot P(5, 3) \cdot C(7, 4)$

31. CREDIT CARD COMPARISONS A comparison of five major credit cards showed that

3 offered cash advances.

3 offered extended payments for all goods and services purchased.

2 required an annual fee of less than $35.

2 offered both cash advances and extended payments.

1 offered extended payments and had an annual fee less than $35.

No card had an annual fee less than $35 and offered both cash advances and extended payments.

How many cards had an annual fee less than $35 and offered cash advances? (Assume that every card had at least one of the three mentioned features.)

32. STUDENT SURVEYS The Department of Foreign Languages of a liberal arts college conducted a survey of its recent graduates to determine the foreign language courses they had taken while undergraduates at the college. Of the 480 graduates,

200 had at least 1 year of Spanish.

178 had at least 1 year of French.

140 had at least 1 year of German.

33 had at least 1 year of Spanish and French.

24 had at least 1 year of Spanish and German.

18 had at least 1 year of French and German.

3 had at least 1 year of all three languages.

How many of the graduates had
a. At least 1 year of at least one of the three languages?
b. At least 1 year of exactly one of the three languages?
c. Less than 1 year of any of the three languages?

33. In how many ways can six different compact discs be arranged on a shelf?

34. In how many ways can three pictures be selected from a group of six different pictures?

35. In how many ways can six different books, four of which are math books, be arranged on a shelf if the math books must be placed next to each other?

36. In how many ways can six people be arranged in a line for a group picture
a. If there are no restrictions?
b. If two people in the group insist on not standing next to each other?

37. Find the number of distinguishable permutations that can be formed from the letters of each word.
a. *CINCINNATI*   **b.** *HONOLULU*

38. How many three-digit numbers can be formed from the numerals in the set $\{1, 2, 3, 4, 5\}$ if
a. Repetition of digits is not allowed?
b. Repetition of digits is allowed?

39. AUTOMOBILE SELECTION An automobile manufacturer has three different subcompact cars in the line. Customers selecting one of these cars have a choice of three engine sizes, four body styles, and three color schemes. How many different selections can a customer make?

40. MENU SELECTIONS Two soups, five entrées, and three desserts are listed on the "Special" menu at the Neptune Restaurant. How many different selections consisting of one soup, one entrée, and one dessert can a customer choose from this menu?

41. INVESTMENTS In a survey conducted by Helena, a financial consultant, it was revealed that of her 400 clients

300 own stocks.

180 own bonds.

160 own mutual funds.

110 own both stocks and bonds.

120 own both stocks and mutual funds.

90 own both bonds and mutual funds.

How many of Helena's clients own stocks, bonds, and mutual funds?

42. POKER From a standard 52-card deck, how many 5-card poker hands can be dealt consisting of
a. Five clubs?   **b.** Three kings and one pair?

43. ELECTIONS In an election being held by the Associated Students Organization, there are six candidates for president, four for vice president, five for secretary, and six for treasurer. How many different possible outcomes are there for this election?

44. TEAM SELECTION There are eight seniors and six juniors in the Math Club at Jefferson High School. In how many ways can a math team consisting of four seniors and two juniors be selected from the members of the Math Club?

45. If order matters, in how many ways can two cards be drawn from a 52-card deck
a. If the first card is replaced before the second card is drawn?
b. If the second card is drawn without replacing the first card?

46. SEATING ARRANGEMENTS In how many ways can seven students be assigned seats in a row containing seven desks if:
a. There are no restrictions?
b. Two of the students must not be seated next to each other?

47. QUALITY CONTROL From a shipment of 60 CPUs, 5 of which are defective, a sample of 4 CPUs is selected at random.
a. In how many different ways can the sample be selected?
b. How many samples contain 3 defective CPUs?
c. How many samples do not contain any defective CPUs?

48. Random Samples A sample of 4 balls is to be selected at random from an urn containing 15 balls numbered 1 to 15. If 6 balls are green, 5 are white, and 4 are black, then:
a. How many different samples can be selected?
b. How many samples can be selected that contain at least 1 white ball?

49. Seating Arrangements In how many ways can three married couples be seated in a row of six seats:
a. If there are no seating restrictions?
b. If men and women must alternate?
c. If each married couple must sit together?

50. Team Selection There are seven boys and five girls in the debate squad at Franklin High School. In how many ways can a four-member debating team be selected:
a. If there are no restrictions?
b. If two boys and two girls must be on the team?
c. If at least two boys must be on the team?

CHAPTER 6　Before Moving On . . .

1. Let $U = \{a, b, c, d, e, f, g\}$, $A = \{a, d, f, g\}$, $B = \{d, f, g\}$, and $C = \{b, c, e, f\}$. Find
a. $A \cap (B \cup C)$
b. $(A \cap C) \cup (B \cup C)$
c. A^c

2. Let A, B, and C be subsets of a universal set U, and suppose that $n(U) = 120$, $n(A) = 20$, $n(A \cap B) = 10$, $n(A \cap C) = 11$, $n(B \cap C) = 9$, and $n(A \cap B \cap C) = 4$. Find $n[A \cap (B \cup C)^c]$.

3. In how many ways can four compact discs be selected from six different compact discs?

4. From a standard 52-card deck, how many 5-card poker hands can be dealt consisting of 3 deuces and 2 face cards?

5. There are six seniors and five juniors in the Chess Club at Madison High School. In how many ways can a team consisting of three seniors and two juniors be selected from the members of the Chess Club?

7

PROBABILITY

© Andrew F. Kazmierski 2010/Shutterstock.com

THE SYSTEMATIC STUDY of probability began in the seventeenth century when certain aristocrats wanted to discover superior strategies to use in the gaming rooms of Europe. Some of the best mathematicians of the period were engaged in this pursuit. Since then, probability has evolved in virtually every sphere of human endeavor in which an element of uncertainty is present.

We begin by introducing some of the basic terminology used in the study of the subject. Then, in Section 7.2, we give the technical meaning of the term *probability*. The rest of this chapter is devoted to the development of techniques for computing the probabilities of the occurrence of certain events.

What is the probability that a randomly chosen couple from a certain large metropolitan area is in the upper-income bracket if both spouses are working? In Example 2, page 415, we show how the income distribution for that metropolitan area can be used to determine this probability.

7.1   Experiments, Sample Spaces, and Events

Terminology

A number of specialized terms are used in the study of probability. We begin by defining the term *experiment*.

> **Experiment**
>
> An **experiment** is an activity with observable results.

The results of the experiment are called the **outcomes** of the experiment. Three examples of experiments are the following:

- Tossing a coin and observing whether it falls heads or tails
- Rolling a die and observing whether the number 1, 2, 3, 4, 5, or 6 shows up
- Testing a spark plug from a batch of 100 spark plugs and observing whether or not it is defective

In our discussion of experiments, we use the following terms:

> **Sample Point, Sample Space, and Event**
>
> **Sample point**: An outcome of an experiment
>
> **Sample space**: The set consisting of all possible sample points of an experiment
>
> **Event**: A subset of a sample space of an experiment

The sample space of an experiment is a universal set whose elements are precisely the outcomes, or the sample points, of the experiment; the events of the experiment are the subsets of the universal set. A sample space associated with an experiment that has a finite number of possible outcomes (sample points) is called a **finite sample space.**

Since the events of an experiment are subsets of a universal set (the sample space of the experiment), we may use the results for set theory given in Chapter 6 to help us study probability. The event B is said to **occur** in a trial of an experiment whenever B contains the observed outcome. We begin by explaining the roles played by the empty set and a universal set when they are viewed as events associated with an experiment. The empty set, $\emptyset$, is called the *impossible event*; it cannot occur because $\emptyset$ has no elements (outcomes). Next, the universal set S is referred to as the *certain event*; it must occur because S contains all the outcomes of the experiment.

This terminology is illustrated in the next several examples.

EXAMPLE 1 Describe the sample space associated with the experiment of tossing a coin and observing whether it falls heads or tails. What are the events of this experiment?

Solution   The two outcomes are heads and tails, and the required sample space is given by $S = \{H, T\}$, where H denotes the outcome heads and T denotes the outcome tails. The events of the experiment, the subsets of S, are

$$\emptyset, \{H\}, \{T\}, S$$

Note that we have included the impossible event, $\emptyset$, and the certain event, S.   ∎

Since the events of an experiment are subsets of the sample space of the experiment, we may talk about the union and intersection of any two events; we can also consider the complement of an event with respect to the sample space.

> **Union of Two Events**
>
> The **union of two events** E and F is the event $E \cup F$.

Thus, the event $E \cup F$ contains the set of outcomes of E and/or F.

> **Intersection of Two Events**
>
> The **intersection of two events** E and F is the event $E \cap F$.

Thus, the event $E \cap F$ contains the set of outcomes common to E and F.

> **Complement of an Event**
>
> The **complement of event** E is the event E^c.

Thus, the event E^c is the set containing all the outcomes in the sample space S that are not in E.

Venn diagrams depicting the union, intersection, and complement of events are shown in Figure 1. These concepts are illustrated in the following example.

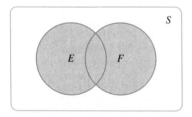

$E \cup F$

(a) The union of two events

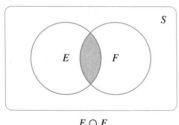

$E \cap F$

(b) The intersection of two events

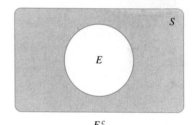

E^c

(c) The complement of the event E

FIGURE 1

EXAMPLE 2 Consider the experiment of rolling a die and observing the number that falls uppermost. Let $S = \{1, 2, 3, 4, 5, 6\}$ denote the sample space of the experiment, and let $E = \{2, 4, 6\}$ and $F = \{1, 3\}$ be events of this experiment. Compute (a) $E \cup F$, (b) $E \cap F$, and (c) F^c. Interpret your results.

Solution

a. $E \cup F = \{1, 2, 3, 4, 6\}$ and is the event that the outcome of the experiment is a 1, a 2, a 3, a 4, or a 6.

b. $E \cap F = \varnothing$ is the impossible event; the number appearing uppermost when a die is rolled cannot be both even and odd at the same time.

c. $F^c = \{2, 4, 5, 6\}$ is precisely the event that the event F does not occur.

If two events cannot occur at the same time, they are said to be mutually exclusive. Using set notation, we have the following definition.

> **Mutually Exclusive Events**
> E and F are **mutually exclusive** if $E \cap F = \emptyset$.

As before, we may use Venn diagrams to illustrate these events. In this case, the two mutually exclusive events are depicted as two nonintersecting circles (Figure 2).

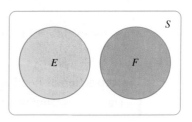

FIGURE 2
Mutually exclusive events

EXAMPLE 3 An experiment consists of tossing a coin three times and observing the resulting sequence of heads and tails.

a. Describe the sample space S of the experiment.
b. Determine the event E that exactly two heads appear.
c. Determine the event F that at least one head appears.

Explore & Discuss

1. Suppose E and F are two complementary events. Must E and F be mutually exclusive? Explain your answer.

2. Suppose E and F are mutually exclusive events. Must E and F be complementary? Explain your answer.

Solution

a. The sample points may be obtained with the aid of a tree diagram (Figure 3).

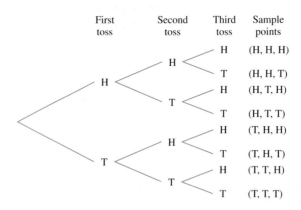

FIGURE 3

The required sample space S is given by

$$S = \{HHH, HHT, HTH, HTT, THH, THT, TTH, TTT\}$$

b. By scanning the sample space S obtained in part (a), we see that the outcomes in which exactly two heads appear are given by the event

$$E = \{HHT, HTH, THH\}$$

c. Proceeding as in part (b), we find

$$F = \{HHH, HHT, HTH, HTT, THH, THT, TTH\}$$

EXAMPLE 4 An experiment consists of rolling a pair of dice and observing the number that falls uppermost on each die.

a. Describe an appropriate sample space S for this experiment.
b. Determine the events $E_2, E_3, E_4, \ldots, E_{12}$ that the sum of the numbers falling uppermost is $2, 3, 4, \ldots, 12$, respectively.

Solution

a. We may represent each outcome of the experiment by an ordered pair of numbers, the first representing the number that appears uppermost on the first die and the second representing the number that appears uppermost on the second die. To distinguish between the two dice, think of the first die as being red and the second as being green. Since there are six possible outcomes for each die, the multiplication principle implies that there are $6 \cdot 6$, or 36, elements in the sample space:

$$S = \{(1, 1), (1, 2), (1, 3), (1, 4), (1, 5), (1, 6),$$
$$(2, 1), (2, 2), (2, 3), (2, 4), (2, 5), (2, 6),$$
$$(3, 1), (3, 2), (3, 3), (3, 4), (3, 5), (3, 6),$$
$$(4, 1), (4, 2), (4, 3), (4, 4), (4, 5), (4, 6),$$
$$(5, 1), (5, 2), (5, 3), (5, 4), (5, 5), (5, 6),$$
$$(6, 1), (6, 2), (6, 3), (6, 4), (6, 5), (6, 6)\}$$

b. With the aid of the results of part (a), we obtain the required list of events, shown in Table 1.

TABLE 1

Sum of Uppermost Numbers	Event
2	$E_2 = \{(1, 1)\}$
3	$E_3 = \{(1, 2), (2, 1)\}$
4	$E_4 = \{(1, 3), (2, 2), (3, 1)\}$
5	$E_5 = \{(1, 4), (2, 3), (3, 2), (4, 1)\}$
6	$E_6 = \{(1, 5), (2, 4), (3, 3), (4, 2), (5, 1)\}$
7	$E_7 = \{(1, 6), (2, 5), (3, 4), (4, 3), (5, 2), (6, 1)\}$
8	$E_8 = \{(2, 6), (3, 5), (4, 4), (5, 3), (6, 2)\}$
9	$E_9 = \{(3, 6), (4, 5), (5, 4), (6, 3)\}$
10	$E_{10} = \{(4, 6), (5, 5), (6, 4)\}$
11	$E_{11} = \{(5, 6), (6, 5)\}$
12	$E_{12} = \{(6, 6)\}$

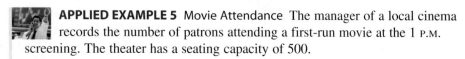 **APPLIED EXAMPLE 5** Movie Attendance The manager of a local cinema records the number of patrons attending a first-run movie at the 1 P.M. screening. The theater has a seating capacity of 500.

a. What is an appropriate sample space for this experiment?
b. Describe the event E that fewer than 50 people attend the screening.
c. Describe the event F that the theater is more than half full at the screening.

Solution

a. The number of patrons at the screening (the outcome) could run from 0 to 500. Therefore, a sample space for this experiment is

$$S = \{0, 1, 2, 3, \ldots, 500\}$$

b. $E = \{0, 1, 2, 3, \ldots, 49\}$
c. $F = \{251, 252, 253, \ldots, 500\}$

APPLIED EXAMPLE 6 Family Composition An experiment consists of recording, in order of their births, the sex composition of a three-child family in which the children were born at different times.

a. Describe an appropriate sample space S for this experiment.
b. Describe the event E that there are two girls and a boy in the family.
c. Describe the event F that the oldest child is a girl.
d. Describe the event G that the oldest child is a girl and the youngest child is a boy.

Solution

a. The sample points of the experiment may be obtained with the aid of the tree diagram shown in Figure 4, where b denotes a boy and g denotes a girl.

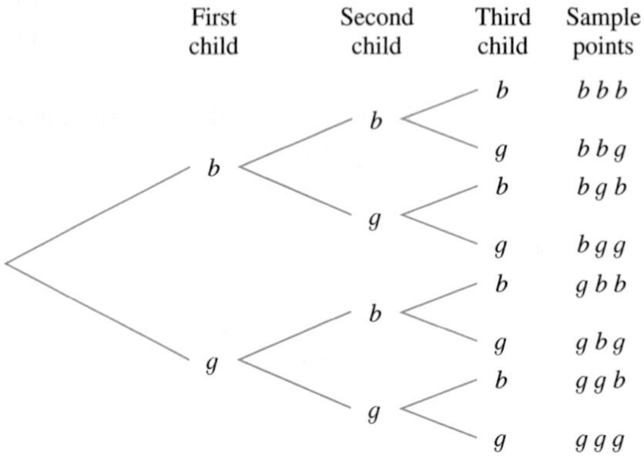

First child	Second child	Third child	Sample points
		b	$b\,b\,b$
	b	g	$b\,b\,g$
b		b	$b\,g\,b$
	g	g	$b\,g\,g$
		b	$g\,b\,b$
	b	g	$g\,b\,g$
g		b	$g\,g\,b$
	g	g	$g\,g\,g$

FIGURE 4
Tree diagram for three-child families

We see from the tree diagram that the required sample space is given by

$$S = \{bbb, bbg, bgb, bgg, gbb, gbg, ggb, ggg\}$$

Using the tree diagram, we find that:
b. $E = \{bgg, gbg, ggb\}$
c. $F = \{gbb, gbg, ggb, ggg\}$
d. $G = \{gbb, ggb\}$

The next example shows that sample spaces may be infinite.

APPLIED EXAMPLE 7 Testing New Products EverBrite is developing a high-amperage, high-capacity battery as a source for powering electric cars. The battery is tested by installing it in a prototype electric car and running the car with a fully charged battery on a test track at a constant speed of 55 mph until the car runs out of power. The distance covered by the car is then observed.

a. What is the sample space for this experiment?
b. Describe the event E that the driving range under test conditions is less than 150 miles.
c. Describe the event F that the driving range is between 200 and 250 miles, inclusive.

Solution

a. Since the distance d covered by the car in any run may be given by any non-negative number, the sample space S is given by

$$S = \{d \mid d \geq 0\}$$

b. The event E is given by

$$E = \{d \mid 0 \le d < 150\}$$

c. The event F is given by

$$F = \{d \mid 200 \le d \le 250\}$$

7.1 Self-Check Exercises

1. A sample of three apples taken from Cavallero's Fruit Stand is examined to determine whether the apples are good or rotten.
   a. What is an appropriate sample space for this experiment?
   b. Describe the event E that exactly one of the apples picked is rotten.
   c. Describe the event F that the first apple picked is rotten.

2. Refer to Self-Check Exercise 1.
   a. Find $E \cup F$.
   b. Find $E \cap F$.
   c. Find F^c.
   d. Are the events E and F mutually exclusive?

Solutions to Self-Check Exercises 7.1 can be found on page 372.

7.1 Concept Questions

1. Explain what is meant by an experiment. Give an example. For the example you have chosen, describe (a) a sample point, (b) the sample space, and (c) an event of the experiment.

2. What does it mean for two events to be mutually exclusive? Give an example of two mutually exclusive events E and F. How can you prove that they are mutually exclusive?

7.1 Exercises

In Exercises 1–6, let $S = \{a, b, c, d, e, f\}$ be a sample space of an experiment and let $E = \{a, b\}$, $F = \{a, d, f\}$, and $G = \{b, c, e\}$ be events of this experiment.

1. Find the events $E \cup F$ and $E \cap F$.

2. Find the events $F \cup G$ and $F \cap G$.

3. Find the events F^c and $E \cap G^c$.

4. Find the events E^c and $F^c \cap G$.

5. Are the events E and F mutually exclusive?

6. Are the events $E \cup F$ and $E \cap F^c$ mutually exclusive?

In Exercises 7–14, let $S = \{1, 2, 3, 4, 5, 6\}$, $E = \{2, 4, 6\}$, $F = \{1, 3, 5\}$, and $G = \{5, 6\}$.

7. Find the event $E \cup F \cup G$.

8. Find the event $E \cap F \cap G$.

9. Find the event $(E \cup F \cup G)^c$.

10. Find the event $(E \cap F \cap G)^c$.

11. Are the events E and F mutually exclusive?

12. Are the events F and G mutually exclusive?

13. Are the events E and F complementary?

14. Are the events F and G complementary?

In Exercises 15–20, let S be any sample space, and let E, F, and G be any three events associated with the experiment. Describe the events using the symbols $\cup$, $\cap$, and ^{c}.

15. The event that E and/or F occurs

16. The event that both E and F occur

17. The event that G does not occur

18. The event that E but not F occurs

19. The event that none of the events E, F, and G occurs

20. The event that E occurs but neither of the events F or G occurs

21. Consider the sample space S of Example 4, page 367.
    a. Determine the event that the number that falls uppermost on the first die is greater than the number that falls uppermost on the second die.
    b. Determine the event that the number that falls uppermost on the second die is double the number that falls uppermost on the first die.

22. Consider the sample space S of Example 4, page 367.
   a. Determine the event that the sum of the numbers falling uppermost is less than or equal to 7.
   b. Determine the event that the number falling uppermost on one die is a 4 and the number falling uppermost on the other die is greater than 4.

23. Let $S = \{a, b, c\}$ be a sample space of an experiment with outcomes a, b, and c. List all the events of this experiment.

24. Let $S = \{1, 2, 3\}$ be a sample space associated with an experiment.
   a. List all events of this experiment.
   b. How many subsets of S contain the number 3?
   c. How many subsets of S contain either the number 2 or the number 3?

25. An experiment consists of selecting a card from a standard deck of playing cards and noting whether the card is black (B) or red (R).
   a. Describe an appropriate sample space for this experiment.
   b. What are the events of this experiment?

26. An experiment consists of selecting a letter at random from the letters in the word *MASSACHUSETTS* and observing the outcomes.
   a. What is an appropriate sample space for this experiment?
   b. Describe the event "the letter selected is a vowel."

27. An experiment consists of tossing a coin, rolling a die, and observing the outcomes.
   a. Describe an appropriate sample space for this experiment.
   b. Describe the event "a head is tossed and an even number is rolled."

28. An experiment consists of spinning the hand of the numbered disc shown in the following figure and then observing the region in which the pointer stops. (If the needle stops on a line, the result is discounted, and the needle is spun again.)

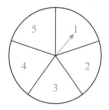

   a. What is an appropriate sample space for this experiment?
   b. Describe the event "the spinner points to the number 2."
   c. Describe the event "the spinner points to an odd number."

29. A die is rolled, and the number that falls uppermost is observed. Let E denote the event that the number shown is a 2, and let F denote the event that the number shown is an even number.
   a. Are the events E and F mutually exclusive?
   b. Are the events E and F complementary?

30. A die is rolled, and the number that falls uppermost is observed. Let E denote the event that the number shown is even, and let F denote the event that the number is an odd number.
   a. Are the events E and F mutually exclusive?
   b. Are the events E and F complementary?

31. QUALITY CONTROL A sample of three transistors taken from a local electronics store was examined to determine whether the transistors were defective (d) or nondefective (n). What is an appropriate sample space for this experiment?

32. MANAGEMENT DECISION From a list of five applicants for a sales position, a, b, c, d, and e, two are selected for the next round of interviews.
   a. Describe an appropriate sample space S for this experiment.
   b. Describe the event E that the interviewees include applicant a.
   c. Describe the event F that the interviewees include applicants a and c.
   d. Describe the event G that the interviewees include applicants d and e.

33. FAMILY COMPOSITION An experiment consists of recording, in order of their births, the sex composition of a four-child family in which the children were born at different times.
   a. Describe an appropriate sample space S for this experiment.
   b. Describe the event E that there are three boys and a girl in the family.
   c. Describe the event F that the youngest child is a girl.
   d. Describe the event G that the oldest and the youngest children are both girls.

34. BLOOD TYPING Human blood is classified by the presence or absence of three main antigens (A, B, and Rh). When a blood specimen is typed, the presence of the A and/or B antigen is indicated by listing the letter A and/or the letter B. If neither the A nor the B antigen is present, the letter O is used. The presence or absence of the Rh antigen is indicated by the symbols $+$ or $-$, respectively. Thus, if a blood specimen is classified as AB^+, it contains the A and the B antigens as well as the Rh antigen. Similarly, O^- blood contains none of the three antigens. Using this information, determine the sample space corresponding to the different blood groups.

35. GAME SHOWS In a television game show, the winner is asked to select three prizes from five different prizes, A, B, C, D, and E.
   a. Describe a sample space of possible outcomes (order is not important).
   b. How many points are there in the sample space corresponding to a selection that includes A?
   c. How many points are there in the sample space corresponding to a selection that includes A and B?
   d. How many points are there in the sample space corresponding to a selection that includes either A or B?

36. AUTOMATIC TELLERS The manager of a local bank observes how long it takes a customer to complete his transactions at the automatic bank teller machine.
   a. Describe an appropriate sample space for this experiment.
   b. Describe the event that it takes a customer between 2 and 3 min to complete his transactions at the automatic teller machines.

37. COMMON STOCKS Robin purchased shares of a machine tool company and shares of an airline company. Let E be the event that the shares of the machine tool company increase in value over the next 6 months, and let F be the event that the shares of the airline company increase in value over the next 6 months. Using the symbols $\cup$, $\cap$, and ^{c}, describe the following events.

a. The shares in the machine tool company do not increase in value.

b. The shares in both the machine tool company and the airline company do not increase in value.

c. The shares of at least one of the two companies increase in value.

d. The shares of only one of the two companies increase in value.

38. CUSTOMER SERVICE SURVEYS The customer service department of Universal Instruments, manufacturer of the Galaxy home computer, conducted a survey among customers who had returned their purchase registration cards. Purchasers of its deluxe model home computer were asked to report the length of time (t) in days before service was required.

a. Describe a sample space corresponding to this survey.

b. Describe the event E that a home computer required service before a period of 90 days had elapsed.

c. Describe the event F that a home computer did not require service before a period of 1 year had elapsed.

39. ASSEMBLY-TIME STUDIES A time study was conducted by the production manager of Vista Vision to determine the length of time in minutes required by an assembly worker to complete a certain task during the assembly of its Pulsar HDTV sets.

a. Describe a sample space corresponding to this time study.

b. Describe the event E that an assembly worker took 2 min or less to complete the task.

c. Describe the event F that an assembly worker took more than 2 min to complete the task.

40. POLITICAL POLLS An opinion poll is conducted among a state's electorate to determine the relationship between their income levels and their stands on a proposition aimed at reducing state income taxes. Voters are classified as belonging to either the low-, middle-, or upper-income group. They are asked whether they favor, oppose, or are undecided about the proposition. Let the letters L, M, and U represent the low-, middle-, and upper-income groups, respectively, and let the letters f, o, and u represent the responses—favor, oppose, and undecided, respectively.

a. Describe a sample space corresponding to this poll.

b. Describe the event E_1 that a respondent favors the proposition.

c. Describe the event E_2 that a respondent opposes the proposition and does not belong to the low-income group.

d. Describe the event E_3 that a respondent does not favor the proposition and does not belong to the upper-income group.

41. QUALITY CONTROL As part of a quality-control procedure, an inspector at Bristol Farms randomly selects ten eggs from each consignment of eggs he receives and records the number of broken eggs.

a. What is an appropriate sample space for this experiment?

b. Describe the event E that at most three eggs are broken.

c. Describe the event F that at least five eggs are broken.

42. POLITICAL POLLS In the opinion poll of Exercise 40, the voters were also asked to indicate their political affiliations—Democrat, Republican, or Independent. As before, let the letters L, M, and U represent the low-, middle-, and upper-income groups, respectively. Let the letters D, R, and I represent Democrat, Republican, and Independent, respectively.

a. Describe a sample space corresponding to this poll.

b. Describe the event E_1 that a respondent is a Democrat.

c. Describe the event E_2 that a respondent belongs to the upper-income group and is a Republican.

d. Describe the event E_3 that a respondent belongs to the middle-income group and is not a Democrat.

43. SHUTTLE BUS USAGE A certain airport hotel operates a shuttle bus service between the hotel and the airport. The maximum capacity of a bus is 20 passengers. On alternate trips of the shuttle bus over a period of 1 week, the hotel manager kept a record of the number of passengers arriving at the hotel in each bus.

a. What is an appropriate sample space for this experiment?

b. Describe the event E that a shuttle bus carried fewer than ten passengers.

c. Describe the event F that a shuttle bus arrived with a full load.

44. SPORTS Eight players, A, B, C, D, E, F, G, and H, are competing in a series of elimination matches of a tennis tournament in which the winner of each preliminary match will advance to the semifinals and the winners of the semifinals will advance to the finals. An outline of the scheduled matches follows. Describe a sample space listing the possible participants in the finals.

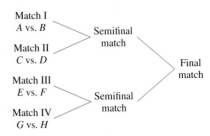

45. An experiment consists of selecting a card at random from a well-shuffled 52-card deck. Let E denote the event that an ace is drawn, and let F denote the event that a spade is drawn. Show that $n(E \cup F) = n(E) + n(F) - n(E \cap F)$.

46. Let S be a sample space for an experiment. Show that if E is any event of an experiment, then E and E^c are mutually exclusive.

47. Let S be a sample space for an experiment, and let E and F be events of this experiment. Show that the events $E \cup F$ and $E^c \cap F^c$ are mutually exclusive.
Hint: Use De Morgan's Law.

48. Let S be a sample space of an experiment with n outcomes. Determine the number of events of this experiment.

In Exercises 49 and 50, determine whether the statement is true or false. If it is true, explain why it is true. If it is false, give an example to show why it is false.

49. If E and F are mutually exclusive and E and G are mutually exclusive, then F and G are mutually exclusive.

50. The numbers 1, 2, and 3 are written separately on three pieces of paper. These slips of paper are then placed in a bowl. If you draw two slips from the bowl, one at a time and without replacement, then the sample space for this experiment consists of six elements.

7.1 Solutions to Self-Check Exercises

1. a. Let g denote a good apple, and let r donate a rotten apple. Thus, the required sample points may be obtained with the aid of a tree diagram (compare with Example 3). The required sample space is given by

$$S = \{ggg, ggr, grg, grr, rgg, rgr, rrg, rrr\}$$

b. By scanning the sample space S obtained in part (a), we identify the outcomes in which exactly one apple is rotten. We find

$$E = \{ggr, grg, rgg\}$$

c. Proceeding as in part (b), we find

$$F = \{rgg, rgr, rrg, rrr\}$$

2. Using the results of Self-Check Exercise 1, we find:
a. $E \cup F = \{ggr, grg, rgg, rgr, rrg, rrr\}$
b. $E \cap F = \{rgg\}$
c. F^c is the set of outcomes in S but not in F. Thus,

$$F^c = \{ggg, ggr, grg, grr\}$$

d. Since $E \cap F \neq \varnothing$, we conclude that E and F are not mutually exclusive.

7.2 Definition of Probability

Finding the Probability of an Event

Let's return to the coin-tossing experiment. The sample space of this experiment is given by $S = \{H, T\}$, where the sample points H and T correspond to the two possible outcomes, heads and tails. If the coin is *unbiased*, then there is *one chance out of two* of obtaining a head (or a tail), and we say that the *probability* of tossing a head (tail) is $\frac{1}{2}$, abbreviated

$$P(H) = \frac{1}{2} \quad \text{and} \quad P(T) = \frac{1}{2}$$

An alternative method of obtaining the values of $P(H)$ and $P(T)$ is based on continued experimentation and does not depend on the assumption that the two outcomes are equally likely. Table 2 summarizes the results of such an exercise.

Observe that the relative frequencies (column 3) differ considerably when the number of trials is small, but as the number of trials becomes very large, the relative frequency approaches the number .5. This result suggests that we assign to $P(H)$ the value $\frac{1}{2}$, as before.

More generally, consider an experiment that may be repeated over and over again under independent and similar conditions. Suppose that in n trials an event E occurs m

TABLE 2

As the Number of Trials Increases, the Relative Frequency Approaches .5

Number of Tosses, n	Number of Heads, m	Relative Frequency of Heads, m/n
10	4	.4000
100	58	.5800
1,000	492	.4920
10,000	5,034	.5034
20,000	10,024	.5012
40,000	20,032	.5008

times. We call the ratio m/n the **relative frequency** of the event E after n repetitions. If this relative frequency approaches some value $P(E)$ as n becomes larger and larger, then $P(E)$ is called the **empirical probability** of E. Thus, the probability $P(E)$ of an event occurring is a measure of the proportion of the time that the event E will occur in the long run. Observe that this method of computing the probability of a head occurring is effective even when a biased coin is used in the experiment. The relative frequency distribution is often referred to as an *observed* or *empirical probability distribution.*

The **probability of an event** is a number that lies between 0 and 1, inclusive. In general, the larger the probability of an event, the more likely that the event will occur. Thus, an event with a probability of .8 is more likely to occur than an event with a probability of .6. An event with a probability of $\frac{1}{2}$, or .5, has a fifty-fifty chance of occurring.

Now suppose we are given an experiment and wish to determine the probabilities associated with certain events of the experiment. This problem could be solved by computing $P(E)$ directly for each event E of interest. In practice, however, the number of events of interest is usually quite large, so this approach is not satisfactory.

The following approach is particularly suitable when the sample space of an experiment is finite.* Let S be a finite sample space with n outcomes; that is,

$$S = \{s_1, s_2, s_3, \ldots, s_n\}$$

Then the events

$$\{s_1\}, \{s_2\}, \{s_3\}, \ldots, \{s_n\}$$

that consist of exactly one point are called the **elementary,** or **simple, events** of the experiment. They are elementary in the sense that any (nonempty) event of the experiment may be obtained by taking a finite union of suitable elementary events. The simple events of an experiment are also **mutually exclusive;** that is, given any two simple events of the experiment, only one can occur.

By assigning probabilities to each of the simple events, we obtain the results shown in Table 3. This table is called a **probability distribution** for the experiment. The function P, which assigns a probability to each of the simple events, is called a **probability function.**

The numbers $P(s_1), P(s_2), \ldots, P(s_n)$ have the following properties:

1. $0 \leq P(s_i) \leq 1$ $i = 1, 2, \ldots, n$
2. $P(s_1) + P(s_2) + \cdots + P(s_n) = 1$
3. $P(\{s_i\} \cup \{s_j\}) = P(s_i) + P(s_j) \ (i \neq j)$ $i = 1, 2, \ldots, n; j = 1, 2, \ldots, n$

The first property simply states that the probability of a simple event must be between 0 and 1, inclusive. The second property states that the sum of the probabilities of all simple events of the sample space is 1. This follows from the fact that the event S is certain to occur. The third property states that the probability of the union of two simple events is given by the sum of their probabilities.

TABLE 3

A Probability Distribution

Simple Event	Probability*
$\{s_1\}$	$P(s_1)$
$\{s_2\}$	$P(s_2)$
$\{s_3\}$	$P(s_3)$
$\vdots$	$\vdots$
$\{s_n\}$	$P(s_n)$

*For simplicity, we use the notation $P(s_i)$ instead of the technically more correct $P(\{s_i\})$.

Exploring with
TECHNOLOGY

We can use a graphing calculator to simulate the coin-tossing experiment described earlier. Associate the outcome "a head" with the number 1 and the outcome "a tail" with the number 0. Select the function **randInt(** on the TI-83/84. (You can find this by pressing $\boxed{\text{MATH}}$ and then moving the cursor to **PRB.**) Select **randInt(** and enter 0, 1) and then press $\boxed{\text{ENTER}}$ repeatedly. This generates 0s and 1s randomly, which simulates the results of tossing an unbiased coin.

---

*For the remainder of the chapter, we assume that all sample spaces are finite.

As we saw earlier, there is no unique method for assigning probabilities to the simple events of an experiment. In practice, the methods that are used to determine these probabilities may range from theoretical considerations of the problem on the one extreme to the reliance on "educated guesses" on the other.

Sample spaces in which the outcomes are equally likely are called **uniform sample spaces.** Assigning probabilities to the simple events in these spaces is relatively easy.

Probability of an Event in a Uniform Sample Space

If

$$S = \{s_1, s_2, \ldots, s_n\}$$

is the sample space for an experiment in which the outcomes are equally likely, then we assign the probabilities

$$P(s_1) = P(s_2) = \cdots = P(s_n) = \frac{1}{n}$$

to each of the simple events $\{s_1\}, \{s_2\}, \ldots, \{s_n\}$.

VIDEO **EXAMPLE 1** A fair die is rolled, and the number that falls uppermost is observed. Determine the probability distribution for the experiment.

Solution   The sample space for the experiment is $S = \{1, 2, 3, 4, 5, 6\}$, and the simple events are accordingly given by the sets $\{1\}, \{2\}, \{3\}, \{4\}, \{5\}$, and $\{6\}$. Since the die is assumed to be fair, the six outcomes are equally likely. We therefore assign a probability of $\frac{1}{6}$ to each of the simple events and obtain the probability distribution shown in Table 4.

TABLE 4

A Probability Distribution

Simple Event	Probability
$\{1\}$	$\frac{1}{6}$
$\{2\}$	$\frac{1}{6}$
$\{3\}$	$\frac{1}{6}$
$\{4\}$	$\frac{1}{6}$
$\{5\}$	$\frac{1}{6}$
$\{6\}$	$\frac{1}{6}$

Explore & Discuss

You suspect that a die is biased.

1. Describe a method you might use to show that your assertion is correct.

2. How would you assign the probability to each outcome 1 through 6 of an experiment that consists of rolling the die and observing the number that lands uppermost?

The next example shows how the *relative frequency* interpretation of probability lends itself to the computation of probabilities.

 APPLIED EXAMPLE 2 Testing New Products Refer to Example 7, Section 7.1. The data shown in Table 5 were obtained in tests involving 200 test runs. Each run was made with a fully charged battery.

a. Describe an appropriate sample space for this experiment.

b. Find the empirical probability distribution for this experiment.

TABLE 5

Data Obtained During 200 Test Runs of an Electric Car

Distance Covered in Miles, x	Frequency of Occurrence
$0 < x \leq 50$	4
$50 < x \leq 100$	10
$100 < x \leq 150$	30
$150 < x \leq 200$	100
$200 < x \leq 250$	40
$250 < x$	16

Solution

a. Let s_1 denote the outcome that the distance covered by the car does not exceed 50 miles; let s_2 denote the outcome that the distance covered by the car is greater than 50 miles but does not exceed 100 miles, and so on. Finally, let s_6 denote the outcome that the distance covered by the car is greater than 250 miles. Then the required sample space is given by

$$S = \{s_1, s_2, s_3, s_4, s_5, s_6\}$$

TABLE 6

A Probability Distribution

Simple Event	Probability
$\{s_1\}$	.02
$\{s_2\}$	.05
$\{s_3\}$	.15
$\{s_4\}$	.50
$\{s_5\}$	.20
$\{s_6\}$	.08

b. To compute the empirical probability distribution for the experiment, we turn to the relative frequency interpretation of probability. Accepting the inaccuracies inherent in a relatively small number of trials (200 runs), we take the probability of s_1 occurring as

$$P(s_1) = \frac{\text{Number of trials in which } s_1 \text{ occurs}}{\text{Total number of trials}}$$

$$= \frac{4}{200} = .02$$

In a similar manner, we assign probabilities to the other simple events, obtaining the probability distribution shown in Table 6. ■

We are now in a position to give a procedure for computing the probability $P(E)$ of an arbitrary event E of an experiment.

> **Finding the Probability of an Event E**
> 1. Determine a sample space S associated with the experiment.
> 2. Assign probabilities to the simple events of S.
> 3. If $E = \{s_1, s_2, s_3, \ldots, s_n\}$, where $\{s_1\}, \{s_2\}, \{s_3\}, \ldots, \{s_n\}$ are simple events, then
> $$P(E) = P(s_1) + P(s_2) + P(s_3) + \cdots + P(s_n)$$
> If E is the empty set, $\varnothing$, then $P(E) = 0$.

The principle stated in Step 3 is called the **addition principle** and is a consequence of Property 3 of the probability function (page 373). This principle allows us to find the probabilities of all other events once the probabilities of the simple events are known.

⚠️ The addition rule in Step 3 applies *only* to the addition of probabilities of simple events.

 APPLIED EXAMPLE 3 Rolling Dice A pair of fair dice is rolled.

a. Calculate the probability that the two dice show the same number.
b. Calculate the probability that the sum of the numbers of the two dice is 6.

Solution From the results of Example 4, Section 7.1, page 367, we see that the sample space S of the experiment consists of 36 outcomes:

$$S = \{(1, 1), (1, 2), \ldots, (6, 5), (6, 6)\}$$

Since both dice are fair, each of the 36 outcomes is equally likely. Accordingly, we assign the probability of $\frac{1}{36}$ to each simple event.

a. The event that the two dice show the same number is given by

$$E = \{(1, 1), (2, 2), (3, 3), (4, 4), (5, 5), (6, 6)\}$$

(Figure 5). Therefore, by the addition principle, the probability that the two dice show the same number is given by

$$P(E) = P[(1, 1)] + P[(2, 2)] + \cdots + P[(6, 6)]$$

$$= \frac{1}{36} + \frac{1}{36} + \cdots + \frac{1}{36} \quad \text{Six terms}$$

$$= \frac{1}{6}$$

b. The event that the sum of the numbers of the two dice is 6 is given by

$$E_6 = \{(1, 5), (2, 4), (3, 3), (4, 2), (5, 1)\}$$

(Figure 6). Therefore, the probability that the sum of the numbers on the two dice is 6 is given by

$$P(E_6) = P[(1, 5)] + P[(2, 4)] + P[(3, 3)] + P[(4, 2)] + P[(5, 1)]$$
$$= \frac{1}{36} + \frac{1}{36} + \cdots + \frac{1}{36} \quad \text{Five terms}$$
$$= \frac{5}{36}$$

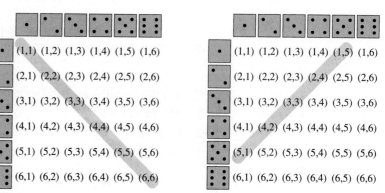

FIGURE **5**
The event that the two dice show the same number

FIGURE **6**
The event that the sum of the numbers on the two dice is 6

APPLIED EXAMPLE 4 Testing New Products Consider the experiment by EverBrite in Example 2. What is the probability that the prototype car will travel more than 150 miles on a fully charged battery?

Solution Using the results of Example 2, we see that the event that the car will travel more than 150 miles on a fully charged battery is given by $E = \{s_4, s_5, s_6\}$. Therefore, the probability that the car will travel more than 150 miles on one charge is given by

$$P(E) = P(s_4) + P(s_5) + P(s_6)$$

or, using the probability distribution for the experiment obtained in Example 2,

$$P(E) = .50 + .20 + .08 = .78$$

7.2 Self-Check Exercises

1. A biased die was rolled repeatedly, and the results of the experiment are summarized in the following table:

Outcome	1	2	3	4	5	6
Frequency of Occurrence	142	173	158	175	162	190

Using the relative frequency interpretation of probability, find the empirical probability distribution for this experiment.

2. In an experiment conducted to study the effectiveness of an eye-level third brake light in the prevention of rear-end col-

lisions, 250 of the 500 highway patrol cars of a certain state were equipped with such lights. At the end of the 1-year trial period, the records revealed that for those equipped with a third brake light there were 14 incidents of rear-end collision. There were 22 such incidents involving the cars not equipped with the accessory. On the basis of these data, what is the probability that a highway patrol car equipped with a third brake light will be rear-ended within a 1-year period? What is the probability that a car not so equipped will be rear-ended within a 1-year period?

Solutions to Self-Check Exercises 7.2 can be found on page 381.

7.2   Concept Questions

1. Define (a) a probability distribution and (b) a probability function. Give examples of each.

2. If $S = \{s_1, s_2, \ldots, s_n\}$ is the sample space for an experiment in which the outcomes are equally likely, what is the probability of each of the simple events $s_1, s_2, \ldots, s_n$? What is this type of sample space called?

3. Suppose $E = \{s_1, s_2, s_3, \ldots, s_n\}$, where E is an event of an experiment and $\{s_1\}, \{s_2\}, \{s_3\}, \ldots, \{s_n\}$ are simple events. If E is nonempty, what is $P(E)$? If E is empty, what is $P(E)$?

7.2   Exercises

In Exercises 1–8, list the simple events associated with each experiment.

1. A nickel and a dime are tossed, and the result of heads or tails is recorded for each coin.

2. A card is selected at random from a standard 52-card deck, and its suit—hearts (h), diamonds (d), spades (s), or clubs (c)—is recorded.

3. OPINION POLLS An opinion poll is conducted among a group of registered voters. Their political affiliation—Democrat (D), Republican (R), or Independent (I)—and their sex—male (m) or female (f)—are recorded.

4. QUALITY CONTROL As part of a quality-control procedure, eight circuit boards are checked, and the number of defective boards is recorded.

5. MOVIE ATTENDANCE In a survey conducted to determine whether movie attendance is increasing (i), decreasing (d), or holding steady (s) among various sectors of the population, participants are classified as follows:

   Group 1: Those aged 10–19

   Group 2: Those aged 20–29

   Group 3: Those aged 30–39

   Group 4: Those aged 40–49

   Group 5: Those aged 50 and older

   The response and age group of each participant are recorded.

6. DURABLE GOODS ORDERS An economist obtains data concerning durable goods orders each month. A record is kept for a 1-year period of any increase (i), decrease (d), or unchanged movement (u) in the number of durable goods orders for each month as compared with the number of such orders in the same month of the previous year.

7. BLOOD TYPES Blood tests are given as a part of the admission procedure at the Monterey Garden Community Hospital. The blood type of each patient (A, B, AB, or O) and the presence or absence of the Rh factor in each patient's blood (Rh^+ or Rh^-) are recorded.

8. METEOROLOGY A meteorologist preparing a weather map classifies the expected average temperature in each of five neighboring states (MN, WI, IA, IL, MO) for the upcoming week as follows:

a. More than 10° below average
b. Normal to 10° below average
c. Higher than normal to 10° above average
d. More than 10° above average

   Using each state's abbreviation and the categories—(a), (b), (c), and (d)—the meteorologist records these data.

9. GRADE DISTRIBUTIONS The grade distribution for a certain class is shown in the following table. Find the probability distribution associated with these data.

Grade	A	B	C	D	F
Frequency of Occurrence	4	10	18	6	2

10. BLOOD TYPES The percentage of the general population that has each blood type is shown in the following table. Determine the probability distribution associated with these data.

Blood Type	A	B	AB	O
Population, %	41	12	3	44

11. FIGHTING INFLATION In a survey of 2000 adults 18 years old and older conducted in 2007, the following question was asked: Is your family income keeping pace with the cost of living? The results of the survey follow:

Answer	Falling behind	Staying even	Increasing faster	Don't know
Respondents	800	880	240	80

Determine the empirical probability distribution associated with these data.

Source: Pew Research Center.

12. TRANSPORTATION FATALITIES The following breakdown of a total of 18,598 transportation fatalities that occurred in 2007 was obtained from records compiled by the U.S. Department of Transportation (DOT).

Mode of Transportation	Car	Train	Bicycle	Plane
Number of Fatalities	16,520	845	698	535

What is the probability that a victim randomly selected from this list of transportation fatalities for 2007 died in:
a. A car crash or a bicycle accident?
b. A train or a plane accident?

Source: U.S. Department of Transportation.

13. **RED-LIGHT RUNNERS** In a survey of 800 likely voters, the following question was asked: Do you support using cameras to identify red-light runners? The results of the survey follow:

Answer	Strongly support	Somewhat support	Somewhat oppose	Strongly oppose	Don't know
Respondents	360	192	88	144	16

What is the probability that a person in the survey selected at random favors using cameras to identify red-light runners?

Source: Public Opinion Strategies.

14. **GREAT RECESSION** In a survey conducted by AlixPartners of 4980 adults 18 years old and older in June 2009, during the "Great Recession," the following question was asked: How long do you think it will take to recover your personal net worth? The results of the survey follow:

Answer (years)	1–2	3–4	5–10	≥10
Respondents	1006	1308	2113	553

a. Determine the empirical probability distribution associated with these data.
b. If a person who participated in the survey is selected at random, what is the probability that he or she expects that it will take 5 or more years to recover his or her personal net worth?

Source: AlixPartners.

15. **CONSUMER SURVEY** In an online survey of 500 adults living with children under the age of 18 years, the participants were asked how many days per week they cook at home. The results of the survey are summarized below:

Number of Days	0	1	2	3	4	5	6	7
Respondents	25	30	45	75	55	100	85	85

Determine the empirical probability distribution associated with these data.

Source: Super Target.

16. **CHECKING INTO A HOTEL ROOM** In a survey of 3019 guests, the following question was asked: What is the first thing you do after checking into a hotel room? The results of the survey follow:

Activity	Respondents
Adjust the thermostat	1027
Turn on the TV	755
Unpack	634
Check out the free toiletries	211
Plug in rechargeable electronics	60
Find the gym	30
Other	302

What is the probability that a person selected at random from the list of guests surveyed would, as a first activity:
a. Adjust the thermostat or plug in rechargeable electronics?
b. Unpack or find the gym?

Source: Tripadvisor.

17. **POLITICAL VIEWS** In a poll conducted among 2000 college freshmen to ascertain the political views of college students, the accompanying data were obtained. Determine the empirical probability distribution associated with these data.

Political Views	A	B	C	D	E
Respondents	52	398	1140	386	24

A: Far left
B: Liberal
C: Middle of the road
D: Conservative
E: Far right

18. **PRODUCT SAFETY SURVEYS** The accompanying data were obtained from a survey of 1500 Americans who were asked: How safe are American-made consumer products? Determine the empirical probability distribution associated with these data.

Rating	A	B	C	D	E
Respondents	285	915	225	30	45

A: Very safe
B: Somewhat safe
C: Not too safe
D: Not safe at all
E: Don't know

19. **TRAFFIC SURVEYS** The number of cars entering a tunnel leading to an airport in a major city over a period of 200 peak hours was observed, and the following data were obtained:

Number of Cars, x	Frequency of Occurrence
$0 < x \le 200$	15
$200 < x \le 400$	20
$400 < x \le 600$	35
$600 < x \le 800$	70
$800 < x \le 1000$	45
$x > 1000$	15

a. Describe an appropriate sample space for this experiment.
b. Find the empirical probability distribution for this experiment.

20. **ARRIVAL TIMES** The arrival times of the 8 A.M. Boston-based commuter train as observed in the suburban town of Sharon over 120 weekdays is summarized below:

Arrival Time, x	Frequency of Occurrence
7:56 A.M. $< x \le$ 7:58 A.M.	4
7:58 A.M. $< x \le$ 8:00 A.M.	18
8:00 A.M. $< x \le$ 8:02 A.M.	50
8:02 A.M. $< x \le$ 8:04 A.M.	32
8:04 A.M. $< x \le$ 8:06 A.M.	9
8:06 A.M. $< x \le$ 8:08 A.M.	4
8:08 A.M. $< x \le$ 8:10 A.M.	3

a. Describe an appropriate sample space for this experiment.

b. Find the empirical probability distribution for this experiment.

21. **CORRECTIVE LENS USE** According to Mediamark Research, during a certain year 84 million out of 179 million adults in the United States corrected their vision by using prescription eyeglasses, bifocals, or contact lenses. (Some respondents use more than one type.) What is the probability that an adult selected at random from the adult population uses corrective lenses?

Source: Mediamark Research.

22. **CORRECTIONAL SUPERVISION** A study conducted by the Corrections Department of a certain state revealed that 163,605 people out of a total adult population of 1,778,314 were under correctional supervision (on probation, on parole, or in jail). What is the probability that a person selected at random from the adult population in that state is under correctional supervision?

23. **LIGHTNING DEATHS** According to data obtained from the National Weather Service, 376 of the 439 people killed by lightning in the United States between 1985 and 1992 were men. (Job and recreational habits of men make them more vulnerable to lightning.) Assuming that this trend holds in the future, what is the probability that a person killed by lightning:

a. Is a male?   **b.** Is a female?

Source: National Weather Service.

24. **QUALITY CONTROL** One light bulb is selected at random from a lot of 120 light bulbs, of which 5% are defective. What is the probability that the light bulb selected is defective?

25. **EFFORTS TO STOP SHOPLIFTING** According to a survey of 176 retailers, 46% of them use electronic tags as protection against shoplifting and employee theft. If one of these retailers is selected at random, what is the probability that the retailer uses electronic tags as antitheft devices?

26. If a ball is selected at random from an urn containing three red balls, two white balls, and five blue balls, what is the probability that it will be a white ball?

27. If a card is drawn at random from a standard 52-card deck, what is the probability that the card drawn is:

a. A diamond?   **b.** A black card?

c. An ace?

28. A pair of fair dice is rolled. What is the probability that:

a. The sum of the numbers shown uppermost is less than 5?

b. At least one 6 is rolled?

29. **TRAFFIC LIGHTS** What is the probability of arriving at a traffic light when it is red if the red signal is lit for 30 sec, the yellow signal for 5 sec, and the green signal for 45 sec?

30. **ROULETTE** What is the probability that a roulette ball will come to rest on an even number other than 0 or 00? (Assume that there are 38 equally likely outcomes consisting of the numbers 1–36, 0, and 00.)

31. **MANAGEMENT DECISIONS** Refer to Exercises 7.1, Problem 32. From a list of five applicants for a sales position, *a, b,* *c, d,* and *e,* two are selected for the next round of interviews. If the applicants are selected at random, what is the probability that the two interviewees chosen:

a. Include applicant *a*?

b. Include applicants *a* and *c*?

c. Include applicants *d* and *e*?

32. **FAMILY COMPOSITION** Refer to Exercises 7.1, Problem 33. An experiment consists of recording the sex composition, in order of their births, of a four-child family in which the children were born at different times. Assuming that a boy is equally likely as a girl to be born into a family, what is the probability that a four-child family chosen at random will have:

a. Three boys and a girl in the family?

b. A youngest child in the family who is a girl?

c. An oldest child and a youngest child in the family who are both girls?

33. **DISPOSITION OF CRIMINAL CASES** Of the 98 first-degree murder cases from 2002 through the first half of 2004 in the Suffolk superior court, 9 cases were thrown out of the system, 62 cases were plea-bargained, and 27 cases went to trial. What is the probability that a case selected at random

a. Was settled through plea bargaining?

b. Went to trial?

Source: Boston Globe.

34. **SWEEPSTAKES** In a sweepstakes sponsored by Gemini Paper Products, 100,000 entries have been received. If 1 grand prize, 5 first prizes, 25 second prizes, and 500 third prizes are to be awarded, what is the probability that a person who has submitted one entry will win:

a. The grand prize?

b. A prize?

35. **POLITICAL POLLS** An opinion poll was conducted among a group of registered voters in a certain state concerning a proposition aimed at limiting state and local taxes. Results of the poll indicated that 35% of the voters favored the proposition, 32% were against it, and the remaining group were undecided. If the results of the poll are assumed to be representative of the opinions of the state's electorate, what is the probability that a registered voter selected at random from the electorate:

a. Favors the proposition?

b. Is undecided about the proposition?

36. **PARENTAL INFLUENCE** In an online survey of 1962 executives from 64 countries conducted by Korn/Ferry International between August and October 2006, the executives were asked whether they would try to influence their children's career choices. Their replies: A (to a very great extent), B (to a great extent), C (to some extent), D (to a small extent), and E (not at all) are recorded below:

Answer	A	B	C	D	E
Respondents	135	404	1057	211	155

What is the probability that a randomly selected respondent's answer was D (to a small extent) or E (not at all)?

Source: Korn/Ferry International.

37. GREEN COMPANIES In a survey conducted in 2007 of 1004 adults 18 years old and older, the following question was asked: How are American companies doing on protecting the environment compared with companies in other countries? The results are summarized below:

Answer	Behind	Equal	Ahead	Don't know
Respondents	382	281	251	90

If an adult in the survey is selected at random, what is the probability that he or she said that American companies are equal or ahead on protecting the environment compared with companies in other countries?

Source: GfK Roper.

38. STAYING IN TOUCH In a poll conducted in 2007, 2000 adults ages 18 years old and older were asked how frequently they are in touch with their parents by phone. The results of the poll are as follows:

Answer	Monthly	Weekly	Daily	Don't know	Less
Respondents, %	11	47	32	2	8

If a person who participated in the poll is selected at random, what is the probability that the person said he or she kept in touch with his or her parents:
a. Once a week?
b. At least once a week?

Source: Pew Research Center.

39. SPENDING METHODS In a survey on consumer spending methods conducted in 2006, the following results were obtained:

Payment Method	Checks	Cash	Credit cards	Debit/ATM cards	Other
Transactions, %	37	14	25	15	9

If a transaction tracked in this survey is selected at random, what is the probability that the transaction was paid for:
a. With a credit card or with a debit/ATM card?
b. With cash or some method other than with a check, a credit card, or a debit/ATM card?

Source: Minute/Visa USA Research Services.

40. SECURITY BREACHES In a survey of 106 senior information technology and data security professionals at major U.S. companies regarding their confidence that they had detected all significant security breaches in the past year, the following responses were obtained:

Answer	Very confident	Moderately confident	Not very confident	Not at all confident
Respondents	21	56	22	7

What is the probability that a respondent in the survey selected at random:
a. Had little or no confidence that he or she had detected all significant security breaches in the past year?

b. Was very confident that he or she had detected all significant security breaches in the past year?

Source: Forsythe Solutions Group.

41. MUSIC VENUES In a survey designed to determine where people listen to music in their home, 1000 people were asked in which room at home they were mostly likely to listen to music. The results are tabulated below:

Room	Living room	Master bedroom	Study/home office	Kitchen	Bathroom	Other
Respondents	448	169	155	100	22	106

If a respondent is selected at random, what is the probability that he or she most likely listens to music:
a. In the living room?
b. In the study/home office or the kitchen?

Source: Phillips Electronics.

42. RETIREMENT BENEFITS VERSUS SALARY In a survey conducted in 2007 of 1402 workers 18 years old and older regarding their opinion on retirement benefits, the following data were obtained: 827 said that it was better to have excellent retirement benefits with a lower-than-expected salary, 477 said that it was better to have a higher-than-expected salary with poor retirement benefits, 42 said "neither," and 56 said "not sure." If a worker in the survey is selected at random, what is the probability that he or she answered that it was better to have:
a. Excellent retirement benefits with a lower-than-expected salary?
b. A higher-than-expected salary with poor retirement benefits?

Source: Transamerica Center for Retirement.

43. AIRLINE SAFETY In an attempt to study the leading causes of airline crashes, the following data were compiled from records of airline crashes from 1959 to 1994 (excluding sabotage and military action):

Primary Factor	Accidents
Pilot	327
Airplane	49
Maintenance	14
Weather	22
Airport/air traffic control	19
Miscellaneous/other	15

Assume that you have just learned of an airline crash and that the data give a generally good indication of the causes of airline crashes. Give an estimate of the probability that the primary cause of the crash was due to pilot error or bad weather.

Source: National Transportation Safety Board.

44. HOUSING APPRECIATION In a survey conducted in the fall 2006, 800 homeowners were asked about their expectations regarding the value of their home in the next few years; the results of the survey are summarized as follows:

Expectations	Homeowners
Decrease	48
Stay the same	152
Increase less than 5%	232
Increase 5–10%	240
Increase more than 10%	128

If a homeowner in the survey is chosen at random, what is the probability that he or she expected his or her home to
a. Stay the same or decrease in value in the next few years?
b. Increase 5% or more in value in the next few years?
Source: S&P, RBC Capital Markets.

45. A pair of fair dice is rolled, and the sum of the two numbers falling uppermost is observed. The probability of obtaining a sum of 2 is the same as that of obtaining a 7 since there is only one way of getting a 2—namely, by each die showing a 1; and there is only one way of obtaining a 7—namely, by one die showing a 3 and the other die showing a 4. What is wrong with this argument?

In Exercises 46–48, determine whether the given experiment has a sample space with equally likely outcomes.

46. A loaded die is rolled, and the number appearing uppermost on the die is recorded.

47. Two fair dice are rolled, and the sum of the numbers appearing uppermost is recorded.

48. A ball is selected at random from an urn containing six black balls and six red balls, and the color of the ball is recorded.

49. Let $S = \{s_1, s_2, s_3, s_4, s_5, s_6\}$ be the sample space associated with an experiment having the following probability distribution:

Outcome	s_1	s_2	s_3	s_4	s_5	s_6
Probability	$\frac{1}{12}$	$\frac{1}{4}$	$\frac{1}{12}$	$\frac{1}{6}$	$\frac{1}{3}$	$\frac{1}{12}$

Find the probability of the event:
a. $A = \{s_1, s_3\}$
b. $B = \{s_2, s_4, s_5, s_6\}$
c. $C = S$

50. Let $S = \{s_1, s_2, s_3, s_4, s_5\}$ be the sample space associated with an experiment having the following probability distribution:

Outcome	s_1	s_2	s_3	s_4	s_5
Probability	$\frac{1}{14}$	$\frac{3}{14}$	$\frac{6}{14}$	$\frac{2}{14}$	$\frac{2}{14}$

Find the probability of the event:
a. $A = \{s_1, s_2, s_4\}$
b. $B = \{s_1, s_5\}$
c. $C = S$

In Exercises 51 and 52, determine whether the statement is true or false. If it is true, explain why it is true. If it is false, give an example to show why it is false.

51. If $S = \{s_1, s_2, \ldots, s_n\}$ is a uniform sample space with n outcomes, then $0 \leq P(s_1) + P(s_2) + \cdots + P(s_n) \leq 1$.

52. Let $S = \{s_1, s_2, \ldots, s_n\}$ be a uniform sample space for an experiment. If $n \geq 5$ and $E = \{s_1, s_2, s_5\}$, then $P(E) = 3/n$.

7.2 Solutions to Self-Check Exercises

1.
$$P(1) = \frac{\text{Number of trials in which a 1 appears uppermost}}{\text{Total number of trials}}$$
$$= \frac{142}{1000}$$
$$= .142$$

Similarly, we compute $P(2), \ldots, P(6)$, obtaining the following probability distribution:

Outcome	1	2	3	4	5	6
Probability	.142	.173	.158	.175	.162	.190

2. The probability that a highway patrol car equipped with a third brake light will be rear-ended within a 1-year period is given by

$$\frac{\text{Number of rear-end collisions involving cars equipped with a third brake light}}{\text{Total number of such cars}} = \frac{14}{250} = .056$$

The probability that a highway patrol car not equipped with a third brake light will be rear-ended within a 1-year period is given by

$$\frac{\text{Number of rear-end collisions involving cars not equipped with a third brake light}}{\text{Total number of such cars}} = \frac{22}{250} = .088$$

7.3   Rules of Probability

Properties of the Probability Function and Their Applications

In this section, we examine some of the properties of the probability function and look at the role they play in solving certain problems. We begin by looking at the generalization of the three properties of the probability function, which were stated for simple events in Section 7.2. Let S be a sample space of an experiment and suppose E and F are events of the experiment. We have the following properties:

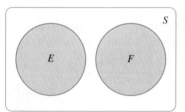

FIGURE 7
If E and F are mutually exclusive events, then $P(E \cup F) = P(E) + P(F)$.

Property 1. $P(E) \geq 0$ for any E.

Property 2. $P(S) = 1$.

Property 3. If E and F are mutually exclusive (that is, only one of them can occur or, equivalently, $E \cap F = \varnothing$), then

$$P(E \cup F) = P(E) + P(F)$$

(Figure 7).

Property 3 may be easily extended to the case involving any finite number of mutually exclusive events. Thus, if $E_1, E_2, \ldots, E_n$ are mutually exclusive events, then

$$P(E_1 \cup E_2 \cup \cdots \cup E_n) = P(E_1) + P(E_2) + \cdots + P(E_n)$$

TABLE 7

Probability Distribution

Score, x	Probability
$x > 700$	.01
$600 < x \leq 700$	.07
$500 < x \leq 600$	.19
$400 < x \leq 500$	.23
$300 < x \leq 400$	.31
$x \leq 300$	.19

APPLIED EXAMPLE 1   SAT Verbal Scores   The superintendent of a metropolitan school district has estimated the probabilities associated with the SAT verbal scores of students from that district. The results are shown in Table 7. If a student is selected at random, what is the probability that his or her SAT verbal score will be:

a. More than 400?
b. Less than or equal to 500?
c. Greater than 400 but less than or equal to 600?

Solution   Let A, B, C, D, E, and F denote, respectively, the event that the score is greater than 700, greater than 600 but less than or equal to 700, greater than 500 but less than or equal to 600, and so forth. Then these events are mutually exclusive. Therefore,

a. The probability that the student's score will be more than 400 is given by

$$P(D \cup C \cup B \cup A) = P(D) + P(C) + P(B) + P(A)$$
$$= .23 + .19 + .07 + .01$$
$$= .5$$

b. The probability that the student's score will be less than or equal to 500 is given by

$$P(D \cup E \cup F) = P(D) + P(E) + P(F)$$
$$= .23 + .31 + .19 = .73$$

c. The probability that the student's score will be greater than 400 but less than or equal to 600 is given by

$$P(C \cup D) = P(C) + P(D)$$
$$= .19 + .23 = .42$$

Property 3 holds if and only if E and F are mutually exclusive. In the general case, we have the following rule:

> **Property 4. Addition Rule**
>
> If E and F are any two events of an experiment, then
> $$P(E \cup F) = P(E) + P(F) - P(E \cap F)$$

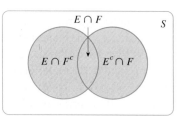

FIGURE 8
$E \cup F = (E \cap F^c) \cup (E \cap F) \cup (E^c \cap F)$

To derive this property, refer to Figure 8. Observe that we can write
$$E = (E \cap F^c) \cup (E \cap F) \quad \text{and} \quad F = (E^c \cap F) \cup (E \cap F)$$
as a union of disjoint sets. Therefore,
$$P(E) = P(E \cap F^c) + P(E \cap F) \quad \text{or} \quad P(E \cap F^c) = P(E) - P(E \cap F)$$
and
$$P(F) = P(E^c \cap F) + P(E \cap F) \quad \text{or} \quad P(E^c \cap F) = P(F) - P(E \cap F)$$

Finally, since $E \cup F = (E \cap F^c) \cup (E \cap F) \cup (E^c \cap F)$ is a union of disjoint sets, we have

$$
\begin{aligned}
P(E \cup F) &= P(E \cap F^c) + P(E \cap F) + P(E^c \cap F) \\
&= P(E) - P(E \cap F) + P(E \cap F) + P(F) - P(E \cap F) \quad \text{Use the earlier results.} \\
&= P(E) + P(F) - P(E \cap F)
\end{aligned}
$$

Note Observe that if E and F are mutually exclusive—that is, if $E \cap F = \varnothing$—then the equation of Property 4 reduces to that of Property 3. In other words, if E and F are mutually exclusive events, then $P(E \cup F) = P(E) + P(F)$. If E and F are not mutually exclusive events, then $P(E \cup F) = P(E) + P(F) - P(E \cap F)$. ■

EXAMPLE 2 A card is drawn from a well-shuffled deck of 52 playing cards. What is the probability that it is an ace or a spade?

Solution Let E denote the event that the card drawn is an ace and let F denote the event that the card drawn is a spade. Then
$$P(E) = \frac{4}{52} \quad \text{and} \quad P(F) = \frac{13}{52}$$

Furthermore, E and F are not mutually exclusive events. In fact, $E \cap F$ is the event that the card drawn is the ace of spades. Consequently,
$$P(E \cap F) = \frac{1}{52}$$

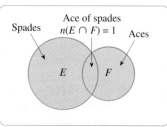

FIGURE 9
$P(E \cup F) = P(E) + P(F) - P(E \cap F)$

The event that a card drawn is an ace or a spade is $E \cup F$, with probability given by

$$
\begin{aligned}
P(E \cup F) &= P(E) + P(F) - P(E \cap F) \\
&= \frac{4}{52} + \frac{13}{52} - \frac{1}{52} = \frac{16}{52} = \frac{4}{13}
\end{aligned}
$$

(Figure 9). This result, of course, can be obtained by arguing that 16 of the 52 cards are either spades or aces of other suits. ■

Explore & Discuss

Let E, F, and G be any three events of an experiment. Use Equation (5) of Section 6.2 to show that

$$P(E \cup F \cup G) = P(E) + P(F) + P(G) - P(E \cap F) - P(E \cap G)$$
$$- P(F \cap G) + P(E \cap F \cap G)$$

If E, F, and G are pairwise mutually exclusive, what is $P(E \cup F \cup G)$?

VIDEO

APPLIED EXAMPLE 3 Quality Control The quality-control department of Vista Vision, manufacturer of the Pulsar 42-inch plasma TV, has determined from records obtained from the company's service centers that 3% of the sets sold experience video problems, 1% experience audio problems, and 0.1% experience both video and audio problems before the expiration of the 90-day warranty. Find the probability that a plasma TV purchased by a consumer will experience video or audio problems before the warranty expires.

Solution   Let E denote the event that a plasma TV purchased will experience video problems within 90 days, and let F denote the event that a plasma TV purchased will experience audio problems within 90 days. Then

$$P(E) = .03 \qquad P(F) = .01 \qquad P(E \cap F) = .001$$

The event that a plasma TV purchased will experience video problems or audio problems before the warranty expires is $E \cup F$, and the probability of this event is given by

$$P(E \cup F) = P(E) + P(F) - P(E \cap F)$$
$$= .03 + .01 - .001$$
$$= .039$$

(Figure 10).

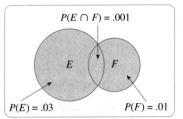

$P(E \cap F) = .001$

E F

$P(E) = .03$ $P(F) = .01$

FIGURE 10
$P(E \cup F) = P(E) + P(F) - P(E \cap F)$

Here is another property of a probability function that is of considerable aid in computing the probability of an event:

Property 5. Rule of Complements
If E is an event of an experiment and E^c denotes the complement of E, then

$$P(E^c) = 1 - P(E)$$

Property 5 is an immediate consequence of Properties 2 and 3. Indeed, we have $E \cup E^c = S$ and $E \cap E^c = \emptyset$, so

$$1 = P(S) = P(E \cup E^c) = P(E) + P(E^c)$$

and therefore,

$$P(E^c) = 1 - P(E)$$

APPLIED EXAMPLE 4 Warranties Refer to Example 3. What is the probability that a Pulsar 42-inch plasma TV bought by a consumer will *not* experience video or audio difficulties before the warranty expires?

Solution   Let E denote the event that a plasma TV bought by a consumer will experience video or audio difficulties before the warranty expires. Then the event that the plasma TV will not experience either problem before the warranty expires is given by E^c, with probability

$$P(E^c) = 1 - P(E)$$
$$= 1 - .039$$
$$= .961$$

Computations Involving the Rules of Probability

We close this section by looking at two additional examples that illustrate the rules of probability.

`VIDEO` **EXAMPLE 5** Let E and F be two mutually exclusive events, and suppose that $P(E) = .1$ and $P(F) = .6$. Compute:

a. $P(E \cap F)$ **b.** $P(E \cup F)$ **c.** $P(E^c)$
d. $P(E^c \cap F^c)$ **e.** $P(E^c \cup F^c)$

Solution

a. Since the events E and F are mutually exclusive—that is, $E \cap F = \varnothing$—we have $P(E \cap F) = 0$.

b. $P(E \cup F) = P(E) + P(F)$ Since E and F are mutually exclusive
$$= .1 + .6$$
$$= .7$$

c. $P(E^c) = 1 - P(E)$ Property 5
$$= 1 - .1$$
$$= .9$$

d. Observe that, by De Morgan's Law, $E^c \cap F^c = (E \cup F)^c$. Hence,

$$P(E^c \cap F^c) = P[(E \cup F)^c]$$ See Figure 11.
$$= 1 - P(E \cup F)$$ Property 5
$$= 1 - .7$$ Use the result of part (b).
$$= .3$$

e. Again using De Morgan's Law, we find

$$P(E^c \cup F^c) = P[(E \cap F)^c]$$
$$= 1 - P(E \cap F)$$
$$= 1 - 0$$ Use the result of part (a).
$$= 1$$

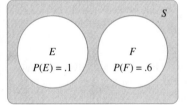

FIGURE 11
$P(E^c \cap F^c) = P[(E \cup F)^c]$

EXAMPLE 6 Let E and F be two events of an experiment with sample space S. Suppose $P(E) = .2$, $P(F) = .1$, and $P(E \cap F) = .05$. Compute:

a. $P(E \cup F)$
b. $P(E^c \cap F^c)$
c. $P(E^c \cap F)$ *Hint:* Draw a Venn diagram.

Solution

a. $P(E \cup F) = P(E) + P(F) - P(E \cap F)$ Property 4
$$= .2 + .1 - .05$$
$$= .25$$

b. Using De Morgan's Law, we have

$$P(E^c \cap F^c) = P[(E \cup F)^c]$$
$$= 1 - P(E \cup F) \qquad \text{Property 5}$$
$$= 1 - .25 \qquad \text{Use the result of part (a).}$$
$$= .75$$

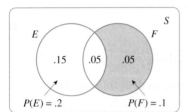

$P(E) = .2$ $P(F) = .1$

FIGURE 12
$P(E^c \cap F)$: the probability that the event F, but not the event E, will occur

c. From the Venn diagram describing the relationship among E, F, and S (Figure 12), we have

$$P(E^c \cap F) = .05 \qquad \text{The shaded subset is the event } E^c \cap F.$$

This result may also be obtained by using the relationship

$$P(E^c \cap F) = P(F) - P(E \cap F)$$
$$= .1 - .05$$
$$= .05$$

7.3 Self-Check Exercises

1. Let E and F be events of an experiment with sample space S. Suppose $P(E) = .4$, $P(F) = .5$, and $P(E \cap F) = .1$. Compute:
   a. $P(E \cup F)$ **b.** $P(E \cap F^c)$

2. Susan Garcia wishes to sell or lease a condominium through a realty company. The realtor estimates that the probability of finding a buyer within a month of the date the property is listed for sale or lease is .3, the probability of finding a lessee is .8, and the probability of finding both a buyer and a lessee is .1. Determine the probability that the property will be sold or leased within 1 month from the date the property is listed for sale or lease.

Solutions to Self-Check Exercises 7.3 can be found on page 391.

7.3 Concept Questions

1. Suppose that S is a sample space of an experiment, E and F are events of the experiment, and P is a probability function. Give the meaning of each of the following statements:
   a. $P(E) = 0$ **b.** $P(F) = 0.5$ **c.** $P(S) = 1$
   d. $P(E \cup F) = P(E) + P(F) - P(E \cap F)$

2. Give an example, based on a real-life situation, illustrating the property $P(E^c) = 1 - P(E)$, where E is an event and E^c is the complement of E.

7.3 Exercises

A pair of dice is rolled, and the number that appears uppermost on each die is observed. In Exercises 1–6, refer to this experiment, and find the probability of the given event.

1. The sum of the numbers is an even number.

2. The sum of the numbers is either 7 or 11.

3. A pair of 1s is thrown.

4. A double is thrown.

5. One die shows a 6, and the other is a number less than 3.

6. The sum of the numbers is at least 4.

An experiment consists of selecting a card at random from a 52-card deck. In Exercises 7–12, refer to this experiment and find the probability of the event.

7. A king of diamonds is drawn.

8. A diamond or a king is drawn.

9. A face card (i.e., a jack, queen, or king) is drawn.

10. A red face card is drawn.

11. An ace is not drawn.

12. A black face card is not drawn.

13. RAFFLES Five hundred raffle tickets were sold. What is the probability that a person holding one ticket will win the first prize? What is the probability that he or she will not win the first prize?

14. TV HOUSEHOLDS The results of a recent television survey of American TV households revealed that 87 out of every 100 TV households have at least one remote control. What is the probability that a randomly selected TV household does not have at least one remote control?

In Exercises 15–24, explain why the statement is incorrect.

15. The sample space associated with an experiment is given by $S = \{a, b, c\}$, where $P(a) = .3$, $P(b) = .4$, and $P(c) = .4$.

16. The probability that a bus will arrive late at the Civic Center is .35, and the probability that it will be on time or early is .60.

17. OFFICE POOLS A person participates in a weekly office pool in which he has one chance in ten of winning the purse. If he participates for 5 weeks in succession, the probability of winning at least one purse is $\frac{5}{10}$.

18. STOCK PRICES The probability that a certain stock will increase in value over a period of 1 week is .6. Therefore, the probability that the stock will decrease in value is .4.

19. A red die and a green die are tossed. The probability that a 6 will appear uppermost on the red die is $\frac{1}{6}$, and the probability that a 1 will appear uppermost on the green die is $\frac{1}{6}$. Hence, the probability that the red die will show a 6 or the green die will show a 1 is $\frac{1}{6} + \frac{1}{6}$.

20. Joanne, a high school senior, has applied for admission to four colleges, A, B, C, and D. She has estimated that the probability that she will be accepted for admission by college A, B, C, and D is .5, .3, .1, and .08, respectively. Thus, the probability that she will be accepted for admission by at least one college is $P(A) + P(B) + P(C) + P(D) = .5 + .3 + .1 + .08 = .98$.

21. The sample space associated with an experiment is given by $S = \{a, b, c, d, e\}$. The events $E = \{a, b\}$ and $F = \{c, d\}$ are mutually exclusive. Hence, the events E^c and F^c are mutually exclusive.

22. POKER A 5-card poker hand is dealt from a 52-card deck. Let A denote the event that a flush is dealt, and let B be the event that a straight is dealt. Then the events A and B are mutually exclusive.

23. RETAIL SALES Mark Owens, an optician, estimates that the probability that a customer coming into his store will purchase one or more pairs of glasses but not contact lenses is .40, and the probability that he will purchase one or more pairs of contact lenses but not glasses is .25. Hence, Owens concludes that the probability that a customer coming into his store will purchase neither a pair of glasses nor a pair of contact lenses is .35.

24. There are eight grades in Garfield Elementary School. If a student is selected at random from the school, then the probability that the student is in the first grade is $\frac{1}{8}$.

25. Let E and F be two events that are mutually exclusive, and suppose $P(E) = .2$ and $P(F) = .5$. Compute:
a. $P(E \cap F)$ **b.** $P(E \cup F)$
c. $P(E^c)$ **d.** $P(E^c \cap F^c)$

26. Let E and F be two events of an experiment with sample space S. Suppose $P(E) = .6$, $P(F) = .4$, and $P(E \cap F) = .2$. Compute:
a. $P(E \cup F)$ **b.** $P(E^c)$
c. $P(F^c)$ **d.** $P(E^c \cap F)$

27. Let $S = \{s_1, s_2, s_3, s_4\}$ be the sample space associated with an experiment having the probability distribution shown in the accompanying table. If $A = \{s_1, s_2\}$ and $B = \{s_1, s_3\}$, find:
a. $P(A)$, $P(B)$ **b.** $P(A^c)$, $P(B^c)$
c. $P(A \cap B)$ **d.** $P(A \cup B)$

Outcome	Probability
s_1	$\frac{1}{8}$
s_2	$\frac{3}{8}$
s_3	$\frac{1}{4}$
s_4	$\frac{1}{4}$

28. Let $S = \{s_1, s_2, s_3, s_4, s_5, s_6\}$ be the sample space associated with an experiment having the probability distribution shown in the accompanying table. If $A = \{s_1, s_2\}$ and $B = \{s_1, s_5, s_6\}$, find:
a. $P(A)$, $P(B)$ **b.** $P(A^c)$, $P(B^c)$
c. $P(A \cap B)$ **d.** $P(A \cup B)$
e. $P(A^c \cap B^c)$ **f.** $P(A^c \cup B^c)$

Outcome	Probability
s_1	$\frac{1}{3}$
s_2	$\frac{1}{8}$
s_3	$\frac{1}{6}$
s_4	$\frac{1}{6}$
s_5	$\frac{1}{12}$
s_6	$\frac{1}{8}$

29. TIRE SAFETY A team of automobile safety experts was asked by a television news station to conduct an experiment in which the tires of 100 randomly chosen cars of its employees were subjected to a safety inspection. It was determined that of the 100 cars inspected, 11 cars failed the tread depth test (at least one tire on the car was worn excessively), 45 cars failed the tire pressure test (at least one tire on the car was overinflated or underinflated), and 4 failed both the tread depth test and the tire pressure test. Find the probability that a car selected at random from this group of cars:
a. Failed only the tire pressure test.
b. Passed both the tread depth test and the tire pressure test.

30. **ALTERNATIVE FUEL VEHICLES** A survey was conducted by the local chapter of an environmental club regarding the ownership of alternative fuel vehicles (AFVs) among the members of the group. An AFV is a vehicle that runs on fuel other than petroleum fuels (petrol and diesel). It was found that of the 80 members of the club surveyed, 22 of them own at least one hybrid car, 12 of them own at least one electric car, and 4 of them own at least one hybrid and at least one electric car. If a member of the club is surveyed, what is the probability that he or she:
   a. Owns only hybrid cars?
   b. Owns no alternative fuel vehicles?

31. **TEACHER ATTITUDES** A nonprofit organization conducted a survey of 2140 metropolitan-area teachers regarding their beliefs about educational problems. The following data were obtained:

    900 said that lack of parental support is a problem.

    890 said that abused or neglected children are problems.

    680 said that malnutrition or students in poor health is a problem.

    120 said that lack of parental support and abused or neglected children are problems.

    110 said that lack of parental support and malnutrition or poor health are problems.

    140 said that abused or neglected children and malnutrition or poor health are problems.

    40 said that lack of parental support, abuse or neglect, and malnutrition or poor health are problems.

    What is the probability that a teacher selected at random from this group said that lack of parental support is the only problem hampering a student's schooling?
    Hint: Draw a Venn diagram.

32. **INVESTMENTS** In a survey of 200 employees of a company regarding their 401(k) investments, the following data were obtained:

    141 had investments in stock funds.

    91 had investments in bond funds.

    60 had investments in money market funds.

    47 had investments in stock funds and bond funds.

    36 had investments in stock funds and money market funds.

    36 had investments in bond funds and money market funds.

    22 had investments in stock funds, bond funds, and money market funds.

    What is the probability that an employee of the company chosen at random:
    a. Had investments in exactly two kinds of investment funds?
    b. Had investments in exactly one kind of investment fund?
    c. Had no investment in any of the three types of funds?

33. **RETAIL SALES** The probability that a shopper in a certain boutique will buy a blouse is .35, that she will buy a pair of pants is .30, and that she will buy a skirt is .27. The probability that she will buy both a blouse and a skirt is .15, that she will buy both a skirt and a pair of pants is .19, and that she will buy both a blouse and a pair of pants is .12. Finally, the probability that she will buy all three items is .08. What is the probability that a customer will buy
   a. Exactly one of these items?
   b. None of these items?

34. **COURSE ENROLLMENTS** Among 500 freshmen pursuing a business degree at a university, 320 are enrolled in an economics course, 225 are enrolled in a mathematics course, and 140 are enrolled in both an economics and a mathematics course. What is the probability that a freshman selected at random from this group is enrolled in:
   a. An economics and/or a mathematics course?
   b. Exactly one of these two courses?
   c. Neither an economics course nor a mathematics course?

35. **CONSUMER SURVEYS** A leading manufacturer of kitchen appliances advertised its products in two magazines: *Good Housekeeping* and the *Ladies Home Journal*. A survey of 500 customers revealed that 140 learned of its products from *Good Housekeeping*, 130 learned of its products from the *Ladies Home Journal*, and 80 learned of its products from both magazines. What is the probability that a person selected at random from this group saw the manufacturer's advertisement in:
   a. Both magazines?
   b. At least one of the two magazines?
   c. Exactly one magazine?

36. **ROLLOVER DEATHS** The following table gives the number of people killed in rollover crashes in various types of vehicles in 2002:

Types of Vehicles	Cars	Pickups	SUVs	Vans
Deaths	4768	2742	2448	698

Find the empirical probability distribution associated with these data. If a fatality due to a rollover crash in 2002 is picked at random, what is the probability that the victim was in:
   a. A car?   b. An SUV?   c. A pickup or an SUV?
   Source: National Highway Traffic Safety Administration.

37. **TAX PREPARATION** A survey in which people were asked how they were planning to prepare their taxes in 2007 revealed the following:

Method of Preparation	Percentage
Computer software	33.9
Accountant	23.6
Tax preparation service	17.4
Spouse, friend, or other relative will prepare	10.8
By hand	14.3

What is the probability that a randomly chosen participant in the survey

a. Was planning to use an accountant or a tax preparation service to prepare his or her taxes?

b. Was not planning to use computer software to prepare his or her taxes and was not planning to do taxes by hand?

Source: National Retail Federation.

38. **WOMEN'S APPAREL** In an online survey for Talbots of 1095 women ages 35 years old and older, the participants were asked what article of clothing women most want to fit perfectly. A summary of the results of the survey follows:

Article of Clothing	Respondents
Jeans	470
Black pantsuit	307
Cocktail dress	230
White shirt	22
Gown	11
Other	55

If a woman who participated in the survey is chosen at random, what is the probability that she most wants:

a. Jeans to fit perfectly?

b. A black pantsuit or a cocktail dress to fit perfectly?

Source: Market Tool's Zoom Panel.

39. **SWITCHING JOBS** Two hundred workers were asked: Would a better economy lead you to switch jobs? The results of the survey follow:

Answer	Very likely	Somewhat likely	Somewhat unlikely	Very unlikely	Don't know
Respondents	40	28	26	104	2

If a worker is chosen at random, what is the probability that he or she:

a. Is very unlikely to switch jobs?

b. Is somewhat likely or very likely to switch jobs?

Source: Accountemps.

40. **401(K) INVESTORS** According to a study conducted in 2003 concerning the participation, by age, of 401(k) investors, the following data were obtained:

Age	20s	30s	40s	50s	60s
Percent	11	28	32	22	7

a. What is the probability that a 401(k) investor selected at random in 2003 was in his or her 20s or 60s?

b. What is the probability that a 401(k) investor selected at random in 2003 was under the age of 50?

Source: Investment Company Institute.

41. **ALTERNATIVE ENERGY SOURCES** In a poll conducted among likely voters by Zogby International, voters were asked their opinion on the best alternative to oil and coal. The results are as follows:

Source	Nuclear	Wind	Fuel cells	Biofuels	Solar	Other/ no answer
Respondents, %	14.2	16.0	3.8	24.3	27.9	13.8

What is the probability that a randomly selected participant in the poll mentioned:

a. Wind or solar energy sources as the best alternative to oil and coal?

b. Nuclear or biofuels as the best alternative to oil and coal?

Source: Zogby International.

42. **ELECTRICITY GENERATION** Electricity in the United States is generated from many sources. The following table gives the sources as well as their shares in the production of electricity:

Source	Coal	Nuclear	Natural gas	Hydropower	Oil	Other
Share, %	50.0	19.3	18.7	6.7	3.0	2.3

If a source for generating electricity is picked at random, what is the probability that it comes from:

a. Coal or natural gas?

b. Nonnuclear sources?

Source: Energy Information Administration.

43. **DOWNLOADING MUSIC** The following table, compiled in 2004, gives the percentage of music downloaded from the United States and other countries by U.S. users:

Country	U.S.	Germany	Canada	Italy	U.K.	France	Japan	Other
Percent	45.1	16.5	6.9	6.1	4.2	3.8	2.5	14.9

a. Verify that the table does give a probability distribution for the experiment.

b. What is the probability that a user who downloads music, selected at random, obtained it from either the United States or Canada?

c. What is the probability that a U.S. user who downloads music, selected at random, does not obtain it from Italy, the United Kingdom (U.K.), or France?

Source: Felix Oberholtzer-Gee and Koleman Strumpf.

44. **PLANS TO KEEP CARS** In a survey conducted to determine how long Americans keep their cars, 2000 automobile owners were asked how long they planned to keep their present cars. The results of the survey follow:

Years Car Is Kept, x	Respondents
$0 \leq x < 1$	60
$1 \leq x < 3$	440
$3 \leq x < 5$	360
$5 \leq x < 7$	340
$7 \leq x < 10$	240
$10 \leq x$	560

Find the probability distribution associated with these data. What is the probability that an automobile owner selected at random from those surveyed planned to keep his or her present car:

a. Less than 5 years?

b. 3 years or more?

45. **ASSEMBLY-TIME STUDIES** A time study was conducted by the production manager of Universal Instruments to determine how much time it took an assembly worker to complete a certain task during the assembly of its Galaxy home computers. Results of the study indicated that 20% of the workers were able to complete the task in less than 3 min, 60% of the workers were able to complete the task in 4 min or less, and 10% of the workers required more than 5 min to complete the task. If an assembly-line worker is selected at random from this group, what is the probability that:

a. He or she will be able to complete the task in 5 min or less?

b. He or she will not be able to complete the task within 4 min?

c. The time taken for the worker to complete the task will be between 3 and 4 min (inclusive)?

46. **DISTRACTED DRIVING** According to a study of 100 drivers in metropolitan Washington, D.C., whose cars were equipped with cameras with sensors, the distractions and the number of incidents (crashes, near crashes, and situations that require an evasive maneuver after the driver was distracted) caused by these distractions are as follows:

Distraction	A	B	C	D	E	F	G	H	I
Driving Incidents	668	378	194	163	133	134	111	111	89

where A = Wireless device (cell phone, PDA)

B = Passenger

C = Something inside car

D = Vehicle

E = Personal hygiene

F = Eating

G = Something outside car

H = Talking/singing

I = Other

If an incident caused by a distraction is picked at random, what is the probability that it was caused by:

a. The use of a wireless device?

b. Something other than personal hygiene or eating?

Source: Virginia Tech Transportation Institute and NHTSA.

47. **GUN-CONTROL LAWS** A poll was conducted among 250 residents of a certain city regarding tougher gun-control laws. The results of the poll are shown in the table:

	Own Only a Handgun	Own Only a Rifle	Own a Handgun and a Rifle	Own Neither	Total
Favor Tougher Laws	0	12	0	138	150
Oppose Tougher Laws	58	5	25	0	88
No Opinion	0	0	0	12	12
Total	58	17	25	150	250

If one of the participants in this poll is selected at random, what is the probability that he or she:

a. Favors tougher gun-control laws?

b. Owns a handgun?

c. Owns a handgun but not a rifle?

d. Favors tougher gun-control laws and does not own a handgun?

48. **RISK OF AN AIRPLANE CRASH** According to a study of Western-built commercial jets involved in crashes from 1988 to 1998, the percentage of airplane crashes that occur at each stage of flight are as follows:

Phase	Percent
On ground, taxiing	4
During takeoff	10
Climbing to cruise altitude	19
En route	5
Descent and approach	31
Landing	31

If one of the doomed flights in the period 1988–1998 is picked at random, what is the probability that it crashed:

a. While taxiing on the ground or while en route?

b. During takeoff or landing?

If the study is indicative of airplane crashes in general, when is the risk of a plane crash the highest?

Source: National Transportation Safety Board.

49. Suppose the probability that Bill can solve a problem is p_1 and the probability that Mike can solve it is p_2. Show that the probability that Bill and Mike working independently can solve the problem is $p_1 + p_2 - p_1 p_2$.

50. Fifty raffle tickets are numbered 1 through 50, and one of them is drawn at random. What is the probability that the number is a multiple of 5 or 7? Consider the following "solution": Since 10 tickets bear numbers that are multiples of 5 and since 7 tickets bear numbers that are multiples of 7, we conclude that the required probability is

$$\frac{10}{50} + \frac{7}{50} = \frac{17}{50}$$

What is wrong with this argument? What is the correct answer?

In Exercises 51–54, determine whether the statement is true or false. If it is true, explain why it is true. If it is false, give an example to show why it is false.

51. If A is a subset of B and $P(B) = 0$, then $P(A) = 0$.

52. If A is a subset of B, then $P(A) \leq P(B)$.

53. If $E_1, E_2, \ldots, E_n$ are events of an experiment, then $P(E_1 \cup E_2 \cup \cdots \cup E_n) = P(E_1) + P(E_2) + \cdots + P(E_n)$.

54. If E is an event of an experiment, then $P(E) + P(E^c) = 1$.

7.3   Solutions to Self-Check Exercises

1. a. Using Property 4, we find

$$P(E \cup F) = P(E) + P(F) - P(E \cap F)$$
$$= .4 + .5 - .1$$
$$= .8$$

b. From the accompanying Venn diagram, in which the subset $E \cap F^c$ is shaded, we see that

$$P(E \cap F^c) = .3$$

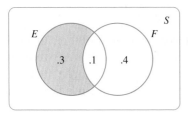

The result may also be obtained by using the relationship

$$P(E \cap F^c) = P(E) - P(E \cap F)$$
$$= .4 - .1 = .3$$

2. Let E denote the event that the realtor will find a buyer within 1 month of the date the property is listed for sale or lease, and let F denote the event that the realtor will find a lessee within the same time period. Then

$$P(E) = .3 \qquad P(F) = .8 \qquad P(E \cap F) = .1$$

The probability of the event that the realtor will find a buyer or a lessee within 1 month of the date the property is listed for sale or lease is given by

$$P(E \cup F) = P(E) + P(F) - P(E \cap F)$$
$$= .3 + .8 - .1 = 1$$

—that is, a certainty.

7.4   Use of Counting Techniques in Probability

Further Applications of Counting Techniques

As we have seen many times before, a problem in which the underlying sample space has a small number of elements may be solved by first determining all such sample points. However, for problems involving sample spaces with a large number of sample points, this approach is neither practical nor desirable.

In this section, we see how the counting techniques studied in Chapter 6 may be employed to help us solve problems in which the associated sample spaces contain large numbers of sample points. In particular, we restrict our attention to the study of uniform sample spaces—that is, sample spaces in which the outcomes are equally likely. For such spaces, we have the following result:

> **Computing the Probability of an Event in a Uniform Sample Space**
>
> Let S be a uniform sample space, and let E be any event. Then
>
> $$P(E) = \frac{\text{Number of outcomes in } E}{\text{Number of outcomes in } S} = \frac{n(E)}{n(S)} \qquad (1)$$

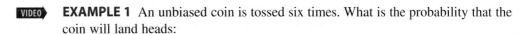

VIDEO   **EXAMPLE 1**   An unbiased coin is tossed six times. What is the probability that the coin will land heads:

a. Exactly three times?
b. At most three times?
c. On the first and the last toss?

Solution

a. Each outcome of the experiment may be represented as a sequence of heads and tails. Using the generalized multiplication principle, we see that the number of outcomes of this experiment is given by 2^6, or 64. Let E denote the event that the coin lands heads exactly three times. Since there are $C(6, 3)$ ways this can occur, we see that the required probability is

$$P(E) = \frac{n(E)}{n(S)} = \frac{C(6, 3)}{64} = \frac{\dfrac{6!}{3!\,3!}}{64} \qquad \text{\small S is a sample space of the experiment.}$$

$$= \frac{\dfrac{6 \cdot 5 \cdot 4}{3 \cdot 2}}{64} = \frac{20}{64} = \frac{5}{16} = .3125$$

b. Let F denote the event that the coin lands heads at most three times. Then $n(F)$ is given by the sum of the number of ways the coin lands heads zero times (no heads!), the number of ways it lands heads exactly once, the number of ways it lands heads exactly twice, and the number of ways it lands heads exactly three times. That is,

$$n(F) = C(6, 0) + C(6, 1) + C(6, 2) + C(6, 3)$$

$$= \frac{6!}{0!\,6!} + \frac{6!}{1!\,5!} + \frac{6!}{2!\,4!} + \frac{6!}{3!\,3!}$$

$$= 1 + 6 + \frac{6 \cdot 5}{2} + \frac{6 \cdot 5 \cdot 4}{3 \cdot 2} = 42$$

Therefore, the required probability is

$$P(F) = \frac{n(F)}{n(S)} = \frac{42}{64} = \frac{21}{32} \approx .6563$$

c. Let F denote the event that the coin lands heads on the first and the last toss. Then $n(F) = 1 \cdot 2 \cdot 2 \cdot 2 \cdot 2 \cdot 1 = 2^4$, so the probability that this event occurs is

$$P(F) = \frac{2^4}{2^6}$$

$$= \frac{1}{2^2}$$

$$= \frac{1}{4}$$

∎

EXAMPLE 2 Two cards are selected at random (without replacement) from a well-shuffled deck of 52 playing cards. What is the probability that:

a. They are both aces?   **b.** Neither of them is an ace?

Solution

a. The experiment consists of selecting 2 cards from a pack of 52 playing cards. Since the order in which the cards are selected is immaterial, the sample points are combinations of 52 cards taken 2 at a time. Now there are $C(52, 2)$ ways of selecting 52 cards taken 2 at a time, so the number of elements in the sample space S is given by $C(52, 2)$. Next, we observe that there are $C(4, 2)$ ways of selecting 2 aces from the 4 in the deck. Therefore, if E denotes the event that the cards selected are both aces, then

$$P(E) = \frac{n(E)}{n(S)}$$

$$= \frac{C(4, 2)}{C(52, 2)} = \frac{\dfrac{4!}{2!\,2!}}{\dfrac{52!}{2!\,50!}} = \frac{4\cdot 3}{2}\cdot\frac{2}{52\cdot 51}$$

$$= \frac{1}{221} \approx .0045$$

b. Let F denote the event that neither of the two cards selected is an ace. Since there are $C(48, 2)$ ways of selecting two cards neither of which is an ace, we find that

$$P(F) = \frac{n(F)}{n(S)} = \frac{C(48, 2)}{C(52, 2)} = \frac{\dfrac{48!}{2!\,46!}}{\dfrac{52!}{2!\,50!}} = \frac{48\cdot 47}{2}\cdot\frac{2}{52\cdot 51}$$

$$= \frac{188}{221} \approx .8507$$

APPLIED EXAMPLE 3 Quality Control A bin in the hi-fi department of Building 20, a bargain outlet, contains 100 blank DVDs, of which 10 are known to be defective. If a customer selects 6 of these DVDs at random, determine the probability:

a. That 2 of them are defective.
b. That at least 1 of them is defective.

Solution

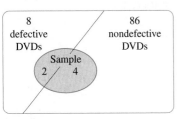

FIGURE 13
A sample of 6 DVDs selected from 90 nondefective DVDs and 10 defective DVDs

a. There are $C(100, 6)$ ways of selecting a set of 6 DVDs from the 100, and this gives $n(S)$, the number of outcomes in the sample space associated with the experiment. Next, we observe that there are $C(10, 2)$ ways of selecting a set of 2 defective DVDs from the 10 defective DVDs and $C(90, 4)$ ways of selecting a set of 4 nondefective DVDs from the 90 non-defective DVDs (Figure 13). Thus, by the multiplication principle, there are $C(10, 2) \cdot C(90, 4)$ ways of selecting 2 defective and 4 nondefective DVDs. Therefore, the probability of selecting 6 DVDs of which 2 are defective is given by

$$\frac{C(10, 2) \cdot C(90, 4)}{C(100, 6)} = \frac{\dfrac{10!}{2!\,8!}\dfrac{90!}{4!\,86!}}{\dfrac{100!}{6!\,94!}}$$

$$= \frac{10\cdot 9}{2}\cdot\frac{90\cdot 89\cdot 88\cdot 87}{4\cdot 3\cdot 2}\cdot\frac{6\cdot 5\cdot 4\cdot 3\cdot 2}{100\cdot 99\cdot 98\cdot 97\cdot 96\cdot 95}$$

$$\approx .096$$

b. Let E denote the event that none of the DVDs selected is defective. Then E^c gives the event that at least 1 of the DVDs is defective. By the rule of complements,

$$P(E^c) = 1 - P(E)$$

To compute $P(E)$, we observe that there are $C(90, 6)$ ways of selecting a set of 6 DVDs that are nondefective. Therefore,

$$P(E) = \frac{C(90, 6)}{C(100, 6)}$$

$$P(E^c) = 1 - \frac{C(90, 6)}{C(100, 6)}$$

$$= 1 - \frac{\dfrac{90!}{6!\,84!}}{\dfrac{100!}{6!\,94!}}$$

$$= 1 - \frac{90 \cdot 89 \cdot 88 \cdot 87 \cdot 86 \cdot 85}{6 \cdot 5 \cdot 4 \cdot 3 \cdot 2} \cdot \frac{6 \cdot 5 \cdot 4 \cdot 3 \cdot 2}{100 \cdot 99 \cdot 98 \cdot 97 \cdot 96 \cdot 95}$$

$$\approx .478$$

The Birthday Problem

VIDEO

APPLIED EXAMPLE 4   The Birthday Problem A group of five people is selected at random. What is the probability that at least two of them have the same birthday?

Solution   For simplicity, we assume that none of the five people was born on February 29 of a leap year. Since the five people were selected at random, we also assume that each of them is equally likely to have any of the 365 days of a year as his or her birthday. If we let A, B, C, D, and F represent the five people, then an outcome of the experiment may be represented by (a, b, c, d, f), where the dates a, b, c, d, and f give the birthdays of A, B, C, D, and F, respectively.

We first observe that since there are 365 possibilities for each of the dates a, b, c, d, and f, the multiplication principle implies that there are

$$\boxed{365} \cdot \boxed{365} \cdot \boxed{365} \cdot \boxed{365} \cdot \boxed{365}$$
$$\quad a \qquad b \qquad c \qquad d \qquad f$$

or 365^5 outcomes of the experiment. Therefore,

$$n(S) = 365^5$$

where S denotes the sample space of the experiment.

Next, let E denote the event that two or more of the five people have the same birthday. It is now necessary to compute $P(E)$. However, a direct computation of $P(E)$ is relatively difficult. It is much easier to compute $P(E^c)$, where E^c is the event that no two of the five people have the same birthday, and then use the relation

$$P(E) = 1 - P(E^c)$$

To compute $P(E^c)$, observe that there are 365 ways (corresponding to the 365 dates) on which A's birthday can occur, followed by 364 ways on which B's birthday could occur if B were not to have the same birthday as A, and so on. Therefore, by the generalized multiplication principle,

$$n(E^c) = \underset{\substack{A\text{'s}\\ \text{birthday}}}{365} \cdot \underset{\substack{B\text{'s}\\ \text{birthday}}}{364} \cdot \underset{\substack{C\text{'s}\\ \text{birthday}}}{363} \cdot \underset{\substack{D\text{'s}\\ \text{birthday}}}{362} \cdot \underset{\substack{F\text{'s}\\ \text{birthday}}}{361}$$

Thus,

$$P(E^c) = \frac{n(E^c)}{n(S)}$$

$$= \frac{365 \cdot 364 \cdot 363 \cdot 362 \cdot 361}{365^5}$$

$$P(E) = 1 - P(E^c)$$

$$= 1 - \frac{365 \cdot 364 \cdot 363 \cdot 362 \cdot 361}{365^5}$$

$$\approx .027$$

TABLE 8

Probability That at Least Two People in a Randomly Selected Group of r People Have the Same Birthday

r	$P(E)$
5	.027
10	.117
15	.253
20	.411
22	.476
23	.507
25	.569
30	.706
40	.891
50	.970

We can extend the result obtained in Example 4 to the general case involving r people. In fact, if E denotes the event that at least two of the r people have the same birthday, an argument similar to that used in Example 4 leads to the result

$$P(E) = 1 - \frac{365 \cdot 364 \cdot 363 \cdots (365 - r + 1)}{365^r}$$

By letting r take on the values 5, 10, 15, 20, . . . , 50, in turn, we obtain the probabilities that at least 2 of 5, 10, 15, 20, . . . , 50 people, respectively, have the same birthday. These results are summarized in Table 8.

The results show that in a group of 23 randomly selected people, the chances are greater than 50% that at least 2 of them will have the same birthday. In a group of 50 people, it is an excellent bet that at least 2 people in the group will have the same birthday.

Explore & Discuss

During an episode of the *Tonight Show*, a talk show host related "The Birthday Problem" to the audience—noting that in a group of 50 or more people, probabilists have calculated that the probability of at least 2 people having the same birthday is very high. To illustrate this point, he proceeded to conduct his own experiment. A person selected at random from the audience was asked to state his birthday. The host then asked whether anyone in the audience had the same birthday. The response was negative. He repeated the experiment. Once again, the response was negative. These results, observed the host, were contrary to expectations. In a later episode of the show, the host explained why this experiment had been improperly conducted. Explain why the host failed to illustrate the point he was trying to make in the earlier episode.

7.4 Self-Check Exercises

1. Four balls are selected at random without replacement from an urn containing ten white balls and eight red balls. What is the probability that all the chosen balls are white?

2. A box contains 20 microchips, of which 4 are substandard. If 2 of the chips are taken from the box, what is the probability that they are both substandard?

Solutions to Self-Check Exercises 7.4 can be found on page 398.

7.4   Concept Questions

1. What is the probability of an event E in a uniform sample space S?

2. Suppose we want to find the probability that at least two people in a group of six randomly selected people have the same birthday.

   a. If S denotes the sample space of this experiment, what is $n(S)$?

   b. If E is the event that two or more of the six people in the group have the same birthday, explain how you would use $P(E^c)$ to determine $P(E)$.

7.4   Exercises

An unbiased coin is tossed five times. In Exercises 1–4, find the probability of the given event.

1. The coin lands heads all five times.

2. The coin lands heads exactly once.

3. The coin lands heads at least once.

4. The coin lands heads more than once.

Two cards are selected at random without replacement from a well-shuffled deck of 52 playing cards. In Exercises 5–8, find the probability of the given event.

5. A pair is drawn.

6. A pair is not drawn.

7. Two black cards are drawn.

8. Two cards of the same suit are drawn.

Four balls are selected at random without replacement from an urn containing three white balls and five blue balls. In Exercises 9–12, find the probability of the given event.

9. Two of the balls are white, and two are blue.

10. All of the balls are blue.

11. Exactly three of the balls are blue.

12. Two or three of the balls are white.

Assume that the probability of a boy being born is the same as the probability of a girl being born. In Exercises 13–16, find the probability that a family with three children will have the given composition.

13. Two boys and one girl

14. At least one girl

15. No girls

16. The two oldest children are girls.

17. An exam consists of ten true-or-false questions. If a student guesses at every answer, what is the probability that he or she will answer exactly six questions correctly?

18. **PERSONNEL SELECTION** Jacobs & Johnson, an accounting firm, employs 14 accountants, of whom 8 are CPAs. If a delegation of 3 accountants is randomly selected from the firm to attend a conference, what is the probability that 3 CPAs will be selected?

19. **QUALITY CONTROL** Two light bulbs are selected at random from a lot of 24, of which 4 are defective. What is the probability that:

    a. Both of the light bulbs are defective?

    b. At least 1 of the light bulbs is defective?

20. A customer at Cavallaro's Fruit Stand picks a sample of 3 oranges at random from a crate containing 60 oranges, of which 4 are rotten. What is the probability that the sample contains 1 or more rotten oranges?

21. **QUALITY CONTROL** A shelf in the Metro Department Store contains 80 colored ink cartridges for a popular ink-jet printer. Six of the cartridges are defective. If a customer selects 2 cartridges at random from the shelf, what is the probability that:

    a. Both are defective?

    b. At least 1 is defective?

22. **QUALITY CONTROL** Electronic baseball games manufactured by Tempco Electronics are shipped in lots of 24. Before shipping, a quality-control inspector randomly selects a sample of 8 from each lot for testing. If the sample contains any defective games, the entire lot is rejected. What is the probability that a lot containing exactly 2 defective games will still be shipped?

23. **PERSONNEL SELECTION** The City Transit Authority plans to hire 12 new bus drivers. From a group of 100 qualified applicants, of whom 60 are men and 40 are women, 12 names are to be selected by lot. Suppose that Mary and John Lewis are among the 100 qualified applicants.

    a. What is the probability that Mary's name will be selected? That both Mary's and John's names will be selected?

    b. If it is stipulated that an equal number of men and women are to be selected (6 men from the group of 60 men and 6 women from the group of 40 women), what is the probability that Mary's name will be selected? That Mary's and John's names will be selected?

24. **PUBLIC HOUSING** The City Housing Authority has received 50 applications from qualified applicants for eight low-

income apartments. Three of the apartments are on the north side of town, and five are on the south side. If the apartments are to be assigned by means of a lottery, what is the probability that:

a. A specific qualified applicant will be selected for one of these apartments?

b. Two specific qualified applicants will be selected for apartments on the same side of town?

25. A student studying for a vocabulary test knows the meanings of 12 words from a list of 20 words. If the test contains 10 words from the study list, what is the probability that at least 8 of the words on the test are words that the student knows?

26. DRIVING TESTS Four different written driving tests are administered by the Motor Vehicle Department. One of these four tests is selected at random for each applicant for a driver's license. If a group consisting of two women and three men apply for a license, what is the probability that:

a. Exactly two of the five will take the same test?

b. The two women will take the same test?

27. BRAND SELECTION A druggist wishes to select three brands of aspirin to sell in his store. He has five major brands to choose from: *A, B, C, D,* and *E*. If he selects the three brands at random, what is the probability that he will select:

a. Brand *B*?

b. Brands *B* and *C*?

c. At least one of the two brands *B* and *C*?

28. BLACKJACK In the game of blackjack, a 2-card hand consisting of an ace and a face card or a 10 is called a blackjack.

a. If a player is dealt 2 cards from a standard deck of 52 well-shuffled cards, what is the probability that the player will receive a blackjack?

b. If a player is dealt 2 cards from 2 well-shuffled standard decks, what is the probability that the player will receive a blackjack?

29. SLOT MACHINES Refer to Exercise 27, Section 6.3, in which the "lucky dollar" slot machine was described. What is the probability that the three "lucky dollar" symbols will appear in the window of the slot machine?

30. ROULETTE In 1959, a world record was set for the longest run on an ungaffed (fair) roulette wheel at the El San Juan Hotel in Puerto Rico. The number 10 appeared six times in a row. What is the probability of the occurrence of this event? (Assume that there are 38 equally likely outcomes consisting of the numbers 1–36, 0, and 00.)

In the Numbers Game, a state lottery, four numbers are drawn with replacement from an urn containing balls numbered 0–9, inclusive. In Exercises 31–34, find the probability that a ticket holder has the indicated winning ticket.

31. All four digits in exact order (the grand prize)

32. Two specified, consecutive digits in exact order (the first two digits, the middle two digits, or the last two digits)

33. One digit (the first, second, third, or fourth digit)

34. Three digits in exact order

A list of poker hands, ranked in order from the highest to the lowest, is shown in the accompanying table along with a description and example of each hand. Use the table to answer Exercises 35–40.

Hand	Description	Example
Straight flush	5 cards in sequence in the same suit	A♥ 2♥ 3♥ 4♥ 5♥
Four of a kind	4 cards of the same rank and any other card	K♥ K♦ K♠ K♣ 2♥
Full house	3 of a kind and a pair	3♥ 3♦ 3♣ 7♥ 7♦
Flush	5 cards of the same suit that are not all in sequence	5♥ 6♥ 9♥ J♥ K♥
Straight	5 cards in sequence but not all of the same suit	10♥ J♦ Q♣ K♠ A♥
Three of a kind	3 cards of the same rank and 2 unmatched cards	K♥ K♦ K♠ 2♥ 4♦
Two pair	2 cards of the same rank and 2 cards of any other rank with an unmatched card	K♥ K♦ 2♥ 2♠ 4♣
One pair	2 cards of the same rank and 3 unmatched cards	K♥ K♦ 5♥ 2♠ 4♥

If a 5-card poker hand is dealt from a well-shuffled deck of 52 cards, what is the probability of being dealt the given hand?

35. A straight flush (Note that an ace may be played as either a high or a low card in a straight sequence—that is, A, 2, 3, 4, 5 or 10, J, Q, K, A. Hence, there are ten possible sequences for a straight in one suit.)

36. A straight (but not a straight flush)

37. A flush (but not a straight flush)

38. Four of a kind

39. A full house

40. Two pairs

41. **ZODIAC SIGNS** There are 12 signs of the Zodiac: Aries, Taurus, Gemini, Cancer, Leo, Virgo, Libra, Scorpio, Sagittarius, Capricorn, Aquarius, and Pisces. Each sign corresponds to a different calendar period of approximately 1 month. Assuming that a person is just as likely to be born under one sign as another, what is the probability that in a group of five people at least two of them
a. Have the same sign?
b. Were born under the sign of Aries?

42. **BIRTHDAY PROBLEM** What is the probability that at least two of the nine justices of the U.S. Supreme Court have the same birthday?

43. **BIRTHDAY PROBLEM** Fifty people are selected at random. What is the probability that none of the people in this group have the same birthday?

44. **BIRTHDAY PROBLEM** There were 42 different presidents of the United States from 1789 through 2000. What is the probability that at least two of them had the same birthday? Compare your calculation with the facts by checking an almanac or some other source.

7.4 Solutions to Self-Check Exercises

1. The probability that all four balls selected are white is given by

$$\frac{\text{The number of ways of selecting 4 white balls from the 10 in the urn}}{\text{The number of ways of selecting any 4 balls from the 18 balls in the urn}}$$

$$= \frac{C(10, 4)}{C(18, 4)}$$

$$= \frac{\dfrac{10!}{4! \, 6!}}{\dfrac{18!}{4! \, 14!}}$$

$$= \frac{10 \cdot 9 \cdot 8 \cdot 7}{4 \cdot 3 \cdot 2} \cdot \frac{4 \cdot 3 \cdot 2}{18 \cdot 17 \cdot 16 \cdot 15}$$

$$\approx .069$$

2. The probability that both chips are substandard is given by

$$\frac{\text{The number of ways of choosing any 2 of the 4 substandard chips}}{\text{The number of ways of choosing any 2 of the 20 chips}}$$

$$= \frac{C(4, 2)}{C(20, 2)}$$

$$= \frac{\dfrac{4!}{2! \, 2!}}{\dfrac{20!}{2! \, 18!}}$$

$$= \frac{4 \cdot 3}{2} \cdot \frac{2}{20 \cdot 19}$$

$$\approx .032$$

7.5 Conditional Probability and Independent Events

Conditional Probability

Suppose that three cities, A, B, and C, are vying to play host to the Summer Olympic Games in 2020. If each city has the same chance of winning the right to host the Games, then the probability of City A hosting the Games is $\frac{1}{3}$. Now suppose City B decides to pull out of contention because of fiscal problems. Then it would seem that City A's chances of playing host will increase. In fact, if the two remaining cities have equal chances of winning, then the probability of City A playing host to the Games is $\frac{1}{2}$.

In general, the probability of an event is affected by the occurrence of other events and/or by the knowledge of information relevant to the event. Basically, the injection of conditions into a problem modifies the underlying sample space of the original problem. This in turn leads to a change in the probability of the event.

EXAMPLE 1 Two cards are drawn without replacement from a well-shuffled deck of 52 playing cards.

a. What is the probability that the first card drawn is an ace?
b. What is the probability that the second card drawn is an ace given that the first card drawn was not an ace?

c. What is the probability that the second card drawn is an ace given that the first card drawn was an ace?

Solution

a. The sample space here consists of 52 equally likely outcomes, 4 of which are aces. Therefore, the probability that the first card drawn is an ace is $\frac{4}{52}$, or $\frac{1}{13}$.

b. The first card having been drawn, there are 51 cards left in the deck. In other words, for the second phase of the experiment, we are working in a *reduced* sample space. If the first card drawn was not an ace, then this modified sample space of 51 points contains 4 "favorable" outcomes (the 4 aces), so the probability that the second card drawn is an ace is given by $\frac{4}{51}$.

c. If the first card drawn was an ace, then there are 3 aces left in the deck of 51 playing cards, so the probability that the second card drawn is an ace is given by $\frac{3}{51}$, or $\frac{1}{17}$.   ■

Observe that in Example 1, the occurrence of the first event reduces the size of the original sample space. The information concerning the first card drawn also leads us to the consideration of modified sample spaces: In part (b), the deck contained four aces, and in part (c), the deck contained three aces.

The probability found in part (b) or part (c) of Example 1 is known as a **conditional probability,** since it is the probability of an event occurring given that another event has already occurred. For example, in part (b), we computed the probability of the event that the second card drawn is an ace *given that* the first card drawn was not an ace. In general, given two events A and B of an experiment, under certain circumstances one may compute the probability of the event B given that the event A has already occurred. This probability, denoted by $P(B \mid A)$, is called the **conditional probability of B given A.**

A formula for computing the conditional probability of B given A may be discovered with the aid of a Venn diagram. Consider an experiment with a uniform sample space S, and suppose that A and B are two events of the experiment (Figure 14).

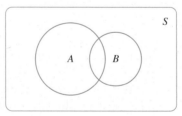

(a) Original sample space

(b) Reduced sample space A. The shaded area is $A \cap B$.

FIGURE **14**

The condition that the event A has occurred tells us that the possible outcomes of the experiment in the second phase are restricted to those outcomes (elements) in the set A. In other words, we may work with the reduced sample space A instead of the original sample space S in the experiment. Next we observe that, with respect to the reduced sample space A, the outcomes in the event B are precisely those elements in the set $A \cap B$. Consequently, the conditional probability of B given A is

$$P(B \mid A) = \frac{\text{Number of elements in } A \cap B}{\text{Number of elements in } A}$$

$$= \frac{n(A \cap B)}{n(A)} \qquad n(A) \neq 0$$

Dividing the numerator and the denominator by $n(S)$, the number of elements in S, we have

$$P(B \mid A) = \frac{\dfrac{n(A \cap B)}{n(S)}}{\dfrac{n(A)}{n(S)}}$$

which is equivalent to the following formula:

> **Conditional Probability of an Event**
>
> If A and B are events in an experiment and $P(A) \neq 0$, then the conditional probability that the event B will occur given that the event A has already occurred is
>
> $$P(B \mid A) = \frac{P(A \cap B)}{P(A)} \qquad \text{(2)}$$

EXAMPLE 2 A pair of fair dice is rolled. What is the probability that the sum of the numbers falling uppermost is 7 if it is known that one of the numbers is a 5?

Solution Let A denote the event that the sum of the numbers falling uppermost is 7, and let B denote the event that one of the numbers is a 5. From the results of Example 4, Section 7.1, we find that

$$A = \{(6, 1), (5, 2), (4, 3), (3, 4), (2, 5), (1, 6)\}$$
$$B = \{(5, 1), (5, 2), (5, 3), (5, 4), (5, 5), (5, 6),$$
$$(1, 5), (2, 5), (3, 5), (4, 5), (6, 5)\}$$

so

$$A \cap B = \{(5, 2), (2, 5)\}$$

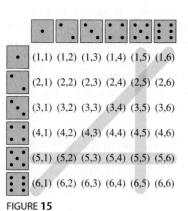

(1,1) (1,2) (1,3) (1,4) (1,5) (1,6)
(2,1) (2,2) (2,3) (2,4) (2,5) (2,6)
(3,1) (3,2) (3,3) (3,4) (3,5) (3,6)
(4,1) (4,2) (4,3) (4,4) (4,5) (4,6)
(5,1) (5,2) (5,3) (5,4) (5,5) (5,6)
(6,1) (6,2) (6,3) (6,4) (6,5) (6,6)

FIGURE 15
$A \cap B = \{(5, 2), (2, 5)\}$

(Figure 15). Since the dice are fair, each outcome of the experiment is equally likely; therefore,

$$P(A \cap B) = \frac{2}{36} \quad \text{and} \quad P(B) = \frac{11}{36} \qquad \text{Recall that } n(S) = 36.$$

Thus, the probability that the sum of the numbers falling uppermost is 7 given that one of the numbers is a 5 is, by virtue of Equation (2),

$$P(A \mid B) = \frac{\dfrac{2}{36}}{\dfrac{11}{36}} = \frac{2}{11}$$

APPLIED EXAMPLE 3 Color Blindness In a test conducted by the U.S. Army, it was found that of 1000 new recruits (600 men and 400 women), 50 of the men and 4 of the women were red-green color-blind. Given that a recruit selected at random from this group is red-green color-blind, what is the probability that the recruit is a male?

Solution Let C denote the event that a randomly selected subject is red-green color-blind, and let M denote the event that the subject is a male recruit. Since 54 out of the 1000 subjects are color-blind, we have

$$P(C) = \frac{54}{1000} = .054$$

Therefore, by Equation (2), the probability that a subject is male given that the subject is red-green color-blind is

$$P(M \mid C) = \frac{P(M \cap C)}{P(C)}$$

$$= \frac{.05}{.054} \approx .926$$

Explore & Discuss

Let A and B be events in an experiment, and suppose that $P(A) \neq 0$. In n trials, the event A occurs m times, the event B occurs k times, and the events A and B occur together l times.

1. Explain why it makes good sense to call the ratio l/m the conditional relative frequency of the event B given the event A.

2. Show that the relative frequencies l/m, m/n, and l/n satisfy the equation

$$\frac{l}{m} = \frac{\dfrac{l}{n}}{\dfrac{m}{n}}$$

3. Explain why the result of part 2 suggests that Equation (2),

$$P(B \mid A) = \frac{P(A \cap B)}{P(A)} \qquad [P(A) \neq 0]$$

is plausible.

In certain problems, the probability of an event B occurring given that A has occurred, written $P(B \mid A)$, is known, and we wish to find the probability of A *and* B occurring. The solution to such a problem is facilitated by the use of the following formula:

Product Rule

$$P(A \cap B) = P(A) \cdot P(B \mid A) \tag{3}$$

This formula is obtained from Equation (2) by multiplying both sides of the equation by $P(A)$. We illustrate the use of the Product Rule in the next several examples.

 APPLIED EXAMPLE 4 Seniors with Driver's Licenses There are 300 seniors at Jefferson High School, of which 140 are males. It is known that 80% of the males and 60% of the females have their driver's license. If a student is selected at random from this senior class, what is the probability that the student is:

a. A male and has a driver's license?

b. A female and does not have a driver's license?

Solution

a. Let M denote the event that the student is a male, and let D denote the event that the student has a driver's license. Then

$$P(M) = \frac{140}{300} \quad \text{and} \quad P(D \mid M) = .8$$

The event that the student selected at random is a male and has a driver's license is $M \cap D$, and by the Product Rule, the probability of this event occurring is given by

$$P(M \cap D) = P(M) \cdot P(D \mid M)$$
$$= \left(\frac{140}{300}\right)(.8) \approx .373$$

b. Let F denote the event that the student is a female. Then D^c is the event that the student does not have a driver's license. We have

$$P(F) = \frac{160}{300} \quad \text{and} \quad P(D^c \mid F) = 1 - .6 = .4$$

Note that we have used the rule of complements in the computation of $P(D^c \mid F)$. The event that the student selected at random is a female and does not have a driver's license is $F \cap D^c$, so, by the Product Rule, the probability of this event occurring is given by

$$P(F \cap D^c) = P(F) \cdot P(D^c \mid F)$$
$$= \left(\frac{160}{300}\right)(.4) \approx .213$$

EXAMPLE 5 Two cards are drawn without replacement from a well-shuffled deck of 52 playing cards. What is the probability that the first card drawn is an ace and the second card drawn is a face card?

Solution   Let A denote the event that the first card drawn is an ace, and let F denote the event that the second card drawn is a face card. Then $P(A) = \frac{4}{52}$. After the first card is drawn, there are 51 cards left in the deck, of which 12 are face cards. Therefore, the probability of drawing a face card given that the first card drawn was an ace is given by

$$P(F \mid A) = \frac{12}{51}$$

By the Product Rule, the probability that the first card drawn is an ace and the second card drawn is a face card is given by

$$P(A \cap F) = P(A) \cdot P(F \mid A)$$
$$= \frac{4}{52} \cdot \frac{12}{51} = \frac{4}{221} \approx .018$$

Explore & Discuss

The Product Rule can be extended to the case involving three or more events. For example, if A, B, and C are three events in an experiment, then it can be shown that

$$P(A \cap B \cap C) = P(A) \cdot P(B \mid A) \cdot P(C \mid A \cap B)$$

1. Explain the formula in words.

2. Suppose 3 cards are drawn without replacement from a well-shuffled deck of 52 playing cards. Use the given formula to find the probability that the 3 cards are aces.

The Product Rule may be generalized to the case involving any finite number of events. For example, in the case involving the three events E, F, and G, it may be shown that

$$P(E \cap F \cap G) = P(E) \cdot P(F \mid E) \cdot P(G \mid E \cap F) \qquad (4)$$

More on Tree Diagrams

Equation (4) and its generalizations may be used to help us solve problems that involve finite stochastic processes. A **finite stochastic process** is an experiment consisting of a finite number of stages in which the outcomes and associated probabilities of each stage depend on the outcomes and associated probabilities of the preceding stages.

We can use tree diagrams to help us solve problems involving finite stochastic processes. Consider, for example, the experiment consisting of drawing 2 cards without replacement from a well-shuffled deck of 52 playing cards. What is the probability that the second card drawn is a face card?

We may think of this experiment as a stochastic process with two stages. The events associated with the first stage are F, that the card drawn is a face card, and F^c, that the card drawn is not a face card. Since there are 12 face cards, we have

$$P(F) = \frac{12}{52} \quad \text{and} \quad P(F^c) = 1 - \frac{12}{52} = \frac{40}{52}$$

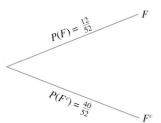

FIGURE 16
F is the event that a face card is drawn.

The outcomes of this trial, together with the associated probabilities, may be represented along two branches of a tree diagram as shown in Figure 16.

In the second trial, we again have two events: G, that the card drawn is a face card, and G^c, that the card drawn is not a face card. But the outcome of the second trial depends on the outcome of the first trial. For example, if the first card drawn was a face card, then the event G that the second card drawn is a face card has probability given by the *conditional probability* $P(G \mid F)$. Since the occurrence of a face card in the first draw leaves 11 face cards in a deck of 51 cards for the second draw, we see that

$$P(G \mid F) = \frac{11}{51} \qquad \begin{array}{l}\text{The probability of drawing a}\\\text{face card given that a face}\\\text{card has already been drawn}\end{array}$$

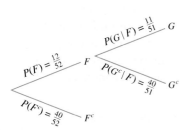

FIGURE 17
G is the event that the second card drawn is a face card.

Similarly, the occurrence of a face card in the first draw leaves 40 that are other than face cards in a deck of 51 cards for the second draw. Therefore, the probability of drawing a card other than a face card in the second draw given that the first card drawn is a face card is

$$P(G^c \mid F) = \frac{40}{51}$$

Using these results, we extend the tree diagram of Figure 16 by displaying another two branches of the tree growing from its upper branch (Figure 17).

To complete the tree diagram, we compute $P(G \mid F^c)$ and $P(G^c \mid F^c)$, the conditional probabilities that the second card drawn is a face card and other than a face card, respectively, given that the first card drawn is not a face card. We find that

$$P(G \mid F^c) = \frac{12}{51} \quad \text{and} \quad P(G^c \mid F^c) = \frac{39}{51}$$

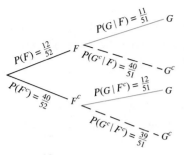

FIGURE 18
Tree diagram showing the two trials of the experiment

This leads to the completion of the tree diagram, shown in Figure 18, in which the branches of the tree that lead to the two outcomes of interest have been highlighted.

Having constructed the tree diagram associated with the problem, we are now in a position to answer the question posed earlier: What is the probability of the second card being a face card? Observe that Figure 18 shows the two ways in which a face card may result in the second draw—namely, the two Gs on the extreme right of the diagram.

Now, by the Product Rule, the probability that the second card drawn is a face card and the first card drawn is a face card (this is represented by the upper branch) is

$$P(G \cap F) = P(F) \cdot P(G \mid F)$$

Similarly, the probability that the second card drawn is a face card and the first card drawn is other than a face card (this corresponds to the other branch) is

$$P(G \cap F^c) = P(F^c) \cdot P(G \mid F^c)$$

Observe that each of these probabilities is obtained by taking the *product of the probabilities appearing on the respective branches*. Since $G \cap F$ and $G \cap F^c$ are mutually exclusive events (why?), the probability that the second card drawn is a face card is given by

$$P(G \cap F) + P(G \cap F^c) = P(F) \cdot P(G \mid F) + P(F^c) \cdot P(G \mid F^c)$$

or, upon replacing the probabilities on the right of the expression by their numerical values,

$$P(G \cap F) + P(G \cap F^c) = \frac{12}{52} \cdot \frac{11}{51} + \frac{40}{52} \cdot \frac{12}{51}$$
$$= \frac{3}{13}$$

APPLIED EXAMPLE 6 Quality Control The panels for the Pulsar 32-inch widescreen LCD HDTVs are manufactured in three locations and then shipped to the main plant of Vista Vision for final assembly. Plants A, B, and C supply 50%, 30%, and 20%, respectively, of the panels used by the company. The quality-control department of the company has determined that 1% of the panels produced by Plant A are defective, whereas 2% of the panels produced by Plants B and C are defective. What is the probability that a randomly selected Pulsar 32-inch HDTV will have a defective panel?

Solution Let A, B, and C denote the events that the HDTV chosen has a panel manufactured in Plant A, Plant B, and Plant C, respectively. Also, let D denote the event that a HDTV has a defective panel. Using the given information, we draw the tree diagram shown in Figure 19. (The events that result in a HDTV with a defective panel being selected are circled.) Taking the product of the probabilities along each branch leading to such an event and then adding them, we obtain the probability that a HDTV chosen at random has a defective panel. Thus, the required probability is given by

$$(.5)(.01) + (.3)(.02) + (.2)(.02) = .005 + .006 + .004$$
$$= .015$$

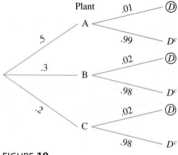

FIGURE 19
Tree diagram showing the probabilities of producing defective panels at each plant

APPLIED EXAMPLE 7 Quality Control A box contains eight 9-volt batteries, of which two are known to be defective. The batteries are selected one at a time without replacement and tested until a nondefective one is found. What is the probability that the number of batteries tested is (a) One? (b) Two? (c) Three?

Solution   We may view this experiment as a multistage process with up to three stages. In the first stage, a battery is selected with a probability of $\frac{6}{8}$ of being nondefective and a probability of $\frac{2}{8}$ of being defective. If the battery selected is good, the experiment is terminated. Otherwise, a second battery is selected with probability of $\frac{6}{7}$ and $\frac{1}{7}$, respectively, of being nondefective and defective. If the second battery selected is good, the experiment is terminated. Otherwise, a third battery is selected with probability of 1 and 0, respectively, of its being nondefective and defective. The tree diagram associated with this experiment is shown in Figure 20, where N denotes the event that the battery selected is nondefective and D denotes the event that the battery selected is defective.

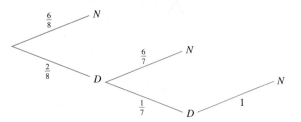

FIGURE 20
In this experiment, batteries are selected until a nondefective one is found.

With the aid of the tree diagram, we see that (a) the probability that only one battery is selected is $\frac{6}{8} = \frac{3}{4}$, (b) the probability that two batteries are selected is $\left(\frac{2}{8}\right)\left(\frac{6}{7}\right)$, or $\frac{3}{14}$, and (c) the probability that three batteries are selected is $\left(\frac{2}{8}\right)\left(\frac{1}{7}\right)(1) = \frac{1}{28}$. ■

Independent Events

Let's return to the experiment of drawing 2 cards in succession without replacement from a well-shuffled deck of 52 playing cards as considered in Example 5. Let E denote the event that the first card drawn is not a face card, and let F denote the event that the second card drawn is a face card. Intuitively, it is clear that the events E and F are *not* independent of each other, because whether or not the first card drawn is a face card affects the likelihood that the second card drawn is a face card.

Next, let's consider the experiment of tossing a coin twice and observing the outcomes: If H denotes the event that the first toss produces heads and T denotes the event that the second toss produces tails, then it is intuitively clear that H and T *are* independent of each other because the outcome of the first toss does not affect the outcome of the second.

In general, two events A and B are independent if the outcome of one does not affect the outcome of the other. Thus, we have

Independent Events

If A and B are **independent events,** then

$$P(A \mid B) = P(A) \quad \text{and} \quad P(B \mid A) = P(B)$$

Using the Product Rule, we can find a simple test to determine the independence of two events. Suppose that A and B are independent and that $P(A) \neq 0$ and $P(B) \neq 0$. Then

$$P(B \mid A) = P(B)$$

Thus, by the Product Rule, we have

$$P(A \cap B) = P(A) \cdot P(B \mid A) = P(A) \cdot P(B)$$

Conversely, if this equation holds, then it can be seen that $P(B \mid A) = P(B)$; that is, A and B are independent. Accordingly, we have the following test for the independence of two events:

> **Test for the Independence of Two Events**
> Two events A and B are independent if and only if
> $$P(A \cap B) = P(A) \cdot P(B) \tag{5}$$

⚠ Do not confuse *independent* events with *mutually exclusive* events. The former pertains to how the occurrence of one event affects the occurrence of another event, whereas the latter pertains to the question of whether the events can occur at the same time.

EXAMPLE 8 Consider the experiment consisting of tossing a fair coin twice and observing the outcomes. Show that the event of heads on the first toss and the event of tails on the second toss are independent events.

Solution Let A denote the event that the outcome of the first toss is a head, and let B denote the event that the outcome of the second toss is a tail. The sample space of the experiment is

$$S = \{(HH), (HT), (TH), (TT)\}$$
$$A = \{(HH), (HT)\}$$
$$B = \{(HT), (TT)\}$$

so

$$A \cap B = \{(HT)\}$$

Next, we compute

$$P(A \cap B) = \frac{1}{4} \qquad P(A) = \frac{1}{2} \qquad P(B) = \frac{1}{2}$$

and observe that Equation (5) is satisfied in this case. Hence, A and B are independent events, as we set out to show. ∎

VIDEO▶ **APPLIED EXAMPLE 9** Medical Surveys A survey conducted by an independent agency for the National Lung Society found that of 2000 women, 680 were heavy smokers and 50 had emphysema. Of those who had emphysema, 42 were also heavy smokers. Using the data in this survey, determine whether the events "being a heavy smoker" and "having emphysema" are independent events.

Solution Let A denote the event that a woman chosen at random in this survey is a heavy smoker, and let B denote the event that a woman chosen at random in this survey has emphysema. Then the probability that a woman is a heavy smoker and has emphysema is given by

$$P(A \cap B) = \frac{42}{2000} = .021$$

Next,

$$P(A) = \frac{680}{2000} = .34 \quad \text{and} \quad P(B) = \frac{50}{2000} = .025$$

so

$$P(A) \cdot P(B) = (.34)(.025) = .0085$$

Since $P(A \cap B) \neq P(A) \cdot P(B)$, we conclude that A and B are not independent events. ■

The solution of many practical problems involves more than two independent events. In such cases, we use the following result.

Explore & Discuss

Let E and F be independent events in a sample space S. Are E^c and F^c independent?

Independence of More Than Two Events

If $E_1, E_2, \ldots, E_n$ are independent events, then

$$P(E_1 \cap E_2 \cap \cdots \cap E_n) = P(E_1) \cdot P(E_2) \cdot \cdots \cdot P(E_n) \qquad \textbf{(6)}$$

Formula (6) states that the probability of the simultaneous occurrence of n independent events is equal to the product of the probabilities of the n events.

▲ It is important to note that the mere requirement that the n events $E_1, E_2, \ldots, E_n$ satisfy Formula (6) is not sufficient to guarantee that the n events are indeed independent. However, a criterion does exist for determining the independence of n events and may be found in more advanced texts on probability.

EXAMPLE 10 It is known that the three events A, B, and C are independent and that $P(A) = .2$, $P(B) = .4$, and $P(C) = .5$. Compute:

a. $P(A \cap B)$ **b.** $P(A \cap B \cap C)$

Solution Using Formulas (5) and (6), we find

a. $P(A \cap B) = P(A) \cdot P(B)$
$= (.2)(.4) = .08$
b. $P(A \cap B \cap C) = P(A) \cdot P(B) \cdot P(C)$
$= (.2)(.4)(.5) = .04$ ■

 APPLIED EXAMPLE 11 Quality Control The Acrosonic model F loudspeaker system has four loudspeaker components: a woofer, a midrange, a tweeter, and an electrical crossover. The quality-control manager of Acrosonic has determined that on the average, 1% of the woofers, 0.8% of the midranges, and 0.5% of the tweeters are defective, while 1.5% of the electrical crossovers are defective. Determine the probability that a loudspeaker system selected at random as it comes off the assembly line (and before final inspection) is not defective. Assume that the defects in the manufacturing of the components are unrelated.

Solution Let A, B, C, and D denote, respectively, the events that the woofer, the midrange, the tweeter, and the electrical crossover are defective. Then

$$P(A) = .01 \qquad P(B) = .008 \qquad P(C) = .005 \qquad P(D) = .015$$

and the probabilities of the corresponding complementary events are

$$P(A^c) = .99 \qquad P(B^c) = .992 \qquad P(C^c) = .995 \qquad P(D^c) = .985$$

The event that a loudspeaker system selected at random is not defective is given by $A^c \cap B^c \cap C^c \cap D^c$. Because the events A, B, C, and D (and therefore also A^c,

B^c, C^c, and D^c) are assumed to be independent, we find that the required probability is given by

$$P(A^c \cap B^c \cap C^c \cap D^c) = P(A^c) \cdot P(B^c) \cdot P(C^c) \cdot P(D^c)$$
$$= (.99)(.992)(.995)(.985)$$
$$\approx .96$$

7.5 Self-Check Exercises

1. Let A and B be events in a sample space S such that $P(A) = .4$, $P(B) = .8$, and $P(A \cap B) = .3$. Find:
   a. $P(A \mid B)$ **b.** $P(B \mid A)$

2. According to a survey cited in *Newsweek*, 29.7% of married survey respondents who married between the ages of 20 and 22 (inclusive), 26.9% of those who married between the ages of 23 and 27, and 45.1% of those who married at age 28 or older said that "their marriage was less than 'very happy.'" Suppose that a survey respondent from each of the three age groups was selected at random. What is the probability that all three respondents said that their marriage was "less than very happy"?

Source: Marc Bain, *Newsweek.*

Solutions to Self-Check Exercises 7.5 can be found on page 412.

7.5 Concept Questions

1. What is conditional probability? Illustrate the concept with an example.

2. If A and B are events in an experiment and $P(A) \neq 0$, then what is the formula for computing $P(B \mid A)$?

3. If A and B are events in an experiment and the conditional probability $P(B \mid A)$ is known, give the formula that can be used to compute the probability of the event that both A and B will occur.

4. **a.** What is the test for determining the independence of two events?
   b. What is the difference between mutually exclusive events and independent events?

7.5 Exercises

1. Let A and B be two events in a sample space S such that $P(A) = .6$, $P(B) = .5$, and $P(A \cap B) = .2$. Find:
   a. $P(A \mid B)$ **b.** $P(B \mid A)$

2. Let A and B be two events in a sample space S such that $P(A) = .4$, $P(B) = .6$, and $P(A \cap B) = .3$. Find:
   a. $P(A \mid B)$ **b.** $P(B \mid A)$

3. Let A and B be two events in a sample space S such that $P(A) = .6$ and $P(B \mid A) = .5$. Find $P(A \cap B)$.

4. Let A and B be the events described in Exercise 1. Find:
   a. $P(A \mid B^c)$ **b.** $P(B \mid A^c)$
   Hint: $(A \cap B^c) \cup (A \cap B) = A$.

In Exercises 5–8, determine whether the events A and B are independent.

5. $P(A) = .3$, $P(B) = .6$, $P(A \cap B) = .18$

6. $P(A) = .6$, $P(B) = .8$, $P(A \cap B) = .2$

7. $P(A) = .5$, $P(B) = .7$, $P(A \cup B) = .85$

8. $P(A^c) = .3$, $P(B^c) = .4$, $P(A \cap B) = .42$

9. If A and B are independent events, $P(A) = .4$, and $P(B) = .6$, find:
   a. $P(A \cap B)$ **b.** $P(A \cup B)$
   c. $P(A \mid B)$ **d.** $P(A^c \cup B^c)$

10. If A and B are independent events, $P(A) = .35$, and $P(B) = .45$, find:
    a. $P(A \cap B)$ **b.** $P(A \cup B)$
    c. $P(A \mid B)$ **d.** $P(A^c \cup B^c)$

11. The accompanying tree diagram represents an experiment consisting of two trials:

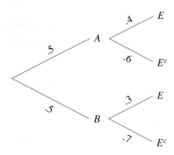

Use the diagram to find:
a. $P(A)$ **b.** $P(E \mid A)$
c. $P(A \cap E)$ **d.** $P(E)$
e. Does $P(A \cap E) = P(A) \cdot P(E)$?
f. Are A and E independent events?

12. The accompanying tree diagram represents an experiment consisting of two trials. Use the diagram to find:
a. $P(A)$ **b.** $P(E \mid A)$
c. $P(A \cap E)$ **d.** $P(E)$
e. Does $P(A \cap E) = P(A) \cdot P(E)$?
f. Are A and E independent events?

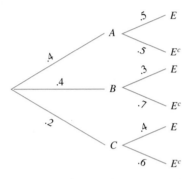

13. An experiment consists of two independent trials. The outcomes of the first trial are A and B with probabilities of occurring equal to .4 and .6. There are also two outcomes, C and D, in the second trial with probabilities of .3 and .7. Draw a tree diagram representing this experiment, and use it to find:
a. $P(A)$ **b.** $P(C \mid A)$
c. $P(A \cap C)$ **d.** $P(C)$
e. Does $P(A \cap C) = P(A) \cdot P(C)$?
f. Are A and C independent events?

14. An experiment consists of two independent trials. The outcomes of the first trial are A, B, and C, with probabilities of occurring equal to .2, .5, and .3, respectively. The outcomes of the second trial are E and F, with probabilities of occurring equal to .6 and .4. Draw a tree diagram representing this experiment. Use this diagram to find:
a. $P(B)$ **b.** $P(F \mid B)$
c. $P(B \cap F)$ **d.** $P(F)$
e. Does $P(B \cap F) = P(B) \cdot P(F)$?
f. Are B and F independent events?

15. A pair of fair dice is rolled. Let E denote the event that the number falling uppermost on the first die is 5, and let F denote the event that the sum of the numbers falling uppermost is 10.
a. Compute $P(F)$.   **b.** Compute $P(E \cap F)$.
c. Compute $P(F \mid E)$.   **d.** Compute $P(E)$.
e. Are E and F independent events?

16. A pair of fair dice is rolled. Let E denote the event that the number falling uppermost on the first die is 4, and let F denote the event that the sum of the numbers falling uppermost is 6.
a. Compute $P(F)$.   **b.** Compute $P(E \cap F)$.
c. Compute $P(F \mid E)$.   **d.** Compute $P(E)$.
e. Are E and F independent events?

17. A pair of fair dice is rolled. What is the probability that the sum of the numbers falling uppermost is less than 9, given that at least one of the numbers is a 6?

18. A pair of fair dice is rolled. What is the probability that the number landing uppermost on the first die is a 4 if it is known that the sum of the numbers landing uppermost is 7?

19. A pair of fair dice is rolled. Let E denote the event that the number landing uppermost on the first die is a 3, and let F denote the event that the sum of the numbers landing uppermost is 7. Determine whether E and F are independent events.

20. A pair of fair dice is rolled. Let E denote the event that the number landing uppermost on the first die is a 3, and let F denote the event that the sum of the numbers landing uppermost is 6. Determine whether E and F are independent events.

21. A card is drawn from a well-shuffled deck of 52 playing cards. Let E denote the event that the card drawn is black and let F denote the event that the card drawn is a spade. Determine whether E and F are independent events. Give an intuitive explanation for your answer.

22. A card is drawn from a well-shuffled deck of 52 playing cards. Let E denote the event that the card drawn is an ace and let F denote the event that the card drawn is a diamond. Determine whether E and F are independent events. Give an intuitive explanation for your answer.

23. **BATTERY LIFE** The probability that a battery will last 10 hr or more is .80, and the probability that it will last 15 hr or more is .15. Given that a battery has lasted 10 hr, find the probability that it will last 15 hr or more.

24. Two cards are drawn without replacement from a well-shuffled deck of 52 playing cards.
a. What is the probability that the first card drawn is a heart?
b. What is the probability that the second card drawn is a heart if the first card drawn was not a heart?
c. What is the probability that the second card drawn is a heart if the first card drawn was a heart?

25. Five black balls and four white balls are placed in an urn. Two balls are then drawn in succession. What is the probability that the second ball drawn is a white ball if
a. The second ball is drawn without replacing the first?
b. The first ball is replaced before the second is drawn?

26. **AUDITING TAX RETURNS** A tax specialist has estimated that the probability that a tax return selected at random will be audited is .02. Furthermore, he estimates that the probability that an audited return will result in additional assessments being levied on the taxpayer is .60. What is the probability that a tax return selected at random will result in additional assessments being levied on the taxpayer?

27. **STUDENT ENROLLMENT** At a certain medical school, $\frac{1}{7}$ of the students are from a minority group. Of the students who belong to a minority group, $\frac{1}{3}$ are black.
    a. What is the probability that a student selected at random from this medical school is black?
    b. What is the probability that a student selected at random from this medical school is black if it is known that the student is a member of a minority group?

28. **EDUCATIONAL LEVEL OF VOTERS** In a survey of 1000 eligible voters selected at random, it was found that 80 had a college degree. Additionally, it was found that 80% of those who had a college degree voted in the last presidential election, whereas 55% of the people who did not have a college degree voted in the last presidential election. Assuming that the poll is representative of all eligible voters, find the probability that an eligible voter selected at random:
    a. Had a college degree and voted in the last presidential election.
    b. Did not have a college degree and did not vote in the last presidential election.
    c. Voted in the last presidential election.
    d. Did not vote in the last presidential election.

29. The probability that Sandy takes her daughter Olivia to the supermarket on Friday is 0.6. If Sandy does bring Olivia to the supermarket on Friday, the probability that she buys Olivia a popsicle is 0.8. What is the probability that Sandy takes Olivia to the supermarket on Friday and buys her a popsicle?

30. Three cards are drawn without replacement from a well-shuffled deck of 52 playing cards. What is the probability that the third card drawn is a diamond?

31. **SELLING A CAR** Jack has decided to advertise the sale of his car by placing flyers in the student union and the dining hall of the college. He estimates that there is a probability of 0.3 that a potential buyer will read the advertisement and that, if it is read, the probability that the reader will buy his car will be 0.2. Using these estimates, find the probability that the person who reads the ad will buy Jack's car.

32. **WINNING BIDS** Brian, a landscape architect, submitted a bid on each of three home landscaping projects. He estimates that the probabilities of winning the bid on Project A, Project B, and Project C are 0.7, 0.6, and 0.5, respectively. Also, the probability of winning a bid on one of the three projects is independent of winning or losing the bids on the other two projects. Find the probability that Brian will:
    a. Win all three of the bids.
    b. Win exactly two of the bids.
    c. Win exactly one bid.

33. **FAMILY COMPOSITION** In a three-child family, what is the probability that all three children are girls given that at least one of the children is a girl? (Assume that the probability of a boy being born is the same as the probability of a girl being born.)

34. A coin is tossed three times. What is the probability that the coin will land heads:
    a. At least twice?
    b. On the second toss, given that heads were thrown on the first toss?
    c. On the third toss, given that tails were thrown on the first toss?

35. **CAR THEFT** Figures obtained from a city's police department seem to indicate that of all motor vehicles reported as stolen, 64% were stolen by professionals, whereas 36% were stolen by amateurs (primarily for joy rides). Of the vehicles presumed stolen by professionals, 24% were recovered within 48 hr, 16% were recovered after 48 hr, and 60% were never recovered. Of the vehicles presumed stolen by amateurs, 38% were recovered within 48 hr, 58% were recovered after 48 hr, and 4% were never recovered.
    a. Draw a tree diagram representing these data.
    b. What is the probability that a vehicle stolen by a professional in this city will be recovered within 48 hr?
    c. What is the probability that a vehicle stolen in this city will never be recovered?

36. **QUALITY CONTROL** An automobile manufacturer obtains the microprocessors used to regulate fuel consumption in its automobiles from three microelectronic firms: A, B, and C. The quality-control department of the company has determined that 1% of the microprocessors produced by Firm A are defective, 2% of those produced by Firm B are defective, and 1.5% of those produced by Firm C are defective. Firms A, B, and C supply 45%, 25%, and 30%, respectively, of the microprocessors used by the company. What is the probability that a randomly selected automobile manufactured by the company will have a defective microprocessor?

37. **COLLEGE ADMISSIONS** The admissions office of a private university released the following admission data for the preceding academic year: From a pool of 3900 male applicants, 40% were accepted by the university, and 40% of these subsequently enrolled. Additionally, from a pool of 3600 female applicants, 45% were accepted by the university, and 40% of these subsequently enrolled. What is the probability that:
    a. A male applicant will be accepted by and subsequently will enroll in the university?
    b. A student who applies for admissions will be accepted by the university?
    c. A student who applies for admission will be accepted by the university and subsequently will enroll?

38. **HOUSING LOANS** The chief loan officer of La Crosse Home Mortgage Company summarized the housing loans extended by the company in 2010 according to type and term of the loan. Her list shows that 70% of the loans were fixed-rate mortgages (F), 25% were adjustable-rate mortgages (A), and 5% belong to some other category (O) (mostly second trust-deed loans and loans extended under the graduated payment plan). Of the fixed-rate mortgages, 80% were 30-year loans and 20% were 15-year loans; of the adjustable-rate mortgages, 40% were 30-year loans and 60% were 15-year loans; finally, of the other loans extended, 30% were 20-year loans, 60% were 10-year loans, and 10% were for a term of 5 years or less.

a. Draw a tree diagram representing these data.

b. What is the probability that a home loan extended by La Crosse has an adjustable rate and is for a term of 15 years?

c. What is the probability that a home loan extended by La Crosse is for a term of 15 years?

39. QUALITY CONTROL It is estimated that 0.80% of a large consignment of eggs in a certain supermarket is broken.

a. What is the probability that a customer who randomly selects a dozen of these eggs receives at least one broken egg?

b. What is the probability that a customer who selects these eggs at random will have to check three cartons before finding a carton without any broken eggs? (Each carton contains a dozen eggs.)

40. QUALITY CONTROL A box contains two defective Christmas tree lights that have been inadvertently mixed with eight nondefective lights. If the lights are selected one at a time without replacement and tested until both defective lights are found, what is the probability that both defective lights will be found after exactly three trials?

41. EMPLOYEE EDUCATION AND INCOME The personnel department of Franklin National Life Insurance Company compiled the accompanying data regarding the income and education of its employees:

	Income $60,000 or Below	Income Above $60,000
Noncollege Graduate	2040	840
College Graduate	400	720

Let A be the event that a randomly chosen employee has a college degree, and let B be the event that the chosen employee's income is more than $60,000.

a. Find each of the following probabilities: $P(A)$, $P(B)$, $P(A \cap B)$, $P(B \mid A)$, and $P(B \mid A^c)$.

b. Are the events A and B independent events?

42. STUDENT FINANCIAL AID The accompanying data were obtained from the financial aid office of a certain university:

	Receiving Financial Aid	Not Receiving Financial Aid	Total
Undergraduates	4,222	3,898	8,120
Graduates	1,879	731	2,610
Total	6,101	4,629	10,730

Let A be the event that a student selected at random from this university is an undergraduate student, and let B be the event that a student selected at random is receiving financial aid.

a. Find each of the following probabilities: $P(A)$, $P(B)$, $P(A \cap B)$, $P(B \mid A)$, and $P(B \mid A^c)$.

b. Are the events A and B independent events?

43. MEDICAL RESEARCH A nationwide survey conducted by the National Cancer Society revealed the following information. Of 10,000 people surveyed, 3200 were "heavy coffee drinkers," and 160 had cancer of the pancreas. Of those who had cancer of the pancreas, 132 were heavy coffee drinkers. Using the data in this survey, determine whether the events "being a heavy coffee drinker" and "having cancer of the pancreas" are independent events.

44. Two cards are drawn without replacement from a well-shuffled deck of 52 cards. Let A be the event that the first card drawn is a heart, and let B be the event that the second card drawn is a red card. Show that the events A and B are dependent events.

45. RELIABILITY OF SECURITY SYSTEMS Before being allowed to enter a maximum-security area at a military installation, a person must pass three independent identification tests: a voice-pattern test, a fingerprint test, and a handwriting test. If the reliability of the first test is 97%, that of the second test is 98.5%, and that of the third is 98.5%, what is the probability that this security system will allow an improperly identified person to enter the maximum-security area?

46. SWITCHING INTERNET SERVICE PROVIDERS (ISPs) According to a survey conducted in 2004 of 1000 American adults with Internet access, one in four households planned to switch ISPs in the next 6 months. Of those who planned to switch, 1% of the households were likely to switch to a satellite connection, 27% to a digital subscriber line (DSL), 28% to cable modem, and 35% to dial-up modem, and 9% didn't know what kind of service provider they would switch to.

a. What is the probability that a randomly selected survey participant who was planning to switch ISPs switched to a dial-up modem connection?

b. What is the probability that a randomly selected survey participant upgraded to high-speed service (satellite, DSL, or cable)?

Source: Ipsos-Insight.

47. PROBABILITY OF TRANSPLANT REJECTION The probabilities that the three patients who are scheduled to receive kidney transplants at General Hospital will suffer rejection are $\frac{1}{2}$, $\frac{1}{3}$, and $\frac{1}{10}$. Assuming that the events (kidney rejection) are independent, find the probability that:

a. At least one patient will suffer rejection.

b. Exactly two patients will suffer rejection.

48. RELIABILITY OF A HOME THEATER SYSTEM In a home theater system, the probability that the video components need repair within 1 year is .01, the probability that the electronic components need repair within 1 year is .005, and the probability that the audio components need repair within 1 year is .001. Assuming that the events are independent, find the probability that:

a. At least one of these components will need repair within 1 year.

b. Exactly one of these components will need repair within 1 year.

49. **PRODUCT RELIABILITY** The proprietor of Cunningham's Hardware Store has decided to install floodlights on the premises as a measure against vandalism and theft. If the probability is .01 that a certain brand of floodlight will burn out within a year, find the minimum number of floodlights that must be installed to ensure that the probability that at least one of them will remain functional for the whole year is at least .99999. (Assume that the floodlights operate independently.)

50. **QUALITY CONTROL** Copykwik has four photocopy machines: A, B, C, and D. The probability that a given machine will break down on a particular day is

$$P(A) = \frac{1}{50} \qquad P(B) = \frac{1}{60} \qquad P(C) = \frac{1}{75} \qquad P(D) = \frac{1}{40}$$

Assuming independence, what is the probability on a particular day that:
a. All four machines will break down?
b. None of the machines will break down?

51. Suppose the probability that an event will occur in one trial is p. Show that the probability that the event will occur at least once in n independent trials is $1 - (1 - p)^n$.

52. Let E be any event in a sample space S.
a. Are E and S independent? Explain your answer.
b. Are E and $\varnothing$ independent? Explain your answer.

53. Let E and F be events such that $F \subset E$. Find $P(E \mid F)$, and interpret your result.

54. Let E and F be mutually exclusive events, and suppose $P(F) \neq 0$. Find $P(E \mid F)$, and interpret your result.

55. Let E and F be independent events; show that E and F^c are independent.

56. Suppose that A and B are mutually exclusive events and that $P(A \cup B) \neq 0$. What is $P(A \mid A \cup B)$?

In Exercises 57–60, determine whether the statement is true or false. If it is true, explain why it is true. If it is false, give an example to show why it is false.

57. If A and B are mutually exclusive and $P(B) \neq 0$, then $P(A \mid B) = 0$.

58. If A is an event of an experiment, then $P(A \mid A^c) \neq 0$.

59. If A and B are events of an experiment, then

$$P(A \cap B) = P(A \mid B) \cdot P(B) = P(B \mid A) \cdot P(A)$$

60. If A and B are independent events with $P(A) \neq 0$ and $P(B) \neq 0$, then $A \cap B \neq \varnothing$.

7.5   Solutions to Self-Check Exercises

1. a. $P(A \mid B) = \dfrac{P(A \cap B)}{P(B)}$ b. $P(B \mid A) = \dfrac{P(A \cap B)}{P(A)}$

   $= \dfrac{.3}{.8} = \dfrac{3}{8}$ $= \dfrac{.3}{.4} = \dfrac{3}{4}$

2. Let A, B, and C denote the events that a respondent who married between the ages of 20 and 22, between the ages of 23 and 27, and at age 28 or older (respectively) said that his or her marriage was "less than very happy." Then the probability of each of these events occurring is $P(A) = .297$, $P(B) = .269$, and $P(C) = .451$. So the probability that all three of the respondents said that his or her marriage was "less than very happy" is

$$P(A) \cdot P(B) \cdot P(C) = (.297)(.269)(.451) \approx .036$$

7.6   Bayes' Theorem

A Posteriori Probabilities

Suppose three machines, A, B, and C, produce similar engine components. Machine A produces 45% of the total components, Machine B produces 30%, and Machine C produces 25%. For the usual production schedule, 6% of the components produced by Machine A do not meet established specifications; for Machine B and Machine C, the corresponding figures are 4% and 3%, respectively. One component is selected at random from the total output and is found to be defective. What is the probability that the component selected was produced by Machine A?

The answer to this question is found by calculating the probability *after* the outcomes of the experiment have been observed. Such probabilities are called **a posteriori probabilities** in contrast to **a priori probabilities**—probabilities that give the likelihood that an event *will* occur, the subject of the last several sections.

Returning to the example under consideration, we need to determine the a posteriori probability for the event that the component selected was produced by Machine A. Toward this end, let A, B, and C denote the events that a component is produced by Machine A, Machine B, and Machine C, respectively. We may represent this experiment with a Venn diagram (Figure 21).

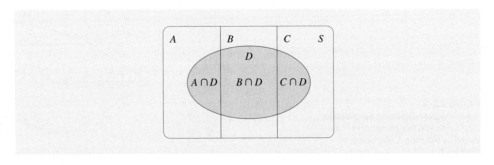

FIGURE 21
D is the event that a defective component is produced by Machine A, Machine B, or Machine C.

The three mutually exclusive events A, B, and C form a **partition** of the sample space S; that is, aside from being mutually exclusive, their union is precisely S. The event D that a component is defective is the shaded area. Again referring to Figure 21, we see that

1. The event D may be expressed as

$$D = (A \cap D) \cup (B \cap D) \cup (C \cap D)$$

2. The event that a component is defective and is produced by Machine A is given by $A \cap D$.

Thus, the a posteriori probability that a defective component selected was produced by Machine A is given by

$$P(A \mid D) = \frac{P(A \cap D)}{P(D)}$$

Upon dividing both the numerator and the denominator by $P(S)$ and observing that the events $A \cap D$, $B \cap D$, and $C \cap D$ are mutually exclusive, we obtain

$$P(A \mid D) = \frac{P(A \cap D)}{P(D)}$$

$$= \frac{P(A \cap D)}{P(A \cap D) + P(B \cap D) + P(C \cap D)} \tag{7}$$

Next, using the Product Rule, we may express

$$P(A \cap D) = P(A) \cdot P(D \mid A)$$
$$P(B \cap D) = P(B) \cdot P(D \mid B)$$
$$P(C \cap D) = P(C) \cdot P(D \mid C)$$

so Equation (7) may be expressed in the form

$$P(A \mid D) = \frac{P(A) \cdot P(D \mid A)}{P(A) \cdot P(D \mid A) + P(B) \cdot P(D \mid B) + P(C) \cdot P(D \mid C)} \tag{8}$$

which is a special case of a result known as **Bayes' Theorem.**

Observe that the expression on the right of Equation (8) involves the probabilities $P(A)$, $P(B)$, and $P(C)$ as well as the conditional probabilities $P(D \mid A)$, $P(D \mid B)$, and $P(D \mid C)$. In fact, by displaying these probabilities on a tree diagram, we obtain Figure 22. We may compute the required probability by substituting the relevant quantities into Equation (8), or we may make use of the following device:

$$P(A \mid D) = \frac{\text{Product of probabilities along the branch through } A \text{ terminating at } D}{\text{Sum of products of the probabilities along each branch terminating at } D}$$

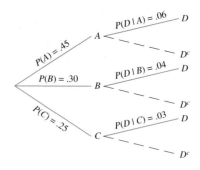

FIGURE 22
A tree diagram displaying the probabilities that a defective component is produced by Machine A, Machine B, or Machine C

In either case, we obtain

$$P(A \mid D) = \frac{(.45)(.06)}{(.45)(.06) + (.30)(.04) + (.25)(.03)}$$
$$\approx .58$$

Before looking at any further examples, let's state the general form of Bayes' Theorem.

Bayes' Theorem

Let $A_1, A_2, \ldots, A_n$ be a partition of a sample space S, and let E be an event of the experiment such that $P(E) \neq 0$ and $P(A_i) \neq 0$ for $1 \leq i \leq n$. Then the a posteriori probability $P(A_i \mid E)$ $(1 \leq i \leq n)$ is given by

$$P(A_i \mid E) = \frac{P(A_i) \cdot P(E \mid A_i)}{P(A_1) \cdot P(E \mid A_1) + P(A_2) \cdot P(E \mid A_2) + \cdots + P(A_n) \cdot P(E \mid A_n)} \quad \textbf{(9)}$$

VIDEO

APPLIED EXAMPLE 1 Quality Control The panels for the Pulsar 32-inch widescreen LCD HDTVs are manufactured in three locations and then shipped to the main plant of Vista Vision for final assembly. Plants A, B, and C supply 50%, 30%, and 20%, respectively, of the panels used by Vista Vision. The quality-control department of the company has determined that 1% of the panels produced by Plant A are defective, whereas 2% of the panels produced by Plants B and C are defective. If a Pulsar 32-inch HDTV is selected at random and the panel is found to be defective, what is the probability that the panel was manufactured in Plant C? (Compare with Example 6, page 404.)

Solution Let A, B, and C denote the events that the set chosen has a panel manufactured in Plant A, Plant B, and Plant C, respectively. Also, let D denote the event that a set has a defective panel. Using the given information, we may draw the tree diagram shown in Figure 23. Next, using Formula (9), we find that the required a posteriori probability is given by

$$P(C \mid D) = \frac{P(C) \cdot P(D \mid C)}{P(A) \cdot P(D \mid A) + P(B) \cdot P(D \mid B) + P(C) \cdot P(D \mid C)}$$
$$= \frac{(.20)(.02)}{(.50)(.01) + (.30)(.02) + (.20)(.02)}$$
$$\approx .27$$

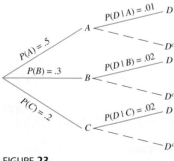

FIGURE 23

$$P(C \mid D) = \frac{\text{Product of probabilities of branches to } D \text{ through } C}{\text{Sum of product of probabilities of branches leading to } D}$$

APPLIED EXAMPLE 2 Income Distributions A study was conducted in a large metropolitan area to determine the annual incomes of married couples in which the husbands were the sole providers and of those in which the husbands and wives were both employed. Table 9 gives the results of this study.

TABLE 9

Annual Family Income, $	Married Couples, %	Income Group with Both Spouses Employed, %
150,000 and over	4	65
100,000–149,999	10	73
75,000–99,999	21	68
50,000–74,999	24	63
30,000–49,999	30	43
Under 30,000	11	28

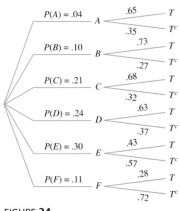

FIGURE **24**

a. What is the probability that a couple selected at random from this area has two incomes?

b. If a randomly chosen couple has two incomes, what is the probability that the annual income of this couple is $150,000 or more?

c. If a randomly chosen couple has two incomes, what is the probability that the annual income of this couple is greater than $49,999?

Solution Let A denote the event that the annual income of the couple is $150,000 or more; let B denote the event that the annual income is between $100,000 and $149,999; let C denote the event that the annual income is between $75,000 and $99,999; and so on. Finally, let T denote the event that both spouses are employed. The probabilities of the occurrence of these events are displayed in Figure 24.

a. The probability that a couple selected at random from this group has two incomes is given by

$$P(T) = P(A) \cdot P(T \mid A) + P(B) \cdot P(T \mid B) + P(C) \cdot P(T \mid C)$$
$$+ P(D) \cdot P(T \mid D) + P(E) \cdot P(T \mid E) + P(F) \cdot P(T \mid F)$$
$$= (.04)(.65) + (.10)(.73) + (.21)(.68) + (.24)(.63)$$
$$+ (.30)(.43) + (.11)(.28)$$
$$= .5528$$

b. Using the results of part (a) and Bayes' Theorem, we find that the probability that a randomly chosen couple has an annual income of $150,000 or more, given that both spouses are employed, is

$$P(A \mid T) = \frac{P(A) \cdot P(T \mid A)}{P(T)} = \frac{(.04)(.65)}{.5528}$$
$$\approx .047$$

c. The probability that a randomly chosen couple has an annual income greater than $49,999, given that both spouses are employed, is

$$P(A \mid T) + P(B \mid T) + P(C \mid T) + P(D \mid T)$$
$$= \frac{P(A) \cdot P(T \mid A) + P(B) \cdot P(T \mid B) + P(C) \cdot P(T \mid C) + P(D) \cdot P(T \mid D)}{P(T)}$$
$$= \frac{(.04)(.65) + (.1)(.73) + (.21)(.68) + (.24)(.63)}{.5528}$$
$$\approx .711$$

7.6 Self-Check Exercises

1. The accompanying tree diagram represents a two-stage experiment. Use the diagram to find $P(B \mid D)$.

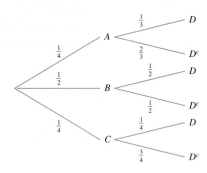

2. In a recent presidential election, it was estimated that the probability that the Republican candidate would be elected was $\frac{3}{5}$ and therefore the probability that the Democratic candidate would be elected was $\frac{2}{5}$ (the two Independent candidates were given little chance of being elected). It was also estimated that if the Republican candidate were elected, then the probability that research for a new manned bomber would continue was $\frac{4}{5}$. But if the Democratic candidate were successful, then the probability that the research would continue was $\frac{3}{10}$. Research was terminated shortly after the successful presidential candidate took office. What is the probability that the Republican candidate won that election?

Solutions to Self-Check Exercises 7.6 can be found on page 422.

7.6 Concept Questions

1. What are a priori probabilities and a posteriori probabilities? Give an example of each.

2. Suppose the events A, B, and C form the partition of a sample space S, and suppose E is an event of an experiment such that $P(E) \neq 0$. Use Bayes' Theorem to write the formula for the a posteriori probability $P(A \mid E)$. (Assume that $P(A)$, $P(B)$, $P(C) \neq 0$.)

3. Refer to Question 2. If E is the event that a product was produced in Factory A, Factory B, or Factory C and $P(E) \neq 0$, what does $P(A \mid E)$ represent?

7.6 Exercises

In Exercises 1–3, refer to the accompanying Venn diagram. An experiment in which the three mutually exclusive events A, B, and C form a partition of the uniform sample space S is depicted in the diagram.

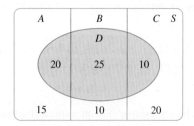

1. Using the information given in the Venn diagram, draw a tree diagram illustrating the probabilities of the events A, B, C, and D.

2. Find: **a.** $P(D)$ **b.** $P(A \mid D)$

3. Find: **a.** $P(D^c)$ **b.** $P(B \mid D^c)$

In Exercises 4–6, refer to the accompanying Venn diagram. An experiment in which the three mutually exclusive events A, B, and C form a partition of the uniform sample space S is depicted in the diagram.

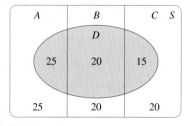

4. Using the information given in the Venn diagram, draw a tree diagram illustrating the probabilities of the events A, B, C, and D.

5. Find: **a.** $P(D)$ **b.** $P(B \mid D)$

6. Find: **a.** $P(D^c)$ **b.** $P(B \mid D^c)$

7. The accompanying tree diagram represents a two-stage experiment. Use the diagram to find:
   a. $P(A) \cdot P(D \mid A)$ b. $P(B) \cdot P(D \mid B)$
   c. $P(A \mid D)$

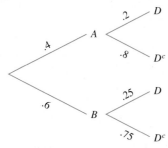

8. The accompanying tree diagram represents a two-stage experiment. Use the diagram to find:
   a. $P(A) \cdot P(D \mid A)$ b. $P(B) \cdot P(D \mid B)$
   c. $P(A \mid D)$

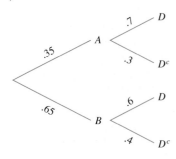

9. The accompanying tree diagram represents a two-stage experiment. Use the diagram to find:
   a. $P(A) \cdot P(D \mid A)$ b. $P(B) \cdot P(D \mid B)$
   c. $P(C) \cdot P(D \mid C)$ d. $P(A \mid D)$

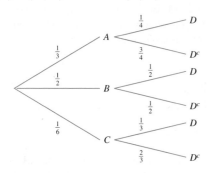

10. The accompanying tree diagram represents a two-stage experiment. Use this diagram to find
    a. $P(A \cap D)$ b. $P(B \cap D)$ c. $P(C \cap D)$ d. $P(D)$
    e. Verify:

$$P(A \mid D) = \frac{P(A \cap D)}{P(D)}$$

$$= \frac{P(A) \cdot P(D \mid A)}{P(A) \cdot P(D \mid A) + P(B) \cdot P(D \mid B) + P(C) \cdot P(D \mid C)}$$

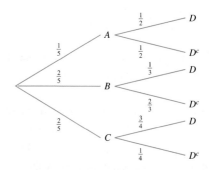

11. The accompanying diagram represents a two-stage experiment. Complete the information on the diagram, and use it to find:
    a. $P(B)$ b. $P(A \mid B)$
    c. $P(B^c)$ d. $P(A \mid B^c)$

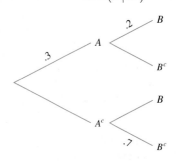

12. The accompanying diagram represents a two-stage experiment. Here, $B = (A \cup C)^c$. Complete the information on the diagram, and use it to find:
    a. $P(D)$ b. $P(B \mid D)$
    c. $P(D^c)$ d. $P(A \mid D^c)$

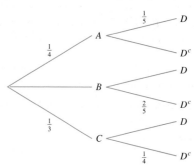

In Exercises 13–16, refer to the following experiment: Two cards are drawn in succession without replacement from a standard deck of 52 cards.

13. What is the probability that the first card is a heart given that the second card is a heart?

14. What is the probability that the first card is a heart given that the second card is a diamond?

15. What is the probability that the first card is a jack given that the second card is an ace?

16. What is the probability that the first card is a face card given that the second card is an ace?

In Exercises 17–20, refer to the following experiment: Urn *A* contains four white balls and six black balls. Urn *B* contains three white balls and five black balls. A ball is drawn from Urn *A* and then transferred to Urn *B*. A ball is then drawn from Urn *B*.

17. Represent the probabilities associated with this two-stage experiment in the form of a tree diagram.

18. What is the probability that the transferred ball was white given that the second ball drawn was white?

19. What is the probability that the transferred ball was black given that the second ball drawn was white?

20. What is the probability that the transferred ball was black given that the second ball drawn was black?

21. **POLITICS** The 1992 U.S. Senate was composed of 57 Democrats and 43 Republicans. Of the Democrats, 38 had served in the military, whereas 28 of the Republicans had seen military service. If a senator selected at random had served in the military, what is the probability that he or she was Republican?

22. **RETIREMENT NEEDS** In a survey of 2000 adults 50 years old and older of whom 60% were retired and 40% were pre-retired, the following question was asked: Do you expect your income needs to vary from year to year in retirement? Of those who were retired, 33% answered no, and 67% answered yes. Of those who were pre-retired, 28% answered no, and 72% answered yes. If a respondent in the survey was selected at random and had answered yes to the question, what is the probability that he or she was retired?
Source: Sun Life Financial.

23. An experiment consists of randomly selecting one of three coins, tossing it, and observing the outcome—heads or tails. The first coin is a two-headed coin, the second is a biased coin such that $P(H) = .75$, and the third is a fair coin.
   a. What is the probability that the coin that is tossed will show heads?
   b. If the coin selected shows heads, what is the probability that this coin is the fair coin?

24. **SEAT-BELT COMPLIANCE** Data compiled by the Highway Patrol Department regarding the use of seat-belts by drivers in a certain area after the passage of a compulsory seat-belt law are shown in the accompanying table.

Drivers	Percentage of Drivers in Group	Percent of Group Stopped for Moving Violation
Group I (using seat-belts)	64	.2
Group II (not using seat-belts)	36	.5

If a driver in that area is stopped for a moving violation, what is the probability that he or she:
a. Will have a seat-belt on?
b. Will not have a seat-belt on?

25. **BLOOD TESTS** If a certain disease is present, then a blood test will reveal it 95% of the time. But the test will also indicate the presence of the disease 2% of the time when in fact the person tested is free of that disease; that is, the test gives a false positive 2% of the time. If 0.3% of the general population actually has the disease, what is the probability that a person chosen at random from the population has the disease given that he or she tested positive?

26. **OPINION POLLS** In a survey to determine the opinions of Americans on health insurers, 400 baby boomers and 600 pre-boomers were asked this question: Do you believe that insurers are very responsible for high health costs? Of the baby boomers, 212 answered in the affirmative, whereas 198 of the pre-boomers answered in the affirmative. If a respondent chosen at random from those surveyed answered the question in the affirmative, what is the probability that he or she is a baby boomer? A pre-boomer?
Source: GfK Roper Consulting.

27. **QUALITY CONTROL** A halogen desk lamp produced by Luminar was found to be defective. The company has three factories where the lamps are manufactured. The percentage of the total number of halogen desk lamps produced by each factory and the probability that a lamp manufactured by that factory is defective are shown in the accompanying table. What is the probability that the defective lamp was manufactured in Factory III?

Factory	Percent of Total Production	Probability of Defective Component
I	35	.015
II	35	.01
III	30	.02

28. **OPINION POLLS** A survey involving 400 likely Democratic voters and 300 likely Republican voters asked the question: Do you support or oppose legislation that would require registration of all handguns? The following results were obtained:

Answer	Democrats, %	Republicans, %
Support	77	59
Oppose	14	31
Don't know/refused	9	10

If a randomly chosen respondent in the survey answered "oppose," what is the probability that he or she is a likely Democratic voter?

29. **AGE DISTRIBUTION OF RENTERS** A study conducted by the Metro Housing Agency in a midwestern city revealed the following information concerning the age distribution of renters within the city.

Age	Adult Population, %	Group Who Are Renters, %
21–44	51	58
45–64	31	45
65 and over	18	60

a. What is the probability that an adult selected at random from this population is a renter?

b. If a renter is selected at random, what is the probability that he or she is in the 21–44 age bracket?

c. If a renter is selected at random, what is the probability that he or she is 45 years old or older?

30. **PRODUCT RELIABILITY** The estimated probability that a Brand A, a Brand B, and a Brand C plasma TV will last at least 30,000 hr is .90, .85, and .80, respectively. Of the 4500 plasma TVs that Ace TV sold in a certain year, 1000 were Brand A, 1500 were Brand B, and 2000 were Brand C. If a plasma TV set sold by Ace TV that year is selected at random and is still working after 30,000 hr of use:
a. What is the probability that it was a Brand A TV?
b. What is the probability that it was not a Brand A TV?

31. **OPINION POLLS** A survey involving 400 likely Democratic voters and 300 likely Republican voters asked the question: Do you support or oppose legislation that would require trigger locks on guns, to prevent misuse by children? The following results were obtained:

Answer	Democrats, %	Republicans, %
Support	88	71
Oppose	7	20
Don't know/refused	5	9

If a randomly chosen respondent in the survey answered "support," what is the probability that he or she is a likely Republican voter?

32. **QUALITY CONTROL** Jansen Electronics has four machines that produce identical components for use in its DVD players. The proportion of the components produced by each machine and the probability of a component produced by that machine being defective are shown in the accompanying table. What is the probability that a component selected at random:
a. Is defective?
b. Was produced by Machine I, given that it is defective?
c. Was produced by Machine II, given that it is defective?

Machine	Proportion of Components Produced	Probability of Defective Component
I	.15	.04
II	.30	.02
III	.35	.02
IV	.20	.03

33. **CRIME RATES** Data compiled by the Department of Justice on the number of people arrested in a certain year for serious crimes (murder, forcible rape, robbery, etc.) revealed that 89% were male and 11% were female. Of the males, 30% were under 18, whereas 27% of the females arrested were under 18.
a. What is the probability that a person arrested for a serious crime in that year was under 18?
b. If a person arrested for a serious crime in that year is known to be under 18, what is the probability that the person is female?
Source: Department of Justice.

34. **RELIABILITY OF MEDICAL TESTS** A medical test has been designed to detect the presence of a certain disease. Among people who have the disease, the probability that the disease will be detected by the test is .95. However, the probability that the test will erroneously indicate the presence of the disease in those who do not actually have it is .04. It is estimated that 4% of the population who take this test have the disease.
a. If the test administered to an individual is positive, what is the probability that the person actually has the disease?
b. If an individual takes the test twice and the test is positive both times, what is the probability that the person actually has the disease? (Assume that the tests are independent.)

35. **RELIABILITY OF MEDICAL TESTS** Refer to Exercise 34. Suppose 20% of the people who were referred to a clinic for the test did in fact have the disease. If the test administered to an individual from this group is positive, what is the probability that the person actually has the disease?

36. **GENDER GAP** A study of the faculty at U.S. medical schools in 2006 revealed that 32% of the faculty were women and 68% were men. Of the female faculty, 31% were full/associate professors, 47% were assistant professors, and 22% were instructors. Of the male faculty, 51% were full/associate professors, 37% were assistant professors, and 12% were instructors. If a faculty member at a U.S. medical school selected at random in 2006 held the rank of full/associate professor, what is the probability that the faculty member was female?
Source: Association of American Medical Colleges.

37. **BEVERAGE RESEARCH** In a study of the scientific research on soft drinks, juices, and milk, 50 studies were fully sponsored by the food industry, and 30 studies were conducted with no corporate ties. Of those that were fully sponsored by the food industry, 14% of the participants found the products unfavorable, 23% were neutral, and 63% found the products favorable. Of those that had no industry funding, 38% found the products unfavorable, 15% were neutral, and 47% found the products favorable.
a. What is the probability that a participant selected at random found the products favorable?
b. If a participant selected at random found the product favorable, what is the probability that he or she belongs to a group that participated in a corporate-sponsored study?
Source: Children's Hospital, Boston.

38. **SELECTION OF SUPREME COURT JUDGES** In a past presidential election, it was estimated that the probability that the Republican candidate would be elected was $\frac{3}{5}$ and therefore the probability that the Democratic candidate would be elected was $\frac{2}{5}$ (the two Independent candidates were given no chance of being elected). It was also estimated that if the Republican candidate were elected, the probability that a conservative, moderate, or liberal judge would be appointed to the Supreme Court (one retirement was expected during the presidential term) was $\frac{1}{2}$, $\frac{1}{3}$, and $\frac{1}{6}$, respectively. If the Democratic candidate were elected, the

probabilities that a conservative, moderate, or liberal judge would be appointed to the Supreme Court would be $\frac{1}{8}$, $\frac{3}{8}$, and $\frac{1}{2}$, respectively. A conservative judge was appointed to the Supreme Court during the presidential term. What is the probability that the Democratic candidate was elected?

39. **PERSONNEL SELECTION** Applicants for temporary office work at Carter Temporary Help Agency who have successfully completed a typing test are then placed in suitable positions by Nancy Dwyer and Darla Newberg. Employers who hire temporary help through the agency return a card indicating satisfaction or dissatisfaction with the work performance of those hired. From past experience it is known that 80% of the employees placed by Nancy are rated as satisfactory, and 70% of those placed by Darla are rated as satisfactory. Darla places 55% of the temporary office help at the agency, and Nancy places the remaining 45%. If a Carter office worker is rated unsatisfactory, what is the probability that he or she was placed by Darla?

40. **MEDICAL RESEARCH** On the basis of data obtained from the National Institute of Dental Research, it has been determined that 42% of 12-year-olds have never had a cavity, 34% of 13-year-olds have never had a cavity, and 28% of 14-year-olds have never had a cavity. Suppose a child is selected at random from a group of 24 junior high school students that includes six 12-year-olds, eight 13-year-olds, and ten 14-year-olds. If this child does not have a cavity, what is the probability that this child is 14 years old?

Source: National Institute of Dental Research.

41. **VOTING PATTERNS** In a recent senatorial election, 50% of the voters in a certain district were registered as Democrats, 35% were registered as Republicans, and 15% were registered as Independents. The incumbent Democratic senator was reelected over her Republican and Independent opponents. Exit polls indicated that she gained 75% of the Democratic vote, 25% of the Republican vote, and 30% of the Independent vote. Assuming that the exit poll is accurate, what is the probability that a vote for the incumbent was cast by a registered Republican?

42. **AUTO-ACCIDENT RATES** An insurance company has compiled the accompanying data relating the age of drivers and the accident rate (the probability of being involved in an accident during a 1-year period) for drivers within that group:

Age Group	Percentage of Insured Drivers	Accident Rate, %
Under 25	16	5.5
25–44	40	2.5
45–64	30	2
65 and over	14	4

What is the probability that an insured driver selected at random:
a. Will be involved in an accident during a particular 1-year period?
b. Who is involved in an accident is under 25?

43. **PERSONAL HABITS** There were 80 male guests at a party. The number of men in each of four age categories is given in the following table. The table also gives the probability that a man in the respective age category will keep his paper money in order of denomination.

Age	Men	Keep Paper Money in Order, %
21–34	25	9
35–44	30	61
45–54	15	80
55 and over	10	80

A man's wallet was retrieved and the paper money in it was kept in order of denomination. What is the probability that the wallet belonged to a male guest between the ages of 35 and 44?

44. **VOTER TURNOUT BY INCOME** Voter turnout drops steadily as income level declines. The following table gives the percentage of eligible voters in a certain city, categorized by income, who responded with "did not vote" in the 2000 presidential election. The table also gives the number of eligible voters in the city, categorized by income.

Income (percentile)	Percent Who "Did Not Vote"	Eligible Voters
0–16	52	4,000
17–33	31	11,000
34–67	30	17,500
68–95	14	12,500
96–100	12	5,000

If an eligible voter from this city who had voted in the election is selected at random, what is the probability that this person had an income in the 17–33 percentile?

Source: The National Election Studies.

45. **THE SOCIAL LADDER** The following table summarizes the results of a poll conducted with 1154 adults.

Annual Household Income, $	Respondents Within That Income Range, %	Respondents Who Call Themselves		
		Rich, %	Middle Class, %	Poor, %
Less than 15,000	11.2	0	24	76
15,000–29,999	18.6	3	60	37
30,000–49,999	24.5	0	86	14
50,000–74,999	21.9	2	90	8
75,000 and higher	23.8	5	91	4

a. What is the probability that a respondent chosen at random calls himself or herself middle class?
b. If a randomly chosen respondent calls himself or herself middle class, what is the probability that the annual household income of that individual is between $30,000 and $49,999, inclusive?
c. If a randomly chosen respondent calls himself or herself middle class, what is the probability that the individual's income is either less than or equal to $29,999 or greater than or equal to $50,000?

Source: New York Times/CBS News; Wall Street Journal Almanac.

46. OBESITY IN CHILDREN Researchers weighed 1976 3-year-olds from low-income families in 20 U.S. cities. Each child is classified by race (white, black, or Hispanic) and by weight (normal weight, overweight, or obese). The results are tabulated as follows:

Race	Children	Weight, %		
		Normal Weight	Overweight	Obese
White	406	68	18	14
Black	1081	68	15	17
Hispanic	489	56	20	24

If a participant in the research is selected at random and is found to be obese, what is the probability that the 3-year-old is white? Hispanic?

Source: American Journal of Public Health.

47. COLLEGE MAJORS The Office of Admissions and Records of a large western university released the accompanying information concerning the contemplated majors of its freshman class:

Major	Freshmen Choosing This Major, %	Females Choosing This Major, %	Males Choosing This Major, %
Business	24	38	62
Humanities	8	60	40
Education	8	66	34
Social science	7	58	42
Natural sciences	9	52	48
Other	44	48	52

What is the probability that:

a. A student selected at random from the freshman class is a female?

b. A business student selected at random from the freshman class is a male?

c. A female student selected at random from the freshman class is majoring in business?

48. VOTER TURNOUT BY PROFESSION The following table gives the percentage of eligible voters grouped according to profession who responded with "voted" in the 2000 presidential election. The table also gives the percentage of people in a survey categorized by their profession.

Profession	Percentage Who Voted	Percentage in Each Profession
Professionals	84	12
White collar	73	24
Blue collar	66	32
Unskilled	57	10
Farmers	68	8
Housewives	66	14

If an eligible voter who participated in the survey and voted in the election is selected at random, what is the probability that this person is a housewife?

Source: The National Election Studies.

49. SLEEPING WITH CELL PHONES In a survey of 920 people aged from 18 through 84 years, of whom 84 belonged to the Millenial Generation (18–29), 224 belonged to Generation X (30–45), 200 belonged to the Baby Boom Generation, and the rest belonged to the Silent Generation (65+), the following question was asked: Who has slept with a cell phone nearby? Of those who answered in the affirmative, 83%, 68%, 50%, and 20% were from the Millenial Generation, Generation X, the Baby Boom Generation, and the Silent Generation, respectively. If a person in the survey is selected at random and has not slept with a cell phone nearby, what is the probability that the person belongs to the Millenial Generation?

Source: Pew Research Center.

50. MEDICAL DIAGNOSES A study was conducted among a certain group of union members whose health insurance policies required second opinions prior to surgery. Of those members whose doctors advised them to have surgery, 20% were informed by a second doctor that no surgery was needed. Of these, 70% took the second doctor's opinion and did not go through with the surgery. Of the members who were advised to have surgery by both doctors, 95% went through with the surgery. What is the probability that a union member who had surgery was advised to do so by a second doctor?

51. SMOKING AND EDUCATION According to the Centers for Disease Control and Prevention, the percentage of adults 25 years old and older who smoke, by educational level, is as follows:

Educational Level	No diploma	GED diploma	High school graduate	Some college	Undergraduate level	Graduate degree
Respondents, %	26	43	25	23	10.7	7

In a group of 140 people, there were 8 with no diploma, 14 with GED diplomas, 40 high school graduates, 24 with some college, 42 with an undergraduate degree, and 12 with a graduate degree. (Assume that these categories are mutually exclusive.) If a person selected at random from this group was a smoker, what is the probability that he or she is a person with a graduate degree?

Source: Centers for Disease Control and Prevention.

7.6 Solutions to Self-Check Exercises

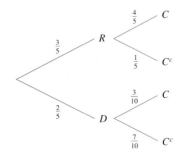

1. Using the probabilities given in the tree diagram and Bayes' Theorem, we have

$$P(B \mid D) = \frac{P(B) \cdot P(D \mid B)}{P(A) \cdot P(D \mid A) + P(B) \cdot P(D \mid B) + P(C) \cdot P(D \mid C)}$$

$$= \frac{\left(\frac{1}{2}\right)\left(\frac{1}{2}\right)}{\left(\frac{1}{4}\right)\left(\frac{1}{3}\right) + \left(\frac{1}{2}\right)\left(\frac{1}{2}\right) + \left(\frac{1}{4}\right)\left(\frac{1}{4}\right)} = \frac{12}{19}$$

2. Let R and D, respectively, denote the event that the Republican and the Democratic candidate won the presidential election. Then $P(R) = \frac{3}{5}$ and $P(D) = \frac{2}{5}$. Also, let C denote the event that research for the new manned bomber continued. These data may be exhibited as in the accompanying tree diagram:

Using Bayes' Theorem, we find that the probability that the Republican candidate had won the election is given by

$$P(R \mid C^c) = \frac{P(R) \cdot P(C^c \mid R)}{P(R) \cdot P(C^c \mid R) + P(D) \cdot P(C^c \mid D)}$$

$$= \frac{\left(\frac{3}{5}\right)\left(\frac{1}{5}\right)}{\left(\frac{3}{5}\right)\left(\frac{1}{5}\right) + \left(\frac{2}{5}\right)\left(\frac{7}{10}\right)} = \frac{3}{10}$$

CHAPTER 7   Summary of Principal Formulas and Terms

FORMULAS

1. Probability of an event in a uniform sample space	$P(E) = \dfrac{n(E)}{n(S)}$
2. Probability of the union of two mutually exclusive events	$P(E \cup F) = P(E) + P(F)$
3. Addition rule	$P(E \cup F) = P(E) + P(F) - P(E \cap F)$
4. Rule of complements	$P(E^c) = 1 - P(E)$
5. Conditional probability	$P(B \mid A) = \dfrac{P(A \cap B)}{P(A)}, \ P(A) \neq 0$
6. Product rule	$P(A \cap B) = P(A) \cdot P(B \mid A)$
7. Test for independence	$P(A \cap B) = P(A) \cdot P(B)$

TERMS

experiment (364)

outcome (364)

sample point (364)

sample space (364)

event (364)

finite sample space (364)

union of two events (365)

intersection of two events (365)

complement of an event (365)

mutually exclusive events (366)

relative frequency (373)

empirical probability (373)

probability of an event (373)

elementary (simple) event (373)

probability distribution (373)

probability function (373)

uniform sample space (374)

addition principle (375)

conditional probability (399)

finite stochastic process (403)

independent events (405)

Bayes' Theorem (413)

Concept Review Questions

Fill in the blanks.

1. An activity with observable results is called a/an _____; an outcome of an experiment is called a/an _____ point, and the set consisting of all possible sample points of an experiment is called a sample _____; a subset of a sample space of an experiment is called a/an _____.

2. The events E and F are mutually exclusive if $E \cap F =$ _____.

3. A sample space in which the outcomes are equally likely is called a/an _____ sample space; if such a space contains n simple events, then the probability of each simple event is _____.

4. The probability of the event B given that the event A has already occurred is called the _____ probability of B given A.

5. If the outcome of one event does not depend on a second event, then the two events are said to be _____.

6. The probability of an event after the outcomes of an experiment have been observed is called a/an _____ _____ _____.

Review Exercises

1. Let E and F be two mutually exclusive events, and suppose $P(E) = .4$ and $P(F) = .2$. Compute:
   a. $P(E \cap F)$ b. $P(E \cup F)$
   c. $P(E^c)$ d. $P(E^c \cap F^c)$
   e. $P(E^c \cup F^c)$

2. Let E and F be two events of an experiment with sample space S. Suppose $P(E) = .3$, $P(F) = .2$, and $P(E \cap F) = .15$. Compute:
   a. $P(E \cup F)$
   b. $P(E^c \cap F^c)$
   c. $P(E^c \cap F)$

3. Let E and F be two mutually exclusive events, and suppose $P(E) = .35$ and $P(F) = .47$. Find:
   a. $P(F^c)$ b. $P(E \cap F^c)$
   c. $P(E \cup F)$ d. $P(E^c \cap F^c)$

4. A die is loaded, and it has been determined that the probability distribution associated with the experiment of rolling the die and observing which number falls uppermost is given by the following:

Simple Event	Probability
{1}	.20
{2}	.12
{3}	.16
{4}	.18
{5}	.15
{6}	.19

   a. What is the probability of the number being even?
   b. What is the probability of the number being either a 1 or a 6?
   c. What is the probability of the number being less than 4?

5. An urn contains six red balls, five black balls, and four green balls. If two balls are selected at random without replacement from the urn, what is the probability that a red ball and a black ball will be selected?

6. **QUALITY CONTROL** The quality-control department of Starr Communications, a manufacturer of video-game DVDs, has determined from records that 1.5% of the DVDs sold have video defects, 0.8% have audio defects, and 0.4% have both audio and video defects. What is the probability that a DVD purchased by a customer:
   a. Will have a video or audio defect?
   b. Will not have a video or audio defect?

7. Let E and F be two events, and suppose that $P(E) = .35$, $P(F) = .55$, and $P(E \cup F) = .70$. Find $P(E \mid F)$.

8. Suppose that $P(E) = .60$, $P(F) = .32$, and $P(E \cap F) = .22$. Are E and F independent?

9. Suppose that E and F are independent events. If $P(E) = .32$ and $P(E \cap F) = .16$, what is $P(F)$?

The accompanying tree diagram represents an experiment consisting of two trials. In Exercises 10–14, use the diagram to find the given probability.

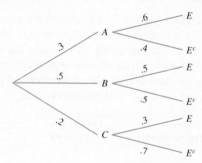

10. $P(A \cap E)$ 11. $P(B \cap E)$

12. $P(C \cap E)$ 13. $P(E)$

14. $P(A \mid E)$

15. An experiment consists of tossing a fair coin three times and observing the outcomes. Let A be the event that at least one head is thrown, and let B be the event that at most two tails are thrown.
    a. Find $P(A)$.   **b.** Find $P(B)$.
    c. Are A and B independent events?

16. **QUALITY CONTROL** In a group of 20 ballpoint pens on a shelf in the stationery department of Metro Department Store, 2 are known to be defective. If a customer selects 3 of these pens, what is the probability that
    a. At least 1 is defective?
    b. No more than 1 is defective?

17. Five people are selected at random. What is the probability that none of the people in this group were born on the same day of the week?

18. A pair of fair dice is rolled. What is the probability that the sum of the numbers falling uppermost is 8 if it is known that the two numbers are different?

19. A fair die is rolled three times. What is the probability that it shows an even number in the first toss, an odd number in the second toss, and a 1 on the third toss? Assume that the outcomes of the tosses are independent.

20. A fair die is rolled, a fair coin is tossed, and a card is drawn from a standard deck of 52 playing cards. Assuming these events are independent, what is the probability that the number falling uppermost on the die is a 6, the coin shows a tail, and the card drawn is a face card?

Three cards are drawn at random without replacement from a standard deck of 52 playing cards. In Exercises 21–25, find the probability of each of the given events.

21. All three cards are aces.

22. All three cards are face cards.

23. The second and third cards are red.

24. The second card is black, given that the first card was red.

25. The second card is a club, given that the first card was black.

26. **ASSEMBLY-TIME STUDIES** The results of a time study conducted by the production manager of Ace Novelty are shown in the accompanying table, where the number of action figures produced each quarter hour during an 8-hour workday has been tabulated. Find the empirical probability distribution associated with this experiment.

Figures Produced (in dozens)	Frequency of Occurrence
30	4
31	0
32	6
33	8
34	6
35	4
36	4

27. **FAMILY INCOME** According to the 2000 U.S. Census, the income distribution of households and families was as follows:

Income, $	0–24,999	25,000–49,999	50,000–74,999
Households and Families	30,261,220	30,965,514	20,540,604

Income, $	75,000–99,999	100,000–124,999	125,000–149,999
Households and Families	10,779,245	5,491,526	2,656,300

Income, $	150,000–199,999	200,000 or more
Households and Families	2,322,038	2,502,675

Find the empirical probability distribution associated with these data.

Source: U.S. Census Bureau.

28. **CONSUMER DECISIONS** Olivia is contemplating buying a laser printer. The probability that she will buy a printer manufactured by Epson, Brother, Canon, and Hewlett-Packard is .23, .18, .31, and .28, respectively. Find the probability that she will buy a laser printer manufactured by:
    a. Epson or Canon.   **b.** Epson, Brother, or Canon.

29. **RETIREMENT EXPECTATIONS** In a survey on retirement, participants were asked this question: Do you think that life will be better, worse, or about the same when you retire? The results of the survey follow:

Answer	Better	Worse	Same	Don't know
Respondent, %	38	18	41	3

If a person in the survey is selected at random, what is the probability that he or she answered that life after retirement would be
    a. The same or better?
    b. The same or worse?
    Source: Bankrate.com, 2007.

30. Consider the composition of a three-child family in which the children were born at different times. Assume that a girl is as likely as a boy at each birth. What is the probability that
    a. There are two girls and a boy in the family?
    b. The oldest child is a girl?
    c. The oldest child is a girl and the youngest child is a boy?

31. **SALES OF PLASMA TVs** The records of Ace Electronics show that of the plasma TVs sold by the company, 26% were manufactured by Panasonic, 15.4% were manufactured by LG, 13.7% were manufactured by Samsung, 13.3% were manufactured by Philips, and 7.3% were manufactured by Hitachi. If a customer chosen at random purchases a plasma TV from Ace Electronics, what is the probability that the set was manufactured by:
    a. Panasonic, LG, Samsung, Philips, or Hitachi?
    b. A company other than those mentioned in part (a)?

32. FIGHTING INFLATION In a survey of 2000 adults, 18 years old and older, conducted in 2007, the following question was asked: Is your family income keeping pace with the cost of living? The results of the survey follow:

Answer	Falling behind	Staying even	Increasing faster	Don't know
Respondents	800	880	240	80

According to the survey, what percentage of the people polled said their family income is:
a. At least keeping pace with the cost of living?
b. Falling behind the cost of living?
Source: Pew Research Center.

33. SALES OF DISASTER-RECOVERY SYSTEMS Jay sells disaster-recovery computer systems to hedge funds. He estimates the probability of Hedge Fund A purchasing a system to be .6 and that of Hedge Fund B purchasing a system to be .5. He also estimates that the probability of both hedge funds purchasing a system is .3. What is the probability that only Hedge Fund A or only Hedge Fund B will purchase a system?

34. FLEX-TIME Of 320 male and 280 female employees at the home office of Gibraltar Insurance Company, 160 of the men and 190 of the women are on flex-time (flexible working hours). Given that an employee selected at random from this group is on flex-time, what is the probability that the employee is a man?

35. QUALITY CONTROL In a manufacturing plant, three machines, A, B, and C, produce 40%, 35%, and 25%, respectively, of the total production. The company's quality-control department has determined that 1% of the items produced by Machine A, 1.5% of the items produced by Machine B, and 2% of the items produced by Machine C are defective. If an item is selected at random and found to be defective, what is the probability that it was produced by Machine B?

36. COLLEGE ADMISSIONS Applicants who wish to be admitted to a certain professional school in a large university are required to take a screening test devised by an educational testing service. From past results, the testing service has estimated that 70% of all applicants are eligible for admission and that 92% of those who are eligible for admission pass the exam, whereas 12% of those who are ineligible for admission pass the exam. Using these results, what is the probability that an applicant for admission:
a. Passed the exam?
b. Passed the exam but was actually ineligible?

37. COMMUTING TIMES Bill commutes to work in the business district of Boston. He takes the train $\frac{3}{5}$ of the time and drives $\frac{2}{5}$ of the time (when he visits clients). If he takes the train, then he gets home by 6:30 P.M. 85% of the time; if he drives, then he gets home by 6:30 P.M. 60% of the time. If Bill gets home by 6:30 P.M., what is the probability that he drove to work?

38. CUSTOMER SURVEYS The sales department of Thompson Drug Company released the accompanying data concerning the sales of a certain pain reliever manufactured by the company.

Pain Reliever	Drug Sold, %	Group Sold in Extra-Strength Dosage, %
Group I (capsule form)	57	38
Group II (tablet form)	43	31

If a customer purchased the extra-strength dosage of this drug, what is the probability that it was in capsule form?

39. OPINION POLLS A survey involving 600 Democrats, 400 Republicans, and 200 Independents asked the question: Do you favor or oppose eliminating taxes on dividends paid to shareholders? The following results were obtained:

Answer	Democrats, %	Republicans, %	Independents, %
Favor	29	66	48
Opposed	71	34	52

If a randomly chosen respondent in the survey answered "favor," what is the probability that he or she is an Independent?
Source: TechnoMetrica Market Intelligence.

40. OPINION POLLS A poll was conducted among 500 registered voters in a certain area regarding their position on a national lottery to raise revenue for the government. The results of the poll are shown in the accompanying table.

Sex	Voters Polled, %	Favoring Lottery, %	Not Favoring Lottery, %	Expressing No Opinion, %
Male	51	62	32	6
Female	49	68	28	4

What is the probability that a registered voter who:
a. Favored a national lottery was a woman?
b. Expressed no opinion regarding the lottery was a woman?

CHAPTER 7   Before Moving On . . .

1. Let $S = \{s_1, s_2, s_3, s_4, s_5, s_6\}$ be the sample space associated with an experiment having the following probability distribution:

Outcome	s_1	s_2	s_3	s_4	s_5	s_6
Probability	$\frac{1}{12}$	$\frac{2}{12}$	$\frac{3}{12}$	$\frac{2}{12}$	$\frac{3}{12}$	$\frac{1}{12}$

Find the probability of the event $A = \{s_1, s_3, s_6\}$.

2. A card is drawn from a well-shuffled 52-card deck. What is the probability that the card drawn is a deuce or a face card?

3. Let E and F be events of an experiment with sample space S. Suppose $P(E) = .5$, $P(F) = .6$, and $P(E \cap F) = .2$. Compute:

a. $P(E \cup F)$ b. $P(E \cap F^c)$

4. Suppose A and B are independent events with $P(A) = .3$ and $P(B) = .6$. Find $P(A \cup B)$.

5. The following tree diagram represents a two-stage experiment. Use the diagram to find $P(A \mid D)$.

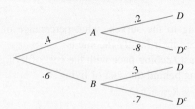

8 PROBABILITY DISTRIBUTIONS AND STATISTICS

Michael Poehlman/Getty Images

STATISTICS IS that branch of mathematics concerned with the collection, analysis, and interpretation of data. In Sections 8.1–8.3, we take a look at descriptive statistics; here, our interest lies in the description and presentation of data in the form of tables and graphs. In the rest of the chapter, we briefly examine inductive statistics, and we see how mathematical tools such as those developed in Chapter 7 may be used in conjunction with these data to help us draw certain conclusions and make forecasts.

Which of two motels should a certain private equity firm purchase? In Example 4, page 441, we show how the occupancy rate and the average daily profit for each motel can be used to help us determine which motel will generate the higher daily profit.

8.1   Distributions of Random Variables

Random Variables

In many situations, it is desirable to assign numerical values to the outcomes of an experiment. For example, if an experiment consists of rolling a die and observing the face that lands uppermost, then it is natural to assign the numbers 1, 2, 3, 4, 5, and 6, respectively, to the outcomes *one, two, three, four, five*, and *six* of the experiment. If we let X denote the outcome of the experiment, then X assumes one of these numbers. Because the values assumed by X depend on the outcomes of a chance experiment, the outcome X is referred to as a random variable.

> **Random Variable**
>
> A **random variable** is a rule that assigns a number to each outcome of a chance experiment.

More precisely, a random variable is a function with domain given by the set of outcomes of a chance experiment and range contained in the set of real numbers.

VIDEO **EXAMPLE 1** A coin is tossed three times. Let the random variable X denote the number of heads that occur in the three tosses.

a. List the outcomes of the experiment; that is, find the domain of the function X.
b. Find the value assigned to each outcome of the experiment by the random variable X.
c. Find the event comprising the outcomes to which a value of 2 has been assigned by X. This event is written $(X = 2)$ and is the event consisting of the outcomes in which two heads occur.

Solution

a. From the results of Example 3, Section 7.1 (page 366), we see that the set of outcomes of the experiment is given by the sample space

$$S = \{\text{HHH, HHT, HTH, THH, HTT, THT, TTH, TTT}\}$$

b. The outcomes of the experiment are displayed in the first column of Table 1. The corresponding value assigned to each such outcome by the random variable X (the number of heads) appears in the second column.
c. With the aid of Table 1, we see that the event $(X = 2)$ is given by the set

$$\{\text{HHT, HTH, THH}\}$$

■

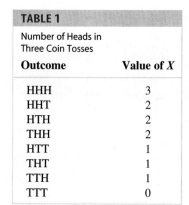

TABLE 1

Number of Heads in Three Coin Tosses

Outcome	Value of X
HHH	3
HHT	2
HTH	2
THH	2
HTT	1
THT	1
TTH	1
TTT	0

TABLE 2

Number of Coin Tosses Before Heads Appear

Outcome	Value of Y
H	1
TH	2
TTH	3
TTTH	4
TTTTH	5
⋮	⋮

EXAMPLE 2 A coin is tossed repeatedly until a head occurs. Let the random variable Y denote the number of coin tosses in the experiment. What are the values of Y?

Solution   The outcomes of the experiment make up the infinite set

$$S = \{\text{H, TH, TTH, TTTH, TTTTH, } \ldots\}$$

These outcomes of the experiment are displayed in the first column of Table 2. The corresponding values assumed by the random variable Y (the number of tosses) appear in the second column.

■

APPLIED EXAMPLE 3 Product Reliability A disposable flashlight is turned on and left on until its battery runs out. Let the random variable Z denote the length (in hours) of the life of the battery. What values may Z assume?

Solution The value of Z may be any nonnegative real number; that is, the possible values of Z comprise the interval $0 \leq Z < \infty$. ◼

One advantage of working with random variables—rather than working directly with the outcomes of an experiment—is that random variables are functions that may be added, subtracted, and multiplied. Because of this, results developed in the field of algebra and other areas of mathematics may be used freely to help us solve problems in probability and statistics.

A random variable is classified into three categories depending on the set of values it assumes. A random variable is called **finite discrete** if it assumes only finitely many values. For example, the random variable X of Example 1 is finite discrete because it may assume values only from the finite set of numbers $\{0, 1, 2, 3\}$. Next, a random variable is said to be **infinite discrete** if it takes on infinitely many values, which may be arranged in a sequence. For example, the random variable Y of Example 2 is infinite discrete because it assumes values from the set $\{1, 2, 3, 4, 5, \ldots\}$, which has been arranged in the form of an infinite sequence. Finally, a random variable is called **continuous** if the values it may assume comprise an interval of real numbers. For example, the random variable Z of Example 3 is continuous because the values it may assume comprise the interval of nonnegative real numbers. For the remainder of this section, unless otherwise noted, *all random variables will be assumed to be finite discrete*.

Probability Distributions of Random Variables

In Section 7.2, we learned how to construct the probability distribution for an experiment. There, the probability distribution took the form of a table that gave the probabilities associated with the outcomes of an experiment. Since the random variable associated with an experiment is related to the outcomes of the experiment, it is clear that we should be able to construct a probability distribution associated with the *random variable* rather than one associated with the outcomes of the experiment. Such a distribution is called the **probability distribution of a random variable** and may be given in the form of a formula or displayed in a table that gives the distinct (numerical) values of the random variable X and the probabilities associated with these values. Thus, if $x_1, x_2, \ldots, x_n$ are the values assumed by the random variable X with associated probabilities $P(X = x_1)$, $P(X = x_2)$, $\ldots$, $P(X = x_n)$, respectively, then the required probability distribution of the random variable X may be expressed in the form of the table shown in Table 3, where $p_i = P(X = x_i)$, $i = 1, 2, \ldots, n$.

The probability distribution of a random variable X satisfies

1. $0 \leq p_i \leq 1$ $i = 1, 2, \ldots, n$
2. $p_1 + p_2 + \cdots + p_n = 1$

In the next several examples, we illustrate the construction and application of probability distributions.

TABLE 3

Probability Distribution for the Random Variable X

x	$P(X = x)$
x_1	p_1
x_2	p_2
x_3	p_3
$\vdots$	$\vdots$
x_n	p_n

EXAMPLE 4

a. Find the probability distribution of the random variable associated with the experiment of Example 1.
b. What is the probability of obtaining at least two heads in the three tosses of the coin?

Solution

a. From the results of Example 1, we see that the values assumed by the random variable X are 0, 1, 2, and 3, corresponding to the events of 0, 1, 2, and 3 heads occurring, respectively. Referring to Table 1 once again, we see that the outcome associated with the event $(X = 0)$ is given by the set $\{TTT\}$. Consequently, the probability associated with the random variable X when it assumes the value 0 is given by

$$P(X = 0) = \frac{1}{8} \qquad \text{Note that } n(S) = 8.$$

Next, observe that the event $(X = 1)$ is given by the set $\{HTT, THT, TTH\}$, so

$$P(X = 1) = \frac{3}{8}$$

In a similar manner, we may compute $P(X = 2)$ and $P(X = 3)$, which gives the probability distribution shown in Table 4.

b. The probability of obtaining at least two heads is given by

$$P(X \geq 2) = P(X = 2) + P(X = 3)$$
$$= \frac{3}{8} + \frac{1}{8} = \frac{1}{2}$$

TABLE 4

Probability Distribution

x	$P(X = x)$
0	$\frac{1}{8}$
1	$\frac{3}{8}$
2	$\frac{3}{8}$
3	$\frac{1}{8}$

EXAMPLE 5 Let X denote the random variable that gives the sum of the faces that fall uppermost when two fair dice are rolled.

a. Find the probability distribution of X.
b. What is the probability that the sum of the faces that fall uppermost is less than or equal to 5? Between 8 and 10, inclusive?

Solution

a. The values assumed by the random variable X are 2, 3, 4, . . . , 12, corresponding to the events $E_2, E_3, E_4, \ldots, E_{12}$ (see Example 4, Section 7.1). The probabilities associated with the random variable X when X assumes the values 2, 3, 4, . . . , 12 are precisely the probabilities $P(E_2), P(E_3), \ldots, P(E_{12})$, respectively, and may be computed in much the same way as the solution to Example 3, Section 7.2. Thus,

$$P(X = 2) = P(E_2) = \frac{1}{36}$$

$$P(X = 3) = P(E_3) = \frac{2}{36}$$

and so on. The required probability distribution of X is given in Table 5.

b. The probability that the sum of the faces that fall uppermost is less than or equal to 5 is given by

$$P(X \leq 5) = P(X = 2) + P(X = 3) + P(X = 4) + P(X = 5)$$
$$= \frac{1}{36} + \frac{2}{36} + \frac{3}{36} + \frac{4}{36} = \frac{10}{36} = \frac{5}{18}$$

The probability that the sum of the faces that fall uppermost is between 8 and 10, inclusive, is given by

$$P(8 \leq X \leq 10) = P(X = 8) + P(X = 9) + P(X = 10)$$
$$= \frac{5}{36} + \frac{4}{36} + \frac{3}{36} = \frac{12}{36} = \frac{1}{3}$$

TABLE 5

x	$P(X = x)$
2	$\frac{1}{36}$
3	$\frac{2}{36}$
4	$\frac{3}{36}$
5	$\frac{4}{36}$
6	$\frac{5}{36}$
7	$\frac{6}{36}$
8	$\frac{5}{36}$
9	$\frac{4}{36}$
10	$\frac{3}{36}$
11	$\frac{2}{36}$
12	$\frac{1}{36}$

VIDEO ▶

APPLIED EXAMPLE 6 Waiting Lines The following data give the number of cars observed waiting in line at the beginning of 2-minute intervals between 3 P.M. and 5 P.M. on a certain Friday at the drive-in teller of Westwood Savings Bank and the corresponding frequency of occurrence.

Cars	0	1	2	3	4	5	6	7	8
Frequency of Occurrence	2	9	16	12	8	6	4	2	1

a. Find the probability distribution of the random variable X, where X denotes the number of cars observed waiting in line.
b. What is the probability that the number of cars observed waiting in line in any 2-minute interval between 3 P.M. and 5 P.M. on a Friday is less than or equal to 3? Between 2 and 4, inclusive? Greater than 6?

TABLE 6

Probability Distribution

x	$P(X = x)$
0	.03
1	.15
2	.27
3	.20
4	.13
5	.10
6	.07
7	.03
8	.02

Solution

a. Dividing each number in the second row of the given table by 60 (the sum of these numbers) gives the respective probabilities associated with the random variable X when X assumes the values 0, 1, 2, ..., 8. (Here, we use the relative frequency interpretation of probability.) For example,

$$P(X = 0) = \frac{2}{60} \approx .03$$

$$P(X = 1) = \frac{9}{60} = .15$$

and so on. The resulting probability distribution is shown in Table 6.
b. The probability that the number of cars observed waiting in line is less than or equal to 3 is given by

$$P(X \le 3) = P(X = 0) + P(X = 1) + P(X = 2) + P(X = 3)$$
$$= .03 + .15 + .27 + .20 = .65$$

The probability that the number of cars observed waiting in line is between 2 and 4, inclusive, is given by

$$P(2 \le X \le 4) = P(2) + P(3) + P(4)$$
$$= .27 + .20 + .13 = .60$$

The probability that the number of cars observed waiting in line is greater than 6 is given by

$$P(X > 6) = P(7) + P(8)$$
$$= .03 + .02 = .05$$ ∎

Histograms

A probability distribution of a random variable may be exhibited graphically by means of a **histogram**. To construct a histogram of a particular probability distribution, first locate the values of the random variable on a number line. Then, above each such number, erect a rectangle with width 1 and height equal to the probability associated with that value of the random variable. For example, the histogram of the probability distribution appearing in Table 4 is shown in Figure 1. The histograms of the proba-

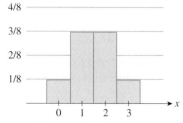

FIGURE 1
Histogram showing the probability distribution for the number of heads occurring in three coin tosses

bility distributions of Examples 5 and 6 are constructed in a similar manner and are displayed in Figures 2 and 3, respectively.

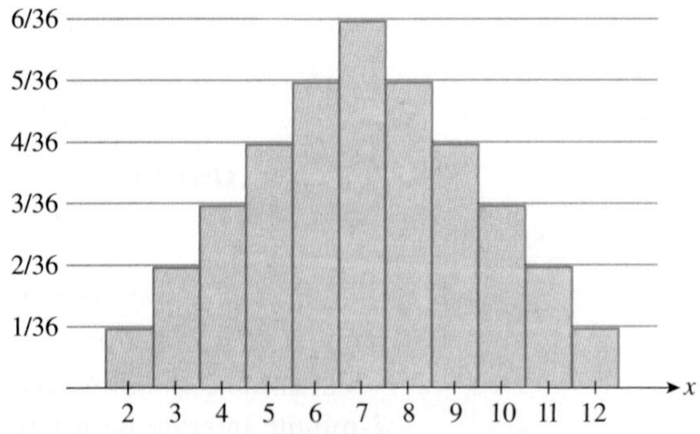

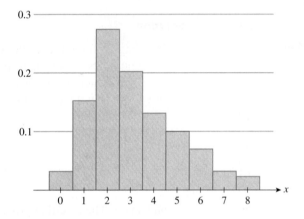

FIGURE 2
Histogram showing the probability distribution for the sum of the uppermost faces of two dice

FIGURE 3
Histogram showing the probability distribution for the number of cars waiting in line

Observe that in each histogram, the area of a rectangle associated with a value of a random variable X gives precisely the probability associated with the value of X. This follows because each such rectangle, by construction, has width 1 and height corresponding to the probability associated with the value of the random variable. Another consequence arising from the method of construction of a histogram is that *the probability associated with more than one value of the random variable X is given by the sum of the areas of the rectangles associated with those values of X.* For example, in the coin-tossing experiment of Example 1, the event of obtaining at least two heads, which corresponds to the event $(X = 2)$ or $(X = 3)$, is given by

$$P(X = 2) + P(X = 3)$$

and may be obtained from the histogram depicted in Figure 1 by adding the areas associated with the values 2 and 3 of the random variable X. We obtain

$$P(X = 2) + P(X = 3) = (1)\left(\frac{3}{8}\right) + (1)\left(\frac{1}{8}\right) = \frac{1}{2}$$

This result provides us with a method of computing the probabilities of events directly from the knowledge of a histogram of the probability distribution of the random variable associated with the experiment.

EXAMPLE 7 Suppose the probability distribution of a random variable X is represented by the histogram shown in Figure 4. Identify the part of the histogram whose area gives the probability $P(10 \leq X \leq 20)$.

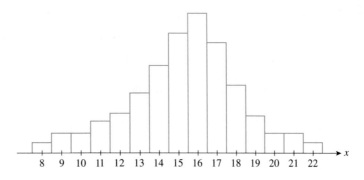

FIGURE **4**

Solution   The event $(10 \le X \le 20)$ is the event consisting of outcomes related to the values 10, 11, 12, . . . , 20 of the random variable X. The probability of this event $P(10 \le X \le 20)$ is therefore given by the shaded area of the histogram in Figure 5.

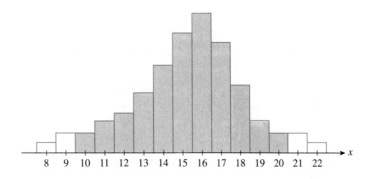

FIGURE **5**
$P(10 \le X \le 20)$

8.1   Self-Check Exercises

1. Three balls are selected at random without replacement from an urn containing four black balls and five white balls. Let the random variable X denote the number of black balls drawn.
   a. List the outcomes of the experiment.
   b. Find the value assigned to each outcome of the experiment by the random variable X.
   c. Find the event consisting of the outcomes to which a value of 2 has been assigned by X.

2. The following data, extracted from the records of Dover Public Library, give the number of books borrowed by the library's members over a 1-month period:

Books	0	1	2	3	4	5	6	7	8
Frequency of Occurrence	780	300	412	205	98	54	57	30	6

   a. Find the probability distribution of the random variable X, where X denotes the number of books checked out over a 1-month period by a randomly chosen member.
   b. Draw the histogram representing this probability distribution.

Solutions to Self-Check Exercises 8.1 can be found on page 436.

8.1   Concept Questions

1. What is a random variable? Give an example.

2. Give an example of (a) a finite discrete random variable, (b) an infinite discrete random variable, and (c) a continuous random variable.

3. Suppose you are given the probability distribution for a random variable X. Explain how you would construct a histogram for this probability distribution. What does the area of each rectangle in the histogram represent?

8.1   Exercises

1. Three balls are selected at random without replacement from an urn containing four green balls and six red balls. Let the random variable X denote the number of green balls drawn.
   a. List the outcomes of the experiment.
   b. Find the value assigned to each outcome of the experiment by the random variable X.
   c. Find the event consisting of the outcomes to which a value of 3 has been assigned by X.

2. A coin is tossed four times. Let the random variable X denote the number of tails that occur.
   a. List the outcomes of the experiment.
   b. Find the value assigned to each outcome of the experiment by the random variable X.
   c. Find the event consisting of the outcomes to which a value of 2 has been assigned by X.

3. A die is rolled repeatedly until a 6 falls uppermost. Let the random variable X denote the number of times the die is rolled. What are the values that X may assume?

4. Cards are selected one at a time without replacement from a well-shuffled deck of 52 cards until an ace is drawn. Let X denote the random variable that gives the number of cards drawn. What values may X assume?

5. Let X denote the random variable that gives the sum of the faces that fall uppermost when two fair dice are rolled. Find $P(X = 7)$.

6. Two cards are drawn from a well-shuffled deck of 52 playing cards. Let X denote the number of aces drawn. Find $P(X = 2)$.

In Exercises 7–12, give the range of values that the random variable X may assume and classify the random variable as finite discrete, infinite discrete, or continuous.

7. $X =$ The number of times a die is thrown until a 2 appears

8. $X =$ The number of defective iPods in a sample of eight iPods

9. $X =$ The distance in miles a commuter travels to work

10. $X =$ The number of hours a child watches television on a given day

11. $X =$ The number of times an accountant takes the CPA examination before passing

12. $X =$ The number of boys in a four-child family

In Exercises 13–16, determine whether the table gives the probability distribution of the random variable X. Explain your answer.

13.

x	−3	−2	−1	0	1	2
$P(X = x)$	0.2	0.4	0.3	−0.2	0.1	0.1

14.

x	−2	−1	0	1	2
$P(X = x)$	0.2	0.1	0.3	0.2	0.1

15.

x	1	2	3	4	5	6
$P(X = x)$	0.3	0.1	0.2	0.2	0.1	0.2

16.

x	−1	0	1	2	3
$P(X = x)$	0.3	0.1	0.2	0.2	0.2

In Exercises 17 and 18, find conditions on the numbers a and/or b such that the table gives the probability distribution of the random variable X.

17.

x	0	2	4	6	8
$P(X = x)$	0.1	0.4	a	0.1	0.2

18.

x	−1	0	1	2	4	5
$P(X = x)$	0.3	a	0.2	0.2	b	0.1

19. The probability distribution of the random variable X is shown in the accompanying table:

x	−10	−5	0	5	10	15	20
$P(X = x)$	.20	.15	.05	.1	.25	.1	.15

Find:
   a. $P(X = -10)$
   b. $P(X \geq 5)$
   c. $P(-5 \leq X \leq 5)$
   d. $P(X \leq 20)$
   e. $P(X < 5)$
   f. $P(X = 3)$

20. The probability distribution of the random variable X is shown in the accompanying table:

x	−5	−3	−2	0	2	3
$P(X = x)$	.17	.13	.33	.16	.11	.10

Find:
   a. $P(X \leq 0)$
   b. $P(X \leq -3)$
   c. $P(-2 \leq X \leq 2)$
   d. $P(X = -2)$
   e. $P(X > 0)$
   f. $P(X = 1)$

21. Suppose that the probability distribution of a random variable X is represented by the accompanying histogram.

Shade the part of the histogram whose area gives the probability $P(17 \leq X \leq 20)$.

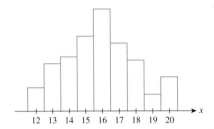

22. **EXAMS** An examination consisting of ten true-or-false questions was taken by a class of 100 students. The probability distribution of the random variable X, where X denotes the number of questions answered correctly by a randomly chosen student, is represented by the accompanying histogram. The rectangle with base centered on the number 8 is missing. What should be the height of this rectangle?

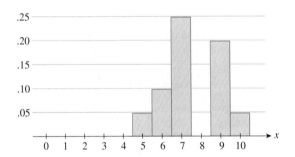

23. Two dice are rolled. Let the random variable X denote the number that falls uppermost on the first die, and let Y denote the number that falls uppermost on the second die.
   a. Find the probability distributions of X and Y.
   b. Find the probability distribution of $X + Y$.

24. **DISTRIBUTION OF FAMILIES BY SIZE** The Public Housing Authority in a certain community conducted a survey of 1000 families to determine the distribution of families by size. The results follow:

Family Size	2	3	4	5	6	7	8
Frequency of Occurrence	350	200	245	125	66	10	4

   a. Find the probability distribution of the random variable X, where X denotes the number of people in a randomly chosen family.
   b. Draw the histogram corresponding to the probability distribution found in part (a).
   c. Find the probability that a family chosen at random from those surveyed has more than five members.

25. **WAITING LINES** The accompanying data were obtained in a study conducted by the manager of SavMore Supermarket.

In this study, the number of customers waiting in line at the express checkout at the beginning of each 3-min interval between 9 A.M. and 12 noon on Saturday was observed.

Customers	0	1	2	3	4
Frequency of Occurrence	1	4	2	7	14

Customers	5	6	7	8	9	10
Frequency of Occurrence	8	10	6	3	4	1

   a. Find the probability distribution of the random variable X, where X denotes the number of customers observed waiting in line.
   b. Draw the histogram representing the probability distribution.
   c. Find the probability that the number of customers waiting in line in any 3-min interval between 9 A.M. and 12 noon is between 1 and 3, inclusive.

26. **MONEY MARKET RATES** The interest rates paid by 30 financial institutions on a certain day for money market deposit accounts are shown in the accompanying table:

Rate, %	3	3.25	3.55	3.56
Institutions	1	7	7	1–

Rate, %	3.58	3.60	3.65	3.85
Institutions	1	8	3	2

Let the random variable X denote the interest rate per year paid by a randomly chosen financial institution on its money market deposit accounts.
   a. Find the probability distribution associated with these data.
   b. Find the probability that the interest rate paid by a financial institution chosen at random is less than 3.56% per year.

27. **TELEVISION PILOTS** After the private screening of a new television pilot, audience members were asked to rate the new show on a scale of 1 to 10 (10 being the highest rating). From a group of 140 people, the following responses were obtained:

Rating	1	2	3	4	5	6	7	8	9	10
Frequency of Occurrence	1	4	3	11	23	21	28	29	16	4

Let the random variable X denote the rating given to the show by a randomly chosen audience member.
   a. Find the probability distribution associated with these data.
   b. What is the probability that the new television pilot got a rating that is higher than 5?

28. U.S. Population by Age The following table gives the 2002 age distribution of the U.S. population:

Group	1	2	3	4	5	6
Age (in years)	Under 5	5–19	20–24	25–44	45–64	65 and over
Number (in thousands)	19,527	59,716	18,611	83,009	66,088	33,590

Let the random variable X denote a randomly chosen age group within the population.
a. Find the probability distribution associated with these data.

b. What percentage of the U.S. population is between 5 and 24 years old, inclusive?

Source: U.S. Census Bureau.

In Exercises 29 and 30, determine whether the statement is true or false. If it is true, explain why it is true. If it is false, give an example to show why it is false.

29. Suppose X is a finite discrete random variable assuming the values $x_1, x_2, \ldots, x_n$ and associated probabilities $p_1, p_2, \ldots, p_n$. Then $p_1 + p_2 + \cdots + p_n = 1$.

30. The area of a histogram associated with a probability distribution is a number between 0 and 1.

8.1 Solutions to Self-Check Exercises

1. a. Using the accompanying tree diagram, we see that the outcomes of the experiment are

$$S = \{BBB, BBW, BWB, BWW, \\ WBB, WBW, WWB, WWW\}$$

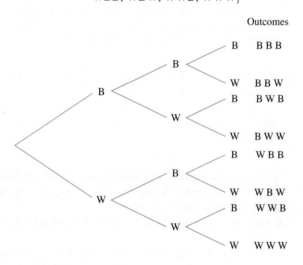

Outcomes

b. Using the results of part (a), we obtain the values assigned to the outcomes of the experiment as follows:

Outcome	BBB	BBW	BWB	BWW
Value	3	2	2	1

Outcome	WBB	WBW	WWB	WWW
Value	2	1	1	0

c. The required event is {BBW, BWB, WBB}.

2. a. We divide each number in the bottom row of the given table by 1942 (the sum of these numbers) to obtain the probabilities associated with the random variable X when X takes on the values 0, 1, 2, 3, 4, 5, 6, 7, and 8. For example,

$$P(X = 0) = \frac{780}{1942} \approx .402$$

$$P(X = 1) = \frac{300}{1942} \approx .154$$

The required probability distribution and histogram follow:

x	0	1	2	3	4
$P(X = x)$	.402	.154	.212	.106	.050

x	5	6	7	8
$P(X = x)$	.028	.029	.015	.003

b.

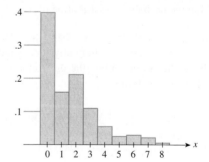

USING TECHNOLOGY

Graphing a Histogram

Graphing Utility

A graphing utility can be used to plot the histogram for a given set of data, as illustrated by the following example.

APPLIED EXAMPLE 1 A survey of 90,000 households conducted in a certain year revealed the following percentage of women who wear a shoe size within the given ranges.

Shoe Size	<5	5–5$\frac{1}{2}$	6–6$\frac{1}{2}$	7–7$\frac{1}{2}$	8–8$\frac{1}{2}$	9–9$\frac{1}{2}$	10–10$\frac{1}{2}$	>10$\frac{1}{2}$
Women, %	1	5	15	27	29	14	7	2

Source: Footwear Market Insights survey.

Let X denote the random variable taking on the values 1 through 8, where 1 corresponds to a shoe size less than 5, 2 corresponds to a shoe size of 5–5$\frac{1}{2}$, and so on.

a. Plot a histogram for the given data.
b. What percentage of women in the survey wear a shoe size within the ranges 7–7$\frac{1}{2}$ or 8–8$\frac{1}{2}$?

Solution

a. Enter the values of X as $x_1 = 1, x_2 = 2, \ldots, x_8 = 8$ and the corresponding values of Y as $y_1 = 1, y_2 = 5, \ldots, y_8 = 2$. Then using the **DRAW** function from the Statistics menu, we draw the histogram shown in Figure T1.

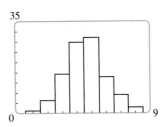

FIGURE **T1**
The histogram for the given data, using the viewing window [0, 9] × [0, 35]

b. The probability that a woman participating in the survey wears a shoe size within the ranges 7–7$\frac{1}{2}$ or 8–8$\frac{1}{2}$ is given by

$$P(X = 4) + P(X = 5) = .27 + .29 = .56$$

This tells us that 56% of the women wear a shoe size within the ranges 7–7$\frac{1}{2}$ or 8–8$\frac{1}{2}$.

Excel

 Excel can be used to plot the histogram for a given set of data, as illustrated by the following example.

 APPLIED EXAMPLE 2 A survey of 90,000 households conducted in a certain year revealed the following percentage of women who wear a shoe size within the given ranges.

Shoe Size	<5	5–5$\frac{1}{2}$	6–6$\frac{1}{2}$	7–7$\frac{1}{2}$	8–8$\frac{1}{2}$	9–9$\frac{1}{2}$	10–10$\frac{1}{2}$	>10$\frac{1}{2}$
Women, %	1	5	15	27	29	14	7	2

Source: Footwear Market Insights survey.

Let X denote the random variable taking on the values 1 through 8, where 1 corresponds to a shoe size less than 5, 2 corresponds to a shoe size of 5–5$\frac{1}{2}$, and so on.

a. Plot a histogram for the given data.
b. What percentage of women in the survey wear a shoe size within the ranges 7–7$\frac{1}{2}$ or 8–8$\frac{1}{2}$?

(*continued*)

Solution

a. Enter the given data in columns A and B onto a spreadsheet, as shown in Figure T2. Highlight the data in column B, and select $\boxed{\Sigma}$ from the Editing group under the Home tab. The sum of the numbers in this column (100) will appear in cell B10. In cell C2, type `=B2/100`, and then press $\boxed{\textbf{Enter}}$. To extend the formula to cell C9, select C2 and move the pointer to the small black box at the lower right corner of that cell. Drag the black $+$ that appears (at the lower right corner of cell C2) through cell C9, and then release it. The probability distribution shown in cells C2 to C9 will then appear on your spreadsheet. Then highlight the data in the Probability column, and select $\boxed{\textbf{Column}}$ from the Charts group under the Insert tab. Click on the first chart type (Clustered Column). Under the Layout tab, click on $\boxed{\textbf{Chart Title}}$ in the Labels group, and select $\boxed{\textbf{Above Chart}}$. Enter `Histogram` as the title. Select $\boxed{\textbf{Primary Horizontal Axis Title}}$ under Axis Titles from the Labels group, select $\boxed{\textbf{Title Below Axis}}$, and then enter `X` as the horizontal axis title. Next, select $\boxed{\textbf{Primary Vertical Axis Title}}$ under Axis Titles followed by $\boxed{\textbf{Rotated Title}}$ and enter `Probability`. Right-click a bar on the chart and select $\boxed{\textbf{Format Data Series}}$. Adjust the slider under Gap Width to 0% in the dialog box that appears, and then click $\boxed{\textbf{Close}}$. Finally, delete the Series 1 legend entry.

	A	B	C
1	X	Frequency	Probability
2	1	1	0.01
3	2	5	0.05
4	3	15	0.15
5	4	27	0.27
6	5	29	0.29
7	6	14	0.14
8	7	7	0.07
9	8	2	0.02
10		100	

FIGURE **T2**
Completed spreadsheet for Example 2

The histogram shown in Figure T3 will appear.

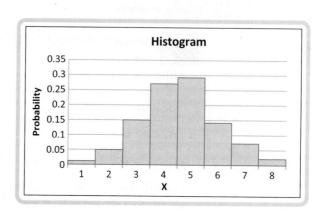

FIGURE **T3**
The histogram for the random variable *X*

Note: Boldfaced words/characters enclosed in a box (for example, $\boxed{\textbf{Enter}}$) indicate an action (click, select, or press) is required. Words/characters printed blue (for example, Chart sub-type) indicate words/characters that appear on the screen. Words/characters printed in a monospace font (for example, `=(-2/3)*A2+2`) indicates words/characters that need to be typed and entered).

b. The probability that a woman participating in the survey wears a shoe size within the ranges $7-7\frac{1}{2}$ or $8-8\frac{1}{2}$ is given by

$$P(X = 4) + P(X = 5) = .27 + .29 = .56$$

This tells us that 56% of the women wear a shoe size within the ranges $7-7\frac{1}{2}$ or $8-8\frac{1}{2}$. ∎

TECHNOLOGY EXERCISES

1. Graph the histogram associated with the data given in Table 1, page 428. Compare your graph with that given in Figure 1, page 431.

2. Graph the histogram associated with the data given in Exercise 24, page 435.

3. Graph the histogram associated with the data given in Exercise 25, page 435.

4. Graph the histogram associated with the data given in Exercise 27, page 435.

8.2 Expected Value

Mean

The average value of a set of numbers is a familiar notion to most people. For example, to compute the average of the four numbers

$$12, 16, 23, 37$$

we simply add these numbers and divide the resulting sum by 4, giving the required average as

$$\frac{12 + 16 + 23 + 37}{4} = \frac{88}{4} = 22$$

In general, we have the following definition:

> **Average, or Mean**
> The **average**, or **mean**, of the n numbers
> $$x_1, x_2, \ldots, x_n$$
> is $\bar{x}$ (read "x bar"), where
> $$\bar{x} = \frac{x_1 + x_2 + \cdots + x_n}{n}$$

TABLE 7

Cars	Frequency of Occurrence
0	2
1	9
2	16
3	12
4	8
5	6
6	4
7	2
8	1

APPLIED EXAMPLE 1 Waiting Times Refer to Example 6, Section 8.1. Find the average number of cars waiting in line at the bank's drive-in teller at the beginning of each 2-minute interval during the period in question.

Solution The number of cars, together with its corresponding frequency of occurrence, are reproduced in Table 7. Observe that the number 0 (of cars) occurs twice, the number 1 occurs 9 times, and so on. There are altogether

$$2 + 9 + 16 + 12 + 8 + 6 + 4 + 2 + 1 = 60$$

numbers to be averaged. Therefore, the required average is given by

$$\frac{(0 \cdot 2) + (1 \cdot 9) + (2 \cdot 16) + (3 \cdot 12) + (4 \cdot 8) + (5 \cdot 6) + (6 \cdot 4) + (7 \cdot 2) + (8 \cdot 1)}{60} \approx 3.1 \qquad \textbf{(1)}$$

or approximately 3.1 cars.

Expected Value

Let's reconsider the expression on the left-hand side of Equation (1), which gives the average of the frequency distribution shown in Table 7. Dividing each term by the denominator, we may rewrite the expression in the form

$$0 \cdot \left(\frac{2}{60}\right) + 1 \cdot \left(\frac{9}{60}\right) + 2 \cdot \left(\frac{16}{60}\right) + 3 \cdot \left(\frac{12}{60}\right) + 4 \cdot \left(\frac{8}{60}\right) + 5 \cdot \left(\frac{6}{60}\right)$$
$$+ 6 \cdot \left(\frac{4}{60}\right) + 7 \cdot \left(\frac{2}{60}\right) + 8 \cdot \left(\frac{1}{60}\right)$$

Observe that each term in the sum is a product of two factors; the first factor is the value assumed by the random variable X, where X denotes the number of cars waiting in line, and the second factor is just the probability associated with that value of the random variable. This observation suggests the following general method for calculating the expected value (that is, the average or mean) of a random variable X that assumes a finite number of values from the knowledge of its probability distribution.

> **Expected Value of a Random Variable X**
>
> Let X denote a random variable that assumes the values $x_1, x_2, \ldots, x_n$ with associated probabilities $p_1, p_2, \ldots, p_n$, respectively. Then the **expected value** of X, denoted by $E(X)$, is given by
>
> $$E(X) = x_1 p_1 + x_2 p_2 + \cdots + x_n p_n \qquad \textbf{(2)}$$

Note The numbers $x_1, x_2, \ldots, x_n$ may be positive, zero, or negative. For example, such a number might be positive if it represents a profit and negative if it represents a loss.

TABLE 8

Probability Distribution

x	$P(X = x)$
0	.03
1	.15
2	.27
3	.20
4	.13
5	.10
6	.07
7	.03
8	.02

APPLIED EXAMPLE 2 Waiting Times Re-solve Example 1 by using the probability distribution associated with the experiment, which is reproduced in Table 8.

Solution Let X denote the number of cars waiting in line. Then the average number of cars waiting in line is given by the expected value of X—that is, by

$$E(X) = (0)(.03) + (1)(.15) + (2)(.27) + (3)(.20) + (4)(.13)$$
$$+ (5)(.10) + (6)(.07) + (7)(.03) + (8)(.02)$$
$$= 3.1 \text{ cars}$$

which agrees with the earlier result.

The expected value of a random variable X is a measure of the central tendency of the probability distribution associated with X. In repeated trials of an experiment with random variable X, the average of the observed values of X gets closer and closer to the expected value of X as the number of trials gets larger and larger. Geometrically, the expected value of a random variable X has the following simple interpretation: If a laminate is made of the histogram of a probability distribution associated with a random variable X, then the expected value of X corresponds to the point on the base of the laminate at which the laminate will balance perfectly when the point is directly over a fulcrum (Figure 6).

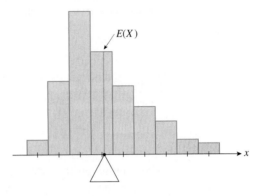

FIGURE 6
Expected value of a random variable X

EXAMPLE 3 Let X denote the random variable that gives the sum of the faces that fall uppermost when two fair dice are rolled. Find the expected value, $E(X)$, of X.

Solution The probability distribution of X, reproduced in Table 9, was found in Example 5, Section 8.1. Using this result, we find

$$E(X) = 2\left(\frac{1}{36}\right) + 3\left(\frac{2}{36}\right) + 4\left(\frac{3}{36}\right) + 5\left(\frac{4}{36}\right) + 6\left(\frac{5}{36}\right) + 7\left(\frac{6}{36}\right)$$
$$+ 8\left(\frac{5}{36}\right) + 9\left(\frac{4}{36}\right) + 10\left(\frac{3}{36}\right) + 11\left(\frac{2}{36}\right) + 12\left(\frac{1}{36}\right)$$
$$= 7$$

Note that, because of the symmetry of the histogram of the probability distribution with respect to the vertical line $x = 7$, the result could have been obtained by merely inspecting Figure 7.

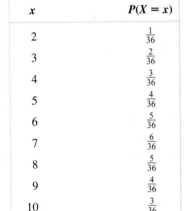

TABLE 9

Probability Distribution

x	$P(X = x)$
2	$\frac{1}{36}$
3	$\frac{2}{36}$
4	$\frac{3}{36}$
5	$\frac{4}{36}$
6	$\frac{5}{36}$
7	$\frac{6}{36}$
8	$\frac{5}{36}$
9	$\frac{4}{36}$
10	$\frac{3}{36}$
11	$\frac{2}{36}$
12	$\frac{1}{36}$

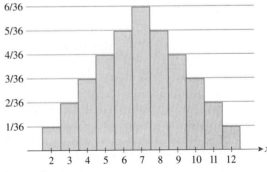

FIGURE 7
Histogram showing the probability distribution for the sum of the uppermost faces of two dice

The next example shows how we can use the concept of expected value to help us make the best investment decision.

VIDEO

APPLIED EXAMPLE 4 Expected Profit A private equity group intends to purchase one of two motels currently being offered for sale in a certain city. The terms of sale of the two motels are similar, although the Regina Inn has 52 rooms and is in a slightly better location than the Merlin Motor Lodge, which has 60 rooms. Records obtained for each motel reveal that the occupancy rates, with corresponding probabilities, during the May–September tourist season are as shown in the following tables.

Regina Inn					
Occupancy Rate	.80	.85	.90	.95	1.00
Probability	.19	.22	.31	.23	.05

Merlin Motor Lodge						
Occupancy Rate	.75	.80	.85	.90	.95	1.00
Probability	.35	.21	.18	.15	.09	.02

The average profit per day for each occupied room at the Regina Inn is $40, whereas the average profit per day for each occupied room at the Merlin Motor Lodge is $36.

a. Find the average number of rooms occupied per day at each motel.
b. If the investors' objective is to purchase the motel that generates the higher daily profit, which motel should they purchase? (Compare the expected daily profit of the two motels.)

Solution

a. Let X denote the occupancy rate at the Regina Inn. Then the average daily occupancy rate at the Regina Inn is given by the expected value of X—that is, by

$$E(X) = (.80)(.19) + (.85)(.22) + (.90)(.31)$$
$$+ (.95)(.23) + (1.00)(.05)$$
$$= .8865$$

The average number of rooms occupied per day at the Regina Inn is

$$(.8865)(52) \approx 46.1$$

or approximately 46.1 rooms. Similarly, letting Y denote the occupancy rate at the Merlin Motor Lodge, we have

$$E(Y) = (.75)(.35) + (.80)(.21) + (.85)(.18) + (.90)(.15)$$
$$+ (.95)(.09) + (1.00)(.02)$$
$$= .8240$$

The average number of rooms occupied per day at the Merlin Motor Lodge is

$$(.8240)(60) \approx 49.4$$

or approximately 49.4 rooms.
b. The expected daily profit at the Regina Inn is given by

$$(46.1)(40) = 1844$$

or $1844. The expected daily profit at the Merlin Motor Lodge is given by

$$(49.4)(36) \approx 1778$$

or approximately $1778. From these results, we conclude that the private equity group should purchase the Regina Inn, which is expected to yield a higher daily profit.

APPLIED EXAMPLE 5 Raffles The Island Club is holding a fund-raising raffle. Ten thousand tickets have been sold for $2 each. There will be a first prize of $3000, 3 second prizes of $1000 each, 5 third prizes of $500 each, and 20 consolation prizes of $100 each. Letting X denote the net winnings (that is, winnings less the cost of the ticket) associated with a ticket, find $E(X)$. Interpret your results.

Solution   The values assumed by X are $(0 - 2)$, $(100 - 2)$, $(500 - 2)$, $(1000 - 2)$, and $(3000 - 2)$—that is, -2, 98, 498, 998, and 2998—which correspond, respectively, to the value of a losing ticket, a consolation prize, a third prize, and so on. The probability distribution of X may be calculated in the usual manner and appears in Table 10. Using the table, we find

$$E(X) = (-2)(.9971) + 98(.0020) + 498(.0005)$$
$$+ 998(.0003) + 2998(.0001)$$
$$= -0.95$$

This expected value gives the long-run average loss (negative gain) of a holder of one ticket; that is, if one participated in such a raffle by purchasing one ticket each time, in the long run, one may expect to lose, on the average, 95 cents per raffle. ■

TABLE 10

Probability Distribution for a Raffle

x	$P(X = x)$
-2	.9971
98	.0020
498	.0005
998	.0003
2998	.0001

APPLIED EXAMPLE 6 Roulette In the game of roulette as played in Las Vegas casinos, the wheel is divided into 38 compartments numbered 1 through 36, 0, and 00. One-half of the numbers 1 through 36 are red, the other half are black, and 0 and 00 are green (Figure 8). Of the many types of bets that may be placed, one type involves betting on the outcome of the color of the winning number. For example, one may place a certain sum of money on *red*. If the winning number is red, one wins an amount equal to the bet placed and the amount of the bet is returned; otherwise, one loses the amount of the bet. Find the expected value of the winnings on a $1 bet placed on *red*.

FIGURE **8**
Roulette wheel

Solution   Let X be a random variable whose values are 1 and -1, which correspond to a win and a loss, respectively. The probabilities associated with the values 1 and -1 are $\frac{18}{38}$ and $\frac{20}{38}$, respectively. Therefore, the expected value is given by

$$E(X) = 1\left(\frac{18}{38}\right) + (-1)\left(\frac{20}{38}\right) = -\frac{2}{38}$$
$$\approx -0.053$$

Thus, if one places a $1 bet on *red* over and over again, one may expect to lose, on the average, approximately 5 cents per bet in the long run. ■

Examples 5 and 6 illustrate games that are not "fair." Of course, most participants in such games are aware of this fact and participate in them for other reasons. In a fair game, neither party has an advantage, a condition that translates into the condition that $E(X) = 0$, where X takes on the values of a player's winnings.

APPLIED EXAMPLE 7 Fair Games Mike and Bill play a card game with a standard deck of 52 cards. Mike selects a card from a well-shuffled deck and receives A dollars from Bill if the card selected is a diamond; otherwise, Mike pays Bill a dollar. Determine the value of A if the game is to be fair.

Solution   Let X denote a random variable whose values are associated with Mike's winnings. Then X takes on the value A with probability $P(X = A) = \frac{1}{4}$ (since there are 13 diamonds in the deck) if Mike wins and takes on the value -1 with probability $P(X = -1) = \frac{3}{4}$ if Mike loses. Since the game is to be a fair one, the expected value $E(X)$ of Mike's winnings must be equal to zero; that is,

$$E(X) = A\left(\frac{1}{4}\right) + (-1)\left(\frac{3}{4}\right) = 0$$

Solving this equation for A gives $A = 3$. Thus, the card game will be fair if Bill makes a $3 payoff when a diamond is drawn.   ■

Odds

In everyday parlance, the probability of the occurrence of an event is often stated in terms of the *odds in favor of* (or *odds against*) the occurrence of the event. For example, one often hears statements such as "The odds that the Dodgers will win the World Series this season are 7 to 5" and "The odds that it will not rain tomorrow are 3 to 2." We will return to these examples later. But first, let us look at a definition that ties together these two concepts.

Odds In Favor Of and Odds Against

If $P(E)$ is the probability of an event E occurring, then

1. The odds in favor of E occurring are

$$\frac{P(E)}{1 - P(E)} = \frac{P(E)}{P(E^c)} \qquad [P(E) \neq 1] \tag{3a}$$

2. The odds against E occurring are

$$\frac{1 - P(E)}{P(E)} = \frac{P(E^c)}{P(E)} \qquad [P(E) \neq 0] \tag{3b}$$

Notes

1. The odds in favor of the occurrence of an event are given by the ratio of the probability of the event occurring to the probability of the event not occurring. The odds against the occurrence of an event are given by the reciprocal of the odds in favor of the occurrence of the event.
2. Whenever possible, odds are expressed as ratios of whole numbers. If the odds in favor of E are $\frac{a}{b}$, we say that the odds in favor of E are a to b. If the odds against E occurring are $\frac{b}{a}$, we say that the odds against E are b to a.   ■

APPLIED EXAMPLE 8 Roulette Find the odds in favor of winning a bet on *red* in American roulette. What are the odds against winning a bet on *red*?

Solution   The probability of winning a bet here—the probability that the ball lands in a red compartment—is given by $P = \frac{18}{38}$. Therefore, using Equation (3a), we see that the odds in favor of winning a bet on *red* are

$$\frac{P(E)}{1 - P(E)} = \frac{\frac{18}{38}}{1 - \frac{18}{38}} \qquad \text{E, event of winning a bet on } red$$

$$= \frac{\frac{18}{38}}{\frac{38 - 18}{38}}$$

$$= \frac{18}{38} \cdot \frac{38}{20}$$

$$= \frac{18}{20} = \frac{9}{10}$$

or 9 to 10. Next, using Equation (3b), we see that the odds against winning a bet on *red* are $\frac{10}{9}$, or 10 to 9.

Now suppose that the odds in favor of the occurrence of an event are a to b. Then Equation (3a) gives

$$\frac{a}{b} = \frac{P(E)}{1 - P(E)}$$

$$a[1 - P(E)] = bP(E) \qquad \text{Cross-multiply.}$$

$$a - aP(E) = bP(E)$$

$$a = (a + b)P(E)$$

$$P(E) = \frac{a}{a + b}$$

which leads us to the following result:

Probability of an Event (Given the Odds)

If the odds in favor of an event E occurring are a to b, then the probability of E occurring is

$$P(E) = \frac{a}{a + b} \tag{4}$$

Equation (4) is often used to determine subjective probabilities, as the next example shows.

[VIDEO] **EXAMPLE 9** Consider each of the following statements.

a. "The odds that the Dodgers will win the World Series this season are 7 to 5."
b. "The odds that it will not rain tomorrow are 3 to 2."

Express each of these odds as a probability of the event occurring.

Robert H. Mason

TITLE   Vice President, Wealth Management Advisor
INSTITUTION   The Mason Group

The Mason Group—a team of Financial Advisors at a major wire house firm—acts as an interface between clients and investment markets. To meet the needs of our private clients, it is important for us to maintain constant contact with them, adjusting their investments when the markets and allocations change and when the clients' goals change.

We often help our clients determine whether their various expected sources of income in retirement will provide them with their desired retirement lifestyle. To begin, we determine the after-tax funds needed in retirement in today's dollars in consultation with the client. Using simple arithmetic, we then look at the duration and amount of their various income flows and their current portfolio allocations (stocks, bonds, cash, etc.). Once we have made this assessment, we take into consideration future possible allocations to arrive at a range of probabilities for portfolio valuation for all years up to and including retirement.

For example, we might tell a client that, on the basis of their given investment plan, there is an 80–95% probability that the expected value of his or her portfolio will increase from $1 million to about $1.5 million by the time the client turns 90; a 50–80% chance that it will increase from $1 million to around $2 million; and a 30–50% chance that it will increase to approximately $2.8 million.

To arrive at these probabilities, we use a deterministic model that assumes that a constant annual rate of return is applied to the portfolio every year of the analysis. We also use probabilistic modeling, taking into account various factors such as economic conditions, the allocation of assets, and market volatility. By using these techniques we are able to arrive at a confidence level, without making any guarantees, that our clients will be able to attain the lifestyle in retirement they desire.

Solution

a. Using Equation (4) with $a = 7$ and $b = 5$ gives the required probability as

$$\frac{7}{7 + 5} = \frac{7}{12} \approx .5833$$

b. Here, the event is that it will not rain tomorrow. Using Equation (4) with $a = 3$ and $b = 2$, we conclude that the probability that it will not rain tomorrow is

$$\frac{3}{3 + 2} = \frac{3}{5} = .6$$

Explore & Discuss

In the movie *Casino*, the executive of the Tangiers Casino, Sam Rothstein (Robert DeNiro), fired the manager of the slot machines in the casino after three gamblers hit three "million dollar" jackpots in a span of 20 minutes. Rothstein claimed that it was a scam and that somebody had gotten into those machines to set the wheels. He was especially annoyed at the slot machine manager's assertion that there was no way to determine this. According to Rothstein, the odds of hitting a jackpot in a four-wheel machine is 1 in $1\frac{1}{2}$ million, and the probability of hitting three jackpots in a row is "in the billions." "It cannot happen! It will not happen!" To see why Rothstein was so indignant, find the odds of hitting the jackpots in three of the machines in quick succession, and comment on the likelihood of this happening.

Median and Mode

In addition to the mean, there are two other measures of central tendency of a group of numerical data: the median and the mode of a group of numbers.

> **Median**
>
> The **median** of a group of numbers arranged in increasing or decreasing order is (a) the middle number if there is an odd number of entries or (b) the mean of the two middle numbers if there is an even number of entries.

 APPLIED EXAMPLE 10 Commuting Times

a. The times, in minutes, Susan took to go to work on nine consecutive working days were

$$46 \quad 42 \quad 49 \quad 40 \quad 52 \quad 48 \quad 45 \quad 43 \quad 50$$

What is the median of her morning commute times?

b. The times, in minutes, Susan took to return home from work on eight consecutive working days were

$$37 \quad 36 \quad 39 \quad 37 \quad 34 \quad 38 \quad 41 \quad 40$$

What is the median of her evening commute times?

Solution

a. Arranging the numbers in increasing order, we have

$$40 \quad 42 \quad 43 \quad 45 \quad 46 \quad 48 \quad 49 \quad 50 \quad 52$$

Here, we have an odd number of entries with the middle number equal to 46, and this gives the required median.

b. Arranging the numbers in increasing order, we have

$$34 \quad 36 \quad 37 \quad 37 \quad 38 \quad 39 \quad 40 \quad 41$$

Here, the number of entries is even, and the required median is

$$\frac{37 + 38}{2} = 37.5$$

> **Mode**
>
> The **mode** of a group of numbers is the number in the group that occurs most frequently.

Note

A group of numerical data may have no mode, a unique mode, or more than one mode.

EXAMPLE 11 Find the mode, if there is one, of the given group of numbers.

a. 1, 2, 3, 4, 6
b. 2, 3, 3, 4, 6, 8
c. 2, 3, 3, 3, 4, 4, 4, 8

Solution

a. The set has no mode because there isn't a number that occurs more frequently than the others.
b. The mode is 3 because it occurs more frequently than the others.
c. The modes are 3 and 4 because each number occurs three times.   ■

Of the three measures of central tendency of a group of numerical data, the mean is by far the most suitable in work that requires mathematical computations.

8.2 Self-Check Exercises

1. Find the expected value of a random variable X having the following probability distribution:

x	-4	-3	-1	0	1	2
$P(X = x)$	.10	.20	.25	.10	.25	.10

2. The developer of Shoreline Condominiums has provided the following estimate of the probability that 20, 25, 30, 35, 40, 45, or 50 of the townhouses will be sold within the first month they are offered for sale.

Units	20	25	30	35	40	45	50
Probability	.05	.10	.30	.25	.15	.10	.05

How many townhouses can the developer expect to sell within the first month they are put on the market?

Solutions to Self-Check Exercises 8.2 can be found on page 452.

8.2 Concept Questions

1. What is the expected value of a random variable? Give an example.

2. What is a fair game? Is the game of roulette as played in American casinos a fair game? Why or why not?

3. a. If the probability of an event E occurring is $P(E)$, what are the odds in favor of E occurring?
   b. If the odds in favor of an event occurring are a to b, what is the probability of E occurring?

8.2 Exercises

1. During the first year at a university that uses a four-point grading system, a freshman took ten three-credit courses and received two As, three Bs, four Cs, and one D.
   a. Compute this student's grade-point average.
   b. Let the random variable X denote the number of points corresponding to a given letter grade. Find the probability distribution of the random variable X and compute $E(X)$, the expected value of X.

2. Records kept by the chief dietitian at the university cafeteria over a 30-week period show the following weekly consumption of milk (in gallons):

Milk	200	205	210	215	220
Weeks	3	4	6	5	4

Milk	225	230	235	240
Weeks	3	2	2	1

   a. Find the average number of gallons of milk consumed per week in the cafeteria.

   b. Let the random variable X denote the number of gallons of milk consumed in a week at the cafeteria. Find the probability distribution of the random variable X and compute $E(X)$, the expected value of X.

3. Find the expected value of a random variable X having the following probability distribution:

x	-5	-1	0	1	5	8
$P(X = x)$	.12	.16	.28	.22	.12	.10

4. Find the expected value of a random variable X having the following probability distribution:

x	0	1	2	3	4	5
$P(X = x)$	$\frac{1}{8}$	$\frac{1}{4}$	$\frac{3}{16}$	$\frac{1}{4}$	$\frac{1}{16}$	$\frac{1}{8}$

5. **EXPECTED EARNINGS** The daily earnings X of an employee who works on a commission basis are given by the following probability distribution. Find the employee's expected earnings.

x (in $)	0	25	50	75
P(X = x)	.07	.12	.17	.14

x (in $)	100	125	150
P(X = x)	.28	.18	.04

6. In a four-child family, what is the expected number of boys? (Assume that the probability of a boy being born is the same as the probability of a girl being born.)

7. EXPECTED SALES On the basis of past experience, the manager of the VideoRama Store has compiled the following table, which gives the probabilities that a customer who enters the VideoRama Store will buy 0, 1, 2, 3, or 4 DVDs. How many DVDs can a customer entering this store be expected to buy?

DVDs	0	1	2	3	4
Probability	.42	.36	.14	.05	.03

8. If a sample of three batteries is selected from a lot of ten, of which two are defective, what is the expected number of defective batteries?

9. AUTO ACCIDENTS The numbers of accidents that occur at a certain intersection known as Five Corners on a Friday afternoon between the hours of 3 P.M. and 6 P.M., along with the corresponding probabilities, are shown in the following table. Find the expected number of accidents during the period in question.

Accidents	0	1	2	3	4
Probability	.935	.030	.020	.010	.005

10. EXPECTED DEMAND The owner of a newsstand in a college community estimates the weekly demand for a certain magazine as follows:

Quantity Demanded	10	11	12	13	14	15
Probability	.05	.15	.25	.30	.20	.05

Find the number of issues of the magazine that the newsstand owner can expect to sell per week.

11. EXPECTED PRODUCT RELIABILITY A bank has two automatic teller machines at its main office and two at each of its three branches. The numbers of machines that break down on a given day, along with the corresponding probabilities, are shown in the following table:

Machines That Break Down	0	1	2	3	4
Probability	.43	.19	.12	.09	.04

Machines That Break Down	5	6	7	8
Probability	.03	.03	.02	.05

Find the expected number of machines that will break down on a given day.

12. EXPECTED SALES The management of the Cambridge Company has projected the sales of its products (in millions of dollars) for the upcoming year, with the associated probabilities shown in the following table:

Sales	20	22	24	26	28	30
Probability	.05	.10	.35	.30	.15	.05

What does the management expect the sales to be next year?

13. INTEREST-RATE PREDICTION A panel of 50 economists was asked to predict the average prime interest rate for the upcoming year. The results of the survey follow:

Interest Rate, %	3.9	4.0	4.1	4.2	4.3	4.4
Economists	3	8	12	14	8	5

On the basis of this survey, what does the panel expect the average prime interest rate to be next year?

14. UNEMPLOYMENT RATES A panel of 64 economists was asked to predict the average unemployment rate for the upcoming year. The results of the survey follow:

Unemployment Rate, %	4.5	4.6	4.7	4.8	4.9	5.0	5.1
Economists	2	4	8	20	14	12	4

On the basis of this survey, what does the panel expect the average unemployment rate to be next year?

15. LOTTERIES In a lottery, 5000 tickets are sold for $1 each. One first prize of $2000, 1 second prize of $500, 3 third prizes of $100, and 10 consolation prizes of $25 are to be awarded. What are the expected net earnings of a person who buys one ticket?

16. LIFE INSURANCE PREMIUMS A man wishes to purchase a 5-year term-life insurance policy that will pay the beneficiary $20,000 in the event that the man's death occurs during the next 5 years. Using life insurance tables, he determines that the probability that he will live another 5 years is .96. What is the minimum amount that he can expect to pay for his premium?
Hint: The minimum premium occurs when the insurance company's expected profit is zero.

17. LIFE INSURANCE PREMIUMS A woman purchased a $20,000, 1-year term-life insurance policy for $260. Assuming that the probability that she will live another year is .992, find the company's expected gain.

18. LIFE INSURANCE POLICIES As a fringe benefit, Dennis Taylor receives a $50,000 life insurance policy from his employer. The probability that Dennis will live another year is .9935. If he purchases the same coverage for himself, what is the minimum amount that he can expect to pay for the policy?

19. EXPECTED PROFIT Max built a spec house at a cost of $450,000. He estimates that he can sell the house for $580,000, $570,000, or $560,000, with probabilities .24, .40, and .36, respectively. What is Max's expected profit?

20. **Investment Analysis** The proprietor of Midland Construction Company has to decide between two projects. He estimates that the first project will yield a profit of $180,000 with a probability of .7 or a profit of $150,000 with a probability of .3; the second project will yield a profit of $220,000 with a probability of .6 or a profit of $80,000 with a probability of .4. Which project should the proprietor choose if he wants to maximize his expected profit?

21. **Cable Television** The management of MultiVision, a cable TV company, intends to submit a bid for the cable television rights in one of two cities, A or B. If the company obtains the rights to City A, the probability of which is .2, the estimated profit over the next 10 years is $10 million; if the company obtains the rights to City B, the probability of which is .3, the estimated profit over the next 10 years is $7 million. The cost of submitting a bid for rights in City A is $250,000 and that in City B is $200,000. By comparing the expected profits for each venture, determine whether the company should bid for the rights in City A or City B.

22. **Expected Auto Sales** Roger Hunt intends to purchase one of two car dealerships currently for sale in a certain city. Records obtained from each of the two dealers reveal that their weekly volume of sales, with corresponding probabilities, are as follows:

Dahl Motors

Cars Sold/Week	5	6	7	8
Probability	.05	.09	.14	.24

Cars Sold/Week	9	10	11	12
Probability	.18	.14	.11	.05

Farthington Auto Sales

Cars Sold/Week	5	6	7	8	9	10
Probability	.08	.21	.31	.24	.10	.06

The average profit/car at Dahl Motors is $543, and the average profit/car at Farthington Auto Sales is $654.
   a. Find the average number of cars sold each week at each dealership.
   b. If Roger's objective is to purchase the dealership that generates the higher weekly profit, which dealership should he purchase? (Compare the expected weekly profit for each dealership.)

23. **Expected Home Sales** Sally Leonard, a real estate broker, is relocating in a large metropolitan area where she has received job offers from Realty Company A and Realty Company B. The number of houses she expects to sell in a year at each firm and the associated probabilities are shown in the following tables:

Company A

Houses Sold	12	13	14	15	16
Probability	.02	.03	.05	.07	.07

Houses Sold	17	18	19	20
Probability	.16	.17	.13	.11

Houses Sold	21	22	23	24
Probability	.09	.06	.03	.01

Company B

Houses Sold	6	7	8	9	10
Probability	.01	.04	.07	.06	.11

Houses Sold	11	12	13	14
Probability	.12	.19	.17	.13

Houses Sold	15	16	17	18
Probability	.04	.03	.02	.01

The average price of a house in the locale of Company A is $308,000, whereas the average price of a house in the locale of Company B is $474,000. If Sally will receive a 3% commission on sales at either company, which job offer should she accept to maximize her expected yearly commission?

24. **Investment Analysis** Bob, the proprietor of Midway Lumber, bases his projections for the annual revenues of the company on the performance of the housing market. He rates the performance of the market as very strong, strong, normal, weak, or very weak. For the next year, Bob estimates that the probabilities for these outcomes are .18, .27, .42, .10, and .03, respectively. He also thinks that the revenues corresponding to these outcomes are $20, $18.8, $16.2, $14, and $12 million, respectively. What is Bob's expected revenue for next year?

25. **Revenue Projection** Maria sees the growth of her business for the upcoming year as being tied to the gross domestic product (GDP). She believes that her business will grow (or contract) at the rate of 5%, 4.5%, 3%, 0%, or −0.5% per year if the GDP grows (or contracts) at the rate of between 2 and 2.5%, between 1.5 and 2%, between 1 and 1.5%, between 0 and 1%, and between −1 and 0%, respectively. Maria has decided to assign a probability of .12, .24, .40, .20, and .04, respectively, to these outcomes. At what rate does Maria expect her business to grow next year?

26. **Weather Predictions** Suppose the probability that it will rain tomorrow is .3.
   a. What are the odds that it will rain tomorrow?
   b. What are the odds that it will not rain tomorrow?

27. **Roulette** In American roulette, as described in Example 6, a player may bet on a split (two adjacent numbers). In this case, if the player bets $1 and either number comes up, the player wins $17 and gets his $1 back. If neither comes up, he loses his $1 bet. Find the expected value of the winnings on a $1 bet placed on a split.

28. **Roulette** If a player placed a $1 bet on *red* and a $1 bet on *black* in a single play in American roulette, what would be the expected value of his winnings?

29. ROULETTE In European roulette, the wheel is divided into 37 compartments numbered 1 through 36 and 0. (In American roulette there are 38 compartments numbered 1 through 36, 0, and 00.) Find the expected value of the winnings on a $1 bet placed on *red* in European roulette.

30. The probability of an event E occurring is .8. What are the odds in favor of E occurring? What are the odds against E occurring?

31. The probability of an event E not occurring is .6. What are the odds in favor of E occurring? What are the odds against E occurring?

32. The odds in favor of an event E occurring are 9 to 7. What is the probability of E occurring?

33. The odds against an event E occurring are 2 to 3. What is the probability of E not occurring?

34. ODDS OF MAKING A SALE Carmen, a computer sales representative, believes that the odds are 8 to 5 that she will clinch the sale of a minicomputer to a certain company. What is the (subjective) probability that Carmen will make the sale?

35. SPORTS Steffi believes that the odds in favor of her winning her tennis match tomorrow are 7 to 5. What is the (subjective) probability that she will win her match tomorrow?

36. SPORTS If a sports forecaster states that the odds of a certain boxer winning a match are 4 to 3, what is the (subjective) probability that the boxer will win the match?

37. ODDS Bob, the proprietor of Midland Lumber, believes that the odds in favor of a business deal going through are 9 to 5. What is the (subjective) probability that this deal will *not* materialize?

38. ROULETTE
  a. Show that, for any number c,
  $$E(cX) = cE(X)$$
  b. Use this result to find the expected loss if a gambler bets $300 on *red* in a single play in American roulette.
  Hint: Use the results of Example 6.

39. If X and Y are random variables and c is any constant, show that
  a. $E(c) = c$
  b. $E(cX) = cE(X)$
  c. $E(X + Y) = E(X) + E(Y)$
  d. $E(X - Y) = E(X) - E(Y)$

40. WAGE RATES The frequency distribution of the hourly wage rates (in dollars) among blue-collar workers in a certain factory is given in the following table. Find the mean (or average) wage rate, the mode, and the median wage rate of these workers.

Wage Rate	10.70	10.80	10.90	11.00	11.10	11.20
Frequency	60	90	75	120	60	45

41. EXAM SCORES In an examination given to a class of 20 students, the following test scores were obtained:

40 45 50 50 55 60 60 75 75 80

80 85 85 85 85 90 90 95 95 100

  a. Find the mean (or average) score, the mode, and the median score.
  b. Which of these three measures of central tendency do you think is the least representative of the set of scores?

42. SAN FRANCISCO WEATHER The normal daily minimum temperatures in degrees Fahrenheit for the months of January through December in San Francisco follow:

46.2 48.4 48.6 49.2 50.7 52.5

53.1 54.2 55.8 54.8 51.5 47.2

Find the average and the median daily minimum temperature in San Francisco for these months.

Source: San Francisco Convention and Visitors Bureau.

43. WAITING TIMES Refer to Example 6, Section 8.1. Find the median of the number of cars waiting in line at the bank's drive-in teller at the beginning of each 2-min interval during the period in question. Compare your answer to the mean obtained in Example 1, Section 8.2.

44. BOSTON WEATHER The relative humidity, in percent, in the morning for the months of January through December in Boston follows:

68 67 69 69 71 73

74 76 79 77 74 70

Find the average and the median of these humidity readings.

Source: National Weather Service Forecast Office.

45. WEIGHT OF POTATO CHIPS The weights, in ounces, of ten packages of potato chips are as follows:

16.1 16 15.8 16 15.9 16.1 15.9 16 16 16.2

Find the average and the median of these weights.

In Exercises 46 and 47, determine whether the statement is true or false. If it is true, explain why it is true. If it is false, give an example to show why it is false.

46. If the odds in favor of an event E occurring are a to b, then the probability of E^c occurring is $b/(a + b)$.

47. A game between two people is fair if the expected value to both people is zero.

8.2 Solutions to Self-Check Exercises

1. $E(X) = (-4)(.10) + (-3)(.20) + (-1)(.25)$
$\quad\quad\quad + (0)(.10) + (1)(.25) + (2)(.10)$
$\quad = -0.8$

2. Let X denote the number of townhouses that will be sold within 1 month of being put on the market. Then the number of townhouses the developer expects to sell within

1 month is given by the expected value of X—that is, by

$E(X) = 20(.05) + 25(.10) + 30(.30) + 35(.25)$
$\quad\quad\quad + 40(.15) + 45(.10) + 50(.05)$
$\quad = 34.25$

or 34 townhouses.

8.3 Variance and Standard Deviation

Variance

The mean, or expected value, of a random variable enables us to express an important property of the probability distribution associated with the random variable in terms of a single number. But the knowledge of the location, or central tendency, of a probability distribution alone is usually not enough to give a reasonably accurate picture of the probability distribution. Consider, for example, the two probability distributions whose histograms appear in Figure 9. Both distributions have the same expected value, or mean, of $\mu = 4$ (the Greek letter μ is read "mu"). Note that the probability distribution with the histogram shown in Figure 9a is closely concentrated about its mean μ, whereas the one with the histogram shown in Figure 9b is widely dispersed or spread about its mean.

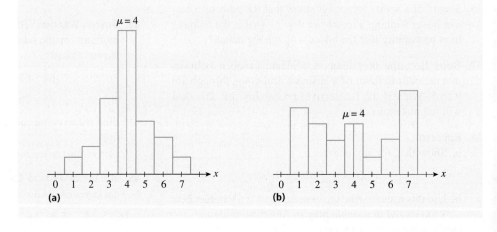

FIGURE 9
The histograms of two probability distributions

As another example, suppose that Olivia has ten packages of Brand A potato chips and ten packages of Brand B potato chips. After carefully measuring the weights of each package, she obtains the following results:

Weight in Ounces									
Brand A 16.1	16	15.8	16	15.9	16.1	15.9	16	16	16.2
Brand B 16.3	15.7	15.8	16.2	15.9	16.1	15.7	16.2	16	16.1

In Example 3, we verify that the mean weights for each of the two brands is 16 ounces. However, a cursory examination of the data now shows that the weights of the Brand B packages exhibit much greater dispersion about the mean than do those of Brand A.

One measure of the degree of dispersion, or spread, of a probability distribution about its mean is given by the *variance* of the random variable associated with the probability distribution. A probability distribution with a small spread about its mean will have a small variance, whereas one with a larger spread will have a larger variance. Thus, the variance of the random variable associated with the probability distribution whose histogram appears in Figure 9a is smaller than the variance of the random variable associated with the probability distribution whose histogram is shown in Figure 9b (see Example 1). Also, as we will see in Example 3, the variance of the random variable associated with the weights of the Brand *A* potato chips is smaller than that of the random variable associated with the weights of the Brand *B* potato chips.

We now define the variance of a random variable.

Variance of a Random Variable *X*

Suppose a random variable has the probability distribution

x	x_1	x_2	x_3	$\cdots$	x_n
$P(X = x)$	p_1	p_2	p_3	$\cdots$	p_n

and expected value

$$E(X) = \mu$$

Then the **variance** of the random variable *X* is

$$\text{Var}(X) = p_1(x_1 - \mu)^2 + p_2(x_2 - \mu)^2 + \cdots + p_n(x_n - \mu)^2 \qquad (5)$$

Let's look a little closer at Equation (5). First, note that the numbers

$$x_1 - \mu, x_2 - \mu, \ldots, x_n - \mu \qquad (6)$$

measure the **deviations** of $x_1, x_2, \ldots, x_n$ from μ, respectively. Thus, the numbers

$$(x_1 - \mu)^2, (x_2 - \mu)^2, \ldots, (x_n - \mu)^2 \qquad (7)$$

measure the squares of the deviations of $x_1, x_2, \ldots, x_n$ from μ, respectively. Next, by multiplying each of the numbers in (7) by the probability associated with each value of the random variable *X*, the numbers are weighted accordingly so that their sum is a measure of the variance of *X* about its mean. An attempt to define the variance of a random variable about its mean in a similar manner using the deviations in (6), rather than their squares, would not be fruitful, since some of the deviations may be positive whereas others may be negative and hence (because of cancellations) the sum will not give a satisfactory measure of the variance of the random variable.

VIDEO **EXAMPLE 1** Find the variance of the random variable *X* and of the random variable *Y* whose probability distributions are shown in the following table. These are the probability distributions associated with the histograms shown in Figure 9a–b.

x	$P(X = x)$	y	$P(Y = y)$
1	.05	1	.2
2	.075	2	.15
3	.2	3	.1
4	.375	4	.15
5	.15	5	.05
6	.1	6	.1
7	.05	7	.25

Solution   The mean of the random variable X is given by

$$\mu_X = (1)(.05) + (2)(.075) + (3)(.2) + (4)(.375) + (5)(.15)$$
$$+ (6)(.1) + (7)(.05)$$
$$= 4$$

Therefore, using Equation (5) and the data from the probability distribution of X, we find that the variance of X is given by

$$\text{Var}(X) = (.05)(1 - 4)^2 + (.075)(2 - 4)^2 + (.2)(3 - 4)^2$$
$$+ (.375)(4 - 4)^2 + (.15)(5 - 4)^2$$
$$+ (.1)(6 - 4)^2 + (.05)(7 - 4)^2$$
$$= 1.95$$

Next, we find that the mean of the random variable Y is given by

$$\mu_Y = (1)(.2) + (2)(.15) + (3)(.1) + (4)(.15) + (5)(.05)$$
$$+ (6)(.1) + (7)(.25)$$
$$= 4$$

so the variance of Y is given by

$$\text{Var}(Y) = (.2)(1 - 4)^2 + (.15)(2 - 4)^2 + (.1)(3 - 4)^2$$
$$+ (.15)(4 - 4)^2 + (.05)(5 - 4)^2$$
$$+ (.1)(6 - 4)^2 + (.25)(7 - 4)^2$$
$$= 5.2$$

Note that $\text{Var}(X)$ is smaller than $\text{Var}(Y)$, which confirms our earlier observations about the spread (or dispersion) of the probability distribution of X and Y, respectively. ∎

Standard Deviation

Because Equation (5), which gives the variance of the random variable X, involves the squares of the deviations, the unit of measurement of $\text{Var}(X)$ is the square of the unit of measurement of the values of X. For example, if the values assumed by the random variable X are measured in units of a gram, then $\text{Var}(X)$ will be measured in units involving the *square* of a gram. To remedy this situation, one normally works with the square root of $\text{Var}(X)$ rather than $\text{Var}(X)$ itself. The former is called the standard deviation of X.

Standard Deviation of a Random Variable X

The **standard deviation** of a random variable X denoted σ (pronounced "sigma"), is defined by

$$\sigma = \sqrt{\text{Var}(X)}$$
$$= \sqrt{p_1(x_1 - \mu)^2 + p_2(x_2 - \mu)^2 + \cdots + p_n(x_n - \mu)^2} \quad \text{(8)}$$

where $x_1, x_2, \ldots, x_n$ denote the values assumed by the random variable X and $p_1 = P(X = x_1), p_2 = P(X = x_2), \ldots, p_n = P(X = x_n)$.

EXAMPLE 2 Find the standard deviations of the random variables X and Y of Example 1.

Solution From the results of Example 1, we have $\text{Var}(X) = 1.95$ and $\text{Var}(Y) = 5.2$. Taking their respective square roots, we have

$$\sigma_X = \sqrt{1.95}$$
$$\approx 1.40$$
$$\sigma_Y = \sqrt{5.2}$$
$$\approx 2.28$$

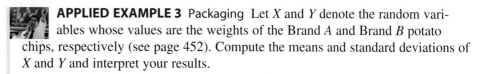 **APPLIED EXAMPLE 3** Packaging Let X and Y denote the random variables whose values are the weights of the Brand A and Brand B potato chips, respectively (see page 452). Compute the means and standard deviations of X and Y and interpret your results.

Solution The probability distributions of X and Y may be computed from the given data as follows:

Brand A			Brand B		
x	Relative Frequency of Occurrence	$P(X = x)$	y	Relative Frequency of Occurrence	$P(Y = y)$
15.8	1	.1	15.7	2	.2
15.9	2	.2	15.8	1	.1
16.0	4	.4	15.9	1	.1
16.1	2	.2	16.0	1	.1
16.2	1	.1	16.1	2	.2
			16.2	2	.2
			16.3	1	.1

The means of X and Y are given by

$$\mu_X = (.1)(15.8) + (.2)(15.9) + (.4)(16.0) + (.2)(16.1)$$
$$+ (.1)(16.2)$$
$$= 16$$
$$\mu_Y = (.2)(15.7) + (.1)(15.8) + (.1)(15.9) + (.1)(16.0)$$
$$+ (.2)(16.1) + (.2)(16.2) + (.1)(16.3)$$
$$= 16$$

Therefore,

$$\text{Var}(X) = (.1)(15.8 - 16)^2 + (.2)(15.9 - 16)^2 + (.4)(16 - 16)^2$$
$$+ (.2)(16.1 - 16)^2 + (.1)(16.2 - 16)^2$$
$$= 0.012$$
$$\text{Var}(Y) = (.2)(15.7 - 16)^2 + (.1)(15.8 - 16)^2 + (.1)(15.9 - 16)^2$$
$$+ (.1)(16 - 16)^2 + (.2)(16.1 - 16)^2 + (.2)(16.2 - 16)^2$$
$$+ (.1)(16.3 - 16)^2$$
$$= 0.042$$

Explore & Discuss

A useful alternative formula for the variance is

$$\sigma^2 = E(X^2) - \mu^2$$

where $E(X^2)$ is the expected value of X^2.

1. Establish the validity of the formula.

2. Use the formula to verify the calculations in Example 3.

so the standard deviations are

$$
\begin{aligned}
\sigma_X &= \sqrt{\mathrm{Var}(X)} \\
&= \sqrt{0.012} \\
&\approx 0.11 \\
\sigma_Y &= \sqrt{\mathrm{Var}(Y)} \\
&= \sqrt{0.042} \\
&\approx 0.20
\end{aligned}
$$

The mean of X and that of Y are both equal to 16. Therefore, the average weight of a package of potato chips of either brand is 16 ounces. However, the standard deviation of Y is greater than that of X. This tells us that the weights of the packages of Brand B potato chips are more widely dispersed about the common mean of 16 than are those of Brand A.

Explore & Discuss

Suppose the mean weight of m packages of Brand A potato chips is μ_1 and the standard deviation from the mean of their weight distribution is σ_1. Also suppose the mean weight of n packages of Brand B potato chips is μ_2 and the standard deviation from the mean of their weight distribution is σ_2.

1. Show that the mean of the combined weights of packages of Brand A and Brand B is

$$
\mu = \frac{m\mu_1 + n\mu_2}{m + n}
$$

2. If $\mu_1 = \mu_2$, show that the standard deviation from the mean of the combined-weight distribution is

$$
\sigma = \left(\frac{m\sigma_1^2 + n\sigma_2^2}{m + n} \right)^{1/2}
$$

3. Refer to Example 3, page 455. Using the results of parts 1 and 2, find the mean and the standard deviation of the combined-weight distribution.

Chebychev's Inequality

The standard deviation of a random variable X may be used in statistical estimations. For example, the following result, derived by the Russian mathematician P. L. Chebychev (1821–1894), gives a bound on the proportion of the values of X lying within k standard deviations of the expected value of X.

Chebychev's Inequality

Let X be a random variable with expected value μ and standard deviation σ. Then the probability that a randomly chosen outcome of the experiment lies between $\mu - k\sigma$ and $\mu + k\sigma$ is at least $1 - (1/k^2)$ where k is the number of standard deviations from the mean; that is,

$$
P(\mu - k\sigma \leq X \leq \mu + k\sigma) \geq 1 - \frac{1}{k^2} \tag{9}
$$

To shed some light on this result, let's take $k = 2$ in Inequality (9) and compute

$$
P(\mu - 2\sigma \leq X \leq \mu + 2\sigma) \geq 1 - \frac{1}{2^2} = 1 - \frac{1}{4} = .75
$$

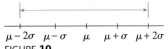

$\mu - 2\sigma \quad \mu - \sigma \quad \mu \quad \mu + \sigma \quad \mu + 2\sigma$

FIGURE 10
At least 75% of the outcomes fall within this interval.

This tells us that at least 75% of the outcomes of the experiment lie within 2 standard deviations of the mean (Figure 10). Taking $k = 3$ in Inequality (9), we have

$$P(\mu - 3\sigma \le X \le \mu + 3\sigma) \ge 1 - \frac{1}{3^2} = 1 - \frac{1}{9} = \frac{8}{9} \approx .89$$

This tells us that at least 89% of the outcomes of the experiment lie within 3 standard deviations of the mean (Figure 11).

FIGURE 11
At least 89% of the outcomes fall within this interval.

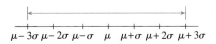

$\mu - 3\sigma \quad \mu - 2\sigma \quad \mu - \sigma \quad \mu \quad \mu + \sigma \quad \mu + 2\sigma \quad \mu + 3\sigma$

EXAMPLE 4 A probability distribution has a mean of 10 and a standard deviation of 1.5. Use Chebychev's inequality to find a bound on the probability that an outcome of the experiment lies between 7 and 13.

Solution   Here, $\mu = 10$ and $\sigma = 1.5$. To determine the value of k, note that $\mu - k\sigma = 7$ and $\mu + k\sigma = 13$. Substituting the appropriate values for μ and σ, we find $k = 2$. Using Chebychev's Inequality (9), we see that a bound on the probability that an outcome of the experiment lies between 7 and 13 is given by

$$P(7 \le X \le 13) \ge 1 - \left(\frac{1}{2^2}\right)$$

$$= \frac{3}{4}$$

—that is, at least 75%.

Note   The results of Example 4 tell us that at least 75% of the outcomes of the experiment lie between $10 - 2\sigma$ and $10 + 2\sigma$—that is, between 7 and 13.

VIDEO   **APPLIED EXAMPLE 5** Industrial Accidents Great Northwest Lumber Company employs 400 workers in its mills. It has been estimated that X, the random variable measuring the number of mill workers who have industrial accidents during a 1-year period, is distributed with a mean of 40 and a standard deviation of 6. Using Chebychev's Inequality (9), find a bound on the probability that the number of workers who will have an industrial accident over a 1-year period is between 30 and 50, inclusive.

Solution   Here, $\mu = 40$ and $\sigma = 6$. We wish to estimate $P(30 \le X \le 50)$. To use Chebychev's Inequality (9), we first determine the value of k from the equation

$$\mu - k\sigma = 30 \quad \text{or} \quad \mu + k\sigma = 50$$

Since $\mu = 40$ and $\sigma = 6$ in this case, we see that k satisfies

$$40 - 6k = 30 \quad \text{and} \quad 40 + 6k = 50$$

from which we deduce that $k = \frac{5}{3}$. Thus, a bound on the probability that the number of mill workers who will have an industrial accident during a 1-year period is between 30 and 50 is given by

$$P(30 \le X \le 50) \ge 1 - \frac{1}{\left(\frac{5}{3}\right)^2}$$

$$= \frac{16}{25}$$

—that is, at least 64%.

8.3 Self-Check Exercises

1. Compute the mean, variance, and standard deviation of the random variable X with probability distribution as follows:

x	-4	-3	-1	0	2	5
$P(X = x)$	.1	.1	.2	.3	.1	.2

2. James recorded the following travel times (the length of time in minutes it took him to drive to work) on ten consecutive days:

55	50	52	48	50	52	46	48	50	51

Calculate the mean and standard deviation of the random variable X associated with these data.

Solutions to Self-Check Exercises 8.3 can be found on page 462.

8.3 Concept Questions

1. **a.** What is the variance of a random variable X?
   b. What is the standard deviation of a random variable X?

2. What does Chebychev's inequality measure?

8.3 Exercises

In Exercises 1–6, the probability distribution of a random variable X is given. Compute the mean, variance, and standard deviation of X.

1.
x	1	2	3	4
$P(X = x)$	.4	.3	.2	.1

2.
x	-4	-2	0	2	4
$P(X = x)$	.1	.2	.3	.1	.3

3.
x	-2	-1	0	1	2
$P(X = x)$	1/16	4/16	6/16	4/16	1/16

4.
x	10	11	12	13	14	15
$P(X = x)$	1/8	2/8	1/8	2/8	1/8	1/8

5.
x	430	480	520	565	580
$P(X = x)$	.1	.2	.4	.2	.1

6.
x	-198	-195	-193	-188	-185
$P(X = x)$	.15	.30	.10	.25	.20

7. The following histograms represent the probability distributions of the random variables X and Y. Determine by inspection which probability distribution has the larger variance.

(a)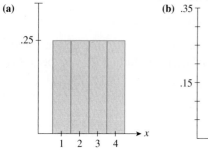

(b)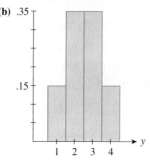

8. The following histograms represent the probability distributions of the random variables X and Y. Determine by inspection which probability distribution has the larger variance.

(a)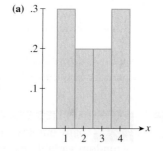

(b)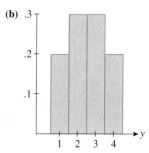

In Exercises 9 and 10, find the variance of the probability distribution for the histogram shown.

9.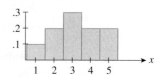

10.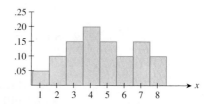

11. An experiment consists of rolling an eight-sided die (numbered 1 through 8) and observing the number that appears uppermost. Find the mean and variance of this experiment.

12. **DRIVING AGE REQUIREMENTS** The minimum age requirement for a regular driver's license differs from state to state. The

frequency distribution for this age requirement in the 50 states is given in the following table:

Minimum Age	15	16	17	18	19	21
Frequency of Occurrence	1	15	4	28	1	1

a. Describe a random variable X that is associated with these data.
b. Find the probability distribution for the random variable X.
c. Compute the mean, variance, and standard deviation of X.

13. **BIRTHRATES** The birthrates in the United States for the years 1997–2006 are given in the following table. (The birthrate is the number of live births/1000 population.)

Year	1997	1998	1999	2000
Birthrate	14.5	14.6	14.7	14.5

Year	2001	2002	2003
Birthrate	14.1	13.9	14.1

Year	2004	2005	2006
Birthrate	14.0	14.0	14.2

a. Describe a random variable X that is associated with these data.
b. Find the probability distribution for the random variable X.
c. Compute the mean, variance, and standard deviation of X.

Source: National Center for Health Statistics.

14. **INVESTMENT ANALYSIS** Paul Hunt is considering two business ventures. The anticipated returns (in thousands of dollars) of each venture are described by the following probability distributions:

Venture A

Earnings	Probability
−20	.3
40	.4
50	.3

Venture B

Earnings	Probability
−15	.2
30	.5
40	.3

a. Compute the mean and variance for each venture.
b. Which investment would provide Paul with the higher expected return (the greater mean)?

c. In which investment would the element of risk be less (that is, which probability distribution has the smaller variance)?

15. **INVESTMENT ANALYSIS** Rosa Walters is considering investing $10,000 in two mutual funds. The anticipated returns from price appreciation and dividends (in hundreds of dollars) are described by the following probability distributions:

Mutual Fund A

Returns	Probability
−4	.2
8	.5
10	.3

Mutual Fund B

Returns	Probability
−2	.2
6	.4
8	.4

a. Compute the mean and variance associated with the returns for each mutual fund.
b. Which investment would provide Rosa with the higher expected return (the greater mean)?
c. In which investment would the element of risk be less (that is, which probability distribution has the smaller variance)?

16. The distribution of the number of chocolate chips (x) in a cookie is shown in the following table. Find the mean and the variance of the number of chocolate chips in a cookie.

x	0	1	2
$P(X = x)$	.01	.03	.05

x	3	4	5
$P(X = x)$	.11	.13	.24

x	6	7	8
$P(X = x)$	.22	.16	.05

17. Equation (5) can also be expressed in the form

$$\text{Var}(X) = (p_1 x_1^2 + p_2 x_2^2 + \cdots + p_n x_n^2) - \mu^2$$

Find the variance of the distribution of Exercise 1 using this equation.

18. Find the variance of the distribution of Exercise 16 using the equation

$$\text{Var}(X) = (p_1 x_1^2 + p_2 x_2^2 + \cdots + p_n x_n^2) - \mu^2$$

19. **HOUSING PRICES** The market research department of the National Real Estate Company conducted a survey among 500 prospective buyers in a suburb of a large metropolitan area to determine the maximum price a prospective buyer would be willing to pay for a house. From the data collected, the distribution that follows was obtained. Compute the mean, variance, and standard deviation of the maximum price x (in thousands of dollars) that these buyers were willing to pay for a house.

Maximum Price Considered, x	$P(X = x)$
380	$\frac{10}{500}$
390	$\frac{20}{500}$
400	$\frac{75}{500}$
410	$\frac{85}{500}$
420	$\frac{70}{500}$
450	$\frac{90}{500}$
480	$\frac{90}{500}$
500	$\frac{55}{500}$
550	$\frac{5}{500}$

20. **AVERAGE RENT** A study of the records of 85,000 apartment units in the greater Boston area revealed the following data:

Year	2002	2003	2004	2005	2006
Average Rent, $	1352	1336	1317	1308	1355

Find the average of the average rent for the 5 years in question. What is the standard deviation for these data?
Source: Northeast Apartment Advisors, Inc.

21. **OCCUPANCY RATE** A study of the records of 85,000 apartment units in the greater Boston area revealed the following data:

Year	2002	2003	2004	2005	2006
Occupancy Rate, %	95.6	94.7	95.2	95.1	96.1

Find the average occupancy rate for the 5-year period. What is the standard deviation for these data?
Source: Northeast Apartment Advisors, Inc.

22. **EXAM SCORES** The following table gives the scores of 30 students in a mathematics examination:

Scores	90–99	80–89	70–79	60–69	50–59
Students	4	8	12	4	2

Find the mean and the standard deviation of the distribution of the given data.
Hint: Assume that all scores lying within a group interval take the middle value of that group.

23. **MARITAL STATUS OF MEN** The number of married men (in thousands) between the ages of 20 and 44 in the United States in 1998 is given in the following table:

Age	20–24	25–29	30–34	35–39	40–44
Men	1332	4219	6345	7598	7633

Find the mean and the standard deviation of the given data.
Hint: See the hint for Exercise 22.
Source: U.S. Census Bureau.

24. **STUCK IN TRAFFIC** The following table gives the extra travel time each year, in hours, for peak-period travelers in urban areas with more than 3 million people:

Urban Area	Annual Hours of Delay per Traveler (in 2007)
Los Angeles–Long Beach–Santa Ana, CA	70
San Francisco–Oakland, CA	55
Atlanta, GA	57
Washington (D.C.–VA–MD)	62
Dallas–Fort Worth–Arlington, TX	53
Houston, TX	56

Find the mean of the extra travel time each year, in hours, for peak-period travelers in urban areas with more than 3 million people. What is the standard deviation for these data?
Source: Texas Transportation Institute.

25. **COST OF TAKING TIME OFF** A survey was conducted of graduates of Harvard College 15 years after graduation. In the survey, the pay of graduates in different fields who had previously taken off 18 months, often to care for children, was compared with pay for graduates who had not taken time off. The average financial penalty for those who had taken time off is summarized in the following table:

Field	M.B.A.	J.D.	Ph.D	B.A. only	M.D.	Other, Masters only
Penalty (%)	−41	−29	−29	−25	−16	−13

Find the mean of the financial penalty for the graduates who had taken time off. What is the standard deviation for these data?
Source: Claudia Golden and Lawrence Katz, Harvard College.

26. **CONVICTION RATES** The following table gives the percentage of homicide cases in Suffolk County, Massachusetts, ending in pleas or verdicts of guilty from 2004 through 2009:

Year	2004	2005	2006	2007	2008	2009
Conviction Rate (%)	81	91	82	75	82	95

Find the mean of the percentage of homicide cases in Suffolk County ending in pleas or verdicts of guilty from 2004 through 2009. What is the standard deviation for these data?

Source: Suffolk County, Massachusetts, District Attorney's office.

27. **HEALTH ISSUES IN MASSACHUSETTS CITIES** A random survey of health issues, conducted by the Department of Public Health of the Commonwealth of Massachusetts, examined the results from the state's seven largest cities. These cities were selected on the basis of their diverse racial and ethnic populations. The percentage of adults reporting fair or poor health for each city in the survey is given in the following table:

City	Boston	Worcester	Springfield	Lowell
Percentage of Adults Reporting Fair or Poor Health	16.3	15.4	22.2	17.2

City	Fall River	Lawrence	New Bedford
Percentage of Adults Reporting Fair or Poor Health	23.2	30.4	26.4

Find the average percentage of adults reporting fair or poor health for the seven cities. What is the standard deviation for these data?

Source: Massachusetts Department of Public Health.

28. **NEW YORK STATE COURTS' TOTAL CASELOAD** The following table gives the total caseload (in millions) in the New York State courts from 2004 through 2009.

Year	2004	2005	2006	2007	2008	2009
Cases	4.2	4.3	4.6	4.5	4.7	4.7

Find the mean of the total caseload in the New York State courts from 2004 through 2009. What is the standard deviation for these data?

Source: New York State Office of Court Administration.

29. **DIABETES IN MASSACHUSETTS CITIES** A random survey of health issues, conducted by the Department of Public Health of the Commonwealth of Massachusetts, examined the results from the state's seven largest cities. These cities were selected on the basis of their diverse racial and ethnic populations. The percentage of adults with diabetes in each city in the survey is given in the following table:

City	Boston	Worcester	Springfield	Lowell
Percentage of Adults with Diabetes	7.2	8.2	12.1	8.7

City	Fall River	Lawrence	New Bedford
Percentage of Adults with Diabetes	11.1	10.9	9.3

Find the average percentage of adults with diabetes in these seven cities. What is the standard deviation for these data?

Source: Massachusetts Department of Public Health.

30. **LIGHTNING INJURIES** The number of injuries due to lightning in the United States from 1999 through 2008 is given in the following table:

Year	1999	2000	2001	2002	2003	2004	2005	2006	2007	2008
Number	243	371	372	256	238	279	309	245	139	207

What is the average number of injuries per year due to lightning in the United States from 1999 through 2008? What is the standard deviation for these data?

Source: National Oceanic and Atmosphere Administration.

31. **GOVERNMENT DEBT** The following table gives the projected debt as a percentage of the gross domestic product (GDP) of nine selected countries for 2011. The study was conducted by the Organization for Economic Co-operation and Development (OECD) in early 2010.

Country	Spain	U.S.	Germany	Portugal
Percentage	67	72	83	88

Country	U.K.	France	Japan	Italy	Greece
Percentage	89	91	113	121	127

Find the mean of the projected debt as a percentage of GDP of the nine countries under consideration. What is the standard deviation for these data?

Source: OECD.

32. **GAS BILL** The monthly gas bill (in dollars) for a typical family of Massachusetts from May 2009 through April 2010 is summarized in the following table:

Month	MAY	JUN	JUL	AUG	SEP	OCT
Amount	89.57	58.99	37.15	37.15	47.64	72.97

Month	NOV	DEC	JAN	FEB	MAR	APR
Amount	145.02	195.46	240.97	242.20	215.14	173.31

Find the mean of the amount of the monthly gas bill for a typical family for the 12-month period under consideration. What is the standard deviation for these data?

Source: Bay State Gas.

33. **HOURS WORKED IN SOME COUNTRIES** The number of average hours worked per year per worker in the United States and five European countries in 2002 is given in the following table:

Country	U.S.	Spain	Great Britain	France	West Germany	Norway
Average Hours Worked	1815	1807	1707	1545	1428	1342

Find the average of the average hours worked per worker in 2002 for workers in the six countries. What is the standard deviation for these data?

Source: Office of Economic Cooperation and Development.

34. ACCESS TO CAPITAL One of the key determinants of economic growth is access to capital. Using 54 variables to create an index of 1–7, with 7 being best possible access to capital, Milken Institute ranked the following as the top ten nations (although technically Hong Kong is not a nation) by the ability of their entrepreneurs to gain access to capital:

Country	Hong Kong	Netherlands	U.K.	Singapore	Switzerland
Index	5.70	5.59	5.57	5.56	5.55

Country	U.S.	Australia	Finland	Germany	Denmark
Index	5.55	5.31	5.24	5.23	5.22

Find the mean of the indices of the top ten nations. What is the standard deviation for these data?

Source: Milken Institute.

35. ACCESS TO CAPITAL Refer to Exercise 34. Milken Institute also ranked the following as the ten worst-performing nations by the ability of their entrepreneurs to gain access to capital:

Country	Peru	Mexico	Bulgaria	Brazil	Indonesia
Index	3.76	3.70	3.66	3.50	3.46

Country	Colombia	Turkey	Argentina	Venezuela	Russia
Index	3.46	3.43	3.20	2.88	2.19

Find the mean of the indices of the ten worst-performing nations. What is the standard deviation for these data?

Source: Milken Institute.

36. ELECTION TURNOUT The percent of the voting-age population who cast ballots in presidential elections from 1932 through 2000 are given in the following table:

Election Year	1932	1936	1940	1944	1948	1952	1956	1960	1964
Turnout, %	53	57	59	56	51	62	59	59	62

Election Year	1968	1972	1976	1980	1984	1988	1992	1996	2000
Turnout %	61	55	54	53	53	50	55	49	51

Find the mean and the standard deviation of the given data.

Source: Federal Election Commission.

37. A probability distribution has a mean of 42 and a standard deviation of 2. Use Chebychev's inequality to find a bound on the probability that an outcome of the experiment lies between

a. 38 and 46.   **b.** 32 and 52.

38. A probability distribution has a mean of 20 and a standard deviation of 3. Use Chebychev's inequality to find a bound on the probability that an outcome of the experiment lies between

a. 15 and 25.   **b.** 10 and 30.

39. A probability distribution has a mean of 50 and a standard deviation of 1.4. Use Chebychev's inequality to find the value of c that guarantees the probability is at least 96% that an outcome of the experiment lies between $50 - c$ and $50 + c$.

40. Suppose X is a random variable with mean μ and standard deviation σ. If a large number of trials is observed, at least what percentage of these values is expected to lie between $\mu - 2\sigma$ and $\mu + 2\sigma$?

41. PRODUCT RELIABILITY The deluxe model hair dryer produced by Roland Electric has a mean expected lifetime of 24 months with a standard deviation of 3 months. Find a bound on the probability that one of these hair dryers will last between 20 and 28 months.

42. PRODUCT RELIABILITY A Christmas tree light has an expected life of 200 hr with a standard deviation of 2 hr.
a. Find a bound on the probability that one of these Christmas tree lights will last between 190 hr and 210 hr.
b. Suppose a large city uses 150,000 of these Christmas tree lights as part of its Christmas decorations. Estimate the number of lights that are likely to require replacement between 180 hr and 220 hr of use.

43. STARTING SALARIES The mean annual starting salary of a new graduate in a certain profession is $52,000 with a standard deviation of $500. Find a bound on the probability that the starting salary of a new graduate in this profession will be between $50,000 and $54,000.

44. QUALITY CONTROL Sugar packaged by a certain machine has a mean weight of 5 lb and a standard deviation of 0.02 lb. For what values of c can the manufacturer of the machinery claim that the sugar packaged by this machine has a weight between $5 - c$ and $5 + c$ lb with probability at least 96%?

In Exercises 45 and 46, determine whether the statement is true or false. If it is true, explain why it is true. If it is false, give an example to show why it is false.

45. Both the variance and the standard deviation of a random variable measure the spread of a probability distribution.

46. Chebychev's inequality is useless when $k \leq 1$.

8.3 Solutions to Self-Check Exercises

1. The mean of the random variable X is

$$\mu = (-4)(.1) + (-3)(.1) + (-1)(.2)$$
$$+ (0)(.3) + (2)(.1) + (5)(.2)$$
$$= 0.3$$

The variance of X is

$$\text{Var}(X) = (.1)(-4 - 0.3)^2 + (.1)(-3 - 0.3)^2$$
$$+ (.2)(-1 - 0.3)^2 + (.3)(0 - 0.3)^2$$
$$+ (.1)(2 - 0.3)^2 + (.2)(5 - 0.3)^2$$
$$= 8.01$$

The standard deviation of X is

$$\sigma = \sqrt{\text{Var}(X)} = \sqrt{8.01} \approx 2.83$$

2. We first compute the probability distribution of X from the given data as follows:

x	Relative Frequency of Occurrence	$P(X = x)$
46	1	.1
48	2	.2
50	3	.3
51	1	.1
52	2	.2
55	1	.1

The mean of X is

$$\mu = (.1)(46) + (.2)(48) + (.3)(50)$$
$$+ (.1)(51) + (.2)(52) + (.1)(55)$$
$$= 50.2$$

The variance of X is

$$\text{Var}(X) = (.1)(46 - 50.2)^2 + (.2)(48 - 50.2)^2$$
$$+ (.3)(50 - 50.2)^2 + (.1)(51 - 50.2)^2$$
$$+ (.2)(52 - 50.2)^2 + (.1)(55 - 50.2)^2$$
$$= 5.76$$

from which we deduce the standard deviation

$$\sigma = \sqrt{5.76}$$
$$= 2.4$$

USING TECHNOLOGY

Finding the Mean and Standard Deviation

The calculation of the mean and standard deviation of a random variable is facilitated by the use of a graphing utility.

 APPLIED EXAMPLE 1 Age Distribution of Company Directors A survey conducted in a certain year of the Fortune 1000 companies revealed the following age distribution of the company directors:

Age	20–24	25–29	30–34	35–39	40–44	45–49	50–54
Directors	1	6	28	104	277	607	1142

Age	55–59	60–64	65–69	70–74	75–79	80–84	85–89
Directors	1413	1424	494	159	62	31	5

Source: Directorship.

Let X denote the random variable taking on the values 1 through 14, where 1 corresponds to the age bracket 20–24, 2 corresponds to the age bracket 25–29, and so on.

a. Plot a histogram for the given data.
b. Find the mean and the standard deviation of these data. Interpret your results.

Solution

a. Enter the values of X as $x_1 = 1$, $x_2 = 2, \ldots, x_{14} = 14$ and the corresponding values of Y as $y_1 = 1$, $y_2 = 6, \ldots, y_{14} = 5$. Then using the **DRAW** function from the Statistics menu of a graphing utility, we obtain the histogram shown in Figure T1.

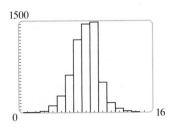

FIGURE **T1**
The histogram for the given data, using the viewing window [0, 16] × [0, 1500]

(*continued*)

b. Using the appropriate function from the Statistics menu, we find that $\bar{x} \approx 7.9193$ and $\sigma x \approx 1.6378$; that is, the mean of X is $\mu \approx 7.9$, and the standard deviation is $\sigma \approx 1.6$. Interpreting our results, we see that the average age of the directors is in the 55- to 60-year-old bracket. ■

TECHNOLOGY EXERCISES

1. a. Graph the histogram associated with the random variable X in Example 1, page 453.
   b. Find the mean and the standard deviation for these data.

2. a. Graph the histogram associated with the random variable Y in Example 1, page 453.
   b. Find the mean and the standard deviation for these data.

3. a. Graph the histogram associated with the data given in Exercise 12, page 458.
   b. Find the mean and the standard deviation for these data.

4. a. Graph the histogram associated with the data given in Exercise 16, page 459.
   b. Find the mean and the standard deviation for these data.

5. A sugar refiner uses a machine to pack sugar in 5-lb cartons. To check the machine's accuracy, cartons are selected at random and weighed. The results follow:

4.98	5.02	4.96	4.97	5.03
4.96	4.98	5.01	5.02	5.06
4.97	5.04	5.04	5.01	4.99
4.98	5.04	5.01	5.03	5.05
4.96	4.97	5.02	5.04	4.97
5.03	5.01	5.00	5.01	4.98

a. Describe a random variable X that is associated with these data.
   b. Find the probability distribution for the random variable X.
   c. Compute the mean and standard deviation of X.

6. The scores of 25 students in a mathematics examination are as follows:

90	85	74	92	68	94	66
87	85	70	72	68	73	72
69	66	58	70	74	88	90
98	71	75	68			

a. Describe a random variable X that is associated with these data.
   b. Find the probability distribution for the random variable X.
   c. Compute the mean and standard deviation of X.

7. HEIGHTS OF WOMEN The following data, obtained from the records of the Westwood Health Club, give the heights (to the nearest inch) of 200 female members of the club:

Height	62	$62\frac{1}{2}$	63	$63\frac{1}{2}$	64	$64\frac{1}{2}$	65	$65\frac{1}{2}$	66
Frequency	2	3	4	8	11	20	32	30	18

Height	$66\frac{1}{2}$	67	$67\frac{1}{2}$	68	$68\frac{1}{2}$	69	$69\frac{1}{2}$	70	$70\frac{1}{2}$	71
Frequency	18	16	8	10	5	5	4	3	2	1

a. Plot a histogram for the given data.
   b. Find the mean and the standard deviation of these data.

8. AGE DISTRIBUTION IN A TOWN The following table gives the distribution of the ages (in years) of the residents (in hundreds) of the town of Monroe who are under the age of 40:

Age	0–3	4–7	8–11	12–15	16–19
Residents	30	42	50	60	50

Age	20–23	24–27	28–31	32–35	36–39
Residents	41	50	45	42	34

Let X denote the random variable taking on the values 1 through 10, where 1 corresponds to the range 0–3, . . . , and 10 corresponds to the range 36–39.
   a. Plot a histogram for the given data.
   b. Find the mean and the standard deviation of X.

8.4 The Binomial Distribution

Bernoulli Trials

An important class of experiments have (or may be viewed as having) two outcomes. For example, in a coin-tossing experiment, the two outcomes are *heads* and *tails*. In the card game played by Mike and Bill (Example 7, Section 8.2), one may view the selection of a diamond as a *win* (for Mike) and the selection of a card of another suit as a *loss* for Mike. For a third example, consider an experiment in which a person is inoculated with a flu vaccine. Here, the vaccine may be classified as being "effective" or "ineffective" with respect to that particular person.

In general, experiments with two outcomes are called **Bernoulli trials,** or **binomial trials.** It is standard practice to label one of the outcomes of a binomial trial a *success* and the other a *failure*. For example, in a coin-tossing experiment, the outcome a *head* may be called a success, in which case the outcome a *tail* is called a failure. Note that by using the terms *success* and *failure* in this way, we depart from their usual connotations.

A sequence of Bernoulli (binomial) trials is called a binomial experiment. More precisely, we have the following definition:

Binomial Experiment

A **binomial experiment** has the following properties:

1. The number of trials in the experiment is fixed.
2. There are two outcomes of each trial: "success" and "failure."
3. The probability of success in each trial is the same.
4. The trials are independent of each other.

In a binomial experiment, it is customary to denote the number of trials by n, the probability of a success by p, and the probability of a failure by q. Because the event of a success and the event of a failure are complementary events, we have the relationship

$$p + q = 1$$

or, equivalently,

$$q = 1 - p$$

The following example involves a binomial experiment.

 EXAMPLE 1 A fair die is rolled four times. Compute the probability of obtaining exactly one 6 in the four throws.

Solution   There are four trials in this experiment. Each trial consists of rolling the die once and observing the face that lands uppermost. We may view each trial as an experiment with two outcomes: a success (S) if the face that lands uppermost is a 6 and a failure (F) if it is any of the other five numbers. Letting p and q denote the probability of success and failure, respectively, of a single trial of the experiment, we find that

$$p = \frac{1}{6} \quad \text{and} \quad q = 1 - \frac{1}{6} = \frac{5}{6}$$

Furthermore, we may assume that the trials of this experiment are independent. Thus, we have a binomial experiment.

With the aid of the multiplication principle, we see that the experiment has 2^4, or 16, outcomes. We can obtain these outcomes by constructing the tree diagram associated with the experiment (see Table 11, where the outcomes are listed according to the number of successes). From the table, we see that the event of obtaining exactly one success in four trials is given by

$$E = \{\text{SFFF, FSFF, FFSF, FFFS}\}$$

with probability given by

$$P(E) = P(\text{SFFF}) + P(\text{FSFF}) + P(\text{FFSF}) + P(\text{FFFS}) \qquad \textbf{(10)}$$

TABLE 11

0 Success	1 Success	2 Successes	3 Successes	4 Successes
FFFF	SFFF	SSFF	SSSF	SSSS
	FSFF	SFSF	SSFS	
	FFSF	SFFS	SFSS	
	FFFS	FSSF	FSSS	
		FSFS		
		FFSS		

Since the trials (throws) are independent, the terms on the right-hand side of Equation (10) may be computed as follows:

$$P(\text{SFFF}) = P(\text{S})P(\text{F})P(\text{F})P(\text{F}) = p \cdot q \cdot q \cdot q = pq^3$$
$$P(\text{FSFF}) = P(\text{F})P(\text{S})P(\text{F})P(\text{F}) = q \cdot p \cdot q \cdot q = pq^3$$
$$P(\text{FFSF}) = P(\text{F})P(\text{F})P(\text{S})P(\text{F}) = q \cdot q \cdot p \cdot q = pq^3$$
$$P(\text{FFFS}) = P(\text{F})P(\text{F})P(\text{F})P(\text{S}) = q \cdot q \cdot q \cdot p = pq^3$$

Therefore, upon substituting these values in Equation (10), we obtain

$$P(E) = pq^3 + pq^3 + pq^3 + pq^3 = 4pq^3$$
$$= 4\left(\frac{1}{6}\right)\left(\frac{5}{6}\right)^3 \approx .386$$

Probabilities in Bernoulli Trials

Let's reexamine the computations we performed in the last example. There, it was found that the probability of obtaining exactly one success in a binomial experiment with four independent trials with probability of success in a single trial p is given by

$$P(E) = 4pq^3 \qquad (\text{where } q = 1 - p) \tag{11}$$

Observe that the coefficient 4 of pq^3 appearing in Equation (11) is precisely the number of outcomes of the experiment with exactly one success and three failures, the outcomes being

$$\text{SFFF} \quad \text{FSFF} \quad \text{FFSF} \quad \text{FFFS}$$

Another way of obtaining this coefficient is to think of the outcomes as arrangements of the letters S and F. Then the number of ways of selecting one position for S from four possibilities is given by

$$C(4, 1) = \frac{4!}{1!\,(4 - 1)!}$$
$$= 4$$

Next, observe that because the trials are independent, each of the four outcomes of the experiment has the same probability, given by

$$pq^3$$

where the exponents 1 and 3 of p and q, respectively, correspond to exactly one success and three failures in the trials that make up each outcome.

As a result of the foregoing discussion, we may write Equation (11) as

$$P(E) = C(4, 1)pq^3 \tag{12}$$

We are also in a position to generalize this result. Suppose that in a binomial experiment the probability of success in any trial is p. What is the probability of obtaining exactly x successes in n independent trials? We start by counting the number of outcomes of the experiment, each of which has exactly x successes. Now, one such outcome involves x successive successes followed by $(n - x)$ failures—that is,

$$\underbrace{\text{SS} \cdots \text{S}}_{x} \underbrace{\text{FF} \cdots \text{F}}_{n-x} \qquad \textbf{(13)}$$

The other outcomes, each of which has exactly x successes, are obtained by rearranging the S's (x of them) and F's ($n - x$ of them). There are $C(n, x)$ ways of arranging these letters. Next, arguing as in Example 1, we see that each such outcome has probability given by

$$p^x q^{n-x}$$

For example, for the outcome (13), we find

$$P(\underbrace{\text{SS} \cdots \text{S}}_{x} \underbrace{\text{FF} \cdots \text{F}}_{(n-x)}) = \underbrace{P(\text{S})P(\text{S}) \cdots P(\text{S})}_{x} \underbrace{P(\text{F})P(\text{F}) \cdots P(\text{F})}_{(n-x)}$$

$$= \underbrace{pp \cdots p}_{x} \underbrace{qq \cdots q}_{n-x}$$

$$= p^x q^{n-x}$$

Let's now state this important result formally.

> **Computation of Probabilities in Bernoulli Trials**
>
> In a binomial experiment in which the probability of success in any trial is p, the probability of exactly x successes in n independent trials is given by
>
> $$C(n, x)p^x q^{n-x}$$

If we let X be the random variable that gives the number of successes in a binomial experiment, then the probability of exactly x successes in n independent trials may be written

$$P(X = x) = C(n, x)p^x q^{n-x} \qquad (x = 0, 1, 2, \ldots, n) \qquad \textbf{(14)}$$

The random variable X is called a **binomial random variable,** and the probability distribution of X is called a **binomial distribution.**

EXAMPLE 2 A fair die is rolled five times. If a 1 or a 6 lands uppermost in a trial, then the throw is considered a success. Otherwise, the throw is considered a failure.

a. Find the probabilities of obtaining exactly 0, 1, 2, 3, 4, and 5 successes in this experiment.

b. Using the results obtained in the solution to part (a), construct the binomial distribution for this experiment, and draw the histogram associated with it.

Solution

a. This is a binomial experiment with X, the binomial random variable, taking on each of the values 0, 1, 2, 3, 4, and 5 corresponding to exactly 0, 1, 2, 3, 4, and 5 successes, respectively, in five trials. Since the die is fair, the probability of a 1 or a 6 landing uppermost in any trial is given by $p = \frac{2}{6} = \frac{1}{3}$, from which it also follows that $q = 1 - p = \frac{2}{3}$. Finally, $n = 5$, since there are five trials (throws of the die) in this experiment. Using Equation (14), we find that the required probabilities are

$$P(X = 0) = C(5, 0)\left(\frac{1}{3}\right)^0\left(\frac{2}{3}\right)^5 = \frac{5!}{0!\ 5!} \cdot \frac{32}{243} \approx .132$$

$$P(X = 1) = C(5, 1)\left(\frac{1}{3}\right)^1\left(\frac{2}{3}\right)^4 = \frac{5!}{1!\ 4!} \cdot \frac{16}{243} \approx .329$$

$$P(X = 2) = C(5, 2)\left(\frac{1}{3}\right)^2\left(\frac{2}{3}\right)^3 = \frac{5!}{2!\ 3!} \cdot \frac{8}{243} \approx .329$$

$$P(X = 3) = C(5, 3)\left(\frac{1}{3}\right)^3\left(\frac{2}{3}\right)^2 = \frac{5!}{3!\ 2!} \cdot \frac{4}{243} \approx .165$$

$$P(X = 4) = C(5, 4)\left(\frac{1}{3}\right)^4\left(\frac{2}{3}\right)^1 = \frac{5!}{4!\ 1!} \cdot \frac{2}{243} \approx .041$$

$$P(X = 5) = C(5, 5)\left(\frac{1}{3}\right)^5\left(\frac{2}{3}\right)^0 = \frac{5!}{5!\ 0!} \cdot \frac{1}{243} \approx .004$$

b. Using these results, we find the required binomial distribution associated with this experiment given in Table 12. Next, we use this table to construct the histogram associated with the probability distribution (Figure 12).

TABLE 12

Probability Distribution

x	P(X = x)
0	.132
1	.329
2	.329
3	.165
4	.041
5	.004

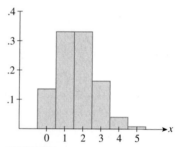

FIGURE **12**
The probability of the number of successes in five throws

EXAMPLE 3 A fair die is rolled five times. If a 1 or a 6 lands uppermost in a trial, then the throw is considered a success. Use the results from Example 2 to answer the following questions:

a. What is the probability of obtaining 0 or 1 success in the experiment?
b. What is the probability of obtaining at least 1 success in the experiment?

Explore & Discuss

Consider the equation

$$P(X = x) = C(n, x)p^x q^{n-x}$$

for the binomial distribution.

1. Construct the histogram with $n = 5$ and $p = .2$, the histogram with $n = 5$ and $p = .5$, and the histogram with $n = 5$ and $p = .8$.

2. Comment on the shape of the histograms, and give an interpretation.

Solution   Using Table 12, we find that

a. The probability of obtaining 0 or 1 success in the experiment is given by

$$P(X = 0) + P(X = 1) = .132 + .329 = .461$$

b. The probability of obtaining at least 1 success in the experiment is given by

$$P(X = 1) + P(X = 2) + P(X = 3) + P(X = 4) + P(X = 5)$$
$$= .329 + .329 + .165 + .041 + .004$$
$$= .868$$

This result may also be obtained by observing that $1 - P(X = 0) = 1 - .132 = .868$.

The following formulas (which we state without proof) will be useful in solving problems that involve binomial experiments.

Mean, Variance, and Standard Deviation of a Random Variable X

If X is a binomial random variable associated with a binomial experiment consisting of n trials with probability of success p and probability of failure q, then the **mean** (expected value), **variance,** and **standard deviation** of X are

$$\mu = E(X) = np \tag{15a}$$
$$\mathrm{Var}(X) = npq \tag{15b}$$
$$\sigma_X = \sqrt{npq} \tag{15c}$$

EXAMPLE 4 For the experiment in Examples 2 and 3, compute the mean, the variance, and the standard deviation of X by (a) using Equations (15a), (15b), and (15c) and (b) using the definition of each term (Sections 8.2 and 8.3).

Solution

a. We use Equations (15a), (15b), and (15c), with $p = \frac{1}{3}$, $q = \frac{2}{3}$, and $n = 5$, obtaining

$$\mu = E(X) = (5)\left(\frac{1}{3}\right) = \frac{5}{3} \approx 1.67$$

$$\mathrm{Var}(X) = (5)\left(\frac{1}{3}\right)\left(\frac{2}{3}\right) = \frac{10}{9} \approx 1.11$$

$$\sigma_X = \sqrt{\mathrm{Var}(X)} \approx \sqrt{1.11} \approx 1.05$$

We leave it to you to interpret the results.

b. Using the definition of expected value and the values of the probability distribution shown in Table 12, we find that

$$\mu = E(X) \approx (0)(.132) + (1)(.329) + (2)(.329)$$
$$+ (3)(.165) + (4)(.041) + (5)(.004)$$
$$\approx 1.67$$

which agrees with the result obtained in part (a). Next, using the definition of variance and $\mu = 1.67$, we find that

$$\mathrm{Var}(X) = (.132)(-1.67)^2 + (.329)(-0.67)^2 + (.329)(0.33)^2$$
$$+ (.165)(1.33)^2 + (.041)(2.33)^2 + (.004)(3.33)^2$$
$$\approx 1.11$$
$$\sigma_X = \sqrt{\mathrm{Var}(X)}$$
$$\approx \sqrt{1.11} \approx 1.05$$

which again agrees with the preceding results.   ■

We close this section by looking at several examples involving binomial experiments. In working through these examples, you may use a calculator, or you may consult Table 1, Binomial Probabilities, Appendix D.

APPLIED EXAMPLE 5 Quality Control A division of Solaron manufactures photovoltaic cells to use in the company's solar energy converters. It is estimated that 5% of the cells manufactured are defective. If a random sample of 20 is selected from a large lot of cells manufactured by the company, what is the probability that it will contain at most 2 defective cells?

Solution We may view this as a binomial experiment. To see this, first note that a fixed number of trials ($n = 20$) corresponds to the selection of exactly 20 photovoltaic cells. Second, observe that there are exactly two outcomes in the experiment: defective ("success") and nondefective ("failure"). Third, the probability of success in each trial is .05 ($p = .05$), and the probability of failure in each trial is .95 ($q = .95$). This assumption is justified by virtue of the fact that the lot from which the cells are selected is "large," so the removal of a few cells will not appreciably affect the percentage of defective cells in the lot in each successive trial. Finally, the trials are independent of each other—once again because of the lot size.

Letting X denote the number of defective cells, we find that the probability of finding at most 2 defective cells in the sample of 20 is given by

$$P(X = 0) + P(X = 1) + P(X = 2)$$
$$= C(20, 0)(.05)^0(.95)^{20} + C(20, 1)(.05)^1(.95)^{19}$$
$$+ C(20, 2)(.05)^2(.95)^{18}$$
$$\approx .3585 + .3774 + .1887$$
$$= .9246$$

Thus, for lots of photovoltaic cells manufactured by Solaron, approximately 92% of the samples will have at most 2 defective cells; equivalently, approximately 8% of the samples will contain more than 2 defective cells. ∎

APPLIED EXAMPLE 6 Success of Heart Transplants The probability that a heart transplant performed at the Medical Center is successful (that is, the patient survives 1 year or more after undergoing such an operation) is .7. Of six patients who have recently undergone such an operation, what is the probability that, 1 year from now,

a. None of the heart recipients will be alive?
b. Exactly three will be alive?
c. At least three will be alive?
d. All will be alive?

Solution   Here, $n = 6$, $p = .7$, and $q = .3$. Let X denote the number of successful operations. Then:

a. The probability that no heart recipients will be alive after 1 year is given by

$$P(X = 0) = C(6, 0)(.7)^0(.3)^6$$
$$= \frac{6!}{0!\,6!} \cdot 1 \cdot (.3)^6$$
$$\approx .0007$$

b. The probability that exactly three heart recipients will be alive after 1 year is given by

$$P(X = 3) = C(6, 3)(.7)^3(.3)^3$$
$$= \frac{6!}{3!\,3!}(.7)^3(.3)^3$$
$$\approx .1852$$

c. The probability that at least three heart recipients will be alive after 1 year is given by

$$P(X = 3) + P(X = 4) + P(X = 5) + P(X = 6)$$
$$= C(6, 3)(.7)^3(.3)^3 + C(6, 4)(.7)^4(.3)^2$$
$$+ C(6, 5)(.7)^5(.3)^1 + C(6, 6)(.7)^6(.3)^0$$
$$= \frac{6!}{3!\,3!}(.7)^3(.3)^3 + \frac{6!}{4!\,2!}(.7)^4(.3)^2 + \frac{6!}{5!\,1!}(.7)^5(.3)^1$$
$$+ \frac{6!}{6!\,0!}(.7)^6 \cdot 1$$
$$\approx .1852 + .3241 + .3025 + .1176$$
$$= .9294$$

d. The probability that all six heart recipients will be alive after 1 year is given by

$$P(X = 6) = C(6, 6)(.7)^6(.3)^0 = \frac{6!}{6!\,0!}(.7)^6 \cdot 1$$
$$\approx .1176$$

APPLIED EXAMPLE 7 Quality Control PAR Bearings manufactures ball bearings packaged in lots of 100 each. The company's quality-control department has determined that 2% of the ball bearings manufactured do not meet the specifications imposed by a buyer. Find the average number of ball bearings per package that fail to meet the buyer's specification.

Solution The experiment under consideration is binomial. The average number of ball bearings per package that fail to meet with the specifications is therefore given by the expected value of the associated binomial random variable. Using Equation (15a), we find that

$$\mu = E(X) = np = (100)(.02) = 2$$

substandard ball bearings in a package of 100.

Equation (15a) also provides us with a useful method for estimating the proportion of defective items in a batch by examining a few random samples, as the following example shows.

APPLIED EXAMPLE 8 Quality Control The ball bearings produced by a certain machine were checked by examining samples of 20. The following table shows the number of substandard ball bearings (they did not meet specified tolerance requirements) contained in a distribution of 100 samples:

Number of Substandard Ball Bearings in a Sample of 20	0	1	2	3	4 or more
Number of Samples	85	10	4	1	0

Find the mean number of substandard ball bearings per sample, and assuming that the distribution is binomial, estimate the percentage of substandard ball bearings in the whole batch.

Solution The mean number of substandard ball bearings per sample is

$$\mu = \frac{1}{100}\big[(85)(0) + (10)(1) + (4)(2) + (1)(3)\big] = 0.21$$

Here, $n = 20$. So Equation (15a) gives

$$0.21 = 20p$$

or $p = .0105$. Thus, approximately 1% of the ball bearings in the group are substandard.

8.4 Self-Check Exercises

1. A binomial experiment consists of four independent trials. The probability of success in each trial is .2.
   a. Find the probabilities of obtaining exactly 0, 1, 2, 3, and 4 successes in this experiment.

b. Construct the binomial distribution, and draw the histogram associated with this experiment.
c. Compute the mean and the standard deviation of the random variable associated with this experiment.

2. A survey shows that 60% of the households in a large metropolitan area have microwave ovens. If ten households are selected at random, what is the probability that five or fewer of these households have microwave ovens?

Solutions to Self-Check Exercises 8.4 can be found on page 474.

8.4 Concept Questions

1. Suppose that you are given a Bernoulli experiment.
   a. How many outcomes are there in each trial?
   b. Can the number of trials in the experiment vary, or is it fixed?
   c. Are the trials in the experiment dependent?
   d. If the probability of success in any trial is p, what is the probability of exactly x successes in n independent trials?

2. Give the formula for the mean, variance, and standard deviation of X, where X is a binomial random variable associated with a binomial experiment consisting of n trials with probability of success p and probability of failure q.

8.4 Exercises

In Exercises 1–6, determine whether the experiment is a binomial experiment. Justify your answer.

1. Rolling a fair die three times and observing the number of times a 6 is thrown

2. Rolling a fair die and observing the number of times the die is thrown until a 6 appears uppermost

3. Rolling a fair die three times and observing the number that appears uppermost

4. A card is selected from a deck of 52 cards, and its color is observed. A second card is then drawn (without replacement), and its color is observed.

5. Recording the number of accidents that occur at a given intersection on four clear days and one rainy day

6. Recording the number of hits a baseball player, whose batting average is .325, gets after being up to bat five times

In Exercises 7–10, find $C(n, x)p^x q^{n-x}$ for the given values of n, x, and p.

7. $n = 4, x = 2, p = \dfrac{1}{3}$ **8.** $n = 6, x = 4, p = \dfrac{1}{4}$

9. $n = 5, x = 3, p = .2$ **10.** $n = 6, x = 5, p = .4$

In Exercises 11–16, use the formula $C(n, x)p^x q^{n-x}$ to determine the probability of the given event.

11. The probability of exactly no successes in five trials of a binomial experiment in which $p = \dfrac{1}{3}$

12. The probability of exactly three successes in six trials of a binomial experiment in which $p = \dfrac{1}{2}$

13. The probability of at least three successes in six trials of a binomial experiment in which $p = \dfrac{1}{2}$

14. The probability of no successful outcomes in six trials of a binomial experiment in which $p = \dfrac{1}{3}$

15. The probability of no failures in five trials of a binomial experiment in which $p = \dfrac{1}{3}$

16. The probability of at least one failure in five trials of a binomial experiment in which $p = \dfrac{1}{3}$

17. A fair die is rolled four times. Calculate the probability of obtaining exactly two 6s.

18. Let X be the number of successes in five independent trials in a binomial experiment in which the probability of success is $p = \dfrac{2}{5}$. Find:
   a. $P(X = 4)$ **b.** $P(2 \le X \le 4)$

19. A binomial experiment consists of five independent trials. The probability of success in each trial is .4.
   a. Find the probabilities of obtaining exactly 0, 1, 2, 3, 4, and 5 successes in this experiment.
   b. Construct the binomial distribution, and draw the histogram associated with this experiment.
   c. Compute the mean and the standard deviation of the random variable associated with this experiment.

20. Let the random variable X denote the number of girls in a five-child family. If the probability of a female birth is .5:
   a. Find the probabilities of 0, 1, 2, 3, 4, and 5 girls in a five-child family.
   b. Construct the binomial distribution, and draw the histogram associated with this experiment.
   c. Compute the mean and the standard deviation of the random variable X.

21. The probability that a fuse produced by a certain manufacturing process will be defective is $\dfrac{1}{50}$. Is it correct to infer from this statement that there is at most 1 defective fuse in each lot of 50 produced by this process? Justify your answer.

22. SPORTS If the probability that a certain tennis player will serve an ace is $\dfrac{1}{4}$, what is the probability that he will serve exactly two aces out of five serves? (Assume that the five serves are independent.)

23. SPORTS If the probability that a certain tennis player will serve an ace is .15, what is the probability that she will serve at least two aces out of five serves? (Assume that the five serves are independent.)

24. **SALES PREDICTIONS** From experience, the manager of Kramer's Book Mart knows that 40% of the people who are browsing in the store will make a purchase. What is the probability that, among ten people who are browsing in the store, at least three will make a purchase?

25. **CUSTOMER SERVICES** Mayco, a mail-order department store, has six telephone lines available for customers who wish to place their orders. If the probability is $\frac{1}{4}$ that any one of the six telephone lines is engaged during business hours, find the probability that all six lines will be in use when a customer calls to place an order.

26. **RESTAURANT VIOLATIONS OF THE HEALTH CODE** Suppose 30% of the restaurants in a certain part of a town are in violation of the health code. If a health inspector randomly selects five of the restaurants for inspection, what is the probability that:
    a. None of the restaurants are in violation of the health code?
    b. One of the restaurants is in violation of the health code?
    c. At least two of the restaurants are in violation of the health code?

27. **ADVERTISEMENTS** An advertisement for Brand *A* chicken noodle soup claims that 60% of all consumers prefer Brand *A* over Brand *B*, the chief competitor's product. To test this claim, David Horowitz, host of *The Consumer Advocate*, selected ten people at random. After tasting both soups, each person was asked to state his or her preference. Assuming that the company's claim is correct, find the probability that:
    a. Six or more people stated a preference for Brand *A*.
    b. Fewer than six people stated a preference for Brand *A*.

28. **VOTERS** In a certain congressional district, it is known that 40% of the registered voters classify themselves as conservatives. If ten registered voters are selected at random from this district, what is the probability that four of them will be conservatives?

29. **VIOLATIONS OF THE BUILDING CODE** Suppose that one third of the new buildings in a town are in violation of the building code. If a building inspector inspects five of the buildings chosen at random, find the probability that:
    a. The first three buildings will pass the inspection and the remaining two will fail the inspection.
    b. Exactly three of the buildings will pass inspection.

30. **EXAMS** A biology quiz consists of eight multiple-choice questions. Five must be answered correctly to receive a passing grade. If each question has five possible answers, of which only one is correct, what is the probability that a student who guesses at random on each question will pass the examination?

31. **BLOOD TYPES** It is estimated that one third of the general population has blood type A+. If a sample of nine people is selected at random, what is the probability that:
    a. Exactly three of them have blood type A+?
    b. At most three of them have blood type A+?

32. **EXAMS** A psychology quiz consists of ten true-or-false questions. If a student knows the correct answer to six of the questions but determines the answers to the remaining questions by flipping a coin, what is the probability that she will obtain a score of at least 90%?

33. **QUALITY CONTROL** The probability that a DVD player produced by VCA Television is defective is estimated to be .02. If a sample of ten players is selected at random, what is the probability that the sample contains:
    a. No defectives?   b. At most two defectives?

34. **QUALITY CONTROL** As part of its quality-control program, the video-game DVDs produced by Starr Communications are subjected to a final inspection before shipment. A sample of six DVDs is selected at random from each lot of DVDs produced, and the lot is rejected if the sample contains one or more defective DVDs. If 1.5% of the DVDs produced by Starr is defective, find the probability that a shipment will be accepted.

35. **ROBOT RELIABILITY** An automobile-manufacturing company uses ten industrial robots as welders on its assembly line. On a given working day, the probability that a robot will be inoperative is .05. What is the probability that on a given working day:
    a. Exactly two robots are inoperative?
    b. More than two robots are inoperative?

36. **ENGINE FAILURES** The probability that an airplane engine will fail in a transcontinental flight is .001. Assuming that engine failures are independent of each other, what is the probability that on a certain transcontinental flight, a four-engine plane will experience:
    a. Exactly one engine failure?
    b. Exactly two engine failures?
    c. More than two engine failures? (*Note:* In this event, the airplane will crash.)

37. **QUALITY CONTROL** The McCormack Company manufactures solar panels. As a part of its quality control, the company checks the day's production by examining samples of 10. The following table shows the number of defective panels contained in a distribution of 40 samples.

Number of Defective Panels in a Sample of 20	0	1	2	3	4	5 or more
Number of Samples		33	3	2	1	1	0

Find the mean number of defective panels per sample, and assuming that the distribution is binomial, estimate the percentage of defective solar panels in the day's production.

38. **QUALITY CONTROL** The panels for the Pulsar 32-inch widescreen LCD HDTVs in a production run were checked by examining samples of 6. The following table shows the number of defective panels contained in a distribution of 30 samples.

Number of Defective Panels in a Sample of 20	0	1	2	3	4 or more
Number of Samples		26	2	1	1	0

Find the mean number of defective panels per sample, and assuming that the distribution is binomial, estimate the percentage of defective panels in the production run.

39. **QUALITY CONTROL** The manager of Toy World has decided to accept a shipment of electronic games if none of a random sample of 20 is found to be defective. What is the probability that he will accept the shipment:
    a. If 10% of the electronic games is defective?
    b. If 5% of the electronic games is defective?

40. **QUALITY CONTROL** Refer to Exercise 39. If the manager's criterion for accepting shipment is that there be no more than 1 defective electronic game in a random sample of 20, what is the probability that he will accept the shipment if 10% of the electronic games is defective?

41. **QUALITY CONTROL** Refer to Exercise 39. If the manager of the store changes his sample size to 10 and decides to accept shipment only if none of the sampled games is defective, what is the probability that he will accept the shipment if 10% of the games is defective?

42. **MAIL-ORDER SALES** Ruth, the owner of a mail-order business, estimates that the probability that a household receiving one of her catalogs will place an order with her is .10. How many catalogs must Ruth send out to ensure that the chances of obtaining at least one order is 50% or better?

43. How many times must a person toss a fair coin to ensure that the chances of obtaining at least one head to be 99% or better?

44. **FLIPPING A COIN** An unbiased coin is tossed 1 million times. Show that the probability is at least .99 that the proportion of times the coin will land heads is between .495 and .505, inclusive. (*Note:* These results show that if an unbiased coin

is tossed a very large number of times, the proportion of times that the coin will land heads is very close to $\frac{1}{2}$.)
Hint: Use Chebychev's inequality.

45. **DRUG TESTING** A new drug has been found to be effective in treating 75% of the people afflicted by a certain disease. If the drug is administered to 500 people who have this disease, what are the mean and the standard deviation of the number of people for whom the drug can be expected to be effective?

46. **COLLEGE GRADUATES** At a certain university, the probability that an entering freshman will graduate within 4 years is .6. From an incoming class of 2000 freshmen, find:
    a. The expected number of students who will graduate within 4 years.
    b. The standard deviation of the number of students who will graduate within 4 years.

In Exercises 47–50, determine whether the statement is true or false. If it is true, explain why it is true. If it is false, give an example to show why it is false.

47. In a binomial trial, the number of outcomes of the experiment may be any finite number.

48. In a binomial experiment with $n = 3$, $P(X = 1 \text{ or } 2) = 3pq$.

49. If the probability that a batter gets a hit is $\frac{1}{4}$ at each time at bat, then the batter is sure to get a hit if she bats four times.

50. The histogram associated with a binomial distribution is symmetric with respect to $x = \frac{n}{2}$ if $p = \frac{1}{2}$.

8.4 Solutions to Self-Check Exercises

1. a. We use Equation (14) with $n = 4$, $p = .2$, and $q = 1 - .2 = .8$, obtaining

$$P(X = 0) = C(4, 0)(.2)^0(.8)^4$$

$$= \frac{4!}{0!\,4!} \cdot 1 \cdot (.8)^4 \approx .410$$

$$P(X = 1) = C(4, 1)(.2)^1(.8)^3$$

$$= \frac{4!}{1!\,3!}(.2)(.8)^3 \approx .410$$

$$P(X = 2) = C(4, 2)(.2)^2(.8)^2$$

$$= \frac{4!}{2!\,2!}(.2)^2(.8)^2 \approx .154$$

$$P(X = 3) = C(4, 3)(.2)^3(.8)^1$$

$$= \frac{4!}{3!\,1!}(.2)^3(.8) \approx .026$$

$$P(X = 4) = C(4, 4)(.2)^4(.8)^0$$

$$= \frac{4!}{4!\,0!}(.2)^4 \cdot 1 \approx .002$$

b. The required binomial distribution and histogram are as follows:

x	$P(X = x)$
0	.410
1	.410
2	.154
3	.026
4	.002

c. The mean is

$$\mu = E(X) = np = (4)(.2)$$
$$= 0.8$$

and the standard deviation is

$$\sigma = \sqrt{npq} = \sqrt{(4)(.2)(.8)}$$
$$= 0.8$$

2. This is a binomial experiment with $n = 10$, $p = .6$, and $q = .4$. Let X denote the number of households that have microwave ovens. Then the probability that five or fewer households have microwave ovens is given by

$$P(X = 0) + P(X = 1) + P(X = 2) + P(X = 3)$$
$$+ P(X = 4) + P(X = 5)$$
$$= C(10, 0)(.6)^0(.4)^{10} + C(10, 1)(.6)^1(.4)^9$$
$$+ C(10, 2)(.6)^2(.4)^8 + C(10, 3)(.6)^3(.4)^7$$
$$+ C(10, 4)(.6)^4(.4)^6 + C(10, 5)(.6)^5(.4)^5$$
$$\approx 0 + .002 + .011 + .042 + .111 + .201$$
$$\approx .367$$

8.5 The Normal Distribution

Probability Density Functions

The probability distributions discussed in the preceding sections were all associated with finite random variables—that is, random variables that take on finitely many values. Such probability distributions are referred to as *finite probability distributions*. In this section, we consider probability distributions associated with a continuous random variable—that is, a random variable that may take on any value lying in an interval of real numbers. Such probability distributions are called **continuous probability distributions.**

Unlike a finite probability distribution, which may be exhibited in the form of a table, a continuous probability distribution is defined by a function f whose domain coincides with the interval of values taken on by the random variable associated with the experiment. Such a function f is called the **probability density function** associated with the probability distribution, and it has the following properties:

1. $f(x)$ is nonnegative for all values of x in its domain.
2. The area of the region between the graph of f and the x-axis is equal to 1 (Figure 13).

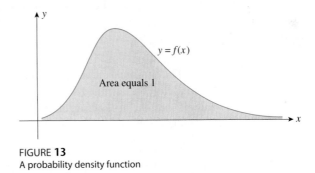

FIGURE 13
A probability density function

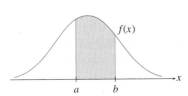

FIGURE 14
$P(a < X < b)$ is given by the area of the shaded region.

Now suppose we are given a continuous probability distribution defined by a probability density function f. Then the probability that the random variable X assumes a value in an interval $a < x < b$ is given by the area of the region between the graph of f and the x-axis from $x = a$ to $x = b$ (Figure 14). We denote the value of this probability by $P(a < X < b)$.* Observe that property 2 of the probability density function states that the probability that a continuous random variable takes on a value lying in its range is 1, a certainty, which is expected. Note the analogy between the areas under the probability density curves and the areas of the histograms associated with finite probability distributions (see Section 8.1).

---

*Because the area under one point of the graph of f is equal to zero, we see that $P(a < X < b) = P(a < X \le b) = P(a \le X < b) = P(a \le X \le b)$.

Normal Distributions

The mean μ and the standard deviation σ of a continuous probability distribution have roughly the same meanings as the mean and standard deviation of a finite probability distribution. Thus, the mean of a continuous probability distribution is a measure of the central tendency of the probability distribution, and the standard deviation of the probability distribution measures its spread about its mean. Both of these numbers will play an important role in the following discussion.

For the remainder of this section, we will discuss a special class of continuous probability distributions known as **normal distributions.** Normal distributions are without a doubt the most important of all the probability distributions. Many phenomena—such as the heights of people in a given population, the weights of newborn infants, the IQs of college students, the actual weights of 16-ounce packages of cereals, and so on—have probability distributions that are normal. The normal distribution also provides us with an accurate approximation to the distributions of many random variables associated with random-sampling problems. In fact, in the next section we will see how a normal distribution may be used to approximate a binomial distribution under certain conditions.

The graph of a normal distribution, which is bell shaped, is called a **normal curve** (Figure 15).

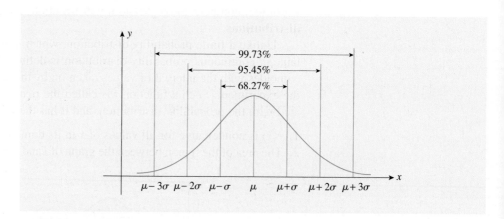

FIGURE **15**
A normal curve

The normal curve (and therefore the corresponding normal distribution) is completely determined by its mean μ and standard deviation σ. In fact, the normal curve has the following characteristics, which are described in terms of these two parameters.*

1. The curve has a peak at $x = \mu$.
2. The curve is symmetric with respect to the vertical line $x = \mu$.
3. The curve always lies above the x-axis but approaches the x-axis as x extends indefinitely in either direction.
4. The area under the curve is 1.
5. For any normal curve, 68.27% of the area under the curve lies within 1 standard deviation of the mean (that is, between $\mu - \sigma$ and $\mu + \sigma$), 95.45% of the area lies within 2 standard deviations of the mean, and 99.73% of the area lies within 3 standard deviations of the mean.

---

*The probability density function associated with this normal curve is given by

$$y = \frac{1}{\sigma\sqrt{2\pi}}\, e^{-(1/2)[(x-\mu)/\sigma]^2}$$

but the direct use of this formula will not be required in our discussion of the normal distribution.

Figure 16 shows two normal curves with different means μ_1 and μ_2 but the same standard deviation. Next, Figure 17 shows two normal curves with the same mean but different standard deviations σ_1 and σ_2. (Which number is smaller?)

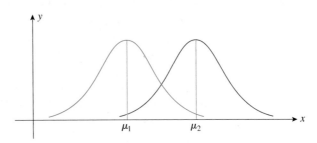

FIGURE 16
Two normal curves that have the same standard deviation but different means

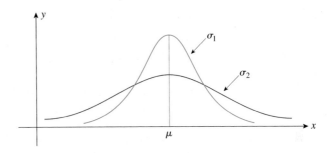

FIGURE 17
Two normal curves that have the same mean but different standard deviations

The mean μ of a normal distribution determines where the center of the curve is located, whereas the standard deviation σ of a normal distribution determines the peakedness (or flatness) of the curve.

As this discussion reveals, there are infinitely many normal curves corresponding to different choices of the parameters μ and σ that characterize such curves. Fortunately, any normal curve may be transformed into any other normal curve (as we will see later), so in the study of normal curves it suffices to single out one such particular curve for special attention. The normal curve with mean $\mu = 0$ and standard deviation $\sigma = 1$ is called the **standard normal curve**. The corresponding distribution is called the **standard normal distribution**. The random variable itself is called the **standard normal random variable** and is commonly denoted by Z.

Exploring with
TECHNOLOGY

Consider the probability density function

$$f(x) = \frac{1}{\sqrt{2\pi}} e^{-x^2/2}$$

which is the formula given in the footnote on page 476 with $\mu = 0$ and $\sigma = 1$.

1. Use a graphing utility to plot the graph of f, using the viewing window $[-4, 4] \times [0, 0.5]$.
2. Use the numerical integration function of a graphing utility to find the area of the region under the graph of f on the intervals $[-1, 1]$, $[-2, 2]$, and $[-3, 3]$, thereby verifying property 5 of normal distributions for the special case in which $\mu = 0$ and $\sigma = 1$.

Computations of Probabilities Associated with Normal Distributions

Areas under the standard normal curve have been extensively computed and tabulated. Table 2, Appendix D, gives the areas of the regions under the standard normal curve to the left of the number z; these areas correspond, of course, to probabilities of the form $P(Z < z)$ or $P(Z \leq z)$. The next several examples illustrate the use of this table in computations involving the probabilities associated with the standard normal variable.

VIDEO

EXAMPLE 1 Let Z be the standard normal variable. Make a sketch of the appropriate region under the standard normal curve, and then find the values of

a. $P(Z < 1.24)$ **b.** $P(Z > 0.5)$
c. $P(0.24 < Z < 1.48)$ **d.** $P(-1.65 < Z < 2.02)$

Solution

FIGURE **18**
$P(Z < 1.24)$

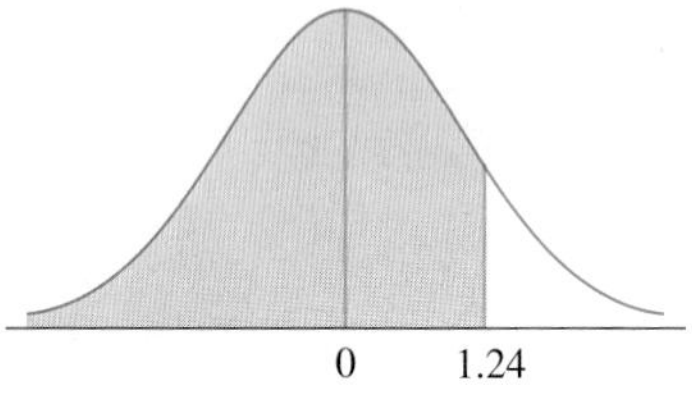

a. The region under the standard normal curve associated with the probability $P(Z < 1.24)$ is shown in Figure 18. To find the area of the required region using Table 2, Appendix D, we first locate the number 1.2 in the column and the number 0.04 in the row, both headed by z, and read off the number 0.8925 appearing in the body of the table. Thus,

$$P(Z < 1.24) = .8925$$

b. The region under the standard normal curve associated with the probability $P(Z > 0.5)$ is shown in Figure 19a. Observe, however, that the required area is, by virtue of the symmetry of the standard normal curve, equal to the shaded area shown in Figure 19b. Thus,

$$\begin{aligned} P(Z > 0.5) &= P(Z < -0.5) \\ &= .3085 \end{aligned}$$

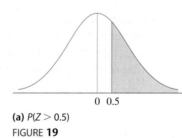

(a) $P(Z > 0.5)$ **(b)** $P(Z < -0.5)$
FIGURE **19**

FIGURE **20**
$P(0.24 < Z < 1.48)$

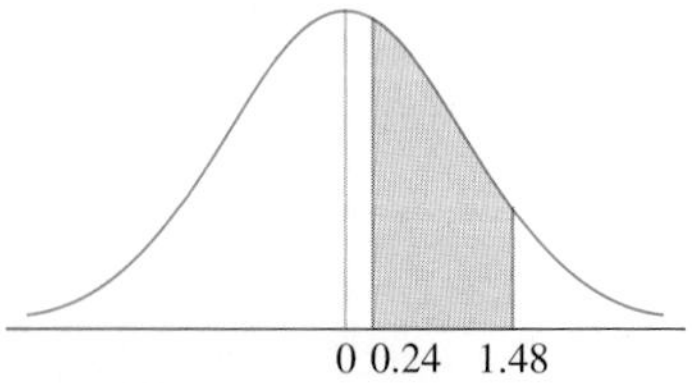

c. The probability $P(0.24 < Z < 1.48)$ is equal to the shaded area shown in Figure 20. This area is obtained by subtracting the area under the curve to the left of $z = 0.24$ from the area under the curve to the left of $z = 1.48$; that is,

$$\begin{aligned} P(0.24 < Z < 1.48) &= P(Z < 1.48) - P(Z < 0.24) \\ &= .9306 - .5948 \\ &= .3358 \end{aligned}$$

FIGURE **21**
$P(-1.65 < Z < 2.02)$

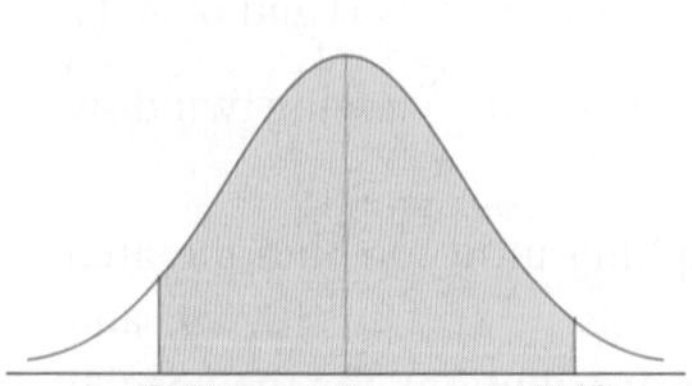

d. The probability $P(-1.65 < Z < 2.02)$ is given by the shaded area shown in Figure 21. We have

$$\begin{aligned} P(-1.65 < Z < 2.02) &= P(Z < 2.02) - P(Z < -1.65) \\ &= .9783 - .0495 \\ &= .9288 \end{aligned}$$

We can calculate the areas under the standard normal curve using the function normalcdf(. This will give a more accurate value than one obtained from the table. To call the function, press [2nd] [VARS], then select 2:normal cdf(. For example, to compute $P(0.24 < Z < 1.48)$, enter

$$\texttt{normalcdf(.24,1.48)}$$

The TI-83/84 screen is shown in Figure 22. The answer (to three decimal places) agrees with the result obtained in Example 1c.

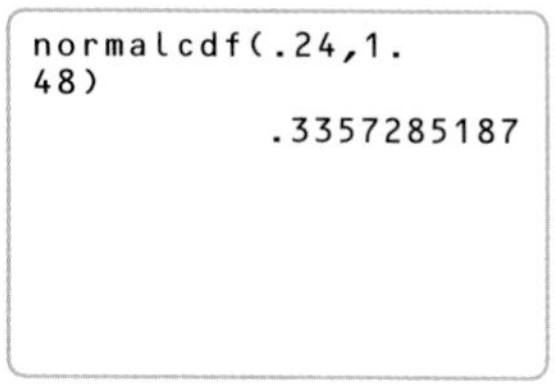

```
normalcdf(.24,1.
48)
            .3357285187
```

FIGURE 22

To find $P(Z < 1.24)$, we write $P(Z < 1.24) = .5 + P(0 < Z < 1.24)$ and enter

$$\texttt{.5+normalcdf(0,1.24)}$$

The TI-83/84 screen is shown in Figure 23. The answer agrees with the result obtained in Example 1a.

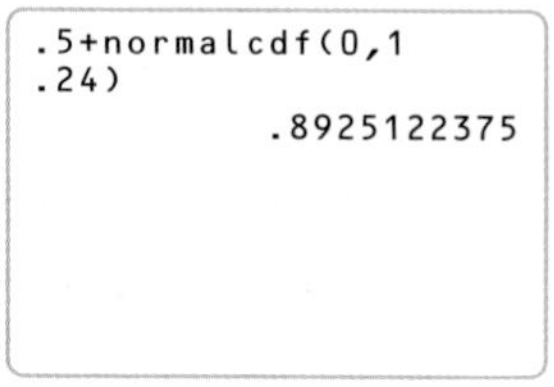

```
.5+normalcdf(0,1
.24)
            .8925122375
```

FIGURE 23

EXAMPLE 2 Let Z be the standard normal random variable. Find the value of z if z satisfies

a. $P(Z < z) = .9474$ **b.** $P(Z > z) = .9115$ **c.** $P(-z < Z < z) = .7888$

Solution

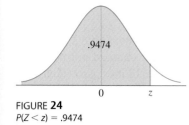

FIGURE 24
$P(Z < z) = .9474$

a. Refer to Figure 24. We want the value of Z such that the area of the region under the standard normal curve and to the left of $Z = z$ is .9474. Locating the number .9474 in Table 2, Appendix D, and reading back, we find that $z = 1.62$.

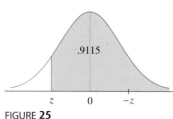

FIGURE 25
$P(Z > z) = .9115$

b. Since $P(Z > z)$, or equivalently, the area of the region to the right of z is greater than 0.5, it follows that z must be negative (Figure 25); hence, $-z$ is positive. Furthermore, the area of the region to the right of z is the same as the area of the region to the left of $-z$. Therefore,

$$P(Z > z) = P(Z < -z)$$
$$= .9115$$

Looking up the table, we find $-z = 1.35$, so $z = -1.35$.

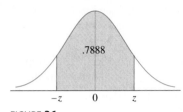

FIGURE **26**
$P(-z < Z < z) = .7888$

c. The region associated with $P(-z < Z < z)$ is shown in Figure 26. Observe that by symmetry, the area of this region is just double that of the area of the region between $Z = 0$ and $Z = z$; that is,

$$P(-z < Z < z) = 2P(0 < Z < z)$$

Furthermore,

$$P(0 < Z < z) = P(Z < z) - \frac{1}{2}$$

(Figure 27). Therefore,

$$\frac{1}{2}P(-z < Z < z) = P(Z < z) - \frac{1}{2}$$

or, solving for $P(Z < z)$, we have

$$P(Z < z) = \frac{1}{2} + \frac{1}{2}P(-z < Z < z)$$

$$= \frac{1}{2}(1 + .7888)$$

$$= .8944$$

Consulting the table, we find $z = 1.25$.

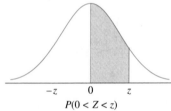

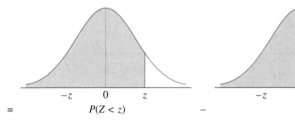

FIGURE **27**

We now turn our attention to the computation of probabilities associated with normal distributions whose means and standard deviations are not necessarily equal to 0 and 1, respectively. As was mentioned earlier, any normal curve may be transformed into the standard normal curve. In particular, it may be shown that if X is a normal random variable with mean μ and standard deviation σ, then it can be transformed into the standard normal random variable Z by means of the substitution

$$Z = \frac{X - \mu}{\sigma}$$

The area of the region under the normal curve (with random variable X) between $x = a$ and $x = b$ is *equal* to the area of the region under the standard normal curve between $z = (a - \mu)/\sigma$ and $z = (b - \mu)/\sigma$. In terms of probabilities associated with these distributions, we have

$$P(a < X < b) = P\left(\frac{a - \mu}{\sigma} < Z < \frac{b - \mu}{\sigma}\right) \tag{16}$$

(Figure 28). Similarly, we have

$$P(X < b) = P\left(Z < \frac{b - \mu}{\sigma}\right) \tag{17}$$

$$P(X > a) = P\left(Z > \frac{a - \mu}{\sigma}\right) \tag{18}$$

Thus, with the help of Equations (16)–(18), computations of probabilities associated with any normal distribution may be reduced to the computations of areas of regions under the standard normal curve.

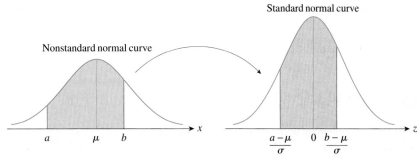

FIGURE 28

Area under the curve between a and b =   Area under the curve between $\dfrac{a-\mu}{\sigma}$ and $\dfrac{b-\mu}{\sigma}$

VIDEO **EXAMPLE 3** Suppose X is a normal random variable with $\mu = 100$ and $\sigma = 20$. Find the values of:

a. $P(X < 120)$ **b.** $P(X > 70)$ **c.** $P(75 < X < 110)$

Solution

a. Using Equation (17) with $\mu = 100$, $\sigma = 20$, and $b = 120$, we have

$$P(X < 120) = P\left(Z < \frac{120 - 100}{20}\right)$$

$$= P(Z < 1) = .8413 \qquad \text{Use the table of values of Z.}$$

b. Using Equation (18) with $\mu = 100$, $\sigma = 20$, and $a = 70$, we have

$$P(X > 70)$$

$$= P\left(Z > \frac{70 - 100}{20}\right)$$

$$= P(Z > -1.5) = P(Z < 1.5) = .9332 \qquad \text{Use the table of values of Z.}$$

c. Using Equation (16) with $\mu = 100$, $\sigma = 20$, $a = 75$, and $b = 110$, we have

$$P(75 < X < 110)$$

$$= P\left(\frac{75 - 100}{20} < Z < \frac{110 - 100}{20}\right)$$

$$= P(-1.25 < Z < 0.5)$$

$$= P(Z < 0.5) - P(Z < -1.25) \qquad \text{See Figure 29.}$$

$$= .6915 - .1056 = .5859 \qquad \text{Use the table of values of Z.}$$

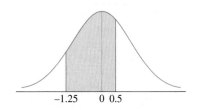

FIGURE 29

8.5 Self-Check Exercises

1. Let Z be a standard normal variable.
   a. Find the value of $P(-1.2 < Z < 2.1)$ by first making a sketch of the appropriate region under the standard normal curve.
   b. Find the value of z if z satisfies $P(-z < Z < z) = .8764$.

2. Let X be a normal random variable with $\mu = 80$ and $\sigma = 10$. Find the values of:
   a. $P(X < 100)$ **b.** $P(X > 60)$ **c.** $P(70 < X < 90)$

Solutions to Self-Check Exercises 8.5 can be found on page 483.

8.5 Concept Questions

1. Consider the following normal curve with mean μ and standard deviation σ:

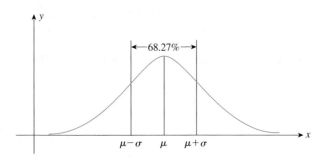

   a. What is the x-coordinate of the peak of the curve?
   b. What can you say about the symmetry of the curve?
   c. Does the curve always lie above the x-axis? What happens to the curve as x extends indefinitely to the left or right?
   d. What is the value of the area under the curve?
   e. Between what values does 68.27% of the area under the curve lie?

2. **a.** What is the difference between a normal curve and a standard normal curve?
   b. If X is a normal random variable with mean μ and standard deviation σ, write $P(a < X < b)$ in terms of the probabilities associated with the standard normal random variable Z.

8.5 Exercises

In Exercises 1–6, find the value of the probability of the standard normal variable Z corresponding to the shaded area under the standard normal curve.

1. $P(Z < 1.45)$

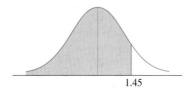

2. $P(Z > 1.11)$

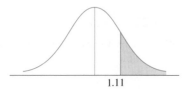

3. $P(Z < -1.75)$

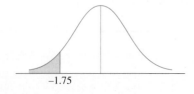

4. $P(0.3 < Z < 1.83)$

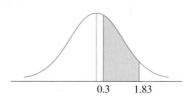

5. $P(-1.32 < Z < 1.74)$

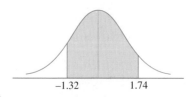

6. $P(-2.35 < Z < -0.51)$

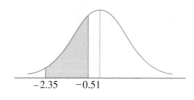

In Exercises 7–14, (a) make a sketch of the area under the standard normal curve corresponding to the probability and (b) find the value of the probability of the standard normal random variable Z corresponding to this area.

7. $P(Z < 1.37)$ **8.** $P(Z > 2.24)$

9. $P(Z < -0.65)$ **10.** $P(0.45 < Z < 1.75)$

11. $P(Z > -1.25)$ **12.** $P(-1.48 < Z < 1.54)$

13. $P(0.68 < Z < 2.02)$ **14.** $P(-1.41 < Z < -0.24)$

15. Let Z be the standard normal variable. Find the values of z if z satisfies:
  a. $P(Z < z) = .8907$ **b.** $P(Z < z) = .2090$

16. Let Z be the standard normal variable. Find the values of z if z satisfies:
  a. $P(Z > z) = .9678$ **b.** $P(-z < Z < z) = .8354$

17. Let Z be the standard normal variable. Find the values of z if z satisfies:
  a. $P(Z > -z) = .9713$ **b.** $P(Z < -z) = .9713$

18. Suppose X is a normal random variable with $\mu = 380$ and $\sigma = 20$. Find the value of:
  a. $P(X < 405)$ **b.** $P(400 < X < 430)$ **c.** $P(X > 400)$

19. Suppose X is a normal random variable with $\mu = 50$ and $\sigma = 5$. Find the value of:
  a. $P(X < 60)$ **b.** $P(X > 43)$ **c.** $P(46 < X < 58)$

20. Suppose X is a normal random variable with $\mu = 500$ and $\sigma = 75$. Find the value of:
  a. $P(X < 750)$ **b.** $P(X > 350)$ **c.** $P(400 < X < 600)$

8.5 Solutions to Self-Check Exercises

1. a. The probability $P(-1.2 < Z < 2.1)$ is given by the shaded area in the accompanying figure:

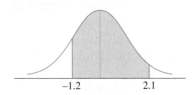

We have
$$P(-1.2 < Z < 2.1) = P(Z < 2.1) - P(Z < -1.2)$$
$$= .9821 - .1151$$
$$= .867$$

b. The region associated with $P(-z < Z < z)$ is shown in the accompanying figure:

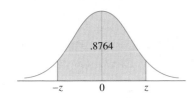

Observe that we have the following relationship:
$$P(Z < z) = \frac{1}{2}[1 + P(-z < Z < z)]$$

(see Example 2c). With $P(-z < Z < z) = .8764$, we find that
$$P(Z < z) = \frac{1}{2}(1 + .8764)$$
$$= .9382$$

Consulting the table, we find $z = 1.54$.

2. Using the transformation (16) and the table of values of Z, we have

a. $P(X < 100) = P\left(Z < \dfrac{100 - 80}{10}\right)$
  $= P(Z < 2)$
  $= .9772$

b. $P(X > 60) = P\left(Z > \dfrac{60 - 80}{10}\right)$
  $= P(Z > -2)$
  $= P(Z < 2)$
  $= .9772$

c. $P(70 < X < 90) = P\left(\dfrac{70 - 80}{10} < Z < \dfrac{90 - 80}{10}\right)$
  $= P(-1 < Z < 1)$
  $= P(Z < 1) - P(Z < -1)$
  $= .8413 - .1587$
  $= .6826$

8.6   Applications of the Normal Distribution

Applications Involving Normal Random Variables

In this section, we look at some applications involving the normal distribution.

APPLIED EXAMPLE 1   Birth Weights of Infants The medical records of infants delivered at the Kaiser Memorial Hospital show that the infants' birth weights in pounds are normally distributed with a mean of 7.4 and a standard deviation of 1.2. Find the probability that an infant selected at random from among those delivered at the hospital weighed more than 9.2 pounds at birth.

Solution   Let X be the normal random variable denoting the birth weights of infants delivered at the hospital. Then the probability that an infant selected at random has a birth weight of more than 9.2 pounds is given by $P(X > 9.2)$. To compute $P(X > 9.2)$, we use Equation (18), Section 8.5, with $\mu = 7.4$, $\sigma = 1.2$, and $a = 9.2$. We find that

$$P(X > 9.2) = P\left(Z > \frac{9.2 - 7.4}{1.2}\right) \qquad P(X > a) = P\left(Z > \frac{a - \mu}{\sigma}\right)$$
$$= P(Z > 1.5)$$
$$= P(Z < -1.5)$$
$$= .0668$$

Thus, the probability that an infant delivered at the hospital weighs more than 9.2 pounds is .0668.

APPLIED EXAMPLE 2   Packaging Idaho Natural Produce Corporation ships potatoes to its distributors in bags whose weights are normally distributed with a mean weight of 50 pounds and standard deviation of 0.5 pound. If a bag of potatoes is selected at random from a shipment, what is the probability that it weighs:

a. More than 51 pounds?
b. Less than 49 pounds?
c. Between 49 and 51 pounds?

Solution   Let X denote the weight of potatoes packed by the company. Then the mean and standard deviation of X are $\mu = 50$ and $\sigma = 0.5$, respectively.

a. The probability that a bag selected at random weighs more than 51 pounds is given by

$$P(X > 51) = P\left(Z > \frac{51 - 50}{0.5}\right) \qquad P(X > a) = P\left(Z > \frac{a - \mu}{\sigma}\right)$$
$$= P(Z > 2)$$
$$= P(Z < -2)$$
$$= .0228$$

b. The probability that a bag selected at random weighs less than 49 pounds is given by

$$P(X < 49) = P\left(Z < \frac{49 - 50}{0.5}\right) \qquad P(X < b) = P\left(Z < \frac{b - \mu}{\sigma}\right)$$
$$= P(Z < -2)$$
$$= .0228$$

c. The probability that a bag selected at random weighs between 49 and 51 pounds is given by

$$P(49 < X < 51)$$

$$= P\left(\frac{49 - 50}{0.5} < Z < \frac{51 - 50}{0.5}\right) \qquad \begin{array}{l} P(a < X < b) \\ = P\left(\frac{a - \mu}{\sigma} < Z < \frac{b - \mu}{\sigma}\right) \end{array}$$

$$= P(-2 < Z < 2)$$

$$= P(Z < 2) - P(Z < -2)$$

$$= .9772 - .0228$$

$$= .9544$$

VIDEO ▶ **APPLIED EXAMPLE 3** College Admissions The grade point average (GPA) of the senior class of Jefferson High School is normally distributed with a mean of 2.7 and a standard deviation of 0.4. If a senior in the top 10% of his or her class is eligible for admission to any of the nine campuses of the state university system, what is the minimum GPA that a senior should have to ensure eligibility for university admission?

Solution Let X denote the GPA of a randomly selected senior at Jefferson High School, and let x denote the minimum GPA that will ensure his or her eligibility for admission to the university. Since only the top 10% are eligible for admission, x must satisfy the equation

$$P(X \geq x) = .1$$

Using Equation (18), Section 8.5, with $\mu = 2.7$ and $\sigma = 0.4$, we find that

$$P(X \geq x) = P\left(Z \geq \frac{x - 2.7}{0.4}\right) = .1 \qquad P(X > a) = P\left(Z > \frac{a - \mu}{\sigma}\right)$$

This is equivalent to the equation

$$P\left(Z < \frac{x - 2.7}{0.4}\right) = .9 \qquad \text{Why?}$$

Consulting Table 2, Appendix D, we find that

$$\frac{x - 2.7}{0.4} = 1.28$$

Upon solving for x, we obtain

$$x = (1.28)(0.4) + 2.7$$

$$\approx 3.2$$

Thus, to ensure eligibility for admission to one of the nine campuses of the state university system, a senior at Jefferson High School should have a minimum of 3.2 GPA.

Approximating Binomial Distributions

As was mentioned in the last section, one important application of the normal distribution is that it provides us with an accurate approximation of other continuous probability distributions. Here, we show how a binomial distribution may be approximated by a suitable normal distribution. This technique leads to a convenient and simple solution to certain problems involving binomial probabilities.

Recall that a binomial distribution is a probability distribution of the form

$$P(X = x) = C(n, x)p^x q^{n-x} \qquad x = 0, 1, 2, \ldots, n \qquad \textbf{(19)}$$

(See Section 8.4.) For small values of n, the arithmetic computations of the binomial probabilities may be done with relative ease. However, if n is large, then the work involved becomes prodigious, even when tables of $P(X = x)$ are available. For example, if $n = 50$, $p = .3$, and $q = .7$, then the probability of ten or more successes is given by

$$P(X \geq 10) = P(X = 10) + P(X = 11) + \cdots + P(X = 50)$$

$$= \frac{50!}{10!\,40!}(.3)^{10}(.7)^{40} + \frac{50!}{11!\,39!}(.3)^{11}(.7)^{39} + \cdots + \frac{50!}{50!\,0!}(.3)^{50}(.7)^{0}$$

TABLE 13

Probability Distribution

x	$P(X = x)$
0	.0000
1	.0000
2	.0002
3	.0011
4	.0046
5	.0148
6	.0370
7	.0739
8	.1201
9	.1602
10	.1762
11	.1602
12	.1201
.	.
.	.
.	.
20	.0000

To see how the normal distribution helps us in such situations, let's consider a coin-tossing experiment. Suppose a fair coin is tossed 20 times and we wish to compute the probability of obtaining 10 or more heads. The solution to this problem may be obtained, of course, by computing

$$P(X \geq 10) = P(X = 10) + P(X = 11) + \cdots + P(X = 20)$$

The inconvenience of this approach for solving the problem at hand has already been pointed out. As an alternative solution, let's begin by interpreting the solution in terms of finding the area of suitable rectangles of the histogram for the distribution associated with the problem. We may use Equation (19) to compute the probability of obtaining exactly x heads in 20 coin tosses. The results lead to the binomial distribution displayed in Table 13.

Using the data from the table, we next construct the histogram for the distribution (Figure 30). The probability of obtaining 10 or more heads in 20 coin tosses is equal to the sum of the areas of the shaded rectangles of the histogram of the binomial distribution shown in Figure 31.

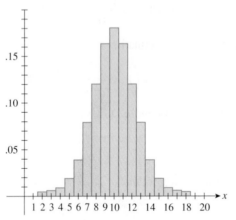

FIGURE **30**
Histogram showing the probability of obtaining x heads in 20 coin tosses

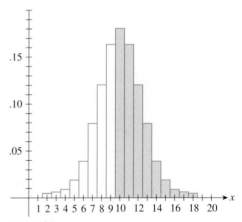

FIGURE **31**
The shaded area gives the probability of obtaining 10 or more heads in 20 coin tosses.

Next, observe that the shape of the histogram suggests that the binomial distribution under consideration may be approximated by a suitable normal distribution. Since the mean and standard deviation of the binomial distribution are given by

$$\mu = np$$
$$= (20)(.5) = 10$$
$$\sigma = \sqrt{npq}$$
$$= \sqrt{(20)(.5)(.5)}$$
$$= 2.24$$

respectively (see Section 8.4), the natural choice of a normal curve for this purpose is one with a mean of 10 and standard deviation of 2.24. Figure 32 shows such a normal curve superimposed on the histogram of the binomial distribution.

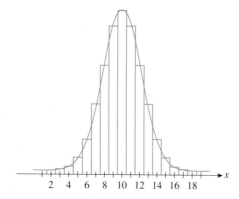

FIGURE 32
Normal curve superimposed on the histogram for a binomial distribution

The good fit suggests that the sum of the areas of the rectangles representing $P(X \geq 10)$, the probability of obtaining 10 or more heads in 20 coin tosses, may be approximated by the area of an appropriate region under the normal curve. To determine this region, let's note that the base of the portion of the histogram representing the required probability extends from $x = 9.5$ on, since the base of the leftmost rectangle in the shaded region is centered at $x = 10$ and the base of each rectangle has length 1 (Figure 33). Therefore, the required region under the normal curve should also have $x \geq 9.5$. Letting Y denote the continuous normal variable, we obtain

$$P(X \geq 10) \approx P(Y \geq 9.5)$$
$$= P(Y > 9.5)$$
$$\approx P\left(Z > \frac{9.5 - 10}{2.24}\right) \qquad P(X > a) = P\left(Z > \frac{a - \mu}{\sigma}\right)$$
$$\approx P(Z > -0.22)$$
$$= P(Z < 0.22)$$
$$= .5871 \qquad \text{Use the table of values of } Z.$$

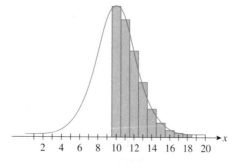

FIGURE 33
$P(X \geq 10)$ is approximated by the area under the normal curve.

The exact value of $P(X \geq 10)$ may be found by computing

$$P(X = 10) + P(X = 11) + \cdots + P(X = 20)$$

in the usual fashion and is equal to .5881. Thus, the normal distribution with suitably chosen mean and standard deviation does provide us with a good approximation of the binomial distribution.

In the general case, the following result, which is a special case of the *central limit theorem*, guarantees the accuracy of the approximation of a binomial distribution by a normal distribution under certain conditions.

THEOREM 1

Suppose we are given a binomial distribution associated with a binomial experiment involving n trials, each with a probability of success p and probability of failure q. Then, if n is large and p is not close to 0 or 1, the binomial distribution may be approximated by a normal distribution with

$$\mu = np \quad \text{and} \quad \sigma = \sqrt{npq}$$

Note   It can be shown that if both np and nq are greater than 5, then the error resulting from this approximation is negligible.   ■

Applications Involving Binomial Random Variables

Next, we look at some applications involving binomial random variables.

APPLIED EXAMPLE 4 Quality Control An automobile manufacturer receives the microprocessors that are used to regulate fuel consumption in its automobiles in shipments of 1000 each from a certain supplier. It has been estimated that, on the average, 1% of the microprocessors manufactured by the supplier are defective. Determine the probability that more than 20 of the microprocessors in a single shipment are defective.

Solution   Let X denote the number of defective microprocessors in a single shipment. Then X has a binomial distribution with $n = 1000$, $p = .01$, and $q = .99$, so

$$\mu = (1000)(.01) = 10$$
$$\sigma = \sqrt{(1000)(.01)(.99)}$$
$$\approx 3.15$$

Approximating the binomial distribution by a normal distribution with a mean of 10 and a standard deviation of 3.15, we find that the probability that more than 20 microprocessors in a shipment are defective is given by

$$P(X > 20) \approx P(Y > 20.5) \qquad \text{Where } Y \text{ denotes the normal random variable}$$
$$= P\left(Z > \frac{20.5 - 10}{3.15}\right) \quad P(X > a) = P\left(Z > \frac{a - \mu}{\sigma}\right)$$
$$\approx P(Z > 3.33)$$
$$\approx P(Z < -3.33)$$
$$= .0004$$

In other words, approximately 0.04% of the shipments containing 1000 microprocessors each will contain more than 20 defective units.   ■

VIDEO

APPLIED EXAMPLE 5 Heart Transplant Survival Rate The probability that a heart transplant performed at the Medical Center is successful (that is, the patient survives 1 year or more after undergoing the surgery) is .7. Of 100 patients who have undergone such an operation, what is the probability that:

a. Fewer than 75 will survive 1 year or more after the operation?
b. Between 80 and 90, inclusive, will survive 1 year or more after the operation?

Solution   Let X denote the number of patients who survive 1 year or more after undergoing a heart transplant at the Medical Center; then X is a binomial random variable. Also, $n = 100$, $p = .7$, and $q = .3$, so

$$\mu = (100)(.7) = 70$$
$$\sigma = \sqrt{(100)(.7)(.3)}$$
$$\approx 4.58$$

Approximating the binomial distribution by a normal distribution with a mean of 70 and a standard deviation of 4.58, we find, upon letting Y denote the associated normal random variable:

a. The probability that fewer than 75 patients will survive 1 year or more is given by

$$P(X < 75) \approx P(Y < 74.5) \qquad \text{Why?}$$
$$\approx P\left(Z < \frac{74.5 - 70}{4.58}\right) \qquad P(X < b) = P\left(Z < \frac{b - \mu}{\sigma}\right)$$
$$\approx P(Z < 0.98)$$
$$= .8365$$

b. The probability that between 80 and 90 patients, inclusive, will survive 1 year or more is given by

$$P(80 \le X \le 90)$$
$$\approx P(79.5 < Y < 90.5)$$
$$\approx P\left(\frac{79.5 - 70}{4.58} < Z < \frac{90.5 - 70}{4.58}\right) \qquad \begin{array}{l} P(a < X < b) \\ = P\left(\dfrac{a - \mu}{\sigma} < Z < \dfrac{b - \mu}{\sigma}\right) \end{array}$$
$$\approx P(2.07 < Z < 4.48)$$
$$= P(Z < 4.48) - P(Z < 2.07)$$
$$= 1 - .9808 \qquad \text{Note: } P(Z < 4.48) \approx 1$$
$$= .0192$$

8.6   Self-Check Exercises

1. The serum cholesterol levels in milligrams per decaliter (mg/dL) in a current Mediterranean population are found to be normally distributed with a mean of 160 and a standard deviation of 50. Scientists at the National Heart, Lung, and Blood Institute consider this pattern ideal for a minimal risk of heart attacks. Find the percentage of the population having blood cholesterol levels between 160 and 180 mg/dL.

2. It has been estimated that 4% of the luggage manufactured by The Luggage Company fails to meet the standards established by the company and is sold as "seconds" to discount and outlet stores. If 500 bags are produced, what is the probability that more than 30 will be classified as "seconds"?

Solutions to Self-Check Exercises 8.6 can be found on page 491.

8.6   Concept Questions

1. What does the central limit theorem allow us to do?

2. Suppose a binomial distribution is associated with a binomial experiment involving n trials, each with a probability of success p and probability of failure q, and suppose n and

p satisfy the other conditions given in the central limit theorem. What are the formulas for μ and σ that can be used to approximate this binomial distribution by a normal distribution?

8.6   Exercises

1. **MEDICAL RECORDS** The medical records of infants delivered at Kaiser Memorial Hospital show that the infants' lengths at birth (in inches) are normally distributed with a mean of 20 and a standard deviation of 2.6. Find the probability that an infant selected at random from among those delivered at the hospital measures:
   a. More than 22 in.
   b. Less than 18 in.
   c. Between 19 and 21 in.

2. **FACTORY WORKERS' WAGES** According to the data released by the Chamber of Commerce of a certain city, the weekly wages of factory workers are normally distributed with a mean of $720 and a standard deviation of $60. What is the probability that a factory worker selected at random from the city makes a weekly wage:
   a. Of less than $720?   b. Of more than $912?
   c. Between $660 and $780?

3. **PRODUCT RELIABILITY** TKK Products manufactures 50-, 60-, 75-, and 100-watt electric light bulbs. Laboratory tests show that the lives of these light bulbs are normally distributed with a mean of 750 hr and a standard deviation of 75 hr. What is the probability that a TKK light bulb selected at random will burn:
   a. For more than 900 hr?
   b. For less than 600 hr?
   c. Between 750 and 900 hr?
   d. Between 600 and 800 hr?

4. **EDUCATION** On average, a student takes dictation at a speed of 100 words/minute midway through an advanced court reporting course at the American Institute of Court Reporting. Assuming that the dictation speeds of the students are normally distributed and that the standard deviation is 20 words/minute, what is the probability that a student randomly selected from the course can take dictation at a speed:
   a. Of more than 120 words/minute?
   b. Between 80 and 120 words/minute?
   c. Of less than 80 words/minute?

5. **IQs** The IQs of students at Wilson Elementary School were measured recently and found to be normally distributed with a mean of 100 and a standard deviation of 15. What is the probability that a student selected at random will have an IQ:
   a. Of 140 or higher?   b. Of 120 or higher?
   c. Between 100 and 120?   d. Of 90 or less?

6. **PRODUCT RELIABILITY** The tread lives of the Super Titan radial tires under normal driving conditions are normally distributed with a mean of 40,000 mi and a standard deviation of 2000 mi. What is the probability that a tire selected at random will have a tread life of more than 35,000 mi? Determine the probability that four tires selected at random still have useful tread lives after 35,000 mi of driving. (Assume that the tread lives of the tires are independent of each other.)

7. **FEMALE FACTORY WORKERS' WAGES** According to data released by the Chamber of Commerce of a certain city, the weekly wages (in dollars) of female factory workers are normally distributed with a mean of 575 and a standard deviation of 50. Find the probability that a female factory worker selected at random from the city makes a weekly wage of $550 to $650.

8. **CIVIL SERVICE EXAMS** To be eligible for further consideration, applicants for certain civil service positions must first pass a written qualifying examination on which a score of 70 or more must be obtained. In a recent examination, it was found that the scores were normally distributed with a mean of 60 points and a standard deviation of 10 points. Determine the percentage of applicants who passed the written qualifying examination.

9. **WARRANTIES** The general manager of the service department of MCA Television has estimated that the time that elapses between the dates of purchase and the dates on which the 50-in. plasma TVs manufactured by the company first require service is normally distributed with a mean of 22 months and a standard deviation of 4 months. If the company gives a 1-year warranty on parts and labor for these TVs, determine the percentage of these TVs manufactured and sold by the company that will require service before the warranty period runs out.

10. **GRADE DISTRIBUTIONS** The scores on an economics examination are normally distributed with a mean of 72 and a standard deviation of 16. If the instructor assigns a grade of A to 10% of the class, what is the lowest score a student may have and still obtain an A?

11. **GRADE DISTRIBUTIONS** The scores on a sociology examination are normally distributed with a mean of 70 and a standard deviation of 10. If the instructor assigns As to 15%, Bs to 25%, Cs to 40%, Ds to 15%, and Fs to 5% of the class, find the cutoff points for grades A–D.

12. **HIGHWAY SPEEDS** The speeds (in miles per hour) of motor vehicles on a certain stretch of Route 3A as clocked at a certain place along the highway are normally distributed with a mean of 64.2 mph and a standard deviation of 8.44 mph. What is the probability that a motor vehicle selected at random is traveling at:
    a. More than 65 mph?
    b. Less than 60 mph?
    c. Between 65 and 70 mph?

In Exercises 13–24, use the appropriate normal distributions to approximate the resulting binomial distributions.

13. A coin is weighted so that the probability of obtaining a head in a single toss is .4. If the coin is tossed 25 times, what is the probability of obtaining:
    a. Fewer than 10 heads?
    b. Between 10 and 12 heads, inclusive?
    c. More than 15 heads?

14. A fair coin is tossed 20 times. What is the probability of obtaining
  a. Fewer than 8 heads?
  b. More than 6 heads?
  c. Between 6 and 10 heads inclusive?

15. **SPORTS** A marksman's chance of hitting a target with each of his shots is 60%. (Assume that the shots are independent of each other.) If he fires 30 shots, what is the probability of his hitting the target
  a. At least 20 times?
  b. Fewer than 10 times?
  c. Between 15 and 20 times, inclusive?

16. **SPORTS** A basketball player has a 75% chance of making a free throw. (Assume that the throws are independent of each other.) What is the probability of her making 100 or more free throws in 120 trials?

17. **QUALITY CONTROL** The manager of C & R Clothiers, a manufacturer of men's dress shirts, has determined that 3% of C & R's shirts do not meet company standards and are sold as "seconds" to discount and outlet stores. What is the probability that in a production run of 200 shirts, fewer than 10 will be classified as "seconds"?

18. **TELEMARKETING** Jorge sells magazine subscriptions over the phone. He estimates that the probability of his making a sale with each attempt is .12. What is the probability of Jorge making more than 10 sales if he makes 80 calls?

19. **INDUSTRIAL ACCIDENTS** Colorado Mining and Mineral has 800 employees engaged in its mining operations. It has been estimated that the probability of a worker meeting with an accident during a 1-year period is .1. What is the probability that more than 70 workers will meet with an accident during the 1-year period?

20. **QUALITY CONTROL** PAR Bearings is the principal supplier of ball bearings for the Sperry Gyroscope Company. It has been determined that 6% of the ball bearings shipped are rejected because they fail to meet tolerance requirements. What is the probability that a shipment of 200 ball bearings contains more than 10 rejects?

21. **DRUG TESTING** An experiment was conducted to test the effectiveness of a new drug in treating a certain disease. The drug was administered to 50 mice that had been previously exposed to the disease. It was found that 35 mice subsequently recovered from the disease. It has been determined that the natural recovery rate from the disease is 0.5.
  a. Determine the probability that 35 or more of the mice not treated with the drug would recover from the disease.
  b. Using the results obtained in part (a), comment on the effectiveness of the drug in the treatment of the disease.

22. **LOAN DELINQUENCIES** The manager of Madison Finance Company has estimated that, because of a recession year, 5% of its 400 loan accounts will be delinquent. If the manager's estimate is correct, what is the probability that 25 or more of the accounts will be delinquent?

23. **CRUISE SHIP BOOKINGS** Because of late cancellations, Neptune Lines, an operator of cruise ships, has a policy of accepting more reservations than there are accommodations available. From experience, 8% of the bookings for the 90-day around-the-world cruise on the S.S. *Drion*, which has accommodations for 2000 passengers, are subsequently canceled. If the management of Neptune Lines has decided, for public relations reasons, that 99% of all booked passengers will obtain accommodation on the ship, determine the largest number of reservations that should be taken for this cruise on the S.S. *Drion*.

24. **THEATER BOOKINGS** Preview Showcase, a research firm, screens pilots of new TV shows before a randomly selected audience and then solicits the audience members' opinions of the shows. Based on past experience, 20% of those who receive complimentary tickets are "no-shows." The theater has a seating capacity of 500. Management has decided, for public relations reasons, that 99% of all ticket holders will be seated. How many tickets should the company send out to prospective viewers for each screening?

8.6 Solutions to Self-Check Exercises

1. Let X be the normal random variable denoting the serum cholesterol levels in milligrams per deciliter in the current Mediterranean population under consideration. Then the percentage of the population having blood cholesterol levels between 160 and 180 mg/dL is given by $P(160 < X < 180)$. To compute $P(160 < X < 180)$, we use Equation (16), Section 8.5, with $\mu = 160$, $\sigma = 50$, $a = 160$, and $b = 180$. We find

$$P(160 < X < 180) = P\left(\frac{160 - 160}{50} < Z < \frac{180 - 160}{50}\right)$$
$$= P(0 < Z < 0.4)$$
$$= P(Z < 0.4) - P(Z < 0)$$
$$= .6554 - .5000$$
$$= .1554$$

Thus, approximately 15.5% of the population has blood cholesterol levels between 160 and 180 mg/dL.

2. Let X denote the number of substandard bags in the production. Then X has a binomial distribution with $n = 500$, $p = .04$, and $q = .96$, so

$$\mu = (500)(.04) = 20$$
$$\sigma = \sqrt{(500)(.04)(.96)} \approx 4.38$$

Approximating the binomial distribution by a normal distribution with a mean of 20 and standard deviation of 4.38, we find that the probability that more than 30 bags in the production of 500 will be substandard is given by

$$P(X > 30) \approx P(Y > 30.5)$$

Where Y denotes the normal random variable

$$\approx P\left(Z > \frac{30.5 - 20}{4.38}\right)$$
$$\approx P(Z > 2.40)$$
$$= P(Z < -2.40)$$
$$= .0082$$

or approximately 0.8%.

| CHAPTER 8 | Summary of Principal Formulas and Terms |

FORMULAS

1. Mean of n numbers	$\bar{x} = \dfrac{x_1 + x_2 + \cdots + x_n}{n}$
2. Expected value	$E(X) = x_1 p_1 + x_2 p_2 + \cdots + x_n p_n$
3. Odds in favor of E occurring	$\dfrac{P(E)}{P(E^c)}$
4. Odds against E occurring	$\dfrac{P(E^c)}{P(E)}$
5. Probability of an event occurring given the odds	$\dfrac{a}{a + b}$
6. Variance of a random variable	$\mathrm{Var}(X) = p_1(x_1 - \mu)^2$ $+ p_2(x_2 - \mu)^2 + \cdots$ $+ p_n(x_n - \mu)^2$
7. Standard deviation of a random variable	$\sigma = \sqrt{\mathrm{Var}(X)}$
8. Chebychev's inequality	$P(\mu - k\sigma \leq X \leq \mu + k\sigma)$ $\geq 1 - \dfrac{1}{k^2}$
9. Probability of x successes in n Bernoulli trials	$C(n, x)p^x q^{n-x}$
10. Binomial random variable: Mean Variance Standard deviation	$\mu = E(X) = np$ $\mathrm{Var}(X) = npq$ $\sigma_X = \sqrt{npq}$

TERMS

random variable (428)

finite discrete random variable (429)

infinite discrete random variable (429)

continuous random variable (429)

probability distribution of a random variable (429)

histogram (431)

average (mean) (439)

expected value (440)

median (447)

mode (447)

variance (453)

standard deviation (454)

Bernoulli (binomial) trial (465)

binomial experiment (465)

binomial random variable (467)

binomial distribution (467)

probability density function (475)

normal distribution (476)

CHAPTER 8   Concept Review Questions

Fill in the blanks.

1. A rule that assigns a number to each outcome of a chance experiment is called a/an _____ variable.

2. If a random variable assumes only finitely many values, then it is called _____ discrete; if it takes on infinitely many values that can be arranged in a sequence, then it is called _____ discrete; if it takes on all real numbers in an interval, then it is said to be _____.

3. The expected value of a random variable X is given by the _____ of the products of the values assumed by the random variable and their associated probabilities. For example, if X assumes the values -2, 3, and 4 with associated probabilities $\frac{1}{2}$, $\frac{1}{4}$, and $\frac{1}{4}$, then its expected value is _____.

4. **a.** If the probability of an event E occurring is $P(E)$, then the odds in favor of E occurring are _____.
   b. If the odds in favor of an event E occurring are a to b, then the probability of E occurring is _____.

5. Suppose a random variable X takes on the values x_1, x_2, $\ldots$, x_n with probabilities p_1, p_2, $\ldots$, p_n and has a mean of μ. Then the variance of X is _____, and the standard deviation of X is _____.

6. In a binomial experiment, the number of trials is _____, there are exactly _____ outcomes in each trial, the probability of "success" in each trial is the _____, and the trials are _____ of each other.

7. A probability distribution that is associated with a continuous random variable is called a/an _____ probability distribution. Such a probability distribution is defined by a/an _____ _____ _____ whose domain is the _____ of values taken on by the random variable associated with the experiment.

8. A binomial distribution may be approximated by a/an _____ distribution with $\mu = np$ and $\sigma = \sqrt{npq}$ if n is _____ and p is not close to _____ or _____.

CHAPTER 8   Review Exercises

1. Three balls are selected at random without replacement from an urn containing three white balls and four blue balls. Let the random variable X denote the number of blue balls drawn.
   a. List the outcomes of this experiment.
   b. Find the value assigned to each outcome of this experiment by the random variable X.
   c. Find the probability distribution of the random variable associated with this experiment.
   d. Draw the histogram representing this distribution.

2. **LIFE INSURANCE POLICIES** A man purchased a $25,000, 1-year term-life insurance policy for $375. Assuming that the probability that he will live for another year is .989, find the company's expected gain.

3. The probability distribution of a random variable X is shown in the following table:

x	$P(X = x)$
0	.1
1	.1
2	.2
3	.3
4	.2
5	.1

   a. Compute $P(1 \le X \le 4)$.
   b. Compute the mean and standard deviation of X.

4. A binomial experiment consists of four trials in which the probability of success in any one trial is $\frac{2}{5}$.
   a. Construct the probability distribution for the experiment.
   b. Compute the mean and standard deviation of the probability distribution.

In Exercises 5–8, let Z be the standard normal variable. Make a rough sketch of the appropriate region under the standard normal curve, and find the probability.

5. $P(Z < 0.5)$ 6. $P(Z < -0.75)$

7. $P(-0.75 < Z < 0.5)$ 8. $P(-0.42 < Z < 0.66)$

In Exercises 9–12, let Z be the standard normal variable. Find z if z satisfies the given value.

9. $P(Z < z) = .9922$ 10. $P(Z < z) = .1469$

11. $P(Z > z) = .9788$

12. $P(-z < Z < z) = .8444$

In Exercises 13–16, let X be a normal random variable with $\mu = 10$ and $\sigma = 2$. Find the value of the given probability.

13. $P(X < 11)$ 14. $P(X > 8)$

15. $P(7 < X < 9)$ 16. $P(6.5 < X < 11.5)$

17. **TRAFFIC** A traffic survey of the speeds of vehicles traveling along a stretch of Hampton Road between 4 P.M. and 6 P.M. yielded the following results:

Speed, mph	30–34	35–39	40–44	45–49	50–54
Probability	.07	.28	.42	.18	.05

Find the average speed of the vehicles.
Hint: Assume that all speeds lying within a group interval take the midvalue of that group.

18. **EXPECTED PROFIT** A buyer for Discount Fashions, an outlet for women's apparel, is considering buying a batch of clothing for $64,000. She estimates that the company will be able

to sell it for $80,000, $75,000, or $70,000 with probabilities of .30, .60, and .10, respectively. On the basis of these estimates, what will be the company's expected gross profit?

19. **Sports** If the probability that a bowler will bowl a strike is .7, what is the probability that he will get exactly two strikes in four attempts? At least two strikes in four attempts? (Assume that the attempts to bowl a strike are independent of each other.)

20. **Heights of Women** The heights of 4000 women who participated in a recent survey were found to be normally distributed with a mean of 64.5 in. and a standard deviation of 2.5 in. What percentage of these women have heights of 67 in. or greater?

21. **Heights of Women** Refer to Exercise 20. Use Chebychev's inequality to estimate the probability that the height of a woman who participated in the survey will fall within 2 standard deviations of the mean—that is, that her height will be between 59.5 and 69.5 in.

22. **Volkswagen's Revenue** The revenue of Volkswagen (in billions of Euros) for the five quarters beginning with the first quarter of 2009 are summarized in the following table:

	2009				2010
Quarter	Q1	Q2	Q3	Q4	Q1
Revenue	24.0	27.2	26.0	28.0	28.6

Find the average quarterly revenue of Volkswagen for the five quarters in question. What is the standard deviation?

Source: Company reports.

23. **Marital Status of Women** The number of single women (in thousands) between the ages of 20 and 44 in the United States in 1998 is given in the following table:

Age	20–24	25–29	30–34	35–39	40–44
Women	6178	3689	2219	1626	1095

Find the mean and the standard deviation of the given data. Hint: Assume that all values lying within a group interval take the middle value of that group.

Source: U.S. Census Bureau.

24. **Quality Control** The proprietor of a hardware store will accept a shipment of ceramic wall tiles if no more than 2 tiles of a random sample of 20 are found to be defective.

What is the probability that he will accept shipment if exactly 10% of the tiles in a certain shipment is defective?

25. **Drug Effectiveness** An experimental drug has been found to be effective in treating 15% of the people afflicted by a certain disease. If the drug is administered to 800 people who have this disease, what are the mean and standard deviation of the number of people for whom the drug can be expected to be effective?

26. **Quality Control** Dayton Iron Works manufactures steel rods to a specification of 1-in. diameter. These rods are accepted by the buyer if they fall within the tolerance limits of 0.995 and 1.005. Assuming that the diameter of the rods is normally distributed about a mean of 1 in. and has a standard deviation of 0.002 in., estimate the percentage of rods that will be rejected by the buyer.

27. **Expected Sales** The division manager of a company claims that 80% of her sales representatives will make or exceed their sales quota in the following month. Assuming that the manager's assessment is correct, what is the probability that the sales quota will be made or exceeded by:
   a. Four of the six sales representatives?
   b. At least four of the sales representatives?

28. **On-Time Arrivals** Diane, who commutes regularly between Los Angeles and San Francisco for business, estimates that the probability that her flight will arrive on time or earlier is .92. Assuming that her assessment is accurate, what is the probability that her flight will arrive on time or earlier:
   a. In three of her next five flights?
   b. In at least three of her next five flights?

29. **Coin Tosses** A coin is biased so that the probability of it landing heads is .6. If the coin is tossed 100 times, what is the probability that heads will appear more than 50 times in the 100 tosses?

30. **Quality Control** A division of Solaron Corporation manufactures photovoltaic cells for use in the company's solar energy converters. It is estimated that 5% of the cells manufactured are defective. In a batch of 200 cells manufactured by the company, what is the probability that it will contain at most 20 defective units?

CHAPTER 8   Before Moving On . . .

1. The values taken on by a random variable X and the frequency of their occurrence are shown in the following table. Find the probability distribution of X.

x	-3	-2	0	1	2	3
Frequency of Occurrence	4	8	20	24	16	8

2. The probability distribution of the random variable X is shown in the following table. Find (a) $P(X \le 0)$ and (b) $P(-4 \le X \le 1)$.

x	-4	-3	-1	0	1	3
$P(X = x)$	.06	.14	.32	.28	.12	.08

3. Find the mean, variance, and standard deviation of a random variable X having the following probability distribution:

x	-3	-1	0	1	3	5
$P(X = x)$	.08	.24	.32	.16	.12	.08

4. A binomial experiment consists of four independent trials, and the probability of success in each trial is 0.3.

  a. Find the probability of obtaining 0, 1, 2, 3, and 4 successes, respectively.

  b. Compute the mean and standard deviation of the random variable associated with this experiment.

5. Let X be a normal random variable with $\mu = 60$ and $\sigma = 5$. Find the values of (a) $P(X < 70)$, (b) $P(X > 50)$, and (c) $P(50 < X < 70)$.

6. A fair coin is tossed 30 times. Using the appropriate normal distribution to approximate a binomial distribution, find the probability of obtaining (a) fewer than 10 heads, (b) between 12 and 16 heads, inclusive, and (c) more than 20 heads.

9

MARKOV CHAINS AND THE THEORY OF GAMES

I N THIS CHAPTER, we look at two important applications of mathematics that are based primarily on matrix theory and the theory of probability. Both of these applications, *Markov chains* and the *theory of games,* though relatively recent developments in the field of mathematics, have wide applications in many practical areas.

After the successful implementation of an urban renewal program, what percentage of the population of a metropolitan area will live in the city, and what percentage of the population will live in the suburbs? In Examples 4 and 5, pages 501–502, we show how we can find the population distribution over the next few years for a population that can be described by a Markov process.

9.1 Markov Chains

Transitional Probabilities

A finite stochastic process, you may recall, is an experiment consisting of a finite number of stages in which the outcomes and associated probabilities at each stage depend on the outcomes and associated probabilities of the *preceding stages*. In this chapter, we are concerned with a special class of stochastic processes—namely, those in which the probabilities associated with the outcomes at any stage of the experiment depend only on the outcomes of the *preceding stage*. Such a process is called a **Markov process,** or a **Markov chain,** named after the Russian mathematician A. A. Markov (1856–1922).

The outcome at any stage of the experiment in a Markov process is called the **state** of the experiment. In particular, the outcome at the current stage of the experiment is called the **current state** of the process. Here is a typical problem involving a Markov chain:

Starting from one state of a process (the current state), determine the probability that the process will be at a particular state at some future time.

APPLIED EXAMPLE 1 Common Stocks An analyst at Weaver and Kline, a stock brokerage firm, observes that the closing price of the preferred stock of an airline company over a short span of time depends only on the stock's previous closing price. At the end of each trading day, the analyst makes a note of the stock's performance for that day, recording the closing price as "higher," "unchanged," or "lower" according to whether the stock closes higher, unchanged, or lower than the previous day's closing price. This sequence of observations may be viewed as a Markov chain. ∎

The transition from one state to another in a Markov chain may be studied with the aid of tree diagrams, as in the next example.

APPLIED EXAMPLE 2 Common Stocks Refer to Example 1. If on a certain day, the stock's closing price is higher than that of the previous day, then the probability that the stock closes higher, unchanged, or lower on the next trading day is .2, .3, and .5, respectively. Next, if the stock's closing price is unchanged from the previous day, then the probability that the stock closes higher, unchanged, or lower on the next trading day is .5, .2, and .3, respectively. Finally, if the stock's closing price is lower than that of the previous day, then the probability that the stock closes higher, unchanged, or lower on the next trading day is .4, .4, and .2, respectively. With the aid of tree diagrams, describe the transition between states and the probabilities associated with these transitions.

Solution The Markov chain being described has three states: higher, unchanged, and lower. If the current state is higher, then the transition to the other states from this state may be displayed by constructing a tree diagram in which the associated probabilities are shown on the appropriate limbs (Figure 1). Tree diagrams describ-

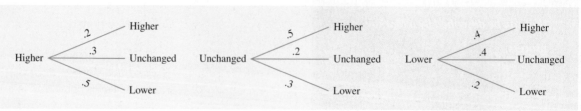

FIGURE **1**
Tree diagrams showing transition probabilities between states

ing the transition from each of the other two possible current states, unchanged and lower, to the other states are constructed in a similar manner. ■

The probabilities encountered in this example are called **transition probabilities** because they are associated with the transition from one state to the next in the Markov process. These transition probabilities may be conveniently represented in the form of a matrix. Suppose for simplicity that we have a Markov chain with three possible outcomes at each stage of the experiment. Let's refer to these outcomes as state 1, state 2, and state 3. Then the transition probabilities associated with the transition from state 1 to each of the states 1, 2, and 3 in the next phase of the experiment are precisely the respective conditional probabilities that the outcome is state 1, state 2, and state 3 *given* that the outcome state 1 has occurred. In short, the desired transition probabilities are $P(\text{state } 1 \mid \text{state } 1)$, $P(\text{state } 2 \mid \text{state } 1)$, and $P(\text{state } 3 \mid \text{state } 1)$, respectively. Thus, we write

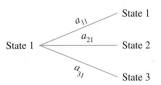

$$a_{11} = P(\text{state } 1 \mid \text{state } 1)$$
$$a_{21} = P(\text{state } 2 \mid \text{state } 1)$$
$$a_{31} = P(\text{state } 3 \mid \text{state } 1)$$

Note that the first subscript in this notation refers to the state in the next stage of the experiment, and the second subscript refers to the current state. Using a tree diagram, we have the following representation:

$$\text{State 1} \left\langle \begin{array}{l} \xrightarrow{a_{11}} \text{State 1} \\ \xrightarrow{a_{21}} \text{State 2} \\ \xrightarrow{a_{31}} \text{State 3} \end{array} \right.$$

Similarly, the transition probabilities associated with the transition from state 2 and state 3 to each of the states 1, 2, and 3 are

$$a_{12} = P(\text{state } 1 \mid \text{state } 2) \quad \text{and} \quad a_{13} = P(\text{state } 1 \mid \text{state } 3)$$
$$a_{22} = P(\text{state } 2 \mid \text{state } 2) \qquad\qquad a_{23} = P(\text{state } 2 \mid \text{state } 3)$$
$$a_{32} = P(\text{state } 3 \mid \text{state } 2) \qquad\qquad a_{33} = P(\text{state } 3 \mid \text{state } 3)$$

These observations lead to the following matrix representation of the transition probabilities:

$$\begin{array}{cc} & \begin{array}{ccc} \text{Current state} & & \\ \text{State 1} & \text{State 2} & \text{State 3} \end{array} \\ \text{Next state} \begin{array}{c} \text{State 1} \\ \text{State 2} \\ \text{State 3} \end{array} & \begin{bmatrix} a_{11} & a_{12} & a_{13} \\ a_{21} & a_{22} & a_{23} \\ a_{31} & a_{32} & a_{33} \end{bmatrix} \end{array}$$

EXAMPLE 3 Use a matrix to represent the transition probabilities obtained in Example 2.

Solution There are three states at each stage of the Markov chain under consideration. Letting state 1, state 2, and state 3 denote the states "higher," "unchanged," and "lower," respectively, we find that

$$a_{11} = .2 \qquad a_{21} = .3 \qquad a_{31} = .5$$

and so on, so the required matrix representation is given by

$$T = \begin{bmatrix} .2 & .5 & .4 \\ .3 & .2 & .4 \\ .5 & .3 & .2 \end{bmatrix}$$

The matrix obtained in Example 3 is a transition matrix. In the general case, we have the following definition:

Transition Matrix

A **transition matrix** associated with a Markov chain with n states is an $n \times n$ matrix T with entries a_{ij} ($1 \le i \le n$, $1 \le j \le n$)

$$T = \begin{matrix} \text{Next} \\ \text{state} \end{matrix} \begin{matrix} \text{State 1} \\ \text{State 2} \\ \vdots \\ \text{State } i \\ \vdots \\ \text{State } n \end{matrix} \begin{bmatrix} a_{11} & a_{12} & \cdots & a_{1j} & \cdots & a_{1n} \\ a_{21} & a_{22} & \cdots & a_{2j} & \cdots & a_{2n} \\ \vdots & \vdots & & \vdots & & \vdots \\ a_{i1} & a_{i2} & \cdots & a_{ij} & \cdots & a_{in} \\ \vdots & \vdots & & \vdots & & \vdots \\ a_{n1} & a_{n2} & \cdots & a_{nj} & \cdots & a_{nn} \end{bmatrix}$$

Current state
State 1   State 2 $\cdots$ State j $\cdots$ State n

having the following properties:

1. $a_{ij} \ge 0$ for all i and j.

2. The sum of the entries in each column of T is 1.

Since $a_{ij} = P(\text{state } i \mid \text{state } j)$ is the probability of the occurrence of an event, it must be nonnegative, and this is precisely what Property 1 implies. Property 2 follows from the fact that the transition from any one of the current states must terminate in one of the n states in the next stage of the experiment. Any square matrix that satisfies properties 1 and 2 is referred to as a **stochastic matrix**.

Explore & Discuss

Let

$$A = \begin{bmatrix} p & q \\ 1-p & 1-q \end{bmatrix} \quad \text{and} \quad B = \begin{bmatrix} r & s \\ 1-r & 1-s \end{bmatrix}$$

be two 2×2 stochastic matrices, where $0 \le p \le 1$, $0 \le q \le 1$, $0 \le r \le 1$, and $0 \le s \le 1$.

1. Show that AB is a 2×2 stochastic matrix.

2. Use the result of part (a) to explain why $A^2, A^3, \ldots, A^n$, where n is a positive integer, are also 2×2 stochastic matrices.

One advantage in representing the transition probabilities in the form of a matrix is that we may use the results from matrix theory to help us solve problems involving Markov processes, as we will see in the next several sections.

Next, for simplicity, let's consider the following Markov process, in which each stage of the experiment has precisely two possible states.

VIDEO▶

APPLIED EXAMPLE 4 Urban–Suburban Population Flow Because of the continued successful implementation of an urban renewal program, it is expected that each year, 3% of the population currently residing in the city will move to the suburbs, and 6% of the population currently residing in the suburbs will move into the city. At present, 65% of the total population of the metropolitan area lives in the city itself, while the remaining 35% lives in the suburbs. Assuming that the total population of the metropolitan area remains constant, what will be the distribution of the population 1 year from now?

Solution This problem may be solved with the aid of a tree diagram and the techniques of Chapter 7. The required tree diagram describing this process is shown in Figure 2. Using the method of Section 7.5, we find that the probability that a person selected at random will be a city dweller 1 year from now is given by

$$(.65)(.97) + (.35)(.06) = .6515$$

In a similar manner, we find that the probability that a person selected at random will reside in the suburbs 1 year from now is given by

$$(.65)(.03) + (.35)(.94) = .3485$$

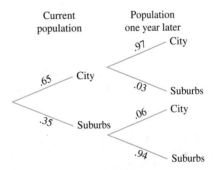

FIGURE 2
Tree diagram showing a Markov process with two states: living in the city and living in the suburbs

Thus, the population of the area 1 year from now may be expected to be distributed as follows: 65.15% living in the city and 34.85% residing in the suburbs. ∎

Let's reexamine the solution to this problem. As we noted earlier, the process under consideration may be viewed as a Markov chain with two possible states at each stage of the experiment: "living in the city" (state 1) and "living in the suburbs" (state 2). The transition matrix associated with this Markov chain is

$$T = \begin{array}{c} \text{State 1} \\ \text{State 2} \end{array} \begin{bmatrix} .97 & .06 \\ .03 & .94 \end{bmatrix} \quad \text{Transition matrix}$$

with column headers State 1, State 2.

Next, observe that the initial (current) probability distribution of the population may be summarized in the form of a column vector of dimension 2 (that is, a 2×1 matrix). Thus,

$$X_0 = \begin{array}{c} \text{State 1} \\ \text{State 2} \end{array} \begin{bmatrix} .65 \\ .35 \end{bmatrix} \quad \text{Initial-state matrix}$$

Using the results of Example 4, we may write the population distribution 1 year later as

$$X_1 = \begin{array}{c} \text{State 1} \\ \text{State 2} \end{array} \begin{bmatrix} .6515 \\ .3485 \end{bmatrix} \quad \text{Distribution after 1 year}$$

You may now verify that

$$TX_0 = \begin{bmatrix} .97 & .06 \\ .03 & .94 \end{bmatrix} \begin{bmatrix} .65 \\ .35 \end{bmatrix} = \begin{bmatrix} .6515 \\ .3485 \end{bmatrix} = X_1$$

so this problem may be solved using matrix multiplication.

 APPLIED EXAMPLE 5 Urban–Suburban Population Flow Refer to Example 4. What is the population distribution of the city after 2 years? After 3 years?

Solution Let X_2 be the column vector representing the population distribution of the metropolitan area after 2 years. We may view X_1, the vector representing the population distribution of the metropolitan area after 1 year, as representing the "initial" probability distribution in this part of our calculation. Thus,

$$X_2 = TX_1 = \begin{bmatrix} .97 & .06 \\ .03 & .94 \end{bmatrix} \begin{bmatrix} .6515 \\ .3485 \end{bmatrix} \approx \begin{bmatrix} .6529 \\ .3471 \end{bmatrix}$$

The vector representing the probability distribution of the metropolitan area after 3 years is given by

$$X_3 = TX_2 \approx \begin{bmatrix} .97 & .06 \\ .03 & .94 \end{bmatrix} \begin{bmatrix} .6529 \\ .3471 \end{bmatrix} \approx \begin{bmatrix} .6541 \\ .3459 \end{bmatrix}$$

That is, after 3 years, the population will be distributed as follows: 65.41% will live in the city, and 34.59% will live in the suburbs.

Distribution Vectors

Observe that in the foregoing computations, we have $X_1 = TX_0$, $X_2 = TX_1 = T^2X_0$, and $X_3 = TX_2 = T^3X_0$. These results are easily generalized. To see this, suppose we have a Markov process in which there are n possible states at each stage of the experiment. Suppose further that the probability of the system initially being in state 1, state 2, . . . , state n is given by $p_1, p_2, \ldots, p_n$, respectively. This distribution may be represented as an n-dimensional vector

$$X_0 = \begin{bmatrix} p_1 \\ p_2 \\ \vdots \\ p_n \end{bmatrix}$$

called a **distribution vector.** If T represents the $n \times n$ transition matrix associated with the Markov process, then the probability distribution of the system after m observations is given by

$$X_m = T^mX_0 \tag{1}$$

  APPLIED EXAMPLE 6 Taxicab Movement To keep track of the location of its cabs, Zephyr Cab has divided a town into three zones: Zone I, Zone II, and Zone III. Zephyr's management has determined from company records that of the passengers picked up in Zone I, 60% are discharged in the same zone, 30% are discharged in Zone II, and 10% are discharged in Zone III. Of those picked up in Zone II, 40% are discharged in Zone I, 30% are discharged in Zone II, and 30% are discharged in Zone III. Of those picked up in Zone III, 30% are discharged in Zone I, 30% are discharged in Zone II, and 40% are discharged in Zone III. At the beginning of the day, 80% of the cabs are in Zone I, 15% are in Zone II, and 5% are in Zone III. Furthermore, a taxi without a passenger will cruise within the zone it is currently in until a pickup is made.

a. Find the transition matrix for the Markov chain that describes the successive locations of a cab.

b. What is the distribution of the cabs after all of them have made one pickup and discharge?

c. What is the distribution of the cabs after all of them have made two pickups and discharges?

Solution Let Zone I, Zone II, and Zone III correspond to state 1, state 2, and state 3, respectively, of the Markov chain.

a. The required transition matrix is given by

$$T = \begin{bmatrix} .6 & .4 & .3 \\ .3 & .3 & .3 \\ .1 & .3 & .4 \end{bmatrix}$$

b. The initial distribution vector associated with the problem is

$$X_0 = \begin{bmatrix} .80 \\ .15 \\ .05 \end{bmatrix}$$

If X_1 denotes the distribution vector after one observation—that is, after all the cabs have made one pickup and discharge—then

$$X_1 = TX_0$$

$$= \begin{bmatrix} .6 & .4 & .3 \\ .3 & .3 & .3 \\ .1 & .3 & .4 \end{bmatrix} \begin{bmatrix} .80 \\ .15 \\ .05 \end{bmatrix} = \begin{bmatrix} .555 \\ .300 \\ .145 \end{bmatrix}$$

That is, 55.5% of the cabs are in Zone I, 30% are in Zone II, and 14.5% are in Zone III.

c. Let X_2 denote the distribution vector after all the cabs have made two pickups and discharges. Then

$$X_2 = TX_1$$

$$= \begin{bmatrix} .6 & .4 & .3 \\ .3 & .3 & .3 \\ .1 & .3 & .4 \end{bmatrix} \begin{bmatrix} .555 \\ .300 \\ .145 \end{bmatrix} = \begin{bmatrix} .4965 \\ .3000 \\ .2035 \end{bmatrix}$$

That is, 49.65% of the cabs are in Zone I, 30% are in Zone II, and 20.35% are in Zone III. You should verify that the same result may be obtained by computing $T^2 X_0$.

Note In this simplified model, we do not take into consideration variable demand and variable delivery time.

9.1 Self-Check Exercises

1. Three supermarkets serve a certain section of a city. During the upcoming year, Supermarket A is expected to retain 80% of its customers, lose 5% of its customers to Supermarket B, and lose 15% to Supermarket C. Supermarket B is expected to retain 90% of its customers and lose 5% of its customers to each of Supermarkets A and C. Supermarket C is expected to retain 75% of its customers, lose 10% to Supermarket A, and lose 15% to Supermarket B. Construct the transition matrix for the Markov chain that describes the expected change in the market share of the three supermarkets.

2. Refer to Self-Check Exercise 1. Currently the market shares of Supermarket A, Supermarket B, and Supermarket C are 0.4, 0.3, and 0.3, respectively.
   a. Find the initial distribution vector for this Markov chain.
   b. What share of the market will be held by each supermarket after 1 year? Assuming that the trend continues, what will be the market share after 2 years?

Solutions to Self-Check Exercises 9.1 can be found on page 507.

9.1 Concept Questions

1. What is a finite stochastic process? What can you say about the finite stochastic processes in a Markov chain?

2. Define the following terms for a Markov chain:
   a. State
   b. Current state
   c. Transition probabilities

3. Consider a transition matrix T for a Markov chain with entries a_{ij}, where $1 \le i \le n$ and $1 \le j \le n$.
   a. If there are n states associated with the Markov chain, what is the size of the matrix T?
   b. Describe the probability that each entry represents. Can an entry be negative?
   c. What is the sum of the entries in each column of T?

9.1 Exercises

In Exercises 1–10, determine which of the matrices are stochastic.

1. $\begin{bmatrix} .4 & .7 \\ .6 & .3 \end{bmatrix}$

2. $\begin{bmatrix} .8 & .2 \\ .3 & .7 \end{bmatrix}$

3. $\begin{bmatrix} \frac{1}{4} & \frac{1}{8} \\ \frac{3}{4} & \frac{7}{8} \end{bmatrix}$

4. $\begin{bmatrix} \frac{1}{3} & 0 & \frac{1}{2} \\ \frac{1}{2} & 1 & 0 \\ \frac{1}{4} & 0 & \frac{1}{2} \end{bmatrix}$

5. $\begin{bmatrix} .3 & .2 & .4 \\ .4 & .7 & .3 \\ .3 & .1 & .2 \end{bmatrix}$

6. $\begin{bmatrix} \frac{1}{3} & \frac{1}{4} & \frac{1}{2} \\ \frac{1}{3} & 0 & -\frac{1}{2} \\ \frac{1}{4} & \frac{3}{4} & \frac{1}{2} \end{bmatrix}$

7. $\begin{bmatrix} .1 & .4 & .3 \\ .7 & .2 & .1 \\ .2 & .4 & .6 \end{bmatrix}$

8. $\begin{bmatrix} 1 & 0 & 0 \\ 0 & 0 & 1 \\ 0 & 1 & 0 \end{bmatrix}$

9. $\begin{bmatrix} .2 & .3 \\ .3 & .1 \\ .5 & .6 \end{bmatrix}$

10. $\begin{bmatrix} .5 & .2 & .3 \\ .2 & .3 & .2 \\ .3 & .4 & .1 \\ 0 & .1 & .4 \end{bmatrix}$

11. The transition matrix for a Markov process is given by

$$T = \begin{array}{c} \\ \text{State 1} \\ \text{State 2} \end{array} \begin{array}{c} \text{State} \\ \begin{array}{cc} 1 & 2 \end{array} \\ \begin{bmatrix} .3 & .6 \\ .7 & .4 \end{bmatrix} \end{array}$$

   a. What does the entry $a_{11} = .3$ represent?
   b. Given that the outcome state 1 has occurred, what is the probability that the next outcome of the experiment will be state 2?
   c. If the initial-state distribution vector is given by

$$X_0 = \begin{array}{c} \text{State 1} \\ \text{State 2} \end{array} \begin{bmatrix} .4 \\ .6 \end{bmatrix}$$

   find TX_0, the probability distribution of the system after one observation.

12. The transition matrix for a Markov process is given by

$$T = \begin{array}{c} \\ \text{State 1} \\ \text{State 2} \end{array} \begin{array}{c} \text{State} \\ \begin{array}{cc} 1 & 2 \end{array} \\ \begin{bmatrix} \frac{1}{6} & \frac{2}{3} \\ \frac{5}{6} & \frac{1}{3} \end{bmatrix} \end{array}$$

   a. What does the entry $a_{22} = \frac{1}{3}$ represent?
   b. Given that the outcome state 1 has occurred, what is the probability that the next outcome of the experiment will be state 2?

c. If the initial-state distribution vector is given by

$$X_0 = \begin{array}{c} \text{State 1} \\ \text{State 2} \end{array} \begin{bmatrix} \frac{1}{4} \\ \frac{3}{4} \end{bmatrix}$$

find TX_0, the probability distribution of the system after one observation.

13. The transition matrix for a Markov process is given by

$$T = \begin{array}{c} \text{State 1} \\ \text{State 2} \end{array} \begin{array}{cc} \overset{\text{State}}{\overset{1 \quad\; 2}{}} \\ \begin{bmatrix} .6 & .2 \\ .4 & .8 \end{bmatrix} \end{array}$$

and the initial-state distribution vector is given by

$$X_0 = \begin{array}{c} \text{State 1} \\ \text{State 2} \end{array} \begin{bmatrix} .5 \\ .5 \end{bmatrix}$$

Find TX_0, and interpret your result with the aid of a tree diagram.

14. The transition matrix for a Markov process is given by

$$T = \begin{array}{c} \text{State 1} \\ \text{State 2} \end{array} \begin{array}{cc} \overset{\text{State}}{\overset{1 \quad\; 2}{}} \\ \begin{bmatrix} \frac{1}{2} & \frac{3}{4} \\ \frac{1}{2} & \frac{1}{4} \end{bmatrix} \end{array}$$

and the initial-state distribution vector is given by

$$X_0 = \begin{array}{c} \text{State 1} \\ \text{State 2} \end{array} \begin{bmatrix} \frac{1}{3} \\ \frac{2}{3} \end{bmatrix}$$

Find TX_0, and interpret your result with the aid of a tree diagram.

In Exercises 15–18, find X_2 (the probability distribution of the system after two observations) for the distribution vector X_0 and the transition matrix T.

15. $X_0 = \begin{bmatrix} .6 \\ .4 \end{bmatrix}$, $T = \begin{bmatrix} .4 & .8 \\ .6 & .2 \end{bmatrix}$

16. $X_0 = \begin{bmatrix} \frac{1}{2} \\ \frac{1}{2} \\ 0 \end{bmatrix}$, $T = \begin{bmatrix} \frac{1}{2} & \frac{1}{3} & \frac{1}{2} \\ 0 & \frac{1}{3} & \frac{1}{4} \\ \frac{1}{2} & \frac{1}{3} & \frac{1}{4} \end{bmatrix}$

17. $X_0 = \begin{bmatrix} \frac{1}{4} \\ \frac{1}{2} \\ \frac{1}{4} \end{bmatrix}$, $T = \begin{bmatrix} \frac{1}{4} & \frac{1}{4} & \frac{1}{2} \\ \frac{1}{4} & \frac{1}{2} & \frac{1}{2} \\ \frac{1}{2} & \frac{1}{4} & 0 \end{bmatrix}$

18. $X_0 = \begin{bmatrix} .25 \\ .40 \\ .35 \end{bmatrix}$, $T = \begin{bmatrix} .1 & .1 & .3 \\ .8 & .7 & .2 \\ .1 & .2 & .5 \end{bmatrix}$

19. PSYCHOLOGY EXPERIMENTS A psychologist conducts an experiment in which a mouse is placed in a T-maze, where it has a choice at the T-junction of turning left and receiving a reward (cheese) or turning right and receiving a mild electric shock (see accompanying figure). At the end of each trial, a record is kept of the mouse's response. It is observed that the mouse is as likely to turn left (state 1) as

right (state 2) during the first trial. In subsequent trials, however, the observation is made that if the mouse had turned left in the previous trial, then on the next trial, the probability that it will turn left is .8, whereas the probability that it will turn right is .2. If the mouse had turned right in the previous trial, then the probability that it will turn right on the next trial is .1, whereas the probability that it will turn left is .9.

a. Using a tree diagram, describe the transitions between states and the probabilities associated with these transitions.

b. Represent the transition probabilities obtained in part (a) in terms of a matrix.

c. What is the initial-state probability vector?

d. Use the results of parts (b) and (c) to find the probability that a mouse will turn left on the second trial.

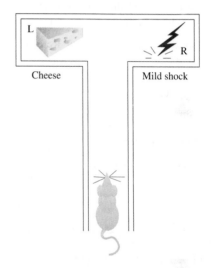

20. SMALL-TOWN REVIVAL At the beginning of 2001, the population of a certain state was 55.4% rural and 44.6% urban. Based on past trends, it is expected that 10% of the population currently residing in the rural areas will move into the urban areas, while 17% of the population currently residing in the urban areas will move into the rural areas in the next decade. What was the population distribution in that state at the beginning of 2011?

21. POLITICAL POLLS Morris Polling conducted a poll 6 months before an election in a state in which a Democrat and a Republican were running for governor and found that 60% of the voters intended to vote for the Republican and 40% intended to vote for the Democrat. In a poll conducted 3 months later, it was found that 70% of those who had earlier stated a preference for the Republican candidate still maintained that preference, whereas 30% of these voters now preferred the Democratic candidate. Of those who had earlier stated a preference for the Democrat, 80% still maintained that preference, whereas 20% now preferred the Republican candidate.

a. If the election were held at this time, who would win?

b. Assuming that this trend continues, which candidate is expected to win the election?

22. COMMUTER TRENDS In a large metropolitan area, 20% of the commuters currently use the public transportation system, whereas the remaining 80% commute via automobile. The city has recently revitalized and expanded its public transportation system. It is expected that 6 months from now 30% of those who are now commuting to work via automobile will switch to public transportation, and 70% will continue to commute via automobile. At the same time, it is expected that 20% of those now using public transportation will commute via automobile and 80% will continue to use public transportation.

a. Construct the transition matrix for the Markov chain that describes the change in the mode of transportation used by these commuters.

b. Find the initial distribution vector for this Markov chain.

c. What percentage of the commuters are expected to use public transportation 6 months from now?

23. URBAN–SUBURBAN POPULATION FLOW Refer to Example 4. If the initial probability distribution is

$$X_0 = \begin{matrix} \text{City} \\ \text{Suburb} \end{matrix} \begin{bmatrix} .80 \\ .20 \end{bmatrix}$$

what will be the population distribution of the city after 1 year? After 2 years?

24. Refer to Example 6. If the initial distribution vector for the location of the taxis is

$$X_0 = \begin{matrix} \text{Zone I} \\ \text{Zone II} \\ \text{Zone III} \end{matrix} \begin{bmatrix} .6 \\ .2 \\ .2 \end{bmatrix}$$

what will be the distribution after all of them have made one pickup and discharge?

25. MARKET SHARE At a certain university, three bookstores—the University Bookstore, the Campus Bookstore, and the Book Mart—currently serve the university community. From a survey conducted at the beginning of the fall quarter, it was found that the University Bookstore and the Campus Bookstore each had 40% of the market, whereas the Book Mart had 20% of the market. Each quarter, the University Bookstore retains 80% of its customers but loses 10% to the Campus Bookstore and 10% to the Book Mart. The Campus Bookstore retains 75% of its customers but loses 10% to the University Bookstore and 15% to the Book Mart. The Book Mart retains 90% of its customers but loses 5% to the University Bookstore and 5% to the Campus Bookstore. If these trends continue, what percentage of the market will each store have at the beginning of the second quarter? The third quarter?

26. MARKET SHARE OF AUTO MANUFACTURERS In a study of the domestic market share of the three major automobile manufacturers A, B, and C in a certain country, it was found that their current market shares were 60%, 30%, and 10%, respectively. Furthermore, it was found that of the customers who bought a car manufactured by A, 75% would again buy a car manufactured by A, 15% would buy a car

manufactured by B, and 10% would buy a car manufactured by C. Of the customers who bought a car manufactured by B, 90% would again buy a car manufactured by B, whereas 5% each would buy cars manufactured by A and C. Finally, of the customers who bought a car manufactured by C, 85% would again buy a car manufactured by C, 5% would buy a car manufactured by A, and 10% would buy a car manufactured by B. Assuming that these sentiments reflect the buying habits of customers in the future, determine the market share that will be held by each manufacturer after the next two model years.

27. COLLEGE MAJORS Records compiled by the admissions office at a state university indicating the percentage of students who change their major each year are shown in the following transition matrix. Of the freshmen now at the university, 30% have chosen their major field in business, 30% in the humanities, 20% in education, and 20% in the natural sciences and other fields. Assuming that this trend continues, find the percentage of these students that will be majoring in each of the given areas in their senior year. Hint: Find $T^3 X_0$.

	Bus.	Hum.	Educ.	Nat. Sc. and others
Business	.80	.10	.20	.10
Humanities	.10	.70	.10	.05
Education	.05	.10	.60	.05
Nat. sci. and others	.05	.10	.10	.80

28. HOMEOWNERS' CHOICE OF ENERGY A study conducted by the Urban Energy Commission in a large metropolitan area indicates the probabilities that homeowners within the area will use certain heating fuels or solar energy during the next 10 years as the major source of heat for their homes. The transition matrix representing the transition probabilities from one state to another is

	Elec.	Gas	Oil	Solar
Electricity	.70	0	0	0
Natural gas	.15	.90	.20	.05
Fuel oil	.05	.02	.75	0
Solar energy	.10	.08	.05	.95

Among homeowners within the area, 20% currently use electricity, 35% use natural gas, 40% use oil, and 5% use solar energy as the major source of heat for their homes. What is the expected distribution of the homeowners who will be using each type of heating fuel or solar energy within the next decade?

In Exercises 29 and 30, determine whether the statement is true or false. If it is true, explain why it is true. If it is false, give an example to show why it is false.

29. A Markov chain is a process in which the outcomes at any stage of the experiment depend on the outcomes of the preceding stages.

30. The sum of the entries in each column of a transition matrix must not exceed 1.

9.1 Solutions to Self-Check Exercises

1. The required transition matrix is

$$T = \begin{bmatrix} .80 & .05 & .10 \\ .05 & .90 & .15 \\ .15 & .05 & .75 \end{bmatrix}$$

2. **a.** The initial distribution vector is

$$X_0 = \begin{bmatrix} .4 \\ .3 \\ .3 \end{bmatrix}$$

   b. The vector representing the market share of each supermarket after 1 year is

$$X_1 = TX_0$$

$$= \begin{bmatrix} .80 & .05 & .10 \\ .05 & .90 & .15 \\ .15 & .05 & .75 \end{bmatrix} \begin{bmatrix} .4 \\ .3 \\ .3 \end{bmatrix} = \begin{bmatrix} .365 \\ .335 \\ .300 \end{bmatrix}$$

That is, after 1 year, Supermarket A will command a 36.5% market share, Supermarket B will have a 33.5% share, and Supermarket C will have a 30% market share.

   The vector representing the market share of the supermarkets after 2 years is

$$X_2 = TX_1$$

$$= \begin{bmatrix} .80 & .05 & .10 \\ .05 & .90 & .15 \\ .15 & .05 & .75 \end{bmatrix} \begin{bmatrix} .365 \\ .335 \\ .300 \end{bmatrix} \approx \begin{bmatrix} .33875 \\ .36475 \\ .29650 \end{bmatrix}$$

That is, 2 years later, the market shares of Supermarkets A, B, and C will be 33.88%, 36.48%, and 29.65%, respectively.

USING TECHNOLOGY

Finding Distribution Vectors

Since the computation of the probability distribution of a system after a certain number of observations involves matrix multiplication, a graphing utility may be used to facilitate the work.

EXAMPLE 1 Consider the problem posed in Example 6, page 502, where

$$T = \begin{bmatrix} .6 & .4 & .3 \\ .3 & .3 & .3 \\ .1 & .3 & .4 \end{bmatrix} \quad \text{and} \quad X_0 = \begin{bmatrix} .80 \\ .15 \\ .05 \end{bmatrix}$$

Verify that

$$X_2 = \begin{bmatrix} .4965 \\ .3000 \\ .2035 \end{bmatrix}$$

as obtained in that example.

Solution First, we enter the matrix X_0 as the matrix A and the matrix T as the matrix B. Then, performing the indicated multiplication, we find that

$$\text{B\textasciicircum 2*A} = \begin{bmatrix} .4965 \\ .3000 \\ .2035 \end{bmatrix}$$

That is,

$$X_2 = T^2X_0 = \begin{bmatrix} .4965 \\ .3000 \\ .2035 \end{bmatrix}$$

as was to be shown.

(*continued*)

TECHNOLOGY EXERCISES

In Exercises 1–2, find X_5 (the probability distribution of the system after five observations) for the distribution vector X_0 and the transition matrix T.

1. $X_0 = \begin{bmatrix} .2 \\ .3 \\ .2 \\ .1 \\ .2 \end{bmatrix}$, $T = \begin{bmatrix} .2 & .2 & .3 & .2 & .1 \\ .1 & .2 & .1 & .2 & .1 \\ .3 & .4 & .1 & .3 & .3 \\ .2 & .1 & .2 & .2 & .2 \\ .2 & .1 & .3 & .1 & .3 \end{bmatrix}$

2. $X_0 = \begin{bmatrix} .1 \\ .2 \\ .2 \\ .3 \\ .2 \end{bmatrix}$, $T = \begin{bmatrix} .3 & .2 & .1 & .3 & .1 \\ .2 & .1 & .2 & .1 & .2 \\ .1 & .2 & .3 & .2 & .2 \\ .1 & .3 & .2 & .3 & .2 \\ .3 & .2 & .2 & .1 & .3 \end{bmatrix}$

3. Refer to Exercise 26 on page 506. Using the same data, determine the market share that will be held by each manufacturer five model years after the study began.

4. Refer to Exercise 25 on page 506. Using the same data, determine the expected market share that each store will have at the beginning of the fourth quarter.

9.2 Regular Markov Chains

Steady-State Distribution Vectors

In Section 9.1, we derived a formula for computing the likelihood that a physical system will be in any one of the possible states associated with each stage of a Markov process describing the system. In this section, we use this formula to help us investigate the long-term trends of certain Markov processes.

APPLIED EXAMPLE 1 Educational Status of Women A survey conducted by the National Commission on the Educational Status of Women reveals that 70% of the daughters of women who have completed 2 or more years of college have also completed 2 or more years of college, whereas 20% of the daughters of women who have had less than 2 years of college have completed 2 or more years of college. If this trend continues, determine, in the long run, the percentage of women in the population who will have completed at least 2 years of college given that currently only 20% of the women have completed at least 2 years of college.

Solution This problem may be viewed as a Markov process with two possible states: "completed 2 or more years of college" (state 1) and "completed less than 2 years of college" (state 2). The transition matrix associated with this Markov chain is given by

$$T = \begin{bmatrix} .7 & .2 \\ .3 & .8 \end{bmatrix}$$

The initial distribution vector is given by

$$X_0 = \begin{bmatrix} .2 \\ .8 \end{bmatrix}$$

To study the long-term trend pertaining to this particular aspect of the educational status of women, let's compute $X_1, X_2, \ldots$, the distribution vectors associated with the Markov process under consideration. These vectors give the percentage of women with 2 or more years of college and that of women with less than 2 years of college after one generation, after two generations, and so on. With the aid of Equation (1), Section 9.1, we find (to four decimal places)

After one generation
$$X_1 = TX_0 = \begin{bmatrix} .7 & .2 \\ .3 & .8 \end{bmatrix} \begin{bmatrix} .2 \\ .8 \end{bmatrix} = \begin{bmatrix} .3 \\ .7 \end{bmatrix}$$

After two generations
$$X_2 = TX_1 = \begin{bmatrix} .7 & .2 \\ .3 & .8 \end{bmatrix} \begin{bmatrix} .3 \\ .7 \end{bmatrix} = \begin{bmatrix} .35 \\ .65 \end{bmatrix}$$

After three generations
$$X_3 = TX_2 = \begin{bmatrix} .7 & .2 \\ .3 & .8 \end{bmatrix} \begin{bmatrix} .35 \\ .65 \end{bmatrix} = \begin{bmatrix} .375 \\ .625 \end{bmatrix}$$

Proceeding further, we obtain the following sequence of vectors:

$$X_4 = \begin{bmatrix} .3875 \\ .6125 \end{bmatrix}$$

$$X_5 \approx \begin{bmatrix} .3938 \\ .6062 \end{bmatrix}$$

$$X_6 \approx \begin{bmatrix} .3969 \\ .6031 \end{bmatrix}$$

$$X_7 \approx \begin{bmatrix} .3984 \\ .6016 \end{bmatrix}$$

$$X_8 \approx \begin{bmatrix} .3992 \\ .6008 \end{bmatrix}$$

$$X_9 \approx \begin{bmatrix} .3996 \\ .6004 \end{bmatrix}$$

After ten generations
$$X_{10} \approx \begin{bmatrix} .3998 \\ .6002 \end{bmatrix}$$

From the results of these computations, we see that as m increases, the probability distribution vector X_m approaches the probability distribution vector

$$\begin{bmatrix} .4 \\ .6 \end{bmatrix} \quad \text{or} \quad \begin{bmatrix} \frac{2}{5} \\ \frac{3}{5} \end{bmatrix}$$

Such a vector is called the **limiting**, or **steady-state, distribution vector** for the system. We interpret these results in the following way: Initially, 20% of the women in the population have completed 2 or more years of college, whereas 80% have completed less than 2 years of college. After one generation, the former has increased to 30% of the population, and the latter has dropped to 70% of the population. The trend continues, and eventually, 40% of all women in future generations will have completed 2 or more years of college, whereas 60% will have completed less than 2 years of college. ■

To explain the foregoing result, let's analyze Equation (1), Section 9.1, more closely. Now, the initial distribution vector X_0 is a constant; that is, it remains fixed throughout our computation of $X_1, X_2, \ldots$. It appears reasonable, therefore, to conjecture that this phenomenon is a result of the behavior of the powers, T^m, of the transition matrix T. Pursuing this line of investigation, we compute

$$T^2 = \begin{bmatrix} .7 & .2 \\ .3 & .8 \end{bmatrix} \begin{bmatrix} .7 & .2 \\ .3 & .8 \end{bmatrix} = \begin{bmatrix} .55 & .3 \\ .45 & .7 \end{bmatrix}$$

$$T^3 = \begin{bmatrix} .7 & .2 \\ .3 & .8 \end{bmatrix} \begin{bmatrix} .55 & .3 \\ .45 & .7 \end{bmatrix} = \begin{bmatrix} .475 & .35 \\ .525 & .65 \end{bmatrix}$$

Proceeding further, we obtain the following sequence of matrices:

$$T^4 = \begin{bmatrix} .4375 & .375 \\ .5625 & .625 \end{bmatrix} \qquad T^5 \approx \begin{bmatrix} .4188 & .3875 \\ .5813 & .6125 \end{bmatrix}$$

$$T^6 \approx \begin{bmatrix} .4094 & .3938 \\ .5906 & .6062 \end{bmatrix} \qquad T^7 \approx \begin{bmatrix} .4047 & .3969 \\ .5953 & .6031 \end{bmatrix}$$

$$T^8 \approx \begin{bmatrix} .4023 & .3984 \\ .5977 & .6016 \end{bmatrix} \qquad T^9 \approx \begin{bmatrix} .4012 & .3992 \\ .5988 & .6008 \end{bmatrix}$$

$$T^{10} \approx \begin{bmatrix} .4006 & .3996 \\ .5994 & .6004 \end{bmatrix} \qquad T^{11} \approx \begin{bmatrix} .4003 & .3998 \\ .5997 & .6002 \end{bmatrix}$$

These results show that the powers T^m of the transition matrix T tend toward a fixed matrix as m gets larger and larger. In this case, the "limiting matrix" is the matrix

$$L = \begin{bmatrix} .40 & .40 \\ .60 & .60 \end{bmatrix} \quad \text{or} \quad \begin{bmatrix} \frac{2}{5} & \frac{2}{5} \\ \frac{3}{5} & \frac{3}{5} \end{bmatrix}$$

Such a matrix is called the **steady-state matrix** for the system. Thus, as was suspected, the long-term behavior of a Markov process such as the one in this example depends on the behavior of the limiting matrix of the powers of the transition matrix—the steady-state matrix for the system. In view of this, the long-term (steady-state) distribution vector for this problem may be found by computing the product

$$LX_0 = \begin{bmatrix} .40 & .40 \\ .60 & .60 \end{bmatrix} \begin{bmatrix} .2 \\ .8 \end{bmatrix} = \begin{bmatrix} .40 \\ .60 \end{bmatrix}$$

which agrees with the result obtained earlier.

Next, since the transition matrix T in this situation seems to have a stabilizing effect over the long term, we are led to wonder whether the steady state would be reached regardless of the initial state of the system. To answer this question, suppose the initial distribution vector is

$$X_0 = \begin{bmatrix} p \\ 1 - p \end{bmatrix}$$

Then, as before, the steady-state distribution vector is given by

$$LX_0 = \begin{bmatrix} .40 & .40 \\ .60 & .60 \end{bmatrix} \begin{bmatrix} p \\ 1 - p \end{bmatrix} = \begin{bmatrix} .40 \\ .60 \end{bmatrix}$$

Thus, the steady state is reached regardless of the initial state of the system!

Regular Markov Chains

The transition matrix T of Example 1 has several important properties, which we emphasized in the foregoing discussion. First, the sequence $T, T^2, T^3, \ldots$ approaches a steady-state matrix in which the columns of the limiting matrix are all equal and all entries are positive. A matrix T having this property is called a *regular* Markov chain.

Regular Markov Chain

A stochastic matrix T is a **regular Markov chain** if the sequence

$$T, T^2, T^3, \ldots$$

approaches a steady-state matrix in which the columns of the limiting matrix are all equal and all the entries are positive.

It can be shown that *a stochastic matrix T is regular if and only if some power of T has entries that are all positive.* Second, as in the case of Example 1, a Markov chain with a regular transition matrix has a steady-state distribution vector whose column is identical to a column in the steady-state matrix; thus, this steady-state distribution vector is always reached regardless of the initial distribution vector.

We will return to computations involving regular Markov chains, but for the moment, let's see how one may determine whether a given matrix is indeed regular.

VIDEO▶ **EXAMPLE 2** Determine which of the following matrices are regular.

a. $\begin{bmatrix} .7 & .2 \\ .3 & .8 \end{bmatrix}$ **b.** $\begin{bmatrix} .4 & 1 \\ .6 & 0 \end{bmatrix}$ **c.** $\begin{bmatrix} 0 & 1 \\ 1 & 0 \end{bmatrix}$

Solution

a. Since all the entries of the matrix are positive, the given matrix is regular. Note that this is the transition matrix of Example 1.

b. In this case, one of the entries of the given matrix is equal to zero. Let's compute

$$\begin{bmatrix} .4 & 1 \\ .6 & 0 \end{bmatrix}^2 = \begin{bmatrix} .4 & 1 \\ .6 & 0 \end{bmatrix}\begin{bmatrix} .4 & 1 \\ .6 & 0 \end{bmatrix} = \begin{bmatrix} .76 & .4 \\ .24 & .6 \end{bmatrix}$$

↑
All entries are positive.

Since the second power of the matrix has entries that are all positive, we conclude that the given matrix is in fact regular.

c. Denote the given matrix by A. Then

$$A = \begin{bmatrix} 0 & 1 \\ 1 & 0 \end{bmatrix}$$

$$A^2 = \begin{bmatrix} 0 & 1 \\ 1 & 0 \end{bmatrix}\begin{bmatrix} 0 & 1 \\ 1 & 0 \end{bmatrix} = \begin{bmatrix} 1 & 0 \\ 0 & 1 \end{bmatrix}$$

Not all entries are positive.

$$A^3 = \begin{bmatrix} 0 & 1 \\ 1 & 0 \end{bmatrix}\begin{bmatrix} 1 & 0 \\ 0 & 1 \end{bmatrix} = \begin{bmatrix} 0 & 1 \\ 1 & 0 \end{bmatrix}$$

Explore & Discuss

Find the set of all 2×2 stochastic matrices with elements that are either 0 or 1.

Observe that $A^3 = A$. It therefore follows that $A^4 = A^2$, $A^5 = A$, and so on. In other words, any power of A must coincide with either A or A^2. Since not all entries of A and A^2 are positive, the same is true of any power of A. We conclude accordingly that the given matrix is not regular.   ■

We now return to the study of regular Markov chains. In Example 1, we found the steady-state distribution vector associated with a regular Markov chain by studying the limiting behavior of a sequence of distribution vectors. Alternatively, as was pointed out in the subsequent discussion, the steady-state distribution vector may also be obtained by first determining the steady-state matrix associated with the regular Markov chain.

Fortunately, there is a relatively simple procedure for finding the steady-state distribution vector associated with a regular Markov process. It does not involve the rather tedious computations required to obtain the sequences in Example 1. The procedure follows.

> ### Finding the Steady-State Distribution Vector
>
> Let T be a regular stochastic matrix. Then the steady-state distribution vector X may be found by solving the vector equation
>
> $$TX = X$$
>
> together with the condition that the sum of the elements of the vector X be equal to 1.

A justification of the foregoing procedure is given in Exercise 29.

VIDEO   **EXAMPLE 3** Find the steady-state distribution vector for the regular Markov chain whose transition matrix is

$$T = \begin{bmatrix} .7 & .2 \\ .3 & .8 \end{bmatrix} \qquad \text{See Example 1.}$$

Solution Let

$$X = \begin{bmatrix} x \\ y \end{bmatrix}$$

be the steady-state distribution vector associated with the Markov process, where the numbers x and y are to be determined. The condition $TX = X$ translates into the matrix equation

$$\begin{bmatrix} .7 & .2 \\ .3 & .8 \end{bmatrix} \begin{bmatrix} x \\ y \end{bmatrix} = \begin{bmatrix} x \\ y \end{bmatrix}$$

or, equivalently, the system of linear equations

$$0.7x + 0.2y = x$$
$$0.3x + 0.8y = y$$

But each of the equations that make up this system of equations is equivalent to the single equation

$$0.3x - 0.2y = 0 \qquad \begin{aligned} &0.7x - x + 0.2y = 0 \\ &0.3x + 0.8y - y = 0 \end{aligned}$$

Next, the condition that the sum of the elements of X is 1 gives

$$x + y = 1$$

Thus, the simultaneous fulfillment of the two conditions implies that x and y are the solutions of the system

$$0.3x - 0.2y = 0$$
$$x + y = 1$$

Solving the first equation for x, we obtain

$$x = \frac{2}{3}y$$

which, upon substitution into the second, yields

$$\frac{2}{3}y + y = 1$$

$$y = \frac{3}{5}$$

Thus, $x = \frac{2}{5}$, and the required steady-state distribution vector is given by

$$X = \begin{bmatrix} \frac{2}{5} \\ \frac{3}{5} \end{bmatrix}$$

which agrees with the result obtained earlier. ■

 APPLIED EXAMPLE 4 Taxicab Movement In Example 6, Section 9.1, we showed that the transition matrix that described the movement of taxis from zone to zone was given by the regular stochastic matrix

$$T = \begin{bmatrix} .6 & .4 & .3 \\ .3 & .3 & .3 \\ .1 & .3 & .4 \end{bmatrix}$$

Use this information to determine the long-term distribution of the taxis in the three zones.

Solution Let

$$X = \begin{bmatrix} x \\ y \\ z \end{bmatrix}$$

be the steady-state distribution vector associated with the Markov process under consideration, where x, y, and z are to be determined. The condition $TX = X$ translates into the matrix equation

$$\begin{bmatrix} .6 & .4 & .3 \\ .3 & .3 & .3 \\ .1 & .3 & .4 \end{bmatrix} \begin{bmatrix} x \\ y \\ z \end{bmatrix} = \begin{bmatrix} x \\ y \\ z \end{bmatrix}$$

or, equivalently, the system of linear equations

$$0.6x + 0.4y + 0.3z = x$$
$$0.3x + 0.3y + 0.3z = y$$
$$0.1x + 0.3y + 0.4z = z$$

The system simplifies into

$$4x - 4y - 3z = 0$$
$$3x - 7y + 3z = 0$$
$$x + 3y - 6z = 0$$

Since $x + y + z = 1$ as well, we are required to solve the system

$$x + y + z = 1$$
$$4x - 4y - 3z = 0$$
$$3x - 7y + 3z = 0$$
$$x + 3y - 6z = 0$$

Using the Gauss–Jordan elimination procedure of Chapter 2, we find that

$$x = \frac{33}{70} \qquad y = \frac{3}{10} \qquad z = \frac{8}{35}$$

or $x \approx 0.47$, $y = 0.30$, and $z \approx 0.23$. Thus, in the long run, approximately 47% of the taxis will be in Zone I, 30% in Zone II, and 23% in Zone III.   ■

9.2 Self-Check Exercises

1. Find the steady-state distribution vector for the regular Markov chain whose transition matrix is

$$T = \begin{bmatrix} .5 & .8 \\ .5 & .2 \end{bmatrix}$$

2. Three supermarkets serve a certain section of a city. During the year, Supermarket A is expected to retain 80% of its customers, lose 5% of its customers to Supermarket B, and lose 15% to Supermarket C. Supermarket B is expected to

retain 90% of its customers and lose 5% to each of Supermarket A and Supermarket C. Supermarket C is expected to retain 75% of its customers, lose 10% to Supermarket A, and lose 15% to Supermarket B. If these trends continue, what will be the market share of each supermarket in the long run?

Solutions to Self-Check Exercises 9.2 can be found on page 516.

9.2 Concept Questions

1. Explain (a) a steady-state distribution vector, (b) a steady-state matrix, and (c) a regular Markov chain.

2. How do you find the steady-state distribution vector given a regular stochastic matrix T associated with a Markov process?

9.2 Exercises

In Exercises 1–8, determine which of the matrices are regular.

1. $\begin{bmatrix} \frac{2}{5} & \frac{3}{4} \\ \frac{3}{5} & \frac{1}{4} \end{bmatrix}$

2. $\begin{bmatrix} 0 & .3 \\ 1 & .7 \end{bmatrix}$

3. $\begin{bmatrix} 1 & .8 \\ 0 & .2 \end{bmatrix}$

4. $\begin{bmatrix} \frac{1}{3} & 0 \\ \frac{2}{3} & 1 \end{bmatrix}$

5. $\begin{bmatrix} \frac{1}{2} & \frac{3}{4} & 0 \\ \frac{1}{2} & 0 & \frac{1}{2} \\ 0 & \frac{1}{4} & \frac{1}{2} \end{bmatrix}$

6. $\begin{bmatrix} 1 & .3 & .1 \\ 0 & .4 & .8 \\ 0 & .3 & .1 \end{bmatrix}$

7. $\begin{bmatrix} .7 & .2 & .3 \\ .3 & .8 & .3 \\ 0 & 0 & .4 \end{bmatrix}$

8. $\begin{bmatrix} 0 & 0 & \frac{1}{4} \\ 1 & 0 & 0 \\ 0 & 1 & \frac{3}{4} \end{bmatrix}$

In Exercises 9–16, find the steady-state vector for the transition matrix.

9. $\begin{bmatrix} \frac{1}{3} & \frac{1}{4} \\ \frac{2}{3} & \frac{3}{4} \end{bmatrix}$

10. $\begin{bmatrix} \frac{4}{5} & \frac{3}{5} \\ \frac{1}{5} & \frac{2}{5} \end{bmatrix}$

11. $\begin{bmatrix} .5 & .2 \\ .5 & .8 \end{bmatrix}$

12. $\begin{bmatrix} .9 & 1 \\ .1 & 0 \end{bmatrix}$

13. $\begin{bmatrix} 0 & \frac{1}{8} & 1 \\ 1 & \frac{5}{8} & 0 \\ 0 & \frac{1}{4} & 0 \end{bmatrix}$

14. $\begin{bmatrix} .6 & .3 & 0 \\ .4 & .4 & .6 \\ 0 & .3 & .4 \end{bmatrix}$

15. $\begin{bmatrix} .2 & 0 & .3 \\ 0 & .6 & .4 \\ .8 & .4 & .3 \end{bmatrix}$

16. $\begin{bmatrix} .1 & .2 & .3 \\ .1 & .2 & .3 \\ .8 & .6 & .4 \end{bmatrix}$

17. **PSYCHOLOGY EXPERIMENTS** A psychologist conducts an experiment in which a mouse is placed in a T-maze, where it has a choice at the T-junction of turning left and receiving a reward (cheese) or turning right and receiving a mild shock. At the end of each trial, a record is kept of the mouse's response. It is observed that the mouse is as likely to turn left (state 1) as right (state 2) during the first trial. In subsequent trials, however, the observation is made that if the mouse had turned left in the previous trial, then the probability that it will turn left in the next trial is .8, whereas the probability that it will turn right is .2. If the mouse had turned right in the previous trial, then the probability that it will turn right in the next trial is .1, whereas the probability that it will turn left is .9. In the long run, what percentage of the time will the mouse turn left at the T-junction?

18. **COMMUTER TRENDS** Within a large metropolitan area, 20% of the commuters currently use the public transportation system, whereas the remaining 80% commute via automobile. The city has recently revitalized and expanded its public transportation system. It is expected that 6 months from now, 30% of those who are now commuting to work via automobile will switch to public transportation, and 70% will continue to commute via automobile. At the same time, it is expected that 20% of those now using public transportation will commute via automobile, and 80% will continue to use public transportation. In the long run, what percentage of the commuters will be using public transportation?

19. **ONE- AND TWO-INCOME FAMILIES** From data compiled over a 10-year period by Manpower, Inc., in a statewide study of married couples in which at least one spouse was working, the following transition matrix was constructed. It gives the transitional probabilities for one and two wage earners among married couples.

		Current State	
		1 Wage Earner	2 Wage Earners
Next State	1 Wage Earner	.72	.12
	2 Wage Earners	.28	.88

At the present time, 48% of the married couples (in which at least one spouse is working) have one wage earner, and 52% have two wage earners. Assuming that this trend continues, what will be the distribution of one- and two-wage earner families among married couples in this area 10 years from now? Over the long run?

20. **PROFESSIONAL WOMEN** From data compiled over a 5-year period by *Women's Daily* in a study of the number of women in the professions, the following transition matrix was constructed. It gives the transitional probabilities for the number of men and women in the professions.

		Current State	
		Men	Women
Next State	Men	.95	.04
	Women	.05	.96

As of the beginning of 1986, 52.9% of professional jobs were held by men. If this trend continues, what percentage of professional jobs will be held by women in the long run?

21. **BUYING TRENDS OF HOME BUYERS** From data collected over the past decade by the Association of Realtors of a certain city, the following transition matrix was obtained. The matrix describes the buying pattern of home buyers who buy single-family homes (*S*) or condominiums (*C*).

		Current State	
		S	C
Next State	S	.85	.35
	C	.15	.65

Currently, 80% of the homeowners live in single-family homes, whereas 20% live in condominiums. If this trend continues, what percentage of homeowners in this city will own single-family homes and condominiums two decades from now? In the long run?

22. **HOMEOWNERS' CHOICE OF ENERGY** A study conducted by the Urban Energy Commission in a large metropolitan area indicates the probabilities that homeowners within the area will use certain heating fuels or solar energy during the next 10 years as the major source of heat for their homes. The following transition matrix represents the transition probabilities from one state to another:

$$
\begin{array}{cccc}
 & \text{Elec.} & \text{Gas} & \text{Oil} & \text{Solar}
\end{array}
$$

	Elec.	Gas	Oil	Solar
Electricity	.70	0	.10	0
Natural gas	.15	.90	.10	.05
Fuel oil	.05	.02	.75	.05
Solar energy	.10	.08	.05	.90

Among the homeowners within the area, 20% currently use electricity, 35% use natural gas, 40% use oil, and 5% use solar energy as the major source of heat for their homes. In the long run, what percentage of homeowners within the area will be using solar energy as their major source of heating fuel?

23. **NETWORK NEWS VIEWERSHIP** A television poll was conducted among regular viewers of the national news in a certain region where the three national networks share the same time slot for the evening news. Results of the poll indicate that 30% of the viewers watch the ABC evening news, 40% watch the CBS evening news, and 30% watch the NBC evening news. Furthermore, it was found that of those viewers who watched the ABC evening news during one week, 80% would again watch the ABC evening news during the next week, 10% would watch the CBS news, and 10% would watch the NBC news. Of those viewers who watched the CBS evening news during one week, 85% would again watch the CBS evening news during the next week, 10% would watch the ABC news, and 5% would watch the NBC news. Of those viewers who watched the NBC evening news during one week, 85% would again watch the NBC news during the next week, 10% would watch ABC, and 5% would watch CBS.

a. What share of the audience consisting of regular viewers of the national news will each network command after 2 weeks?

b. In the long run, what share of the audience will each network command?

24. **NETWORK NEWS VIEWERSHIP** Refer to Exercise 23. If the initial distribution vector is

$$
X_0 = \begin{matrix} \text{ABC} \\ \text{CBS} \\ \text{NBC} \end{matrix} \begin{bmatrix} .40 \\ .40 \\ .20 \end{bmatrix}
$$

what share of the audience will each network command in the long run?

25. **GENETICS** In a certain species of roses, a plant with geno-type (genetic makeup) *AA* has red flowers, a plant with genotype *Aa* has pink flowers, and a plant with genotype *aa* has white flowers, where *A* is the dominant gene and *a* is the recessive gene for color. If a plant with one genotype is crossed with another plant, then the color of the off-spring's flowers is determined by the genotype of the parent plants. If a plant of each genotype is crossed with a pink-flowered plant, then the transition matrix used to determine the color of the offspring's flowers is given by

$$
\begin{array}{cc}
 & \text{Parent} \\
 & \text{Red} \quad \text{Pink} \quad \text{White}
\end{array}
$$

$$
\begin{array}{cc}
\text{Red } (AA) \\
\text{Offspring} \quad \text{Pink } (Aa) \text{ or } (aA) \\
\text{White } (aa)
\end{array}
\begin{bmatrix}
\frac{1}{2} & \frac{1}{4} & 0 \\
\frac{1}{2} & \frac{1}{2} & \frac{1}{2} \\
0 & \frac{1}{4} & \frac{1}{2}
\end{bmatrix}
$$

If the offspring of each generation are crossed only with pink-flowered plants, what percentage of the plants will have red flowers in the long run? Pink flowers? White flowers?

26. **MARKET SHARE OF AUTO MANUFACTURERS** In a study of the domestic market share of the three major automobile man-ufacturers *A*, *B*, and *C* in a certain country, it was found that of the customers who bought a car manufactured by *A*, 75% would again buy a car manufactured by *A*, 15% would buy a car manufactured by *B*, and 10% would buy a car manu-factured by *C*. Of the customers who bought a car manu-factured by *B*, 90% would again buy a car manufactured by *B*, whereas 5% each would buy cars manufactured by *A* and *C*. Finally, of the customers who bought a car manufactured by *C*, 85% would again buy a car manufactured by *C*, 5% would buy a car manufactured by *A*, and 10% would buy a car manufactured by *B*. Assuming that these sentiments reflect the buying habits of customers in the future model years, determine the market share that will be held by each manufacturer in the long run.

In Exercises 27 and 28, determine whether the statement is true or false. If it is true, explain why it is true. If it is false, give an example to show why it is false.

27. A stochastic matrix *T* is a regular Markov chain if the pow-ers of *T* approach a fixed matrix whose columns are all equal.

28. To find the steady-state distribution vector *X*, we solve the system

$$
TX = X
$$
$$
x_1 + x_2 + \cdots + x_n = 1
$$

where *T* is the regular stochastic matrix associated with the Markov process and

$$
X = \begin{bmatrix} x_1 \\ x_2 \\ \vdots \\ x_n \end{bmatrix}
$$

29. Let *T* be a regular stochastic matrix. Show that the steady-state distribution vector *X* may be found by solving the vector equation *TX = X* together with the condition that the sum of the elements of *X* is 1.

Hint: Take the initial distribution to be *X*, the steady-state distri-bution vector. Then, when *n* is large, $X \approx T^n X$. (Why?) Multiply both sides of the last equation by *T* (on the left), and consider the resulting equation when *n* is large.

9.2   Solutions to Self-Check Exercises

1. Let

$$
X = \begin{bmatrix} x \\ y \end{bmatrix}
$$

be the steady-state distribution vector associated with the Markov process, where the numbers *x* and *y* are to be deter-mined. The condition *TX = X* translates into the matrix equation

$$
\begin{bmatrix} .5 & .8 \\ .5 & .2 \end{bmatrix} \begin{bmatrix} x \\ y \end{bmatrix} = \begin{bmatrix} x \\ y \end{bmatrix}
$$

which is equivalent to the system of linear equations

$$
0.5x + 0.8y = x
$$
$$
0.5x + 0.2y = y
$$

Each equation in the system is equivalent to the equation

$$
0.5x - 0.8y = 0
$$

Next, the condition that the sum of the elements of *X* is 1 gives

$$
x + y = 1
$$

Thus, the simultaneous fulfillment of the two conditions implies that *x* and *y* are the solutions of the system

$$
0.5x - 0.8y = 0
$$
$$
x + \quad y = 1
$$

Solving the first equation for *x*, we obtain

$$
x = \frac{8}{5} y
$$

which, upon substitution into the second, yields

$$
\frac{8}{5} y + y = 1
$$

$$
y = \frac{5}{13}
$$

Therefore, $x = \frac{8}{13}$, and the required steady-state distribution vector is

$$\begin{bmatrix} \frac{8}{13} \\ \frac{5}{13} \end{bmatrix}$$

2. The transition matrix for the Markov process under consideration is

$$T = \begin{bmatrix} .80 & .05 & .10 \\ .05 & .90 & .15 \\ .15 & .05 & .75 \end{bmatrix}$$

Now, let

$$X = \begin{bmatrix} x \\ y \\ z \end{bmatrix}$$

be the steady-state distribution vector associated with the Markov process under consideration, where x, y, and z are to be determined. The condition $TX = X$ is

$$\begin{bmatrix} .80 & .05 & .10 \\ .05 & .90 & .15 \\ .15 & .05 & .75 \end{bmatrix} \begin{bmatrix} x \\ y \\ z \end{bmatrix} = \begin{bmatrix} x \\ y \\ z \end{bmatrix}$$

or, equivalently, the system of linear equations as follows:

$$0.80x + 0.05y + 0.10z = x$$
$$0.05x + 0.90y + 0.15z = y$$
$$0.15x + 0.05y + 0.75z = z$$

This system simplifies to

$$4x - y - 2z = 0$$
$$x - 2y + 3z = 0$$
$$3x + y - 5z = 0$$

Since $x + y + z = 1$ as well, we are required to solve the system

$$4x - y - 2z = 0$$
$$x - 2y + 3z = 0$$
$$3x + y - 5z = 0$$
$$x + y + z = 1$$

Using the Gauss–Jordan elimination procedure, we find

$$x = \frac{1}{4} \qquad y = \frac{1}{2} \qquad z = \frac{1}{4}$$

Therefore, in the long run, Supermarkets A and C will each have 25% of the customers, and Supermarket B will have 50% of the customers.

USING TECHNOLOGY

Finding the Long-Term Distribution Vector

The problem of finding the long-term distribution vector for a regular Markov chain ultimately rests on the problem of solving a system of linear equations. As such, the **rref** or equivalent function of a graphing utility proves indispensable, as the following example shows.

EXAMPLE 1 Find the steady-state distribution vector for the regular Markov chain whose transition matrix is

$$T = \begin{bmatrix} .4 & .2 & .1 \\ .3 & .4 & .5 \\ .3 & .4 & .4 \end{bmatrix}$$

Solution Let

$$\begin{bmatrix} x \\ y \\ z \end{bmatrix}$$

be the steady-state distribution vector, where x, y, and z are to be determined. The condition $TX = X$ translates into the matrix equation

$$\begin{bmatrix} .4 & .2 & .1 \\ .3 & .4 & .5 \\ .3 & .4 & .4 \end{bmatrix} \begin{bmatrix} x \\ y \\ z \end{bmatrix} = \begin{bmatrix} x \\ y \\ z \end{bmatrix}$$

(continued)

or, equivalently, the system of linear equations

$$0.4x + 0.2y + 0.1z = x$$
$$0.3x + 0.4y + 0.5z = y$$
$$0.3x + 0.4y + 0.4z = z$$

Because $x + y + z = 1$, we are required to solve the system

$$-0.6x + 0.2y + 0.1z = 0$$
$$0.3x - 0.6y + 0.5z = 0$$
$$0.3x + 0.4y - 0.6z = 0$$
$$x + y + z = 1$$

Entering this system into the graphing calculator as the augmented matrix

$$A = \begin{bmatrix} -.6 & .2 & .1 & 0 \\ .3 & -.6 & .5 & 0 \\ .3 & .4 & -.6 & 0 \\ 1 & 1 & 1 & 1 \end{bmatrix}$$

and then using the **rref** function, we obtain the equivalent system (to two decimal places)

$$\begin{bmatrix} 1 & 0 & 0 & .20 \\ 0 & 1 & 0 & .42 \\ 0 & 0 & 1 & .38 \\ 0 & 0 & 0 & 0 \end{bmatrix}$$

Therefore, $x \approx 0.20$, $y \approx 0.42$, and $z \approx 0.38$, and so the required steady-state distribution vector is approximately

$$\begin{bmatrix} .20 \\ .42 \\ .38 \end{bmatrix}$$

TECHNOLOGY EXERCISES

In Exercises 1 and 2, find the steady-state vector for the matrix T.

1.
$$T = \begin{bmatrix} .2 & .2 & .3 & .2 & .1 \\ .1 & .2 & .1 & .2 & .1 \\ .3 & .4 & .1 & .3 & .3 \\ .2 & .1 & .2 & .2 & .2 \\ .2 & .1 & .3 & .1 & .3 \end{bmatrix}$$

2.
$$T = \begin{bmatrix} .3 & .2 & .1 & .3 & .1 \\ .2 & .1 & .2 & .1 & .2 \\ .1 & .2 & .3 & .2 & .2 \\ .1 & .3 & .2 & .3 & .2 \\ .3 & .2 & .2 & .1 & .3 \end{bmatrix}$$

3. Verify that the steady-state vector for Example 4, page 513, is (to two decimal places)

$$X = \begin{bmatrix} .47 \\ .30 \\ .23 \end{bmatrix}$$

Absorbing Markov Chains

Absorbing Markov Chains

In this section, we investigate the long-term trends of a certain class of Markov chains that involve transition matrices that are not regular. In particular, we study Markov chains in which the transition matrices, known as absorbing stochastic matrices, have the special properties that we now describe.

Consider the stochastic matrix

$$\begin{bmatrix} 1 & 0 & .2 & 0 \\ 0 & 1 & .3 & 1 \\ 0 & 0 & .5 & 0 \\ 0 & 0 & 0 & 0 \end{bmatrix}$$

associated with a Markov process. Interpreting it in the usual fashion, we see that after one observation, the probability is 1 (a certainty) that an object previously in state 1 will remain in state 1. Similarly, we see that an object previously in state 2 must remain in state 2. Next, we find that an object previously in state 3 has a probability of .2 of going to state 1, a probability of .3 of going to state 2, a probability of .5 of remaining in state 3, and no chance of going to state 4. Finally, an object previously in state 4 must, after one observation, end up in state 2.

This stochastic matrix exhibits certain special characteristics. First, as observed earlier, an object in state 1 or state 2 must stay in state 1 or state 2, respectively. Such states are called absorbing states. In general, an **absorbing state** is one from which it is impossible for an object to leave. To identify the absorbing states of a stochastic matrix, we simply examine each column of the matrix. If column i has a 1 in the a_{ii} position (that is, on the main diagonal of the matrix) and zeros elsewhere in that column, then and only then is state i an absorbing state.

Second, observe that states 3 and 4, although not absorbing states, have the property that an object in each of these states has a possibility of going to an absorbing state. For example, an object currently in state 3 has a probability of .2 of ending up in state 1, an absorbing state, and an object in state 4 must end up in state 2, also an absorbing state, after one transition.

Absorbing Stochastic Matrix

An **absorbing stochastic matrix** has the following properties:

1. There is at least one absorbing state.
2. It is possible to go from each nonabsorbing state to an absorbing state in one or more steps.

A Markov chain is said to be an **absorbing Markov chain** if the transition matrix associated with the process is an absorbing stochastic matrix.

VIDEO ▶ **EXAMPLE 1** Determine whether the following matrices are absorbing stochastic matrices.

a.
$$\begin{bmatrix} .7 & 0 & .1 & 0 \\ 0 & 1 & .5 & 0 \\ .3 & 0 & .2 & 0 \\ 0 & 0 & .2 & 1 \end{bmatrix}$$

b.
$$\begin{bmatrix} 1 & 0 & 0 & 0 \\ 0 & 1 & 0 & 0 \\ 0 & 0 & .5 & .4 \\ 0 & 0 & .5 & .6 \end{bmatrix}$$

Solution

a. States 2 and 4 are both absorbing states. Furthermore, even though state 1 is not an absorbing state, there is a possibility (with probability .3) that an object may go from this state to state 3. State 3 itself is nonabsorbing, but an object in that state has a probability of .5 of going to the absorbing state 2 and a probability of .2 of going to the absorbing state 4. Thus, the given matrix is an absorbing stochastic matrix.

b. States 1 and 2 are absorbing states. However, it is impossible for an object to go from the nonabsorbing states 3 and 4 to either or both of the absorbing states. Thus, the given matrix is not an absorbing stochastic matrix.   ▪

Given an absorbing stochastic matrix, it is always possible, by suitably reordering the states if necessary, to rewrite it so that the absorbing states appear first. Then the resulting matrix can be partitioned into four submatrices,

$$\begin{array}{cc} \text{Absorbing} & \text{Nonabsorbing} \end{array}$$
$$\left[\begin{array}{c|c} I & S \\ \hline O & R \end{array}\right]$$

where I is an identity matrix whose order is determined by the number of absorbing states and O is a zero matrix. The submatrices R and S correspond to the nonabsorbing states. As an example, the absorbing stochastic matrix of Example 1(a),

$$\begin{array}{c} \\ 1 \\ 2 \\ 3 \\ 4 \end{array} \begin{array}{cccc} 1 & 2 & 3 & 4 \\ \left[\begin{array}{cccc} .7 & 0 & .1 & 0 \\ 0 & 1 & .5 & 0 \\ .3 & 0 & .2 & 0 \\ 0 & 0 & .2 & 1 \end{array}\right] \end{array} \quad \text{may be written as} \quad \begin{array}{c} \\ 4 \\ 2 \\ 1 \\ 3 \end{array} \begin{array}{cccc} 4 & 2 & 1 & 3 \\ \left[\begin{array}{cc|cc} 1 & 0 & 0 & .2 \\ 0 & 1 & 0 & .5 \\ \hline 0 & 0 & .7 & .1 \\ 0 & 0 & .3 & .2 \end{array}\right] \end{array}$$

upon reordering the states as indicated.

APPLIED EXAMPLE 2 Gambler's Ruin   John has decided to risk $2 in the following game of chance. He places a $1 bet on each repeated play of the game in which the probability of his winning $1 is .4, and he continues to play until he has accumulated a total of $3 or he has lost all of his money. Write the transition matrix for the related absorbing Markov chain.

Solution   There are four states in this Markov chain, which correspond to John accumulating a total of $0, $1, $2, and $3. Since the first and last states listed are absorbing states, we will list these states first, resulting in the transition matrix

$$\begin{array}{c} \\ \\ \$0 \\ \$3 \\ \$1 \\ \$2 \end{array} \begin{array}{cc} \overbrace{\hphantom{\$0\ \ \$3}}^{\text{Absorbing}} & \overbrace{\hphantom{\$1\ \ \$2}}^{\text{Nonabsorbing}} \\ \begin{array}{cccc} \$0 & \$3 & \$1 & \$2 \end{array} \\ \left[\begin{array}{cc|cc} 1 & 0 & .6 & 0 \\ 0 & 1 & 0 & .4 \\ \hline 0 & 0 & 0 & .6 \\ 0 & 0 & .4 & 0 \end{array}\right] \end{array}$$

which is constructed as follows: Since the state "$0" is an absorbing state, we see that $a_{11} = 1$, $a_{21} = a_{31} = a_{41} = 0$. Similarly, the state "$3" is an absorbing state, so $a_{22} = 1$, and $a_{12} = a_{32} = a_{42} = 0$. To construct the column corresponding to the nonabsorbing state "$1," we note that there is a probability of .6 (John loses) in going from an accumulated amount of $1 to $0, so $a_{13} = .6$; $a_{23} = a_{33} = 0$ because it is not feasible to go from an accumulated amount of $1 to either an accumulated amount of $3 or $1 in one transition (play). Finally, there is a probability of .4 (John wins) in going from an accumulated amount of $1 to an accumulated amount of $2, so $a_{43} = .4$. The last column of the transition matrix is constructed by reasoning in a similar manner.   ■

The following question arises in connection with the last example: If John continues to play the game as originally planned, what is the probability that he will depart from the game victorious—that is, leave with an accumulated amount of $3?

To answer this question, we have to look at the long-term trend of the relevant Markov chain. Taking a cue from our work in the last section, we may compute the powers of the transition matrix associated with the Markov chain. Just as in the case of regular stochastic matrices, it turns out that the powers of an absorbing stochastic matrix approach a steady-state matrix. However, instead of demonstrating this, we use the following result, which we state without proof, for computing the steady-state matrix:

Finding the Steady-State Matrix for an Absorbing Stochastic Matrix

Suppose an absorbing stochastic matrix A has been partitioned into submatrices

$$A = \left[\begin{array}{c|c} I & S \\ \hline O & R \end{array}\right]$$

Then the *steady-state matrix* of A is given by

$$\left[\begin{array}{c|c} I & S(I - R)^{-1} \\ \hline O & O \end{array}\right]$$

where the order of the identity matrix appearing in the expression $(I - R)^{-1}$ is chosen to have the same order as R.

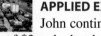 **APPLIED EXAMPLE 3** Gambler's Ruin (continued) Refer to Example 2. If John continues to play the game until either he has accumulated a sum of $3 or he has lost all of his money, what is the probability that he will accumulate $3?

Solution The transition matrix associated with the Markov process is (see Example 2)

$$A = \left[\begin{array}{cc|cc} 1 & 0 & .6 & 0 \\ 0 & 1 & 0 & .4 \\ \hline 0 & 0 & 0 & .6 \\ 0 & 0 & .4 & 0 \end{array}\right]$$

We need to find the steady-state matrix of A. In this case,

$$R = \begin{bmatrix} 0 & .6 \\ .4 & 0 \end{bmatrix} \quad \text{and} \quad S = \begin{bmatrix} .6 & 0 \\ 0 & .4 \end{bmatrix}$$

so

$$I - R = \begin{bmatrix} 1 & 0 \\ 0 & 1 \end{bmatrix} - \begin{bmatrix} 0 & .6 \\ .4 & 0 \end{bmatrix} = \begin{bmatrix} 1 & -.6 \\ -.4 & 1 \end{bmatrix}$$

Using the formula in Section 2.6 for finding the inverse of a 2 × 2 matrix, we find that (to two decimal places)

$$(I - R)^{-1} = \begin{bmatrix} 1.32 & .79 \\ .53 & 1.32 \end{bmatrix}$$

VIDEO

Explore & Discuss

Consider the stochastic matrix

$$A = \begin{bmatrix} 1 & 0 & a \\ 0 & 1 & b \\ 0 & 0 & 1-a-b \end{bmatrix}$$

where a and b satisfy $0 < a < 1$, $0 < b < 1$, and $0 < a + b < 1$.

1. Find the steady-state matrix.
2. What is the probability that state 3 will be absorbed in state 2?

so

$$S(I-R)^{-1} = \begin{bmatrix} .6 & 0 \\ 0 & .4 \end{bmatrix}\begin{bmatrix} 1.32 & .79 \\ .53 & 1.32 \end{bmatrix} = \begin{bmatrix} .79 & .47 \\ .21 & .53 \end{bmatrix}$$

Therefore, the required steady-state matrix of A is given by

$$\begin{bmatrix} I & S(I-R)^{-1} \\ \hline O & O \end{bmatrix} = \begin{array}{c} \\ \$0 \\ \$3 \\ \$1 \\ \$2 \end{array}\begin{array}{cccc} \$0 & \$3 & \$1 & \$2 \end{array}\begin{bmatrix} 1 & 0 & .79 & .47 \\ 0 & 1 & .21 & .53 \\ \hline 0 & 0 & 0 & 0 \\ 0 & 0 & 0 & 0 \end{bmatrix}$$

From this result, we see that if he starts with \$2, the probability is .53 that John will leave the game with an accumulated amount of \$3—that is, that he wins \$1.   ■

Our last example shows an application of Markov chains in the field of genetics.

APPLIED EXAMPLE 4 Genetics   In a certain species of flowers, a plant of genotype (genetic makeup) *AA* has red flowers, a plant of genotype *Aa* has pink flowers, and a plant of genotype *aa* has white flowers, where *A* is the dominant gene and *a* is the recessive gene for color. If a plant of one genotype is crossed with another plant, then the color of the offspring's flowers is determined by the genotype of the parent plants. If the offspring are crossed successively with plants of genotype *AA* only, show that in the long run, all the flowers produced by the plants will be red.

Solution   First, let's construct the transition matrix associated with the resulting Markov chain. In crossing a plant of genotype *AA* with another of the same genotype *AA*, the offspring will inherit one dominant gene from each parent and thus will have genotype *AA*. Therefore, the probabilities of the offspring being genotype *AA*, *Aa*, and *aa* are 1, 0, and 0, respectively.

Next, in crossing a plant of genotype *AA* with one of genotype *Aa*, the probability of the offspring having genotype *AA* (inheriting an *A* gene from the first parent and an *A* from the second) is $\frac{1}{2}$; the probability of the offspring having genotype *Aa* (inheriting an *A* gene from the first parent and an *a* gene from the second parent) is $\frac{1}{2}$; finally, the probability of the offspring being of genotype *aa* is 0 since this is clearly impossible.

A similar argument shows that when a plant of genotype *AA* is crossed with one of genotype *aa*, the probabilities of the offspring having genotype *AA*, *Aa*, and *aa* are 0, 1, and 0, respectively.

The required transition matrix is thus given by

Absorbing state
↓

$$T = \begin{array}{c} AA \\ Aa \\ aa \end{array}\begin{array}{ccc} AA & Aa & aa \end{array}\begin{bmatrix} 1 & \frac{1}{2} & 0 \\ 0 & \frac{1}{2} & 1 \\ 0 & 0 & 0 \end{bmatrix}$$

Observe that the state *AA* is an absorbing state. Furthermore, it is possible to go from each of the other two nonabsorbing states to the absorbing state *AA*. Thus, the Markov chain is an absorbing Markov chain. To determine the long-term effects of this experiment, let's compute the steady-state matrix of *T*. Partitioning *T* in the usual manner, we find

$$T = \begin{bmatrix} 1 & \frac{1}{2} & 0 \\ 0 & \frac{1}{2} & 1 \\ 0 & 0 & 0 \end{bmatrix}$$

so

$$R = \begin{bmatrix} \frac{1}{2} & 1 \\ 0 & 0 \end{bmatrix} \quad \text{and} \quad S = \begin{bmatrix} \frac{1}{2} & 0 \end{bmatrix}$$

Next, we compute

$$I - R = \begin{bmatrix} 1 & 0 \\ 0 & 1 \end{bmatrix} - \begin{bmatrix} \frac{1}{2} & 1 \\ 0 & 0 \end{bmatrix} = \begin{bmatrix} \frac{1}{2} & -1 \\ 0 & 1 \end{bmatrix}$$

and, using the formula for finding the inverse of a 2×2 matrix in Section 2.6,

$$(I - R)^{-1} = \begin{bmatrix} 2 & 2 \\ 0 & 1 \end{bmatrix}$$

Thus,

$$S(I - R)^{-1} = \begin{bmatrix} \frac{1}{2} & 0 \end{bmatrix} \begin{bmatrix} 2 & 2 \\ 0 & 1 \end{bmatrix} = \begin{bmatrix} 1 & 1 \end{bmatrix}$$

Therefore, the steady-state matrix of T is given by

$$\begin{bmatrix} I & S(I-R)^{-1} \\ O & O \end{bmatrix} = \begin{matrix} & \\ AA \\ Aa \\ aa \end{matrix} \begin{matrix} AA & Aa & aa \\ \begin{bmatrix} 1 & 1 & 1 \\ 0 & 0 & 0 \\ 0 & 0 & 0 \end{bmatrix} \end{matrix}$$

Interpreting the steady-state matrix of T, we see that the long-term result of crossing the offspring with plants of genotype AA leads only to the absorbing state AA. In other words, such a procedure will result in the production of plants that will bear only red flowers, as we set out to demonstrate. ∎

9.3 Self-Check Exercises

1. Let

$$T = \begin{bmatrix} .2 & 0 & 0 \\ .3 & 1 & .6 \\ .5 & 0 & .4 \end{bmatrix}$$

a. Show that T is an absorbing stochastic matrix.
b. Rewrite T so that the absorbing states appear first, partition the resulting matrix, and identify the submatrices R and S.
c. Compute the steady-state matrix of T.

2. There is a trend toward increased use of computer-aided transcription (CAT) and electronic recording (ER) as alternatives to manual transcription (MT) of court proceedings by court stenographers in a certain state. Suppose the following stochastic matrix gives the transition matrix associated with the Markov process over the past decade:

$$\begin{matrix} & \text{CAT} & \text{ER} & \text{MT} \end{matrix}$$
$$T = \begin{matrix} \text{CAT} \\ \text{ER} \\ \text{MT} \end{matrix} \begin{bmatrix} 1 & .3 & .2 \\ 0 & .6 & .3 \\ 0 & .1 & .5 \end{bmatrix}$$

Determine the probability that a court now using electronic recording or manual transcribing of its proceedings will eventually change to CAT.

Solutions to Self-Check Exercises 9.3 can be found on page 525.

9.3 Concept Questions

1. What is an absorbing stochastic matrix?

2. Suppose the absorbing stochastic matrix A has been partitioned into submatrices

$$\left[\begin{array}{c|c} I & S \\ \hline O & R \end{array}\right]$$

Write the expression representing the steady-state matrix of A.

9.3 Exercises

In Exercises 1–8, determine whether the matrix is an absorbing stochastic matrix.

1. $\begin{bmatrix} \frac{2}{5} & 0 \\ \frac{3}{5} & 1 \end{bmatrix}$

2. $\begin{bmatrix} 1 & 0 \\ 0 & 1 \end{bmatrix}$

3. $\begin{bmatrix} 1 & .5 & 0 \\ 0 & 0 & 1 \\ 0 & .5 & 0 \end{bmatrix}$

4. $\begin{bmatrix} 1 & 0 & 0 \\ 0 & .7 & .2 \\ 0 & .3 & .8 \end{bmatrix}$

5. $\begin{bmatrix} \frac{1}{8} & 0 & 0 \\ \frac{1}{4} & 1 & 0 \\ \frac{5}{8} & 0 & 1 \end{bmatrix}$

6. $\begin{bmatrix} 1 & 0 & 0 & 0 \\ 0 & \frac{5}{8} & 0 & \frac{1}{6} \\ 0 & \frac{1}{8} & 1 & 0 \\ 0 & \frac{1}{4} & 0 & \frac{5}{6} \end{bmatrix}$

7. $\begin{bmatrix} 1 & 0 & .3 & 0 \\ 0 & 1 & .2 & 0 \\ 0 & 0 & .1 & .5 \\ 0 & 0 & .4 & .5 \end{bmatrix}$

8. $\begin{bmatrix} 1 & 0 & 0 & 0 \\ 0 & 1 & 0 & 0 \\ 0 & 0 & .2 & .6 \\ 0 & 0 & .8 & .4 \end{bmatrix}$

In Exercises 9–14, rewrite each absorbing stochastic matrix so that the absorbing states appear first, partition the resulting matrix, and identify the submatrices R and S.

9. $\begin{bmatrix} .6 & 0 \\ .4 & 1 \end{bmatrix}$

10. $\begin{bmatrix} \frac{1}{4} & 0 & 0 \\ \frac{1}{4} & 1 & 0 \\ \frac{1}{2} & 0 & 1 \end{bmatrix}$

11. $\begin{bmatrix} 0 & .2 & 0 \\ .5 & .4 & 0 \\ .5 & .4 & 1 \end{bmatrix}$

12. $\begin{bmatrix} .5 & 0 & .3 \\ 0 & 1 & .1 \\ .5 & 0 & .6 \end{bmatrix}$

13. $\begin{bmatrix} .4 & .2 & 0 & 0 \\ .2 & .3 & 0 & 0 \\ 0 & .3 & 1 & 0 \\ .4 & .2 & 0 & 1 \end{bmatrix}$

14. $\begin{bmatrix} .1 & 0 & 0 & 0 \\ .2 & 1 & 0 & .2 \\ .3 & 0 & 1 & 0 \\ .4 & 0 & 0 & .8 \end{bmatrix}$

In Exercises 15–24, compute the steady-state matrix of each stochastic matrix.

15. $\begin{bmatrix} .55 & 0 \\ .45 & 1 \end{bmatrix}$

16. $\begin{bmatrix} \frac{3}{5} & 0 \\ \frac{2}{5} & 1 \end{bmatrix}$

17. $\begin{bmatrix} 1 & .2 & .3 \\ 0 & .4 & .2 \\ 0 & .4 & .5 \end{bmatrix}$

18. $\begin{bmatrix} \frac{1}{5} & 0 & 0 \\ 0 & 1 & \frac{3}{8} \\ \frac{4}{5} & 0 & \frac{5}{8} \end{bmatrix}$

19. $\begin{bmatrix} \frac{1}{2} & 0 & \frac{1}{3} & 0 \\ \frac{1}{2} & 1 & 0 & 0 \\ 0 & 0 & \frac{2}{3} & 0 \\ 0 & 0 & 0 & 1 \end{bmatrix}$

20. $\begin{bmatrix} 1 & \frac{1}{8} & \frac{1}{3} & 0 \\ 0 & \frac{1}{8} & 0 & 0 \\ 0 & \frac{1}{4} & \frac{2}{3} & 0 \\ 0 & \frac{1}{2} & 0 & 1 \end{bmatrix}$

21. $\begin{bmatrix} 1 & 0 & \frac{1}{4} & \frac{1}{3} \\ 0 & 1 & \frac{1}{4} & \frac{1}{3} \\ 0 & 0 & \frac{1}{2} & 0 \\ 0 & 0 & 0 & \frac{1}{3} \end{bmatrix}$

22. $\begin{bmatrix} 1 & 0 & .2 & .1 \\ 0 & 1 & .4 & .2 \\ 0 & 0 & 0 & .4 \\ 0 & 0 & .4 & .3 \end{bmatrix}$

23. $\begin{bmatrix} 1 & 0 & 0 & .2 & .1 \\ 0 & 1 & 0 & .1 & .2 \\ 0 & 0 & 1 & .3 & .1 \\ 0 & 0 & 0 & .2 & .2 \\ 0 & 0 & 0 & .2 & .4 \end{bmatrix}$

24. $\begin{bmatrix} 1 & 0 & \frac{1}{4} & \frac{1}{3} & 0 \\ 0 & 1 & 0 & \frac{1}{3} & \frac{1}{2} \\ 0 & 0 & \frac{1}{4} & \frac{1}{3} & 0 \\ 0 & 0 & \frac{1}{2} & 0 & \frac{1}{2} \\ 0 & 0 & 0 & 0 & 0 \end{bmatrix}$

25. **BROADBAND INTERNET SERVICE** As more and more people switch to broadband Internet service, the demand for dial-up Internet service will continue to drop. Suppose the transition matrix

$$A = \begin{array}{c} \\ B \\ D \end{array} \begin{array}{c} B \quad\ D \\ \begin{bmatrix} .80 & 0 \\ .20 & 1 \end{bmatrix} \end{array}$$

describes this Markov process, where B denotes broadband Internet service and D denotes dial-up Internet service.

a. Show that A is an absorbing stochastic matrix, and rewrite it so that the absorbing state appears first. Partition the resulting matrix, and identify the submatrices R and S.

b. Compute the steady-state matrix of A, and interpret your results.

26. Diane has decided to play the following game of chance. She places a $1 bet on each repeated play of the game in which the probability of her winning $1 is .5. She has further decided to continue playing the game until she either has accumulated a total of $3 or has lost all her money. What is the probability that Diane will eventually leave the game a winner if she started with a capital of $1? Of $2?

27. Refer to Exercise 26. Suppose Diane has decided to stop playing only after she has accumulated a sum of $4 or has lost all her money. All other conditions being the same,

what is the probability that Diane will leave the game a winner if she started with a capital of $1? Of $2? Of $3?

28. **VIDEO RECORDERS** Over the years, consumers are turning more and more to newer and much improved video-recording devices. The following transition matrix describes the Markov chain associated with this process. Here V stands for VHS recorders, D stands for DVD recorders, and H stands for high-definition video recorders.

$$A = \begin{array}{c} \\ V \\ D \\ H \end{array} \begin{array}{ccc} V & D & H \\ \begin{bmatrix} .10 & 0 & 0 \\ .70 & .60 & 0 \\ .20 & .40 & 1 \end{bmatrix} \end{array}$$

a. Show that A is an absorbing stochastic matrix and rewrite it so that the absorbing state appears first. Partition the resulting matrix, and identify the submatrices R and S.
b. Compute the steady-state matrix of A and interpret your results.

29. **EDUCATION RECORDS** The registrar of Computronics Institute has compiled the following statistics on the progress of the school's students in their 2-year computer programming course leading to an associate degree: Of beginning students in a particular year, 75% successfully complete their first year of study and move on to the second year, whereas 25% drop out of the program; of second-year students in a particular year, 90% go on to graduate at the end of the year, whereas 10% drop out of the program.
a. Construct the transition matrix associated with this Markov process.
b. Compute the steady-state matrix.
c. Determine the probability that a beginning student enrolled in the program will complete the course successfully.

30. **EDUCATION RECORDS** The registrar of a law school has compiled the following statistics on the progress of the school's students working toward the LLB degree: Of the first-year students in a particular year, 85% successfully complete their course of studies and move on to the second year, whereas 15% drop out of the program; of the second-year students in a particular year, 92% go on to the third year, whereas 8% drop out of the program; of the third-year students in a particular year, 98% go on to graduate at the end of the year, whereas 2% drop out of the program.
a. Construct the transition matrix associated with the Markov process.
b. Find the steady-state matrix.
c. Determine the probability that a beginning law student enrolled in the program will go on to graduate.

In Exercises 31 and 32, determine whether the statement is true or false. If it is true, explain why it is true. If it is false, give an example to show why it is false.

31. An absorbing stochastic matrix need not contain an absorbing state.

32. In partitioning an absorbing matrix into subdivisions,

$$A = \begin{bmatrix} I & S \\ \hline O & R \end{bmatrix}$$

the identity matrix I is chosen to have the same order as R.

33. **GENETICS** Refer to Example 4. If the offspring are crossed successively with plants of genotype aa only, show that in the long run, all the flowers produced by the plants will be white.

9.3 Solutions to Self-Check Exercises

1. a. State 2 is an absorbing state. States 1 and 3 are not absorbing, but each has a possibility (with probability .3 and .6) that an object may go from these states to state 2. Therefore, the matrix T is an absorbing stochastic matrix.
b. Denoting the states as indicated, we rewrite

$$\begin{array}{c} \\ 1 \\ 2 \\ 3 \end{array} \begin{array}{ccc} 1 & 2 & 3 \\ \begin{bmatrix} .2 & 0 & 0 \\ .3 & 1 & .6 \\ .5 & 0 & .4 \end{bmatrix} \end{array}$$

in the form

$$\begin{array}{c} \\ 2 \\ 3 \\ 1 \end{array} \begin{array}{ccc} 2 & 3 & 1 \\ \begin{bmatrix} 1 & .6 & .3 \\ 0 & .4 & .5 \\ 0 & 0 & .2 \end{bmatrix} \end{array}$$

We see that

$$S = \begin{bmatrix} .6 & .3 \end{bmatrix} \quad \text{and} \quad R = \begin{bmatrix} .4 & .5 \\ 0 & .2 \end{bmatrix}$$

c. We compute

$$I - R = \begin{bmatrix} 1 & 0 \\ 0 & 1 \end{bmatrix} - \begin{bmatrix} .4 & .5 \\ 0 & .2 \end{bmatrix} = \begin{bmatrix} .6 & -.5 \\ 0 & .8 \end{bmatrix}$$

and, using the formula for finding the inverse of a 2×2 matrix in Section 2.6,

$$(I - R)^{-1} = \begin{bmatrix} 1.67 & 1.04 \\ 0 & 1.25 \end{bmatrix}$$

so

$$S(I - R)^{-1} = \begin{bmatrix} .6 & .3 \end{bmatrix} \begin{bmatrix} 1.67 & 1.04 \\ 0 & 1.25 \end{bmatrix} = \begin{bmatrix} 1 & 1 \end{bmatrix}$$

Therefore, the steady-state matrix of T is

$$\left[\begin{array}{c|cc} 1 & 1 & 1 \\ \hline 0 & 0 & 0 \\ 0 & 0 & 0 \end{array}\right]$$

2. We want to compute the steady-state matrix of T. Note that T is in the form

$$\left[\begin{array}{c|c} I & S \\ \hline O & R \end{array}\right]$$

where

$$S = [.3 \quad .2] \quad \text{and} \quad R = \begin{bmatrix} .6 & .3 \\ .1 & .5 \end{bmatrix}$$

We compute

$$I - R = \begin{bmatrix} 1 & 0 \\ 0 & 1 \end{bmatrix} - \begin{bmatrix} .6 & .3 \\ .1 & .5 \end{bmatrix} = \begin{bmatrix} .4 & -.3 \\ -.1 & .5 \end{bmatrix}$$

and, using the inverse formula in Section 2.6,

$$(I - R)^{-1} = \begin{bmatrix} 2.94 & 1.76 \\ 0.59 & 2.36 \end{bmatrix}$$

so

$$S(I - R)^{-1} = [.3 \quad .2] \begin{bmatrix} 2.94 & 1.76 \\ 0.59 & 2.36 \end{bmatrix} = [1 \quad 1]$$

Therefore, the steady-state matrix of T is

$$\begin{array}{c} \text{CAT} \quad \text{ER} \quad \text{MT} \\ \begin{array}{c} \text{CAT} \\ \text{ER} \\ \text{MT} \end{array} \left[\begin{array}{c|cc} 1 & 1 & 1 \\ \hline 0 & 0 & 0 \\ 0 & 0 & 0 \end{array}\right] \end{array}$$

Interpreting the steady-state matrix of T, we see that in the long run all courts in this state will use computer-aided transcription.

9.4 Game Theory and Strictly Determined Games

The theory of games is a relatively new branch of mathematics and owes much of its development to John von Neumann (1903–1957), one of the mathematical giants of the 20th century. John Harsanyi, John Nash, and Reinhard Selten won the Nobel Prize in Economics in 1994 for their work in this field. Basically, the theory of games combines matrix methods with the theory of probability to determine the optimal strategies to be employed by two or more opponents involved in a competitive situation, with each opponent seeking to maximize his or her "gains," or, equivalently, to minimize his or her "losses." As such, the players may be poker players, managers of rival corporations seeking to extend their share of the market, campaign managers, or generals of opposing armies, to name a few.

For simplicity, we limit our discussion to games with two players. Such games are, naturally enough, called two-person games.

Two-Person Games

APPLIED EXAMPLE 1 Coin-Matching Game Richie and Chuck play a coin-matching game in which each player selects a side of a penny without prior knowledge of the other's choice. Then, upon a predetermined signal, both players disclose their choices simultaneously. Chuck agrees to pay Richie a sum of $3 if both choose heads; if Richie chooses heads and Chuck chooses tails, then Richie pays Chuck $6; if Richie chooses tails and Chuck chooses heads, then Chuck pays Richie $2; finally, if both Richie and Chuck choose tails, then Chuck pays Richie $1. In this game, the objective of each player is to discover a strategy that will ensure that his winnings are maximized (equivalently, that his losses are minimized). ∎

The coin-matching game is an example of a **zero-sum game**—that is, a game in which the payoff to one party results in an equal loss to the other. For such games, the sum of the payments made by both players at the end of each play adds up to zero.

To facilitate the analysis of the problem, we represent the given data in the form of a matrix called a **payoff matrix**:

$$\begin{array}{cc} & \begin{array}{cc} \text{Heads} & \text{Tails} \end{array} \\ R\text{'s moves} \begin{array}{c} \text{Heads} \\ \text{Tails} \end{array} & \begin{bmatrix} 3 & -6 \\ 2 & 1 \end{bmatrix} \end{array}$$

Each row of the matrix corresponds to one of the two possible moves by Richie (referred to as the row player, R), whereas each column corresponds to one of the two possible moves by Chuck (referred to as the column player, C). Each entry in the matrix represents the payoff from C to R. For example, the entry $a_{11} = 3$ represents a $3 payoff from Chuck to Richie (C to R) when Richie chooses to play row 1 (heads) and Chuck chooses to play column 1 (heads). On the other hand, the entry $a_{12} = -6$ represents (because it's negative) a $6 payoff to C (from R) when R chooses to play row 1 (heads) and C chooses to play column 2 (tails). (Interpret the meaning of $a_{21} = 2$ and $a_{22} = 1$ for yourself.)

More generally, suppose we are given a two-person game with two players R and C. Furthermore, suppose that R has m possible moves $R_1, R_2, \ldots, R_m$ and that C has n possible moves $C_1, C_2, \ldots, C_n$. Then we can represent the game in terms of an $m \times n$ matrix in which each row of the matrix represents one of the m possible moves of R and each column of the matrix represents one of the n possible moves of C:

$$\begin{array}{cc} & \begin{array}{ccccccc} C_1 & C_2 & \cdots & C_j & \cdots & C_n \end{array} \\ R\text{'s moves} \begin{array}{c} R_1 \\ R_2 \\ \vdots \\ R_i \\ \vdots \\ R_m \end{array} & \begin{bmatrix} a_{11} & a_{12} & \cdots & a_{1j} & \cdots & a_{1n} \\ a_{21} & a_{22} & \cdots & a_{2j} & \cdots & a_{2n} \\ \vdots & \vdots & & \vdots & & \vdots \\ a_{i1} & a_{i2} & \cdots & a_{ij} & \cdots & a_{in} \\ \vdots & \vdots & & \vdots & & \vdots \\ a_{m1} & a_{m2} & \cdots & a_{mj} & \cdots & a_{mn} \end{bmatrix} \end{array}$$

The entry a_{ij} in the ith row and jth column of the (payoff) matrix represents the payoff to R when R chooses move R_i and C chooses move C_j. In this context, note that a payoff to R means, in actuality, a payoff to C in the event that the value of a_{ij} is negative.

EXAMPLE 2 The payoff matrix associated with a game is given by

$$\begin{array}{cc} & \begin{array}{ccc} C_1 & C_2 & C_3 \end{array} \\ R\text{'s moves} \begin{array}{c} R_1 \\ R_2 \end{array} & \begin{bmatrix} 1 & -2 & 3 \\ 4 & -5 & -1 \end{bmatrix} \end{array}$$

Give an interpretation of this payoff matrix.

Solution In this two-person game, player R has two possible moves, whereas player C has three possible moves. The payoffs are determined as follows: If R chooses R_1, then

R wins 1 unit if C chooses C_1.
R loses 2 units if C chooses C_2.
R wins 3 units if C chooses C_3.

If R chooses R_2, then

R wins 4 units if C chooses C_1.
R loses 5 units if C chooses C_2.
R loses 1 unit if C chooses C_3.

PORTFOLIO

Christian Derrick

TITLE   Technical Director, Europe
INSTITUTION   SpiderCloud Wireless

SpiderCloud Wireless is the start-up company that introduced the first enterprise radio access network (E-RAN) systems into mobile networks. E-RAN technology allows for superior indoor coverage and capacity as well as high-value services for a mobile operator's most important customer, the business user. As the Technical Director, Europe, I am responsible for working with European mobile operators to develop and deliver new wireless technologies.

At SpiderCloud, we draw on our knowledge of mathematics to understand the strategic decisions of our mobile partners. Applying our knowledge of game theory, for example, we can begin to answer a variety of questions such as: How will mobile operators price their voice, data, and SMS plans? And how will suppliers price their cell phone equipment?

Let's consider the first question. If each mobile operator offered identical pricing plans, one would predict that a price reduction by an operator would lead to an increase in that operator's market share. But price, of course, is not the only factor a consumer takes into consideration when selecting a plan. Consumers also consider other variables such as the operator's brand name and reputation, the device that is bundled with the plan, the geographical coverage of the operator's network, and a range of add-on options.

Game theory helps mobile operators to factor the perceived value of these factors into their pricing plans. Operators use game theory to evaluate the likely outcomes of changes in pricing in response to both their competitors' actions and their competitors' responses to their own actions. This helps operators to maximize their profits. Working at SpiderCloud, I have learned that an in-depth knowledge of game theory, including Nash equilibrium and the prisoner's dilemma, is extremely useful for predicting the behavior of players in a complex business environment.

Optimal Strategies

Let's return to the payoff matrix of Example 1 and see how it may be used to help us determine the "best" strategy for each of the two players R and C. For convenience, this matrix is reproduced here:

$$
\begin{array}{cc}
 & \begin{array}{cc} C\text{'s moves} \\ C_1 \quad\ C_2 \end{array} \\
R\text{'s moves} \quad \begin{array}{c} R_1 \\ R_2 \end{array} & \begin{bmatrix} 3 & -6 \\ 2 & 1 \end{bmatrix}
\end{array}
$$

Let's first consider the game from R's point of view. Since the entries in the payoff matrix represent payoffs to R, his initial reaction might be to seek out the largest entry in the matrix and consider the row containing such an entry as a possible move. Thus, he is led to the consideration of R_1 as a possible move.

Let's examine this choice a little more closely. To be sure, R would realize the largest possible payoff to himself ($3) if C chose C_1; but if C chose C_2, then R would lose $6! Since R does not know beforehand what C's move will be, a more prudent approach on R's part would be to assume that no matter what row he chooses, C will counter with a move (column) that will result in the smallest payoff to R. To maximize the payoff to himself under these circumstances, R would then select from among the moves (rows) the one in which the smallest payoff is as large as possible. This strategy for R, which is called, for obvious reasons, the **maximin strategy,** may be summarized as follows:

Maximin Strategy

1. For each row of the payoff matrix, find the smallest entry in that row.
2. Choose the row for which the entry found in step 1 is as large as possible. This row constitutes R's "best" move.

For the problem under consideration, we can organize our work as follows:

$$\begin{bmatrix} 3 & -6 \\ 2 & 1 \end{bmatrix} \quad \begin{matrix} \text{Row} \\ \text{minima} \\ -6 \\ ① \end{matrix} \quad \leftarrow \text{Larger of the row minima}$$

From these results, it is seen that R's "best" move is row 2. By choosing this move, R stands to win at least \$1.

Next, let's consider the game from C's point of view. His objective is to minimize the payoff to R. This is accomplished by choosing the column whose largest payoff is as small as possible. This strategy for C, which is called the **minimax strategy,** may be summarized as follows:

Minimax Strategy

1. For each column of the payoff matrix, find the largest entry in that column.
2. Choose the column for which the entry found in step 1 is as small as possible. This column constitutes C's "best" move.

We can organize the work involved in determining C's "best" move as follows:

$$\begin{bmatrix} 3 & -6 \\ 2 & 1 \end{bmatrix}$$

$$\text{Column maxima} \quad 3 \quad ①$$
$$\uparrow$$
$$\text{Smaller of the column maxima}$$

From these results, we see that C's "best" move is column 2. By choosing this move, C stands to lose at most \$1.

VIDEO

EXAMPLE 3 For the game with the following payoff matrix, determine the maximin and minimax strategies for each player.

$$\begin{bmatrix} -3 & -2 & 4 \\ -2 & 0 & 3 \\ 6 & -1 & 1 \end{bmatrix}$$

Solution We determine the minimum of each row and the maximum of each column of the payoff matrix, and we then display these numbers by circling the largest of the row minima and the smallest of the column maxima:

$$\begin{bmatrix} -3 & -2 & 4 \\ -2 & 0 & 3 \\ 6 & -1 & 1 \end{bmatrix} \quad \begin{matrix} \text{Row} \\ \text{minima} \\ -3 \\ -2 \\ \text{-1} \end{matrix} \quad \leftarrow \text{Largest of the row minima}$$

$$\text{Column maxima} \quad 6 \quad ⓪ \quad 4$$
$$\uparrow$$
$$\text{Smallest of the column maxima}$$

From these results, we conclude that the maximin strategy (for the row player) is to play row 3, whereas the minimax strategy (for the column player) is to play column 2.

EXAMPLE 4 Determine the maximin and minimax strategies for each player in a game whose payoff matrix is given by

$$\begin{bmatrix} 3 & 4 & -4 \\ 2 & -1 & -3 \end{bmatrix}$$

Solution Proceeding as in Example 3, we obtain the following:

Row
minima

$$\begin{bmatrix} 3 & 4 & -4 \\ 2 & -1 & -3 \end{bmatrix} \begin{matrix} -4 \\ \text{-3} \end{matrix} \quad \leftarrow \text{Larger of the row minima}$$

Column maxima   3   4   -3
↑
Smallest of the column maxima

from which we conclude that the maximin strategy for the row player is to play row 2, whereas the minimax strategy for the column player is to play column 3.

In arriving at the maximin and minimax strategies for the respective players, we have assumed that both players always act rationally, with the knowledge that their opponents will always act rationally. This means that each player adopts a strategy of always making the same move and assumes that his opponent is always going to counter that move with a move that will maximize the payoff to the opponent. Thus, each player adopts the pure strategy of always making the move that will minimize the payoff his opponent can receive and thereby maximize the payoff to himself.

This raises the following question: Suppose a game is played repeatedly and one of the players realizes that the opponent is employing his maximin (or minimax) strategy. Can this knowledge be used to the player's advantage? To obtain a partial answer to this question, let's consider the game posed in Example 3. There, the minimax strategy for the column player is to play column 2. Suppose, in repeated plays of the game, a player consistently plays that column and this strategy becomes known to the row player. The row player may then change the strategy from playing row 3 (the maximin strategy) to playing row 2, thereby reducing losses from 1 unit to zero. Thus, at least for this game, the knowledge that a player is employing the maximin or minimax strategy can be used to the opponent's advantage.

There is, however, a class of games in which the knowledge that a player is using the maximin (or minimax) strategy proves of no help to the opponent. Consider the game of Example 4. There, the row player's maximin strategy is to play row 2, and the column player's minimax strategy is to play column 3. Suppose, in repeated plays of the game, R (the row player) has discovered that C (the column player) consistently chooses to play column 3 (the minimax strategy). Can this knowledge be used to R's advantage? Now, other than playing row 2 (the maximin strategy), R may choose to play row 1. But if R makes this choice, then he would lose 4 units instead of 3 units! Clearly, in this case, the knowledge that C is using the minimax strategy cannot be used to advantage. R's optimal (best) strategy is the maximin strategy.

Optimal Strategy

The **optimal strategy** in a game is the strategy that is most profitable to a particular player.

Next, suppose that in repeated plays of the game, C has discovered that R consistently plays row 2 (his optimal strategy). Can this knowledge be used to C's advantage? Another glance at the payoff matrix reveals that by playing column 1, C stands to lose 2 units, and by playing column 2, he stands to win 1 unit, as compared with winning 3 units by playing column 3, as called for by the minimax strategy. Thus, as in the case of R, C does not benefit from knowing his opponent's move. Furthermore, his optimal strategy coincides with the minimax strategy.

This game, in which the row player cannot benefit from knowing that his or her opponent is using the minimax strategy and the column player cannot benefit from knowing that his or her opponent is using the maximin strategy, is said to be strictly determined.

Strictly Determined Game

A **strictly determined game** is characterized by the following properties:

1. There is an entry in the payoff matrix that is *simultaneously* the smallest entry in its row and the largest entry in its column. This entry is called the **saddle point** for the game.

2. The optimal strategy for the row player is the maximin strategy, obtained by choosing the row containing the saddle point. The optimal strategy for the column player is the minimax strategy, obtained by choosing the column containing the saddle point.

The saddle point of a strictly determined game is also referred to as the **value of the game.** If the value of a strictly determined game is positive, then the game favors the row player. If the value is negative, the game favors the column player. If the value of the game is zero, the game is called a **fair game.**

Returning to the coin-matching game discussed earlier, we conclude that Richie's optimal strategy consists of playing row 2 repeatedly, whereas Chuck's optimal strategy consists of playing column 2 repeatedly. Furthermore, the value of the game is 1, implying that the game favors the row player, Richie.

EXAMPLE 5 A two-person, zero-sum game is defined by the payoff matrix

$$A = \begin{bmatrix} 1 & 2 & -3 \\ -1 & 2 & -2 \\ 2 & 3 & -4 \end{bmatrix}$$

a. Show that the game is strictly determined, and find the saddle point(s) for the game.
b. What is the optimal strategy for each player?
c. What is the value of the game? Does the game favor one player over the other?

Solution

a. First, we determine the minimum of each row and the maximum of each column of the payoff matrix A and display these minima and maxima as follows:

$$\begin{bmatrix} 1 & 2 & -3 \\ -1 & 2 & \boxed{-2} \\ 2 & 3 & -4 \end{bmatrix} \begin{matrix} \text{Row} \\ \text{minima} \\ -3 \\ -2 \leftarrow \text{Largest of the row minima} \\ -4 \end{matrix}$$

Column maxima   2   3 -2
                            $\uparrow$
                  Smallest of the column maxima

From these results, we see that the circled entry, -2, is simultaneously the smallest entry in its row and the largest entry in its column. Therefore, the game is strictly determined, with the entry $a_{23} = -2$ as its saddle point.

b. From these results, we see that the optimal strategy for the row player is to make the move represented by the second row of the matrix, and the optimal strategy for the column player is to make the move represented by the third column.

c. The value of the game is -2, which implies that if both players adopt their best strategy, the column player will win 2 units in a play. Consequently, the game favors the column player.   ∎

A game may have more than one saddle point, as the next example shows.

EXAMPLE 6 A two-person, zero-sum game is defined by the payoff matrix

$$A = \begin{bmatrix} 4 & 5 & 4 \\ -2 & -5 & -3 \\ 4 & 6 & 8 \end{bmatrix}$$

a. Show that the game is strictly determined, and find the saddle points for the game.
b. Discuss the optimal strategies for the players.
c. Does the game favor one player over the other?

Solution

a. Proceeding as in the previous example, we obtain the following information:

We see that each of the circled entries, 4, is simultaneously the smallest entry in the row and the largest entry in the column containing it. Therefore, the game is strictly determined, and in this case, it has two saddle points: the entry $a_{11} = 4$ and the entry $a_{31} = 4$. In general, it can be shown that every saddle point of a payoff matrix must have the same value.

b. Since the game has two saddle points, both lying in the first column and in the first and third rows of the payoff matrix, we see that the row player's optimal strategy consists of playing either row 1 or row 3 consistently, whereas the column player's optimal strategy consists of playing column 1 repeatedly.

c. The value of the game is 4, which implies that it favors the row player.   ∎

APPLIED EXAMPLE 7 Bidding for Rights Two television subscription companies, UBS and Telerama, are planning to extend their operations to a certain city. Each has the option of making its services available to prospective subscribers with a special introductory subscription rate. It is estimated that if both UBS and Telerama offer the special subscription rate, each will get 50% of the market, whereas if UBS offers the special subscription rate and Telerama does not, UBS will get 70% of the market. If Telerama offers the special subscription rate and UBS does not, it is estimated that UBS will get 40% of the market. It is estimated that if both companies elect not to offer the special subscription rate, UBS will get 60% of the market.

a. Construct the payoff matrix for the game.
b. Show that the game is strictly determined.
c. Determine the optimal strategy for each company, and find the value of the game.

Solution

a. The required payoff matrix is given by

Telerama

		Intro. rate	Usual rate
	Intro. rate	.50	.70
UBS	Usual rate	.40	.60

b. The entry $a_{11} = .50$ is the smaller entry in its row and the larger entry in its column. Therefore, the entry $a_{11} = .50$ is a saddle point of the game, and the game is strictly determined.

c. The entry $a_{11} = .50$ is the only saddle point of the game, so UBS's optimal strategy is to choose row 1, and Telerama's optimal strategy is to choose column 1. In other words, both companies should offer their potential customers their respective introductory subscription rates. ∎

Explore & Discuss

A two-person, zero-sum game is defined by the payoff matrix

$$A = \begin{bmatrix} a & a \\ c & d \end{bmatrix}$$

1. Show that the game is strictly determined.
2. What can you say about the game with the following payoff matrix?

$$B = \begin{bmatrix} a & b \\ c & c \end{bmatrix}$$

9.4 Self-Check Exercises

1. A two-person, zero-sum game is defined by the payoff matrix

$$A = \begin{bmatrix} -2 & 1 & 3 \\ 3 & 2 & 2 \\ 2 & -1 & 4 \end{bmatrix}$$

a. Show that the game is strictly determined, and find the saddle point(s) for the game.
b. What is the optimal strategy for each player?
c. What is the value of the game? Does the game favor one player over the other?

2. The management of Delta Corporation, a construction and development company, is deciding whether to go ahead with the construction of a large condominium complex. A financial analysis of the project indicates that if Delta goes ahead with the development and the home mortgage rate drops 1 point or more by next year, when the complex is expected to be completed, it will stand to make a profit of $750,000. If Delta goes ahead with the development and

the mortgage rate stays within 1 point of the current rate by next year, Delta will stand to make a profit of $600,000. If Delta goes ahead with the development and the mortgage rate increases 1 point or more by next year, Delta will stand to make a profit of $350,000. If Delta does not go ahead with the development and the mortgage rate drops 1 point or more by next year, Delta will stand to make a profit of $400,000. If Delta does not go ahead with the development and the mortgage rate stays within 1 point of the current rate by next year, Delta will stand to make a profit of $350,000. Finally, if Delta does not go ahead with the development and the mortgage rate increases 1 point or more by next year, Delta stands to make $250,000.

a. Represent this information in the form of a payoff matrix.
b. Assuming that the home mortgage rate trend is volatile over the next year, determine whether or not Delta should go ahead with the project.

Solutions to Self-Check Exercises 9.4 can be found on page 535.

9.4   Concept Questions

1. a. What is the maximin strategy for the row player in a two-person game that is represented by a payoff matrix?

b. What is the minimax strategy for the column player in a two-person game that is represented by a payoff matrix?

2. a. How do you find the saddle point in the payoff matrix for a strictly determined game?

b. What is the optimal strategy for the row player in a strictly determined game? The column player?

9.4   Exercises

In Exercises 1–8, determine the maximin and minimax strategies for each two-person, zero-sum matrix game.

1. $\begin{bmatrix} 2 & 3 \\ 4 & 1 \end{bmatrix}$

2. $\begin{bmatrix} -1 & 3 \\ 2 & 5 \end{bmatrix}$

3. $\begin{bmatrix} 1 & 3 & 2 \\ 0 & -1 & 4 \end{bmatrix}$

4. $\begin{bmatrix} 1 & 4 & -2 \\ 4 & 6 & -3 \end{bmatrix}$

5. $\begin{bmatrix} 3 & 2 & 1 \\ 1 & -2 & 3 \\ 6 & 4 & 1 \end{bmatrix}$

6. $\begin{bmatrix} 1 & 4 \\ 2 & -2 \\ 3 & 0 \end{bmatrix}$

7. $\begin{bmatrix} 4 & 2 & 1 \\ 1 & 0 & -1 \\ 2 & 1 & 3 \end{bmatrix}$

8. $\begin{bmatrix} -1 & 1 & 2 \\ 3 & 1 & 1 \\ -1 & 1 & 2 \\ 3 & 2 & -1 \end{bmatrix}$

In Exercises 9–18, determine whether the two-person, zero-sum matrix game is strictly determined. If a game is strictly determined,
a. Find the saddle point(s) of the game.
b. Find the optimal strategy for each player.
c. Find the value of the game.
d. Determine whether the game favors one player over the other.

9. $\begin{bmatrix} 2 & 3 \\ 1 & -4 \end{bmatrix}$

10. $\begin{bmatrix} 1 & 0 \\ 0 & -1 \end{bmatrix}$

11. $\begin{bmatrix} 1 & 3 & 2 \\ -1 & 4 & -6 \end{bmatrix}$

12. $\begin{bmatrix} 3 & 2 \\ -1 & -2 \\ 4 & 1 \end{bmatrix}$

13. $\begin{bmatrix} 1 & 3 & 4 & 2 \\ 0 & 2 & 6 & -4 \\ -1 & -3 & -2 & 1 \end{bmatrix}$

14. $\begin{bmatrix} 2 & 4 & 2 \\ 0 & 3 & 0 \\ -1 & -2 & 1 \end{bmatrix}$

15. $\begin{bmatrix} 1 & 2 \\ 0 & 3 \\ -1 & 2 \\ 2 & -2 \end{bmatrix}$

16. $\begin{bmatrix} -1 & 2 & 4 \\ 2 & 3 & 5 \\ 0 & 1 & -3 \\ -2 & 4 & -2 \end{bmatrix}$

17. $\begin{bmatrix} 1 & -1 & 3 & 2 \\ 1 & 0 & 2 & 2 \\ -2 & 2 & 3 & -1 \end{bmatrix}$

18. $\begin{bmatrix} 3 & -1 & 0 & -4 \\ 2 & 1 & 0 & 2 \\ -3 & 1 & -2 & 1 \\ -1 & -1 & -2 & 1 \end{bmatrix}$

19. Robin and Cathy play a game of matching fingers. On a predetermined signal, both players simultaneously extend 1, 2, or 3 fingers from a closed fist. If the sum of the number of fingers extended is even, then Robin receives an amount in dollars equal to that sum from Cathy. If the sum of the number of fingers extended is odd, then Cathy receives an amount in dollars equal to that sum from Robin.

a. Construct the payoff matrix for the game.

b. Find the maximin and the minimax strategies for Robin and Cathy, respectively.

c. Is the game strictly determined?

d. If the answer to part (c) is yes, what is the value of the game?

20. MANAGEMENT DECISIONS Brady's, a conventional department store, and ValueMart, a discount department store, are both considering opening new stores at one of two possible sites: the Civic Center and North Shore Plaza. The strategies available to the management of each store are given in the following payoff matrix, where each entry represents the amounts (in hundreds of thousands of dollars) either gained or lost by one business from or to the other as a result of the sites selected.

$$\begin{array}{c} \\ \text{Brady's} \end{array} \begin{array}{cc} & \begin{array}{cc} \text{ValueMart} \\ \text{Center} \quad \text{Plaza} \end{array} \\ \begin{array}{c} \text{Civic Center} \\ \text{North Shore Plaza} \end{array} & \begin{bmatrix} 2 & -2 \\ 3 & -4 \end{bmatrix} \end{array}$$

a. Show that the game is strictly determined.

b. What is the value of the game?

c. Determine the best strategy for the management of each store (that is, determine the ideal locations for each store).

21. FINANCIAL ANALYSIS The management of Acrosonic is faced with the problem of deciding whether to expand the production of its line of electrostatic loudspeaker systems. It has been estimated that an expansion will result in an annual profit of $200,000 for Acrosonic if the general economic climate is good. On the other hand, an expansion during a period of economic recession will cut Acrosonic's annual profit to $120,000. As an alternative, Acrosonic may hold the production of its electrostatic loudspeaker systems at the current level and expand its line of conventional loudspeaker systems. In this event, the company will make a profit of $50,000 in an expanding economy (because many potential customers will be expected to buy electrostatic loudspeaker systems from other competitors) and a profit of $150,000 in a recessionary economy.

a. Construct the payoff matrix for this game.

Hint: The row player is the management of the company, and the column player is the economy.

b. Should management recommend expanding the company's line of electrostatic loudspeaker systems?

22. **FINANCIAL ANALYSIS** The proprietor of Belvedere's is faced with the problem of deciding whether to expand her restaurant facilities now or to wait until some future date to do so. If she expands the facilities now and the economy experiences a period of growth during the coming year, she will make a net profit of $442,000; if she expands now and a period of zero growth follows, then she will make a net profit of $40,000; and if she expands now and an economic recession follows, she will suffer a net loss of $108,000. If she does not expand the restaurant now and the economy experiences a period of growth during the coming year, she will make a net profit of $280,000; if she does not expand now and a period of zero growth follows, she will make a net profit of $190,000. Finally, if she does not expand now and an economic recession follows, she will make a net profit of $100,000.

a. Represent this information in the form of a payoff matrix.

b. Determine whether the owner of the restaurant should expand her facilities at this time.

23. **MARKET SHARE** Roland's Barber Shop and Charley's Barber Shop are both located in the business district of a certain town. Roland estimates that if he raises the price of a haircut by $1, he will increase his market share by 3% if Charley raises his price by the same amount; he will decrease his market share by 1% if Charley holds his price at the same level; and he will decrease his market share by 3% if Charley lowers his price by $1. If Roland keeps his price the same, he will increase his market share by 2% if Charley raises his price by $1; he will keep the same market share if Charley holds the price at the same level; and he will decrease his market share by 2% if Charley lowers his price by $1. Finally, if Roland lowers the price he charges by $1, his market share will increase by 5% if Charley raises his prices by the same amount; he will increase his market share by 2% if Charley holds his price at the same level; and he will increase his market share by 1% if Charley lowers his price by $1.

a. Construct the payoff matrix for this game.

b. Show that the game is strictly determined.

c. If neither party is willing to lower the price he charges for a haircut, show that both should keep their present price structures.

In Exercises 24–26, determine whether the statement is true or false. If it is true, explain why it is true. If it is false, give an example to show why it is false.

24. In a zero-sum game, the payments made by the players at the end of each play add up to zero.

25. In a strictly determined game, the value of the game is given by the saddle point of the game.

26. If the value of a strictly determined game is not negative, it favors the row player.

9.4 Solutions to Self-Check Exercises

1. a. Displaying the minimum of each row and the maximum of each column of the payoff matrix A, we obtain

$$
\begin{array}{c}
\\
\begin{bmatrix} -2 & 1 & 3 \\ 3 & ② & 2 \\ 2 & -1 & 4 \end{bmatrix}
\begin{array}{l} -2 \\ 2 \\ -1 \end{array}
\end{array}
\begin{array}{l} \\ \leftarrow \text{Largest of the row minima} \end{array}
$$

Row minima

Column maxima 3   2   4

↑
Smallest of the column maxima

From these results, we see that the circled entry, 2, is simultaneously the smallest entry in its row and the largest entry in its column. Therefore, the game is strictly determined, with the entry $a_{22} = 2$ as its saddle point.

b. From these results, we see that the optimal strategy for the row player is to make the move represented by the second row of the matrix, and the optimal strategy for the column player is to make the move represented by the second column.

c. The value of the game is 2, which implies that if both players adopt their best strategy, the row player will win 2 units in a play. Consequently, the game favors the row player.

2. a. We may review this situation as a game in which the row player is Delta and the column player is the home mortgage rate. The required payoff matrix is

Mortgage rate

		Decrease	Steady	Increase
Delta	Project	$\begin{bmatrix} 750 $	$ 600 $	$ 350 \\ $
Corp.	No project	$ 400 $	$ 350 $	$ 250 \end{bmatrix}$

(All figures are in thousands of dollars.)

b. From part (a), the payoff matrix under consideration is

$$
\begin{bmatrix} 750 & 600 & 350 \\ 400 & 350 & 250 \end{bmatrix}
$$

Proceeding in the usual manner, we find

From these results, we see that the entry $a_{13} = 350$ is a saddle point, and the game is strictly determined. We can also conclude that the company should go ahead with the project.

$$
\begin{bmatrix}
750 & 600 & \boxed{350} \\
400 & 350 & 250
\end{bmatrix}
\begin{array}{l}
\text{Row} \\
\text{minima} \\
350 \;\leftarrow\; \begin{array}{l}\text{Largest of the}\\\text{row minima}\end{array} \\
250
\end{array}
$$

Column maxima   750   600   350
↑
Smallest of the column maxima

9.5 Games with Mixed Strategies

In Section 9.4, we discussed strictly determined games and found that the optimal strategy for the row player is to select the row containing a saddle point for the game, and the optimal strategy for the column player is to select the column containing a saddle point. Furthermore, in repeated plays of the game, each player's optimal strategy consists of making the same move over and over again, since the discovery of the opponent's optimal strategy cannot be used to advantage. Such strategies are called **pure strategies.** In this section, we look at games that are not strictly determined and the strategies associated with such games.

Mixed Strategies

As a simple example of a game that is not strictly determined, let's consider the following slightly modified version of the coin-matching game played by Richie and Chuck (see Example 1, Section 9.4). Suppose Richie wins $3 if both parties choose heads and $1 if both choose tails and loses $2 if one chooses heads and the other tails. Then the payoff matrix for this game is given by

$$
\begin{array}{c}
\hspace{3.2cm} C\text{'s moves} \\
\hspace{3cm} \begin{array}{cc} C_1 & C_2 \\ \text{(heads)} & \text{(tails)} \end{array} \\
R\text{'s moves} \quad \begin{array}{c} R_1 \text{ (heads)} \\ R_2 \text{ (tails)} \end{array}
\begin{bmatrix} 3 & -2 \\ -2 & 1 \end{bmatrix}
\end{array}
$$

A quick examination of this matrix reveals that it contains no entry that is simultaneously the smallest entry in its row and the largest entry in its column; that is, the game has no saddle point and is therefore not strictly determined. What strategy might Richie adopt for the game? Offhand, it would seem that he should consistently select row 1, since he stands to win $3 by playing this row and only $1 by playing row 2 at a risk, in either case, of losing $2. However, if Chuck discovers that Richie is playing row 1 consistently, he would counter this strategy by playing column 2, causing Richie to lose $2 on each play! In view of this, Richie is led to consider a strategy whereby he chooses row 1 some of the time and row 2 at other times. A similar analysis of the game from Chuck's point of view suggests that he might consider choosing column 1 some of the time and column 2 at other times. Such strategies are called **mixed strategies.**

From a practical point of view, there are many ways in which a player may choose moves in a game with mixed strategies. For example, in the game just mentioned, if Richie decides to play heads half the time and tails the other half of the time, he could toss an unbiased coin before each move and let the outcome of the toss determine which move he should make. Here is another more general but less practical way of deciding on the choice of a move: Having determined beforehand the proportion of the time row 1 is to be chosen (and therefore the proportion of the time row 2 is to be chosen), Richie might construct a spinner (Figure 3) in which the areas of the two sectors

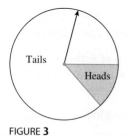

FIGURE 3

reflect these proportions and let the move be decided by the outcome of a spin. These two methods for determining a player's move in a game with mixed strategies guarantee that the strategy will not fall into a pattern that will be discovered by the opponent.

From a mathematical point of view, we may describe the mixed strategy of a row player in terms of a row vector whose dimension coincides with the number of possible moves the player has. For example, if Richie had decided on a strategy in which he chose to play row 1 half the time and row 2 the other half of the time, then this strategy is represented by the row vector

$$[.5 \quad .5]$$

Similarly, the mixed strategy for a column player may be represented by a column vector of appropriate dimension. For example, returning to our illustration, suppose Chuck has decided that 20% of the time he will choose column 1 and 80% of the time he will choose column 2. This strategy is represented by the column vector

$$\begin{bmatrix} .2 \\ .8 \end{bmatrix}$$

Expected Value of a Game

For the purpose of comparing the merits of a player's different mixed strategies in a game, it is convenient to introduce a number called the expected value of a game. The **expected value of a game** measures the average payoff to the row player when both players adopt a particular set of mixed strategies. We now explain this notion using a 2×2 matrix game whose payoff matrix has the general form

$$A = \begin{bmatrix} a_{11} & a_{12} \\ a_{21} & a_{22} \end{bmatrix}$$

Suppose that in repeated plays of the game, the row player R adopts the mixed strategy

$$P = [p_1 \quad p_2]$$

(that is, the player selects row 1 with probability p_1 and row 2 with probability p_2), and the column player C adopts the mixed strategy

$$Q = \begin{bmatrix} q_1 \\ q_2 \end{bmatrix}$$

(that is, the column player selects column 1 with probability q_1 and column 2 with probability q_2). Now, in each play of the game, there are four possible outcomes, which may be represented by the ordered pairs

(row 1, column 1)

(row 1, column 2)

(row 2, column 1)

(row 2, column 2)

where the first number of each ordered pair represents R's selection and the second number of each ordered pair represents C's selection. Since the choice of moves is made by one player without knowing the other's choice, each pair of events (for example, the events "row 1" and "column 1") constitutes a pair of independent events. Therefore, the probability of R choosing row 1 and C choosing column 1, $P(\text{row 1, column 1})$, is given by

$$P(\text{row 1, column 1}) = P(\text{row 1}) \cdot P(\text{column 1})$$
$$= p_1 q_1$$

In a similar manner, we compute the probability of each of the other three outcomes. These calculations, together with the payoffs associated with each of the four possible outcomes, may be summarized as follows:

Outcome	Probability	Payoff
(row 1, column 1)	p_1q_1	a_{11}
(row 1, column 2)	p_1q_2	a_{12}
(row 2, column 1)	p_2q_1	a_{21}
(row 2, column 2)	p_2q_2	a_{22}

Then the *expected payoff E* of the game is the sum of the products of the payoffs and the corresponding probabilities (see Section 8.2). Thus,

$$E = p_1q_1a_{11} + p_1q_2a_{12} + p_2q_1a_{21} + p_2q_2a_{22}$$

In terms of the matrices P, A, and Q, we have the following relatively simple expression for E:

$$E = PAQ$$

which you may verify (Exercise 22). This result may be generalized as follows:

Expected Value of a Game
Let

$$P = [p_1 \quad p_2 \quad \cdots \quad p_m] \quad \text{and} \quad Q = \begin{bmatrix} q_1 \\ q_2 \\ \vdots \\ q_n \end{bmatrix}$$

be the vectors representing the mixed strategies for the row player R and the column player C, respectively, in a game with the $m \times n$ payoff matrix

$$A = \begin{bmatrix} a_{11} & a_{12} & \cdots & a_{1n} \\ a_{21} & a_{22} & \cdots & a_{2n} \\ \vdots & \vdots & & \vdots \\ a_{m1} & a_{m2} & \cdots & a_{mn} \end{bmatrix}$$

Then the expected value of the game is given by

$$E = PAQ = [p_1 \quad p_2 \quad \cdots \quad p_m] \begin{bmatrix} a_{11} & a_{12} & \cdots & a_{1n} \\ a_{21} & a_{22} & \cdots & a_{2n} \\ \vdots & \vdots & & \vdots \\ a_{m1} & a_{m2} & \cdots & a_{mn} \end{bmatrix} \begin{bmatrix} q_1 \\ q_2 \\ \vdots \\ q_n \end{bmatrix}$$

We now look at several examples involving the computation of the expected value of a game.

APPLIED EXAMPLE 1 Coin-Matching Game Consider a coin-matching game played by Richie and Chuck with the payoff matrix (in dollars) given by

$$A = \begin{bmatrix} 3 & -2 \\ -2 & 1 \end{bmatrix}$$

Compute the expected payoff of the game if Richie adopts the mixed strategy P and Chuck adopts the mixed strategy Q, where

a. $P = [.5 \quad .5]$ and $Q = \begin{bmatrix} .5 \\ .5 \end{bmatrix}$

b. $P = [.8 \quad .2]$ and $Q = \begin{bmatrix} .1 \\ .9 \end{bmatrix}$

Solution

a. We compute

$$E = PAQ = [.5 \quad .5] \begin{bmatrix} 3 & -2 \\ -2 & 1 \end{bmatrix} \begin{bmatrix} .5 \\ .5 \end{bmatrix}$$

$$= [.5 \quad -.5] \begin{bmatrix} .5 \\ .5 \end{bmatrix}$$

$$= 0$$

Thus, in repeated plays of the game, it may be expected that in the long term, the payoff to each player is 0.

b. We compute

$$E = PAQ = [.8 \quad .2] \begin{bmatrix} 3 & -2 \\ -2 & 1 \end{bmatrix} \begin{bmatrix} .1 \\ .9 \end{bmatrix}$$

$$= [2 \quad -1.4] \begin{bmatrix} .1 \\ .9 \end{bmatrix}$$

$$= -1.06$$

That is, in the long run, Richie may be expected to lose $1.06 on the average in each play. ∎

VIDEO **EXAMPLE 2** The payoff matrix for a certain game is given by

$$A = \begin{bmatrix} 1 & -2 \\ -1 & 2 \\ 3 & -3 \end{bmatrix}$$

a. Find the expected payoff to the row player if the row player R uses her maximin pure strategy and the column player C uses her minimax pure strategy.

b. Find the expected payoff to the row player if R uses her maximin strategy 50% of the time and chooses each of the other two rows 25% of the time, while C chooses each column 50% of the time.

Solution

a. The maximin and minimax strategies for the row and column players, respectively, may be found by using the method of Section 9.4. Thus,

$$\begin{bmatrix} 1 & -2 \\ -1 & 2 \\ 3 & -3 \end{bmatrix} \begin{matrix} -2 \\ \ominus \!\!1 \leftarrow \text{Largest of the row minima} \\ -3 \end{matrix}$$

Row minima

Column maxima   3   ②
↑
Smaller of the column maxima

From these results, we see that R's optimal pure strategy is to choose row 2, whereas C's optimal pure strategy is to choose column 2. Furthermore, if both players use these strategies, then the expected payoff to R is 2 units.

b. In this case, R's mixed strategy may be represented by the row vector

$$P = [.25 \quad .50 \quad .25]$$

and C's mixed strategy may be represented by the column vector

$$Q = \begin{bmatrix} .5 \\ .5 \end{bmatrix}$$

The expected payoff to the row player will then be given by

$$E = PAQ = [.25 \quad .50 \quad .25] \begin{bmatrix} 1 & -2 \\ -1 & 2 \\ 3 & -3 \end{bmatrix} \begin{bmatrix} .5 \\ .5 \end{bmatrix}$$

$$= [.5 \quad -.25] \begin{bmatrix} .5 \\ .5 \end{bmatrix}$$

$$= .125$$

In Section 9.4, we studied optimal strategies associated with strictly determined games and found them to be precisely the maximin and minimax pure strategies adopted by the row and column players. We now look at optimal mixed strategies associated with matrix games that are not strictly determined. In particular, we state, without proof, the optimal mixed strategies to be adopted by the players in a 2×2 matrix game.

As we saw earlier, a player in a nonstrictly determined game should adopt a mixed strategy, since a pure strategy will soon be detected by the opponent, who may then use this knowledge to his advantage in devising a counterstrategy. Since there are infinitely many mixed strategies for each player in such a game, the question arises as to how an optimal mixed strategy may be discovered for each player. An optimal mixed strategy for a player is one in which the row player maximizes his expected payoff and the column player simultaneously minimizes the row player's expected payoff.

More precisely, the optimal mixed strategy for the row player is arrived at by using the following argument: The row player anticipates that any mixed strategy he adopts will be met by a counterstrategy by the column player that will minimize the row player's payoff. Consequently, the row player adopts the mixed strategy for which the expected payoff to the row player (when the column player uses his best counterstrategy) is maximized.

Similarly, the optimal mixed strategy for the column player is arrived at by using the following argument: The column player anticipates that the row player will choose a counterstrategy that will maximize the row player's payoff regardless of the mixed strategy he (the column player) chooses. Consequently, the column player adopts the mixed strategy for which the expected payoff to the row player (who will use his best counterstrategy) is minimized.

Without going into details, let's note that the problem of finding the optimal mixed strategies for the players in a nonstrictly determined game is equivalent to the problem of solving a related linear programming problem. However, for a 2×2 nonstrictly determined game, the optimal mixed strategies for the players may be found by employing the formulas contained in the following result, which we state without proof.

Optimal Strategies for Nonstrictly Determined Games

Let

$$\begin{bmatrix} a & b \\ c & d \end{bmatrix}$$

be the payoff matrix for a nonstrictly determined game. Then the **optimal mixed strategy for the row player** is given by

$$P = [p_1 \quad p_2] \tag{2a}$$

where

$$p_1 = \frac{d - c}{a + d - b - c} \quad \text{and} \quad p_2 = 1 - p_1$$

and the **optimal mixed strategy for the column player** is given by

$$Q = \begin{bmatrix} q_1 \\ q_2 \end{bmatrix} \tag{2b}$$

where

$$q_1 = \frac{d - b}{a + d - b - c} \quad \text{and} \quad q_2 = 1 - q_1$$

Furthermore, the **value of the game** is given by the expected value of the game, $E = PAQ$, where P and Q are the optimal mixed strategies for the row and column players, respectively. Thus,

$$E = PAQ$$
$$= \frac{ad - bc}{a + d - b - c} \tag{2c}$$

The next example illustrates the use of these formulas in finding the optimal mixed strategies and in finding the value of a 2×2 (nonstrictly determined) game.

 APPLIED EXAMPLE 3 Coin-Matching Game (continued) Consider the coin-matching game played by Richie and Chuck with the payoff matrix

$$A = \begin{bmatrix} 3 & -2 \\ -2 & 1 \end{bmatrix} \quad \text{See Example 1.}$$

a. Find the optimal mixed strategies for both Richie and Chuck.
b. Find the value of the game. Does it favor one player over the other?

Solution

a. The game under consideration has no saddle point and is accordingly nonstrictly determined. Using Equation (2a) with $a = 3$, $b = -2$, $c = -2$, and $d = 1$, we find that

$$p_1 = \frac{d - c}{a + d - b - c} = \frac{1 - (-2)}{3 + 1 - (-2) - (-2)} = \frac{3}{8}$$
$$p_2 = 1 - p_1$$
$$= 1 - \frac{3}{8}$$
$$= \frac{5}{8}$$

so Richie's optimal mixed strategy is given by

$$P = [p_1 \quad p_2]$$

$$= [\tfrac{3}{8} \quad \tfrac{5}{8}]$$

Using Equation (2b), we find that

$$q_1 = \frac{d - b}{a + d - b - c} = \frac{1 - (-2)}{3 + 1 - (-2) - (-2)} = \frac{3}{8}$$

$$q_2 = 1 - q_1$$

$$= 1 - \frac{3}{8}$$

$$= \frac{5}{8}$$

giving Chuck's optimal mixed strategy as

$$Q = \begin{bmatrix} \tfrac{3}{8} \\ \tfrac{5}{8} \end{bmatrix}$$

b. The value of the game may be found by computing the matrix product PAQ, where P and Q are the vectors found in part (a). Equivalently, using Equation (2c), we find that

$$E = \frac{ad - bc}{a + d - b - c}$$

$$= \frac{(3)(1) - (-2)(-2)}{3 + 1 - (-2) - (-2)}$$

$$= -\frac{1}{8}$$

Since the value of the game is negative, we conclude that the coin-matching game with the given payoff matrix favors Chuck (the column player) over Richie. Over the long run, in repeated plays of the game, where each player uses his optimal strategy, Chuck is expected to win $\frac{1}{8}$, or 12.5¢, on the average per play.   ∎

APPLIED EXAMPLE 4 Investment Strategies As part of their investment strategy, the Carringtons have earmarked $40,000 for short-term investments in the stock market and the money market. The performance of the investments depends on the prime rate (that is, the interest rate that banks charge their best customers). An increase in the prime rate generally favors their investment in the money market, whereas a decrease in the prime rate generally favors their investment in the stock market. Suppose the following payoff matrix gives the percentage increase or decrease in the value of each investment for each state of the prime rate:

	Prime rate up	Prime rate down
Money market investment	15	10
Stock market investment	−5	25

a. Determine the optimal investment strategy for the Carringtons' short-term investment of $40,000.
b. What short-term profit can the Carringtons expect to make on their investments?

Solution

a. We treat the problem as a matrix game in which the Carringtons are the row player. Letting $p = [p_1 \quad p_2]$ denote their optimal strategy, we find that

$$p_1 = \frac{d - c}{a + d - b - c} = \frac{25 - (-5)}{15 + 25 - 10 - (-5)} \qquad a = 15, b = 10, c = -5, \text{ and } d = 25$$

$$= \frac{30}{35} = \frac{6}{7}$$

$$p_2 = 1 - p_1 = 1 - \frac{6}{7} = \frac{1}{7}$$

Thus, the Carringtons should put $(\frac{6}{7})(\$40,000)$, or approximately \$34,300, into the money market and $(\frac{1}{7})(\$40,000)$, or approximately \$5700, into the stock market.

b. The expected value of the game is given by

$$E = \frac{ad - bc}{a + d - b - c}$$

$$= \frac{(15)(25) - (10)(-5)}{15 + 25 - 10 - (-5)} = \frac{425}{35}$$

$$\approx 12.14$$

Thus, the Carringtons can expect to make a short-term profit of 12.14% on their total investment of \$40,000—that is, a profit of $(0.1214)(40,000)$, or \$4856. ■

Explore & Discuss

A two-person, zero-sum game is defined by the payoff matrix

$$A = \begin{bmatrix} x & 1 - x \\ 1 - x & x \end{bmatrix}$$

1. For what value(s) of x is the game strictly determined? For what value(s) of x is the game not strictly determined?

2. What is the value of the game?

9.5 Self-Check Exercises

1. The payoff matrix for a game is given by

$$A = \begin{bmatrix} 2 & 3 & -1 \\ -3 & 2 & -2 \\ 3 & -2 & 2 \end{bmatrix}$$

a. Find the expected payoff to the row player if the row player R uses the maximin pure strategy and the column player C uses the minimax pure strategy.

b. Find the expected payoff to the row player if R uses the maximin strategy 40% of the time and chooses each of the other two rows 30% of the time while C uses the minimax strategy 50% of the time and chooses each of the other two columns 25% of the time.

c. Which pair of strategies favors the row player?

2. A farmer has allocated 2000 acres of her farm for planting two crops. Crop A is more susceptible to frost than Crop B is. If there is no frost in the growing season, then she can expect to make \$40/acre from Crop A and \$25/acre from Crop B. If there is mild frost, the expected profits are \$20/acre from Crop A and \$30/acre from Crop B. How many acres of each crop should the farmer cultivate to maximize her profits? What profit could she expect to make using this optimal strategy?

Solutions to Self-Check Exercises 9.5 can be found on page 546.

9.5   Concept Questions

1. What does the expected value of a game measure?

2. Suppose

$$\begin{bmatrix} a & b \\ c & d \end{bmatrix}$$

is the payoff matrix for a nonstrictly determined game.
  a. What is the optimal mixed strategy for the column player?
  b. What is the optimal mixed strategy for the row player?
  c. What is the value of the game?

9.5   Exercises

In Exercises 1–6, find the expected payoff E of each game whose payoff matrix and strategies P and Q (for the row and column players, respectively) are given.

1. $\begin{bmatrix} 3 & 1 \\ -4 & 2 \end{bmatrix}$, $P = [\frac{1}{2} \quad \frac{1}{2}]$, $Q = \begin{bmatrix} \frac{3}{5} \\ \frac{2}{5} \end{bmatrix}$

2. $\begin{bmatrix} -1 & 4 \\ 3 & -2 \end{bmatrix}$, $P = [.8 \quad .2]$, $Q = \begin{bmatrix} .6 \\ .4 \end{bmatrix}$

3. $\begin{bmatrix} -4 & 3 \\ 2 & 1 \end{bmatrix}$, $P = [\frac{1}{3} \quad \frac{2}{3}]$, $Q = \begin{bmatrix} \frac{3}{4} \\ \frac{1}{4} \end{bmatrix}$

4. $\begin{bmatrix} 1 & 2 \\ -3 & 1 \end{bmatrix}$, $P = [\frac{3}{5} \quad \frac{2}{5}]$, $Q = \begin{bmatrix} \frac{1}{3} \\ \frac{2}{3} \end{bmatrix}$

5. $\begin{bmatrix} 2 & 0 & -2 \\ 1 & -1 & 3 \\ 2 & 1 & -4 \end{bmatrix}$, $P = [.2 \quad .6 \quad .2]$, $Q = \begin{bmatrix} .2 \\ .6 \\ .2 \end{bmatrix}$

6. $\begin{bmatrix} 1 & -4 & 2 \\ 2 & 1 & -1 \\ 2 & -2 & 0 \end{bmatrix}$, $P = [.2 \quad .3 \quad .5]$, $Q = \begin{bmatrix} .6 \\ .2 \\ .2 \end{bmatrix}$

7. The payoff matrix for a game is given by

$$\begin{bmatrix} 1 & -2 \\ -2 & 3 \end{bmatrix}$$

Compute the expected payoffs of the game for the pairs of strategies in parts (a–d). Which of these strategies is most advantageous to R?

a. $P = [1 \quad 0]$, $Q = \begin{bmatrix} 1 \\ 0 \end{bmatrix}$

b. $P = [0 \quad 1]$, $Q = \begin{bmatrix} 1 \\ 0 \end{bmatrix}$

c. $P = [\frac{1}{2} \quad \frac{1}{2}]$, $Q = \begin{bmatrix} \frac{1}{2} \\ \frac{1}{2} \end{bmatrix}$

d. $P = [.5 \quad .5]$, $Q = \begin{bmatrix} .8 \\ .2 \end{bmatrix}$

8. The payoff matrix for a game is

$$\begin{bmatrix} 3 & 1 & 1 \\ 0 & 2 & 0 \\ -1 & 0 & 2 \end{bmatrix}$$

Compute the expected payoffs of the game for the pairs of strategies in parts (a–d). Which of these strategies is most advantageous to R?

a. $P = [\frac{1}{3} \quad \frac{1}{3} \quad \frac{1}{3}]$, $Q = \begin{bmatrix} \frac{1}{3} \\ \frac{1}{3} \\ \frac{1}{3} \end{bmatrix}$

b. $P = [\frac{1}{4} \quad \frac{1}{2} \quad \frac{1}{4}]$, $Q = \begin{bmatrix} \frac{1}{8} \\ \frac{3}{8} \\ \frac{1}{2} \end{bmatrix}$

c. $P = [.4 \quad .3 \quad .3]$, $Q = \begin{bmatrix} .6 \\ .2 \\ .2 \end{bmatrix}$

d. $P = [.1 \quad .5 \quad .4]$, $Q = \begin{bmatrix} .3 \\ .3 \\ .4 \end{bmatrix}$

9. The payoff matrix for a game is

$$\begin{bmatrix} -3 & 3 & 2 \\ -3 & 1 & 1 \\ 1 & -2 & 1 \end{bmatrix}$$

a. Find the expected payoff to the row player if the row player R uses the maximin pure strategy and the column player C uses the minimax pure strategy.
b. Find the expected payoff to the row player if R uses the maximin strategy 50% of the time and chooses each of the other two rows 25% of the time, while C uses the minimax strategy 60% of the time and chooses each of the other columns 20% of the time.
c. Which of these pairs of strategies is most advantageous to the row player?

10. The payoff matrix for a game is

$$\begin{bmatrix} 4 & -3 & 3 \\ -4 & 2 & 1 \\ 3 & -5 & 2 \end{bmatrix}$$

a. Find the expected payoff to the row player if the row player R uses the maximin pure strategy and the column player C uses the minimax pure strategy.
b. Find the expected payoff to the row player if R uses the maximin strategy 40% of the time and chooses each of the other two rows 30% of the time, while C uses the

minimax strategy 50% of the time and chooses each of the other columns 25% of the time.

c. Which of these pairs of strategies is most advantageous to the row player?

In Exercises 11–16, find the optimal strategies, P and Q, for the row and column players, respectively. Also compute the expected payoff E of each matrix game and determine which player it favors, if any, if the row and column players use their optimal strategies.

11. $\begin{bmatrix} 4 & 1 \\ 2 & 3 \end{bmatrix}$ **12.** $\begin{bmatrix} 2 & 5 \\ 3 & -6 \end{bmatrix}$ **13.** $\begin{bmatrix} -1 & 2 \\ 1 & -3 \end{bmatrix}$

14. $\begin{bmatrix} -1 & 3 \\ 2 & 0 \end{bmatrix}$ **15.** $\begin{bmatrix} -2 & -6 \\ -8 & -4 \end{bmatrix}$ **16.** $\begin{bmatrix} 2 & 5 \\ -2 & 4 \end{bmatrix}$

17. Consider the coin-matching game played by Richie and Chuck (see Examples 1 and 3) with the payoff matrix

$$A = \begin{bmatrix} 4 & -2 \\ -2 & 1 \end{bmatrix}$$

a. Find the optimal strategies for Richie and Chuck.

b. Find the value of the game. Does it favor one player over the other?

18. INVESTMENT STRATEGIES As part of their investment strategy, the Carringtons have decided to put $100,000 into stock market investments and also into purchasing precious metals. The performance of the investments depends on the state of the economy in the next year. In an expanding economy, it is expected that their stock market investment will outperform their investment in precious metals, whereas an economic recession will have precisely the opposite effect. Suppose the following payoff matrix gives the expected percentage increase or decrease in the value of each investment for each state of the economy:

	Expanding economy	Economic recession
Stock market investment	20	−5
Commodity investment	10	15

a. Determine the optimal investment strategy for the Carringtons' investment of $100,000.

b. What profit can the Carringtons expect to make on their investments over the year if they use their optimal investment strategy?

19. INVESTMENT STRATEGIES The Maxwells have decided to invest $40,000 in the common stocks of two companies listed on the New York Stock Exchange. One of the companies derives its revenue mainly from its worldwide operation of a chain of hotels, whereas the other company is a domestic major brewery. It is expected that if the economy is in a state of growth, then the hotel stock should outperform the brewery stock; however, the brewery stock is expected to hold its own better than the hotel stock in a recessionary period. Suppose the following payoff matrix gives the expected percentage increase or decrease in the value of each investment for each state of the economy:

	Expanding economy	Economic recession
Investment in hotel stock	25	−5
Investment in brewery stock	10	15

a. Determine the optimal investment strategy for the Maxwells' investment of $40,000.

b. What profit can the Maxwells expect to make on their investments if they use their optimal investment strategy?

20. CAMPAIGN STRATEGIES Bella Robinson and Steve Carson are running for a seat in the U.S. Senate. If both candidates campaign only in the major cities of the state, then Robinson will get 60% of the votes; if both candidates campaign only in the rural areas, then Robinson will get 55% of the votes; if Robinson campaigns exclusively in the city and Carson campaigns exclusively in the rural areas, then Robinson will get 40% of the votes; finally, if Robinson campaigns exclusively in the rural areas and Carson campaigns exclusively in the city, then Robinson will get 45% of the votes.

a. Construct the payoff matrix for the game, and show that it is not strictly determined.

b. Find the optimal strategy for both Robinson and Carson.

21. ADVERTISEMENTS Two dentists, Lydia Russell and Jerry Carlton, are planning to establish practices in a newly developed community. Both have allocated approximately the same total budget for advertising in the local newspaper and for the distribution of fliers announcing their practices. Because of the location of their offices, Russell will get 48% of the business if both dentists advertise only in the local newspaper; if both dentists advertise through fliers, then Russell will get 45% of the business; if Russell advertises exclusively in the local newspaper and Carlton advertises exclusively through fliers, then Russell will get 65% of the business. Finally, if Russell advertises through fliers exclusively and Carlton advertises exclusively in the local newspaper, then Russell will get 50% of the business.

a. Construct the payoff matrix for the game, and show that it is not strictly determined.

b. Find the optimal strategy for both Russell and Carlton.

22. Let

$$\begin{bmatrix} a_{11} & a_{12} \\ a_{21} & a_{22} \end{bmatrix}$$

be the payoff matrix with a 2×2 matrix game. Assume that either the row player uses the optimal mixed strategy $P = [p_1 \quad p_2]$, where

$$p_1 = \frac{d - c}{a + d - b - c} \quad \text{and} \quad p_2 = 1 - p_1$$

or the column player uses the optimal mixed strategy

$$Q = \begin{bmatrix} q_1 \\ q_2 \end{bmatrix}$$

where

$$q_1 = \frac{d - b}{a + d - b - c} \quad \text{and} \quad q_2 = 1 - q_1$$

Show by direct computation that the expected value of the game is given by $E = PAQ$.

23. Let

$$\begin{bmatrix} a & b \\ c & d \end{bmatrix}$$

be the payoff matrix associated with a nonstrictly determined 2×2 matrix game. Prove that the expected payoff of the game is given by

$$E = \frac{ad - bc}{a + d - b - c}$$

Hint: Compute $E = PAQ$, where P and Q are the optimal strategies for the row and column players, respectively.

9.5   **Solutions to Self-Check Exercises**

1. a. From the following calculations,

we see that R's optimal pure strategy is to choose row 1, whereas C's optimal pure strategy is to choose column 3. Furthermore, if both players use their respective optimal strategies, then the expected payoff to R is -1 unit.

b. R's mixed strategy may be represented by the row vector

$$P = [.4 \quad .3 \quad .3]$$

and C's mixed strategy may be represented by the column vector

$$Q = \begin{bmatrix} .25 \\ .25 \\ .50 \end{bmatrix}$$

The expected payoff to the row player will then be given by

$$E = PAQ = [.4 \quad .3 \quad .3] \begin{bmatrix} 2 & 3 & -1 \\ -3 & 2 & -2 \\ 3 & -2 & 2 \end{bmatrix} \begin{bmatrix} .25 \\ .25 \\ .50 \end{bmatrix}$$

$$= [.4 \quad .3 \quad .3] \begin{bmatrix} .75 \\ -1.25 \\ 1.25 \end{bmatrix}$$

$$= .3$$

c. From the results of parts (a) and (b), we see that the mixed strategies of part (b) will be better for R.

2. We may view this problem as a matrix game with the farmer as the row player and the weather as the column player. The payoff matrix for the game is

$$\begin{array}{cc} & \begin{array}{cc} \text{No} & \text{Mild} \\ \text{frost} & \text{frost} \end{array} \\ \begin{array}{c} \text{Crop } A \\ \text{Crop } B \end{array} & \begin{bmatrix} 40 & 20 \\ 25 & 30 \end{bmatrix} \end{array}$$

The game under consideration has no saddle point and is accordingly nonstrictly determined. Letting $p = [p_1 \quad p_2]$ denote the farmer's optimal strategy and using the formula for determining the optimal mixed strategies for a 2×2 game with $a = 40$, $b = 20$, $c = 25$, and $d = 30$, we find

$$p_1 = \frac{d - c}{a + d - b - c} = \frac{30 - 25}{40 + 30 - 20 - 25} = \frac{5}{25} = \frac{1}{5}$$

$$p_2 = 1 - p_1 = 1 - \frac{1}{5} = \frac{4}{5}$$

Therefore, the farmer should cultivate $(\frac{1}{5})(2000)$, or 400, acres of Crop A and 1600 acres of Crop B. By using her optimal strategy, the farmer can expect to realize a profit of

$$E = \frac{ad - bc}{a + d - b - c}$$

$$= \frac{(40)(30) - (20)(25)}{40 + 30 - 20 - 25}$$

$$= 28$$

or \$28/acre—that is, a total profit of $(28)(2000)$, or \$56,000.

CHAPTER 9   Summary of Principal Formulas and Terms

FORMULAS

1. Steady-state matrix for an absorbing stochastic matrix	If $A = \left[\begin{array}{c:c} I & S \\ \hline O & R \end{array}\right]$ then the steady-state matrix of A is $\left[\begin{array}{c:c} I & S(I - R)^{-1} \\ \hline O & O \end{array}\right]$
2. Expected value of a game	$E = PAQ =$ $[p_1 \quad p_2 \quad \cdots \quad p_m] \begin{bmatrix} a_{11} & a_{12} & \cdots & a_{1n} \\ a_{21} & a_{22} & \cdots & a_{2n} \\ \vdots & \vdots & & \vdots \\ a_{m1} & a_{m2} & \cdots & a_{mn} \end{bmatrix} \begin{bmatrix} q_1 \\ q_2 \\ \vdots \\ q_n \end{bmatrix}$
3. Optimal strategy for a nonstrictly determined game	$P = [p_1 \quad p_2]$, where $\quad p_1 = \dfrac{d - c}{a + d - b - c}$ and $\quad p_2 = 1 - p_1$ and $\quad Q = \begin{bmatrix} q_1 \\ q_2 \end{bmatrix}$ where $\quad q_1 = \dfrac{d - b}{a + d - b - c}$ and $\quad q_2 = 1 - q_1$ The expected value of the game is $E = PAQ$ $\quad = \dfrac{ad - bc}{a + d - b - c}$

TERMS

Markov chain (process) (498)

transition matrix (500)

stochastic matrix (500)

steady-state (limiting) distribution vector (509)

steady-state matrix (510)

regular Markov chain (510)

absorbing state (519)

absorbing stochastic matrix (519)

absorbing Markov chain (519)

zero-sum game (526)

maximin strategy (528)

minimax strategy (529)

optimal strategy (530)

strictly determined game (531)

saddle point (531)

value of the game (531)

fair game (531)

pure strategy (536)

mixed strategy (536)

expected value of a game (537)

CHAPTER 9   Concept Review Questions

Fill in the blanks.

1. A Markov chain is a stochastic process in which the _____ associated with the outcomes at any stage of the experiment depend only on the outcomes of the _____ stage.

2. The outcome at any stage of the experiment in a Markov process is called the _____ of the experiment; the outcome at the current stage of the experiment is called the current _____.

3. The probabilities in a Markov chain are called _____ probabilities because they are associated with the transition from one state to the next in the Markov process.

4. A transition matrix associated with a Markov chain with n states is a/an _____ matrix T with entries satisfying the following conditions: (a) All entries are _____, and (b) the sum of the entries in each column of T is _____.

5. If the probability distribution vector X_N associated with a Markov process approaches a fixed vector as N gets larger and larger, then the fixed vector is called the steady-state _____ vector for the system. To find this vector, we are led to finding the limit of T^m, which (if it exists) is called the _____ matrix.

6. A stochastic matrix T is a/an _____ Markov chain if T^m approaches a steady-state matrix in which the _____ of the limiting matrix are all _____ and all the entries are _____. To find the steady-state distribution vector X, we solve the vector equation _____ together with the condition that the sum of the _____ of the vector X is equal to _____.

7. In an absorbing stochastic matrix, (a) there is at least one _____ state, a state in which it is impossible for an object to _____, and (b) it is possible to go from each nonabsorbing state to an absorbing state in one or more _____.

8. **a.** A game in which the payoff to one party results in an equal loss to the other is called a/an _____ game.
   b. The strategy employed by the row player in which he or she selects from among the rows one in which the smallest payoff is as large as possible is called the _____ strategy. The strategy in which C chooses from among the columns one in which the largest payoff is as small as possible, is called the _____ strategy.

9. A strategy that is most profitable to a particular player is called an _____ strategy.

10. In a strictly determined game, an entry in the payoff matrix that is simultaneously the smallest entry in the row and the largest entry in the column is called a/an _____ _____; the optimal strategy for the row player in a strictly determined game is the _____ strategy, obtained by choosing the _____ containing the _____ point; the optimal strategy for the column player is the _____ strategy, obtained by choosing the _____ containing the _____ point.

CHAPTER 9   Review Exercises

In Exercises 1–4, determine which of the following are regular stochastic matrices.

1. $\begin{bmatrix} 1 & -2 \\ 0 & -8 \end{bmatrix}$

2. $\begin{bmatrix} .3 & 1 \\ .7 & 0 \end{bmatrix}$

3. $\begin{bmatrix} \frac{1}{2} & 0 & \frac{1}{3} \\ 0 & 0 & \frac{1}{3} \\ \frac{1}{2} & 1 & \frac{1}{3} \end{bmatrix}$

4. $\begin{bmatrix} .3 & 0 & .5 \\ .2 & 1 & 0 \\ .1 & 0 & .5 \end{bmatrix}$

In Exercises 5 and 6, find X_2 (the probability distribution of the system after two observations) for the distribution vector X_0 and the transition matrix T.

5. $X_0 = \begin{bmatrix} \frac{1}{2} \\ \frac{1}{2} \\ 0 \end{bmatrix}$, $T = \begin{bmatrix} 0 & \frac{1}{4} & \frac{3}{5} \\ \frac{2}{5} & \frac{1}{2} & \frac{1}{5} \\ \frac{3}{5} & \frac{1}{4} & \frac{1}{5} \end{bmatrix}$

6. $X_0 = \begin{bmatrix} .35 \\ .25 \\ .40 \end{bmatrix}$, $T = \begin{bmatrix} .2 & .1 & .3 \\ .5 & .4 & .4 \\ .3 & .5 & .3 \end{bmatrix}$

In Exercises 7–10, determine whether the matrix is an absorbing stochastic matrix.

7. $\begin{bmatrix} 1 & .6 & .1 \\ 0 & .2 & .6 \\ 0 & .2 & .3 \end{bmatrix}$

8. $\begin{bmatrix} .3 & .2 & .1 \\ .7 & .5 & .3 \\ 0 & .3 & .6 \end{bmatrix}$

9. $\begin{bmatrix} .32 & .22 & .44 \\ .68 & .78 & .56 \\ 0 & 0 & 0 \end{bmatrix}$

10. $\begin{bmatrix} .31 & .35 & 0 \\ .32 & .40 & 0 \\ .37 & .25 & 1 \end{bmatrix}$

In Exercises 11–14, find the steady-state matrix for the transition matrix.

11. $\begin{bmatrix} .6 & .3 \\ .4 & .7 \end{bmatrix}$

12. $\begin{bmatrix} .5 & .4 \\ .5 & .6 \end{bmatrix}$

13. $\begin{bmatrix} .6 & .4 & .3 \\ .2 & .2 & .2 \\ .2 & .4 & .5 \end{bmatrix}$

14. $\begin{bmatrix} .1 & .2 & .6 \\ .3 & .4 & .2 \\ .6 & .4 & .2 \end{bmatrix}$

15. **URBANIZATION OF FARMLAND** A study conducted by the State Department of Agriculture in a Sunbelt state reveals an increasing trend toward urbanization of the farmland within the state. Ten years ago, 50% of the land within the state was used for agricultural purposes (A), 15% had been urbanized (U), and the remaining 35% was neither agricultural nor urban (N). Since that time, 10% of the agricultural land has been converted to urban land, 5% has been used for other purposes, and the remaining 85% is still agricultural. Of the urban land, 95% has remained urban, whereas 5% of it has been used for other nonagricultural purposes. Of the land that was neither agricultural nor urban, 10% has been converted to agricultural land, 5% has been urbanized, and the remaining 85% remains unchanged.
   a. Construct the transition matrix for the Markov chain that describes the shift in land use within the state.
   b. Find the probability vector describing the distribution of land within the state 10 years ago.
   c. Assuming that this trend continues, find the probability vector describing the distribution of land within the state 10 years from now.

16. **Automobile Survey** *Auto Trend* magazine conducted a survey among automobile owners in a certain area of the country to determine what type of car they now own and what type of car they expect to own 4 years from now. For purposes of classification, automobiles mentioned in the survey were placed into three categories: large, intermediate, and small. Results of the survey follow:

| | | Present car | |
	Large	Intermediate	Small
Future car — Large	.3	.1	.1
Intermediate	.3	.5	.2
Small	.4	.4	.7

Assuming that these results indicate the long-term buying trend of car owners within the area, what will be the distribution of cars (relative to size) in this area over the long run?

In Exercises 17–20, determine whether each game within the given payoff matrix is strictly determined. If so, give the optimal pure strategies for the row player and the column player and also give the value of the game.

17. $\begin{bmatrix} 1 & 2 \\ 3 & 5 \\ 4 & 6 \end{bmatrix}$

18. $\begin{bmatrix} 1 & 0 & 3 \\ 2 & -1 & -2 \end{bmatrix}$

19. $\begin{bmatrix} 1 & 3 & 6 \\ -2 & 4 & 3 \\ -5 & -4 & -2 \end{bmatrix}$

20. $\begin{bmatrix} 4 & 3 & 2 \\ -6 & 3 & -1 \\ 2 & 3 & 4 \end{bmatrix}$

In Exercises 21–24, find the expected payoff E of each game whose payoff matrix and strategies P and Q (for the row and column players, respectively) are given.

21. $\begin{bmatrix} 4 & 8 \\ 6 & -12 \end{bmatrix}, P = [\frac{1}{2} \ \ \frac{1}{2}], Q = \begin{bmatrix} \frac{1}{4} \\ \frac{3}{4} \end{bmatrix}$

22. $\begin{bmatrix} 3 & 0 & -3 \\ 2 & 1 & 2 \end{bmatrix}, P = [\frac{1}{3} \ \ \frac{2}{3}], Q = \begin{bmatrix} \frac{1}{3} \\ \frac{1}{3} \\ \frac{1}{3} \end{bmatrix}$

23. $\begin{bmatrix} 3 & -1 & 2 \\ 1 & 2 & 4 \\ -2 & 3 & 6 \end{bmatrix}, P = [.2 \ \ .4 \ \ .4], Q = \begin{bmatrix} .2 \\ .6 \\ .2 \end{bmatrix}$

24. $\begin{bmatrix} 2 & -2 & 3 \\ 1 & 2 & -1 \\ -1 & 2 & 3 \end{bmatrix}, P = [.2 \ \ .4 \ \ .4], Q = \begin{bmatrix} .3 \\ .3 \\ .4 \end{bmatrix}$

In Exercises 25–28, find the optimal strategies, P and Q, for the row player and the column player, respectively. Also compute the expected payoff E of each matrix game if the row and column players adopt their optimal strategies and determine which player it favors, if any.

25. $\begin{bmatrix} 1 & -2 \\ 0 & 3 \end{bmatrix}$

26. $\begin{bmatrix} 4 & -7 \\ -5 & 6 \end{bmatrix}$

27. $\begin{bmatrix} 3 & -6 \\ 1 & 2 \end{bmatrix}$

28. $\begin{bmatrix} 12 & 10 \\ 6 & 14 \end{bmatrix}$

29. **Pricing Products** Two competing music stores, Disco-Mart and Stereo World, each have the option of selling a certain popular compact disc (CD) label at a price of either $7/CD or $8/CD. If both sell the label at the same price, they are each expected to get 50% of the business. If Disco Mart sells the label at $7/CD and Stereo World sells the label at $8/CD, DiscoMart is expected to get 70% of the business; if DiscoMart sells the label at $8/CD and Stereo World sells the label at $7/CD, DiscoMart is expected to get 40% of the business.
   a. Represent this information in the form of a payoff matrix.
   b. Determine the optimal price that each company should sell the CD label for to ensure that it captures the largest possible expected market share.

30. **Maximizing Production** The management of a division of National Motor Corporation that produces compact and subcompact cars has estimated that the quantity demanded of their compact models is 1500 units/week if the price of oil increases at a higher than normal rate, whereas the quantity demanded of their subcompact models is 2500 units/week under similar conditions. However, the quantity demanded of their compact models and subcompact models is 3000 units and 2000 units/week, respectively, if the price of oil increases at a normal rate. Determine the percentages of compact and subcompact cars the division should plan to manufacture to maximize the expected number of cars demanded each week.

CHAPTER 9   Before Moving On . . .

1. The transition matrix for a Markov process is

$$T = \begin{array}{c} \text{State 1} \\ \text{State 2} \end{array} \begin{bmatrix} .3 & .4 \\ .7 & .6 \end{bmatrix}$$

and the initial-state distribution vector is

$$X_0 = \begin{array}{c} \text{State 1} \\ \text{State 2} \end{array} \begin{bmatrix} .6 \\ .4 \end{bmatrix}$$

Find X_2.

2. Find the steady-state vector for the transition matrix

$$T = \begin{bmatrix} \frac{1}{3} & \frac{1}{4} \\ \frac{2}{3} & \frac{3}{4} \end{bmatrix}$$

3. Compute the steady-state matrix of the absorbing stochastic matrix

$$\begin{bmatrix} \frac{1}{3} & 0 & 0 \\ 0 & 1 & \frac{1}{4} \\ \frac{2}{3} & 0 & \frac{3}{4} \end{bmatrix}$$

4. A two-person, zero-sum game is defined by the matrix

$$A = \begin{bmatrix} 2 & 3 & -1 \\ -1 & 2 & -3 \\ 3 & 4 & -2 \end{bmatrix}$$

a. Show that the game is strictly determined, and find the saddle point for the game.

b. What is the optimal strategy for each player?

c. What is the value of the game? Does the game favor one player over the other?

5. The payoff matrix for a certain game is

$$A = \begin{bmatrix} 2 & -1 \\ 3 & 2 \\ -3 & 4 \end{bmatrix}$$

a. Find the expected payoff to the row player if the row player R uses her maximin pure strategy and the column player C uses his minimax pure strategy.

b. Find the expected payoff to the row player if R uses her maximin strategy 40% of the time and chooses each of the other two rows 30% of the time, while C chooses the minimax strategy 60% of the time.

6. The payoff matrix for a certain game is

$$\begin{bmatrix} 3 & 1 \\ -2 & 2 \end{bmatrix}$$

a. Find the optimal strategies, P and Q, for the row and column players, respectively.

b. Find the expected payoff E of the game, and determine which player it favors, if any, if the row and column players use their optimal strategies.

APPENDIX A
INTRODUCTION TO LOGIC

ONE OF THE earliest records of humanity's efforts to understand the reasoning process can be found in Aristotle's work *Organon* (third century B.C.), in which he presented his ideas on logical arguments. Up until the present day, Aristotelian logic has been the basis for traditional logic, the systematic study of valid inferences.

The field of mathematics known as symbolic logic, in which symbols are used to replace ordinary language, had its beginnings in the eighteenth and nineteenth centuries with the works of the German mathematician Gottfried Wilhelm Leibniz (1646–1716) and the English mathematician George Boole (1815–1864). Boole introduced algebraic-type operations to the field of logic, thereby providing us with a systematic method of combining statements. Boolean algebra is the basis of modern-day computer technology as well as being central to the study of pure mathematics.

In this appendix, we introduce the fundamental concepts of symbolic logic. Beginning with the definitions of statements and their truth values, we proceed to a discussion of the combination of statements and valid arguments. In Section A.6, we present an application of symbolic logic that is widely used in computer technology: switching networks.

A.1   Propositions and Connectives

We use deductive reasoning in many of the things we do. Whether in a formal debate or in an expository article, we use language to express our thoughts. In English, sentences are used to express assertions, questions, commands, and wishes. In our study of logic, we will be concerned with only one type of sentence, the declarative sentence.

> **Proposition**
> A **proposition**, or *statement*, is a declarative sentence that can be classified as either true or false but not both.

Commands, requests, questions, and exclamations are examples of sentences that are not propositions.

EXAMPLE 1 Which of the following are propositions?

a. Toronto is the capital of Ontario.
b. Close the door!
c. There are 100 trillion connections among the neurons in the human brain.
d. Who is the chief justice of the Supreme Court?
e. The new television sit-com is a successful show.
f. The 2010 Summer Olympic Games were held in Montreal.
g. $x + 3 = 8$
h. How wonderful!
i. Either seven is an odd number or it is even.

Solution   Statements (a), (c), (e), (f), and (i) are propositions. Statement (c) would be difficult to verify, but the validity of the statement can at least theoretically be determined. Statement (e) is a proposition if we assume that the meaning of the term *successful* has been defined. For example, one might use the Nielsen ratings to determine the success of a new show. Statement (f) is a proposition that is false.

Statements (b), (d), (g), and (h) are *not* propositions. Statement (b) is a command, (d) is a question, and (h) is an exclamation. Statement (g) is an open sentence that cannot be classified as true or false. For example, if $x = 5$, then $5 + 3 = 8$ and the sentence is true. On the other hand, if $x = 4$, then $4 + 3 \neq 8$ and the sentence is false. ■

Having considered what is meant by a proposition, we now discuss the ways in which propositions may be combined. For example, the two propositions

a. Toronto is the capital of Ontario

and

b. Toronto is the largest city in Canada

may be joined to form the proposition

c. Toronto is the capital of Ontario and is the largest city in Canada.

Propositions (a) and (b) are called **prime**, or *simple*, **propositions** because they are simple statements expressing a single complete thought. Propositions that are combinations of two or more propositions, such as proposition (c), are called **compound propositions.** In the ensuing discussion, we use the lowercase letters p, q, r, and so on to denote prime propositions, and the uppercase letters P, Q, R, and so on to denote compound propositions.

The words that are used to combine propositions are called logical connectives. The basic connectives that we will consider are given in Table 1 along with their symbols. We discuss the first three in this section and the remaining two in Section A.3.

TABLE 1

Name	Logical Connective	Symbol
Conjunction	and	$\wedge$
Disjunction	or	$\vee$
Negation	not	$\sim$
Conditional	if . . . then	$\rightarrow$
Biconditional	if and only if	$\leftrightarrow$

Conjunction

A conjunction is a statement of the form "p and q" and is represented symbolically by

$$p \wedge q$$

The conjunction $p \wedge q$ is true if *both* p and q are true; it is false otherwise.

We have already encountered a conjunction in an earlier example. The two propositions

p: Toronto is the capital of Ontario

q: Toronto is the largest city in Canada

were combined to form the conjunction

$p \wedge q$: Toronto is the capital of Ontario and is the largest city in Canada.

Disjunction

A disjunction is a proposition of the form "p or q" and is represented symbolically by

$$p \vee q$$

The disjunction $p \vee q$ is false if *both* statements p and q are false; it is true in all other cases.

The use of the word *or* in this definition is meant to convey the meaning "one or the other, or both." Since this disjunction is true when *both* p and q are true, as well as when only one of p and q is true, it is often referred to as an inclusive disjunction.

EXAMPLE 2 Consider the propositions

p: Dorm residents can purchase meal plans.

q: Dorm residents can purchase à la carte cards.

The disjunction is

$p \vee q$: Dorm residents can purchase meal plans or à la carte cards. ■

The disjunction in Example 2 is true when dorm residents can purchase either meal plans or à la carte cards or both meal plans and à la carte cards.

Exclusive Disjunction

An **exclusive disjunction** is a proposition of the form either "*p* or *q*" and is denoted by

$$p \veebar q$$

The disjunction $p \veebar q$ is true if *either p* or *q* is true but not both.

In contrast to an inclusive disjunction, an exclusive disjunction is *false* when both *p* and *q* are true. In Example 2, the exclusive disjunction would not be true if dorm residents could buy both meal plans and à la carte cards. The difference between exclusive and inclusive disjunctions is further illustrated in the next example.

EXAMPLE 3 Consider the propositions

p: The base price of each condominium unit includes a private deck.

q: The base price of each condominium unit includes a private patio.

Find the exclusive disjunction $p \veebar q$.

Solution   The exclusive disjunction is

$p \veebar q$: The base price of each condominium unit includes either a private deck or a patio, but not both.

Observe that this statement is not true when both *p* and *q* are true. In other words, the base price of each condominium unit does not include both a private deck and a patio. ■

In our everyday use of language, the meaning of the word *or* is not always clear. In legal documents, the two cases are distinguished by the words *and/or* (inclusive) and *either/or* (exclusive). In mathematics, we use the word *or* in the inclusive sense unless otherwise specified.

Negation

A **negation** is a proposition of the form "not *p*" and is represented symbolically by

$$\sim p$$

The proposition $\sim p$ is true if *p* is false and vice versa.

EXAMPLE 4 Form the negation of the proposition

p: The price of the New York Stock Exchange Composite Index rose today.

Solution   The negation is

$\sim p$: The price of the New York Stock Exchange Composite Index did not rise today. ■

EXAMPLE 5 Consider the two propositions

p: The birthrate declined in the United States last year.

q: The population of the United States increased last year.

Write the following statements in symbolic form:

a. Last year, the birthrate declined, and the population increased in the United States.

b. Either the birthrate declined or the population increased in the United States last year, but not both.

c. It is not true that the birthrate declined and the population increased in the United States last year.

Solution   The symbolic form of each statement is given by

a. $p \wedge q$ **b.** $p \veebar q$ **c.** $\sim(p \wedge q)$ ∎

A.1   Exercises

In Exercises 1–14, determine whether the statement is a proposition.

1. The defendant was convicted of grand larceny.

2. Who won the 2008 presidential election?

3. The first month of the year is February.

4. The number 2 is odd.

5. $x - 1 \geq 0$

6. Keep off the grass!

7. Coughing may be caused by a lack of water in the air.

8. The first McDonald's fast-food restaurant was opened in California.

9. Exercise protects men and women from sudden heart attacks.

10. If voters do not pass the proposition, then taxes will be increased.

11. Don't swim immediately after eating!

12. What ever happened to Baby Jane?

13. $x + 1 = 1$

14. A major corporation will enter or expand operations into the home-security products market this year.

In Exercises 15–20, identify the logical connective that is used in the statement.

15. Housing starts in the United States did not increase last month.

16. Mel Bieber's will is valid, and he was of sound mind and memory when he made the will.

17. Americans are saving less and spending more this year.

18. You traveled on your job, and you were not reimbursed.

19. Both loss of appetite and irritability are symptoms of mental stress.

20. Prices for many imported goods have either stayed flat or dropped slightly this year.

In Exercises 21–26, state the negation of the proposition.

21. New orders for manufactured goods fell last month.

22. The space shuttle was not launched on January 24.

23. Drinking alcohol during pregnancy affects the size and weight of babies.

24. Not all patients suffering from influenza lose weight.

25. The commuter airline industry is now undergoing a shakeup.

26. The Dow Jones Industrial Average registered its fourth consecutive decline today.

27. Let p and q denote the propositions

   p: Domestic car sales increased over the past year.

   q: Foreign car sales decreased over the past year.

   Express the following compound propositions in words:
   a. $p \vee q$ **b.** $p \wedge q$ **c.** $p \veebar q$
   d. $\sim p$ **e.** $\sim p \vee q$ **f.** $\sim p \vee \sim q$

28. Let p and q denote the propositions

   p: Every employee is required to be fingerprinted.

   q: Every employee is required to take an oath of allegiance.

   Express the following compound propositions in words:
   a. $p \vee q$ **b.** $p \wedge q$ **c.** $\sim p \vee \sim q$
   d. $\sim p \wedge \sim q$ **e.** $p \vee \sim q$

29. Let p and q denote the propositions

   p: The doctor recommended surgery to treat Sam's hyperthyroidism.

   q: The doctor recommended radioactive iodine to treat Sam's hyperthyroidism.

   a. State the exclusive disjunction for these propositions in words.

   b. State the inclusive disjunction for these propositions in words.

30. Let p and q denote the propositions

    p: The investment newsletter recommended buying bond mutual funds.

    q: The investment newsletter recommended buying stock mutual funds.

  a. State the exclusive disjunction for these propositions in words.

  b. State the inclusive disjunction for these propositions in words.

31. Let p and q denote the propositions

    p: The SAT verbal scores improved in this school district last year.

    q: The SAT math scores improved in this school district last year.

  Express each of the following statements symbolically.

  a. The SAT verbal scores and the SAT math scores improved in this school district last year.

  b. Either the SAT verbal scores or the SAT math scores improved in this school district last year.

  c. Neither the SAT verbal scores nor the SAT math scores improved in this school district last year.

  d. It is not true that the SAT math scores did not improve in this school district last year.

32. Let p and q denote the propositions

    p: Laura purchased a flat screen television.

    q: Laura did not purchase a DVD player.

  Express each of the following statements symbolically.

  a. Laura purchased either a flat screen television or a DVD player or both a flat screen television and a DVD player.

  b. Laura purchased a flat screen television and a DVD player.

  c. It is not true that Laura purchased a DVD player.

  d. Laura purchased neither a flat screen television nor a DVD player.

33. Let p, q, and r denote the propositions

    p: The popularity of prime-time soaps increased this year.

    q: The popularity of prime-time situation comedies increased this year.

    r: The popularity of prime-time detective shows decreased this year.

  Express each of the following propositions in words.

  a. $\sim p \wedge \sim q$ **b.** $\sim p \vee r$

  c. $\sim(\sim r) \vee \sim q$ **d.** $\sim p \veebar \sim q$

A.2 Truth Tables

A primary objective of studying logic is to determine whether a given proposition is true or false. In other words, we wish to determine the **truth value** of a given statement.

Consider, for example, the conjunction $p \wedge q$ formed from the prime propositions p and q. There are four possible cases:

1. p is true and q is true.
2. p is true and q is false.
3. p is false and q is true.
4. p is false and q is false.

By definition, the conjunction is true when both p and q are true, and it is false otherwise. We can summarize this information in the form of a truth table, as shown in Table 2.

In a similar manner, we can construct the truth tables for inclusive disjunction, exclusive disjunction, and negation (Tables 3a–c).

TABLE 2

Conjunction

p	q	$p \wedge q$
T	T	T
T	F	F
F	T	F
F	F	F

TABLE 3

p	q	$p \vee q$		p	q	$p \veebar q$		p	$\sim p$
T	T	T		T	T	F		T	F
T	F	T		T	F	T		F	T
F	T	T		F	T	T			
F	F	F		F	F	F			

(a) Inclusive disjunction   **(b)** Exclusive disjunction   **(c)** Negation

In general, when we are given a compound proposition, we are concerned with the problem of finding every possible combination of truth values associated with the compound proposition. To systematize this procedure, we construct a truth table exhibiting all possible truth values for the given proposition. The next several examples illustrate this method.

EXAMPLE 1 Construct the truth table for the proposition $\sim p \vee q$.

Solution   The truth table is constructed in the following manner.

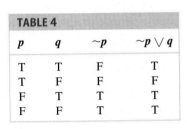

TABLE 4

p	q	$\sim p$	$\sim p \vee q$
T	T	F	T
T	F	F	F
F	T	T	T
F	F	T	T

1. The two prime propositions p and q are placed at the head of the first two columns (Table 4).
2. The two propositions containing the connectives, $\sim p$ and $\sim p \vee q$, are placed at the head of the next two columns.
3. The possible truth values for p are entered in the column headed by p, and then the possible truth values for q are entered in the column headed by q. Notice that the *possible* T *values are always exhausted first.*
4. The possible truth values for the negation $\sim p$ are entered in the column headed by $\sim p$, and then the possible truth values for the disjunction $\sim p \vee q$ are entered in the column headed by $\sim p \vee q$. ■

EXAMPLE 2 Construct the truth table for the proposition $\sim p \vee (p \wedge q)$.

Solution   Proceeding as in the previous example, we construct the truth table as shown in Table 5. Since the given proposition is the disjunction of the propositions $\sim p$ and $(p \wedge q)$, columns are introduced for $\sim p$, $p \wedge q$, and $\sim p \vee (p \wedge q)$.

TABLE 5

p	q	$\sim p$	$p \wedge q$	$\sim p \vee (p \wedge q)$
T	T	F	T	T
T	F	F	F	F
F	T	T	F	T
F	F	T	F	T

The following is an example involving three prime propositions.

EXAMPLE 3 Construct the truth table for the proposition $(p \vee q) \vee (r \wedge \sim p)$.

Solution   Following the method of the previous example, we construct the truth table as shown in Table 6.

TABLE 6

p	q	r	$p \vee q$	$\sim p$	$r \wedge \sim p$	$(p \vee q) \vee (r \wedge \sim p)$
T	T	T	T	F	F	T
T	T	F	T	F	F	T
T	F	T	T	F	F	T
T	F	F	T	F	F	T
F	T	T	T	T	T	T
F	T	F	T	T	F	T
F	F	T	F	T	T	T
F	F	F	F	T	F	F

Observe that the truth table in Example 3 contains eight rows, whereas the truth tables in Examples 1 and 2 contain four rows. In general, *if a compound proposition $P(p, q, \ldots)$ contains the n prime propositions $p, q, \ldots$, then the corresponding truth table contains 2^n rows.* For example, since the compound proposition in Example 3 contains three prime propositions, its corresponding truth table contains 2^3, or 8, rows.

A.2   Exercises

In Exercises 1–18, construct a truth table for each compound proposition.

1. $p \vee \sim q$

2. $\sim p \wedge \sim q$

3. $\sim(\sim p)$

4. $\sim(p \wedge q)$

5. $p \vee \sim p$

6. $\sim(\sim p \vee \sim q)$

7. $\sim p \wedge (p \vee q)$

8. $(p \vee \sim q) \wedge q$

9. $(p \vee q) \wedge (p \wedge \sim q)$

10. $(p \vee q) \wedge \sim p$

11. $(p \vee q) \wedge \sim(p \vee q)$

12. $(p \vee q) \vee (\sim p \wedge q)$

13. $(p \vee q) \wedge (p \vee r)$

14. $p \wedge (q \vee r)$

15. $(p \wedge q) \vee \sim r$

16. $(\sim p \vee q) \wedge \sim r$

17. $(p \wedge \sim q) \vee (p \wedge r)$

18. $\sim(p \wedge q) \vee (q \wedge r)$

19. If a compound proposition consists of the prime propositions p, q, r, and s, how many rows does its corresponding truth table contain?

A.3   The Conditional and the Biconditional Connectives

In this section, we introduce two other connectives: the conditional and the biconditional. We also discuss three variations of conditional statements: the inverse, the contrapositive, and the converse.

We often use expressions of the form

If it rains, *then* the baseball game will be postponed

to specify the conditions under which a statement will be true. The "if . . . then" statement is the building block on which deductive reasoning is based, and it is important to understand its use in forming logical proofs.

> **Conditional Statement**
>
> A **conditional statement** is a proposition of the form "if p, then q" and is represented symbolically by
>
> $$p \rightarrow q$$
>
> The connective "if . . . then" is called the **conditional connective**; the proposition p is called the **hypothesis**; and the proposition q is called the **conclusion**. A conditional statement is false if the hypothesis is true and the conclusion is false; it is true in all other cases.

TABLE 7

p	q	$p \rightarrow q$
T	T	T
T	F	F
F	T	T
F	F	T

The truth table determined by the conditional $p \rightarrow q$ is shown in Table 7.

One question that is often asked is: Why is a conditional statement true when its hypothesis is false? We can answer this question by considering the following conditional statement made by a mother to her son:

If you do your homework, then you may watch TV.

Think of the statement consisting of the two prime propositions

p: You do your homework

q: You may watch TV

as a *promise* made by the mother to her son. Four cases arise:

1. The son does his homework, and his mother lets him watch TV.
2. The son does his homework, and his mother does not let him watch TV.
3. The son does not do his homework, and his mother lets him watch TV.
4. The son does not do his homework, and his mother does not let him watch TV.

In case 1, p and q are both true, the promise has been kept, and consequently, $p \rightarrow q$ is true. In case 2, p is true and q is false, and the mother has broken her promise. Therefore, $p \rightarrow q$ is false. In cases 3 and 4, p is not true, and the promise is *not* broken. Thus, $p \rightarrow q$ is regarded as a true statement. In other words, the conditional statement is regarded as false only if the "promise" is broken.

There are several equivalent expressions for the conditional connective "if p then q." Among them are the following:

1. p implies q
2. p only if q
3. q if p
4. q whenever p
5. Suppose p, then q

Care should be taken not to confuse the conditional "q if p" with the conditional $q \rightarrow p$, because the two statements have quite different meanings. For example, the conditional $p \rightarrow q$ formed from the two propositions

p: There is a fire

q: You call the fire department

is

> If there is a fire, then you call the fire department.

The conditional $q \rightarrow p$ is

> If you call the fire department, then there is a fire.

Obviously, the two statements have quite different meanings.

We refer to statements that are variations of the conditional $p \rightarrow q$ as **logical variants**. We define three logical variants of the conditional $p \rightarrow q$ as follows:

1. The **converse** is the compound statement "if q, then p" and is represented symbolically by

$$q \rightarrow p$$

2. The **contrapositive** is the compound statement "if not q, then not p" and is represented symbolically by

$$\sim q \rightarrow \sim p$$

3. The **inverse** is the compound statement "if not p, then not q" and is represented symbolically by

$$\sim p \rightarrow \sim q$$

EXAMPLE 1 Given the two propositions

p: You vote in the presidential election.

q: You are a registered voter.

a. State the conditional $p \to q$.

b. State the converse, the contrapositive, and the inverse of $p \to q$.

Solution

a. The conditional is "If you vote in the presidential election, then you are a registered voter."

b. The converse is "If you are a registered voter, then you vote in the presidential election." The contrapositive is "If you are not a registered voter, then you do not vote in the presidential election." The inverse is "If you do not vote in the presidential election, then you are not a registered voter."

The truth table for the conditional $p \to q$ and its three logical variants is shown in Table 8. Notice that the conditional $p \to q$ and its contrapositive $\sim q \to \sim p$ have identical truth tables. In other words, the conditional statement and its contrapositive have the same meaning.

TABLE 8

p	q	Conditional $p \to q$	Converse $q \to p$	$\sim p$	$\sim q$	Contrapositive $\sim q \to \sim p$	Inverse $\sim p \to \sim q$
T	T	T	T	F	F	T	T
T	F	F	T	F	T	F	T
F	T	T	F	T	F	T	F
F	F	T	T	T	T	T	T

> **Logical Equivalence**
>
> Two propositions P and Q are **logically equivalent**, denoted by
>
> $$P \Leftrightarrow Q$$
>
> if they have identical truth tables.

Referring once again to the truth table in Table 8, we see that $p \to q$ is logically equivalent to its contrapositive. Similarly, the converse of a conditional statement is logically equivalent to the inverse.

It is sometimes easier to prove the contrapositive of a conditional statement than it is to prove the conditional itself. We may use this to our advantage in establishing a proof, as shown in the next example.

EXAMPLE 2 Prove that if n^2 is an odd number, then n is an odd number.

Solution   Let p and q be the propositions

p: n^2 is odd.

q: n is an odd number.

Since $p \to q$ is logically equivalent to $\sim q \to \sim p$, it suffices to prove $\sim q \to \sim p$. Thus, we wish to prove that if n is not an odd number, then n^2 is an even number and consequently is not odd. If n is even, then $n = 2k$, where k is an integer. Therefore,

$$n^2 = (2k)(2k) = 2(2k^2)$$

Since $2(2k^2)$ is a multiple of 2, it is an even number. Thus, we have shown that the contrapositive $\sim q \to \sim p$ is true, and it follows that the conditional $p \to q$ is also true.

We now turn our attention to the last of the five basic connectives.

> **Biconditional Propositions**
>
> Statements of the form "p if and only if q" are called **biconditional propositions** and are represented symbolically by
>
> $$p \leftrightarrow q$$
>
> The connective "if and only if" is called the *biconditional connective*. The biconditional $p \leftrightarrow q$ is true whenever p and q are *both true* or *both false*.

TABLE 9

p	q	$p \leftrightarrow q$
T	T	T
T	F	F
F	T	F
F	F	T

The truth table for $p \leftrightarrow q$ is shown in Table 9.

EXAMPLE 3 Let p and q be the propositions

p: Mark is going to the senior prom.

q: Linda is going to the senior prom.

State the biconditional $p \leftrightarrow q$.

Solution   The required statement is

Mark is going to the senior prom

if and only if

Linda is going to the senior prom.

As suggested by its name, the biconditional statement is actually composed of two conditional statements. For instance, an *equivalent expression* for the biconditional statement in Example 3 is given by the conjunction of the two conditional statements

Mark is going to the senior prom
if Linda is going to the senior prom.

Linda is going to the senior prom
if Mark is going to the senior prom.

Thus, "p if q, and q if p" is equivalent to "p if and only if q."

The equivalent expressions that are most commonly used in forming conditional and biconditional statements are summarized in Table 10. The words *necessary* and *sufficient* occur frequently in mathematical proofs. When we say that p is **sufficient** for q we mean that *when p is true, q is also true*—that is, $p \rightarrow q$. In like manner, when we say that p is **necessary** for q, we mean that *if p is not true, then q is not true*—that is, $\sim p \rightarrow \sim q$. But this last expression is logically equivalent to $q \rightarrow p$. Thus, when we say that p is necessary and sufficient for q, we mean $p \rightarrow q$ and $q \rightarrow p$. Example 4 illustrates the use of these expressions.

TABLE 10

		Equivalent Form
Conditional Statement	If p, then q	p is sufficient for q p only if q q is necessary for p q, if p
Biconditional Statement	p if and only if q	If p then q; if q then p p is necessary and sufficient for q

EXAMPLE 4 Let p and q be the propositions

p: The stock market goes up.

q: Interest rates decrease.

Represent the following statements symbolically:

a. If interest rates decrease, then the stock market goes up.
b. If interest rates do not decrease, then the stock market does not go up.
c. The stock market will go up if and only if interest rates decrease.
d. Decreasing interest rates is a sufficient condition for the stock market to go up.
e. Decreasing interest rates is a necessary and sufficient condition for a rising stock market.

Solution

a. $q \rightarrow p$ **b.** $\sim q \rightarrow \sim p$, or $p \rightarrow q$ **c.** $p \leftrightarrow q$
d. $q \rightarrow p$ **e.** $q \leftrightarrow p$

     Just as there is an order of precedence when we use the arithmetical operations $\times$, $\div$, $+$, and $-$, we must also observe an order of precedence when we use the logical connectives. The following list dictates the order of precedence for logical connectives.

> **Order of Precedence of Logical Connectives**
>
> $$\sim, \quad \wedge, \quad \vee, \quad \rightarrow, \quad \leftrightarrow$$

     Thus, the connective $\sim$ should be applied first, followed by $\wedge$, and so on. For example, using the order of precedence, we see that $p \wedge r \vee s$ is $(p \wedge r) \vee s$.
     Also, as in the case of arithmetical operations, parentheses can be used to override the order of precedence.

A.3   Exercises

In Exercises 1–4, write the converse, the contrapositive, and the inverse of the conditional statement.

1. $p \rightarrow \sim q$ **2.** $\sim p \rightarrow \sim q$

3. $q \rightarrow p$ **4.** $\sim p \rightarrow q$

In Exercises 5 and 6, refer to the following propositions p and q:

     p: It is snowing

     q: The temperature is below freezing.

5. Express the conditional and the biconditional of p and q in words.

6. Express the converse, contrapositive, and inverse of the conditional $p \rightarrow q$ in words.

In Exercises 7 and 8, refer to the following propositions p and q:

p: The company's union and management reach a settlement.

q: The workers do not strike.

7. Express the conditional and biconditional of p and q in words.

8. Express the converse, contrapositive, and inverse of the conditional $p \rightarrow q$ in words.

In Exercises 9–12, determine whether the statement is true or false.

9. A conditional proposition and its converse are logically equivalent.

10. The converse and the inverse of a conditional proposition are logically equivalent.

11. A conditional proposition and its inverse are logically equivalent.

12. The converse and the contrapositive of a conditional proposition are logically equivalent.

13. Consider the conditional statement "If the owner lowers the selling price of the house, then I will buy it." Under what conditions is the conditional statement false?

14. Consider the biconditional statement "I will buy the house if and only if the owner lowers the selling price." Under what conditions is the biconditional statement false?

In Exercises 15–28, construct a truth table for the compound proposition.

15. $\sim(p \to q)$

16. $\sim(q \to \sim p)$

17. $\sim(p \to q) \land p$

18. $(p \to q) \lor (q \to p)$

19. $(p \to \sim q) \veebar \sim p$

20. $(p \to q) \land (\sim p \lor q)$

21. $(p \to q) \leftrightarrow (\sim q \to \sim p)$

22. $(p \to q) \leftrightarrow (\sim p \lor q)$ 23. $(p \land q) \to (p \lor q)$

24. $\sim q \to (\sim p \land \sim q)$ 25. $(p \lor q) \to \sim r$

26. $(p \leftrightarrow q) \lor r$ 27. $p \to (q \lor r)$

28. $[(p \to q) \lor (q \to r)] \to (p \to r)$

In Exercises 29–36, determine whether the compound propositions are logically equivalent.

29. $\sim p \lor q; p \to q$ 30. $\sim(p \lor q); \sim p \land \sim q$

31. $q \to p; \sim p \to \sim q$ 32. $\sim p \to q; \sim p \lor q$

33. $p \land q; p \to \sim q$ 34. $\sim(p \land \sim q); \sim p \lor q$

35. $(p \to q) \to r; (p \lor q) \lor r$

36. $p \lor (q \land r); (p \lor q) \land (p \lor r)$

37. Let p and q denote the following propositions:

   p: Taxes are increased.

   q: The federal deficit increases.

   Represent the following statements symbolically.
   a. If taxes are increased, then the federal deficit will not increase.
   b. If taxes are not increased, then the federal deficit will increase.
   c. The federal deficit will not increase if and only if taxes are increased.
   d. Increased taxation is a sufficient condition for halting the growth of the federal deficit.
   e. Increased taxation is a necessary and sufficient condition for halting the growth of the federal deficit.

38. Let p and q denote the following propositions:

   p: The unemployment rate decreases.

   q: Consumer confidence improves.

   Represent the following statements symbolically.
   a. If the unemployment rate does not decrease, consumer confidence will not improve.
   b. Consumer confidence will improve if and only if the unemployment rate does not decrease.
   c. A decreasing unemployment rate is a sufficient condition for consumer confidence to improve.
   d. A decreasing unemployment rate is a necessary and sufficient condition for consumer confidence to improve.

A.4   Laws of Logic

Just as the laws of algebra help us to perform operations with real numbers, the **laws of logic** provide us with a systematic method of simplifying statements.

Laws of Logic

Let p, q, and r be any three propositions. Then

1. $p \land p \Leftrightarrow p$	*Idempotent law for conjunction*
2. $p \lor p \Leftrightarrow p$	*Idempotent law for disjunction*
3. $(p \land q) \land r \Leftrightarrow p \land (q \land r)$	*Associative law for conjunction*
4. $(p \lor q) \lor r \Leftrightarrow p \lor (q \lor r)$	*Associative law for disjunction*
5. $p \land q \Leftrightarrow q \land p$	*Commutative law for conjunction*
6. $p \lor q \Leftrightarrow q \lor p$	*Commutative law for disjunction*
7. $p \land (q \lor r) \Leftrightarrow (p \land q) \lor (p \land r)$	*Distributive law for conjunction*
8. $p \lor (q \land r) \Leftrightarrow (p \lor q) \land (p \lor r)$	*Distributive law for disjunction*
9. $\sim(p \lor q) \Leftrightarrow \sim p \land \sim q$	*De Morgan's Law*
10. $\sim(p \land q) \Leftrightarrow \sim p \lor \sim q$	*De Morgan's Law*

To verify any of these laws, we need only construct a truth table to show that the given statements are logically equivalent. We illustrate this procedure in the next example.

EXAMPLE 1 Prove the distributive law for conjunction.

Solution   We wish to prove that $p \wedge (q \vee r)$ is logically equivalent to $(p \wedge q) \vee (p \wedge r)$. This is easily done by constructing the associated truth table, as shown in Table 11. Since the entries in the last two columns are the same, we conclude that $p \wedge (q \vee r) \Leftrightarrow (p \wedge q) \vee (p \wedge r)$.

TABLE 11

p	q	r	$q \vee r$	$p \wedge q$	$p \wedge r$	$p \wedge (q \vee r)$	$(p \wedge q) \vee (p \wedge r)$
T	T	T	T	T	T	T	T
T	T	F	T	T	F	T	T
T	F	T	T	F	T	T	T
T	F	F	F	F	F	F	F
F	T	T	T	F	F	F	F
F	T	F	T	F	F	F	F
F	F	T	T	F	F	F	F
F	F	F	F	F	F	F	F

The proofs of the other laws are left to you as an exercise.

De Morgan's Laws, Laws 9 and 10, are useful in forming the negation of a statement. For example, if we wish to state the negation of the proposition

> Steve plans to major in business administration or economics

we can represent the statement symbolically by $p \vee q$, where the prime propositions are

p: Steve plans to major in business administration.

q: Steve plans to major in economics.

Then the negation of $p \vee q$ is $\sim(p \vee q)$. Using De Morgan's Laws, we have

$$\sim(p \vee q) \Leftrightarrow \sim p \wedge \sim q$$

Thus, the required statement is

> Steve does not plan to major in business administration, *and* he does not plan to major in economics.

Up to this point, we have considered propositions that have both true and false entries in their truth tables. Some statements have the property that they are always true; other propositions have the property that they are always false.

Tautologies and Contradictions

A **tautology** is a statement that is always true.

A **contradiction** is a statement that is always false.

EXAMPLE 2 Show that

a. $p \vee \sim p$ is a tautology.   **b.** $p \wedge \sim p$ is a contradiction.

Solution

a. The truth table associated with $p \vee \sim p$ is shown in Table 12a. Since all the entries in the last column are Ts, the proposition is a tautology.

b. The truth table for $p \wedge \sim p$ is shown in Table 12b. Since all the entries in the last column are Fs, the proposition is a contradiction.

TABLE 12

p	$\sim p$	$p \vee \sim p$	p	$\sim p$	$p \wedge \sim p$
T	F	T	T	F	F
F	T	T	F	T	F

(a) (b)

In Section A.3, we defined logically equivalent statements as statements that have identical truth tables. The definition of equivalence may also be restated in terms of a tautology.

> **Logical Equivalence**
>
> Two propositions P and Q are **logically equivalent** if the biconditional $P \leftrightarrow Q$ is a tautology.

Consider, for example, the prime propositions p and q. Let's look more closely at the truth table for $p \leftrightarrow q$ (Table 13a).

TABLE 13

	p	q	$p \leftrightarrow q$	p	q	$p \leftrightarrow q$
Case 1	T	T	T	T	T	T
Case 2	T	F	F	F	F	T
Case 3	F	T	F			
Case 4	F	F	T			

(a) (b)

If the biconditional is always true, then the second and third cases shown in the truth table are excluded, and we are left with the truth table in Table 13b. Notice that the entries in each row of the p and q columns are identical. In other words, p and q have identical truth values and hence are logically equivalent.

In addition to the ten laws stated earlier, we have the following six laws involving tautologies and contradictions.

> **Laws of Logic**
>
> Let t be a tautology, and let c be a contradiction. Then
>
> **11.** $p \vee \sim p \Leftrightarrow t$ **12.** $p \wedge \sim p \Leftrightarrow c$ **15.** $p \vee c \Leftrightarrow p$
> **13.** $p \vee t \Leftrightarrow t$ **14.** $p \wedge t \Leftrightarrow p$ **16.** $p \wedge c \Leftrightarrow c$

It now remains only to show how these laws are used to simplify proofs.

EXAMPLE 3 Using the laws of logic, show that

$$p \lor (\sim p \land q) \Leftrightarrow (p \lor q)$$

Solution

$$
\begin{aligned}
p \lor (\sim p \land q) &\Leftrightarrow (p \lor \sim p) \land (p \lor q) & \text{By Law 8} \\
&\Leftrightarrow t \land (p \lor q) & \text{By Law 11} \\
&\Leftrightarrow p \lor q & \text{By Law 14}
\end{aligned}
$$

EXAMPLE 4 Using the laws of logic, show that

$$\sim(p \lor q) \lor (\sim p \land q) \Leftrightarrow \sim p$$

Solution

$$
\begin{aligned}
\sim(p \lor q) \lor (\sim p \land q) & & \\
&\Leftrightarrow (\sim p \land \sim q) \lor (\sim p \land q) & \text{By Law 9} \\
&\Leftrightarrow \sim p \land (\sim q \lor q) & \text{By Law 7} \\
&\Leftrightarrow \sim p \land t & \text{By Law 11} \\
&\Leftrightarrow \sim p & \text{By Law 14}
\end{aligned}
$$

A.4 Exercises

1. Prove the idempotent law for conjunction, $p \land p \Leftrightarrow p$.

2. Prove the idempotent law for disjunction, $p \lor p \Leftrightarrow p$.

3. Prove the associative law for conjunction, $(p \land q) \land r \Leftrightarrow p \land (q \land r)$.

4. Prove the associative law for disjunction, $(p \lor q) \lor r \Leftrightarrow p \lor (q \lor r)$.

5. Prove the commutative law for conjunction, $p \land q \Leftrightarrow q \land p$.

6. Prove the commutative law for disjunction, $p \lor q \Leftrightarrow q \lor p$.

7. Prove the distributive law for disjunction, $p \lor (q \land r) \Leftrightarrow (p \lor q) \land (p \lor r)$.

8. Prove De Morgan's Laws
   a. $\sim(p \lor q) \Leftrightarrow \sim p \land \sim q$ **b.** $\sim(p \land q) \Leftrightarrow \sim p \lor \sim q$

In Exercises 9–18, determine whether the statement is a tautology, a contradiction, or neither.

9. $(p \to q) \leftrightarrow (\sim p \lor q)$ **10.** $(p \veebar q) \land (p \leftrightarrow q)$

11. $p \to (p \lor q)$ **12.** $(p \to q) \lor (q \to p)$

13. $(p \to q) \leftrightarrow (\sim q \to \sim p)$

14. $p \land (p \to q) \to q$

15. $(p \to q) \land (\sim q) \to (\sim p)$

16. $[(p \to q) \land (q \to r)] \to (p \to r)$

17. $[(p \to q) \lor (q \to r)] \to (p \to r)$

18. $[p \land (q \lor r)] \leftrightarrow [(p \land q) \lor (p \land r)]$

19. Let p and q denote the statements

   p: The candidate opposes changes in the Social Security system.

   q: The candidate supports immigration reform.

   Use De Morgan's Laws to state the negation of $p \land q$ and the negation of $p \lor q$.

20. Let p and q denote the statements

   p: The recycling bill was passed by the voters.

   q: The tax on oil and hazardous materials was not approved by the voters.

   Use De Morgan's Laws to state the negation of $p \land q$ and the negation of $p \lor q$.

In Exercises 21–26, use the laws of logic to prove the propositions.

21. $[p \land (q \lor \sim q) \lor (p \land q)] \Leftrightarrow p \lor (p \land q)$

22. $p \lor (\sim p \land \sim q) \Leftrightarrow p \lor \sim q$

23. $(p \land \sim q) \lor (p \land \sim r) \Leftrightarrow p \land (\sim q \lor \sim r)$

24. $(p \lor q) \lor \sim q \Leftrightarrow t$

25. $p \land \sim(q \land r) \Leftrightarrow (p \land \sim q) \lor (p \land \sim r)$

26. $p \lor (q \lor r) \Leftrightarrow r \lor (q \lor p)$

A.5 Arguments

In this section, we discuss arguments and the methods that are used to determine the validity of arguments.

> **Argument**
>
> An **argument** or **proof** consists of a set of propositions $p_1, p_2, \ldots, p_n$, called the *premises*, and a proposition q, called the *conclusion*. An argument is *valid* if and only if the conclusion is true whenever the premises are all true. An argument that is *not* valid is called a *fallacy*, or an *invalid* argument.

The next example illustrates the form in which an argument is presented. Notice that the premises are written separately above the horizontal line and the conclusion is written below the line.

EXAMPLE 1 An argument is presented in the following way:

Premises: If Pam studies diligently, she passes her exams.

Pam studies diligently.

Conclusion: Pam passes her exams.

To determine the validity of an argument, we first write the argument in symbolic form and then construct the associated truth table containing the prime propositions, the premises, and the conclusion. We then *check the rows in which the premises are all true. If the conclusion in each of these rows is also true, then the argument is valid. Otherwise, it is a fallacy.*

EXAMPLE 2 Determine the validity of the argument in Example 1.

Solution   The symbolic form of the argument is

$$p \rightarrow q$$
$$\frac{p}{\therefore q}$$

Observe that the conclusion is preceded by the symbol $\therefore$, which is used to represent the word *therefore*. The truth table associated with this argument is shown in Table 14. Observe that only row 1 contains true values for both premises. Since the conclusion is also true in this row, we conclude that the argument is valid.

TABLE 14

Propositions		Premises		Conclusion
p	q	$p \rightarrow q$	p	q
T	T	T	T	T
T	F	F	T	F
F	T	T	F	T
F	F	T	F	F

EXAMPLE 3 Determine the validity of the argument

> If Michael is overtired, then he is grumpy.
> Michael is grumpy.
> Therefore, Michael is overtired.

Solution The argument is written symbolically as follows:

$$p \rightarrow q$$
$$q$$
$$\therefore p$$

The associated truth table is shown in Table 15. Observe that the entries for the premises in the third row are both true, but the corresponding entry for the conclusion is false. We conclude that the argument is a fallacy.

TABLE 15

p	q	$p \rightarrow q$	q	p
T	T	T	T	T
T	F	F	F	T
F	T	T	T	F
F	F	T	F	F

When we consider the validity of an argument, we are concerned only with the *form* of the argument and not the truth or falsity of the premises. In other words, the conclusion of an argument may follow validly from the premises, but the premises themselves may be false. The next example demonstrates this point.

EXAMPLE 4 Determine the validity of the argument

> If I drive a car, then I eat lunch.
> If I eat lunch, then I play Wii.
> Therefore, if I drive a car, then I play Wii.

Solution The symbolic form of the argument is

$$p \rightarrow q$$
$$q \rightarrow r$$
$$\therefore p \rightarrow r$$

The associated truth table is shown in Table 16. Since the conclusion is true in each of the rows that contain true values for both premises, we conclude that the argument is valid. Note that the validity of the argument is not affected by the truth or falsity of the premise "If I drive a car, then I eat lunch."

TABLE 16

p	q	r	$p \rightarrow q$	$q \rightarrow r$	$p \rightarrow r$	
T	T	T	T	T	T	(✓)
T	T	F	T	F	F	
T	F	T	F	T	T	
T	F	F	F	T	F	
F	T	T	T	T	T	(✓)
F	T	F	T	F	T	
F	F	T	T	T	T	(✓)
F	F	F	T	T	T	(✓)

A question that may already have arisen in your mind is: How does one determine the validity of an argument if the associated truth table does not contain true values for all the premises? The next example provides the answer to this question.

EXAMPLE 5 Determine the validity of the argument

> The door is locked.
>
> The door is unlocked.
> _____
>
> Therefore, the door is locked.

Solution The symbolic form of the argument is

$$p$$
$$\underline{\sim p}$$
$$\therefore p$$

The associated truth table is shown in Table 17. Observe that no rows contain true values for both premises. Nevertheless, the argument is considered to be valid, since the condition that the conclusion is true whenever the premises are all true is not violated. Again, we remind you that the validity of an argument is not determined by the truth or falsity of its premises; rather, it is determined only by the form of the argument. ∎

TABLE 17

p	$\sim p$	p
T	F	T
F	T	F

The next proposition provides us with an alternative method for determining the validity of an argument.

> **Proposition**
>
> Suppose an argument consists of the premises $p_1, p_2, \ldots, p_n$ and conclusion q. Then, the argument is valid if and only if the proposition
>
> $$(p_1 \wedge p_2 \wedge \cdots \wedge p_n) \to q$$
>
> is a tautology.

To prove this proposition, we must show that (a) if an argument is valid, then the given proposition is a tautology, and (b) if the given proposition is a tautology, then the argument is valid.

Proof of (a) Since the argument is valid, it follows that q is true whenever all of the premises $p_1, p_2, \ldots, p_n$ are true. But the conjunction $(p_1 \wedge p_2 \wedge \cdots \wedge p_n)$ is true when all the premises are true (by the definition of conjunction). Hence, q is true whenever the conjunction is true, and we conclude that the conditional $(p_1 \wedge p_2 \wedge \cdots \wedge p_n) \to q$ is true. (Recall that a conditional statement is always true when its hypothesis is false. Hence, to show that a conditional is a tautology, we need only prove that its conclusion is always true when its hypothesis is true.)

Proof of (b) Since the given proposition is a tautology, it is always true. Therefore, q is true when the conjunction

$$p_1 \wedge p_2 \wedge \cdots \wedge p_n$$

is true. But the conjunction is true when all of the premises $p_1, p_2, \ldots, p_n$ are true. Hence, q is true whenever the premises are all true, and the argument is valid. ∎

Having proved this proposition, we can now use it to determine the validity of an argument. If we are given an argument, we construct a truth table for $(p_1 \wedge p_2 \wedge \cdots \wedge p_n) \to q$. If the truth table contains all Ts in its last column, then the argument is valid; otherwise, it is invalid. This method of proof is illustrated in the next example.

EXAMPLE 6 Determine the validity of the argument

> You return the book on time, or you will have to pay a fine.
>
> You do not return the book on time.
>
> Therefore, you will have to pay a fine.

Solution The symbolic form of the argument is

$$p \vee q$$
$$\underline{\qquad \sim p}$$
$$\therefore q$$

Following the method described, we construct the truth table for

$$[(p \vee q) \wedge \sim p] \rightarrow q$$

as shown in Table 18. Since the entries in the last column are all Ts, the proposition is a tautology, and we conclude that the argument is valid.

TABLE 18

p	q	$p \vee q$	$\sim p$	$(p \vee q) \wedge \sim p$	$[(p \vee q) \wedge \sim p] \rightarrow q$
T	T	T	F	F	T
T	F	T	F	F	T
F	T	T	T	T	T
F	F	F	T	F	T

By familiarizing ourselves with a few of the most commonly used argument forms, we can simplify the problem of determining the validity of an argument. Some of the argument forms most commonly used are the following:

1. **Modus ponens** (a manner of affirming), or rule of detachment

$$p \rightarrow q$$
$$\underline{\qquad p \qquad}$$
$$\therefore q$$

2. **Modus tollens** (a manner of denying)

$$p \rightarrow q$$
$$\underline{\qquad \sim q \qquad}$$
$$\therefore \sim p$$

3. **Law of syllogisms**

$$p \rightarrow q$$
$$\underline{q \rightarrow r}$$
$$\therefore p \rightarrow r$$

The truth tables verifying modus ponens and the law of syllogisms have already been constructed (see Tables 14 and 16, respectively). The verification of modus tollens is left to you as an exercise. The next two examples illlustrate the use of these argument forms.

EXAMPLE 7 Determine the validity of the argument

> If the battery is dead, the car will not start.
>
> The car starts.
>
> Therefore, the battery is not dead.

Solution   As before, we express the argument in symbolic form. Thus,

$$p \rightarrow q$$
$$\underline{\sim q}$$
$$\therefore \sim p$$

Identifying the form of this argument as modus tollens, we conclude that the given argument is valid.

EXAMPLE 8 Determine the validity of the argument

If mortgage rates are lowered, housing sales increase.

If housing sales increase, then the prices of houses increase.

Therefore, if mortgage rates are lowered, the prices of houses increase.

Solution   The symbolic form of the argument is

$$p \rightarrow q$$
$$\underline{q \rightarrow r}$$
$$\therefore p \rightarrow r$$

Using the law of syllogisms, we conclude that the argument is valid.

A.5 Exercises

In Exercises 1–16, determine whether the argument is valid.

1. $p \rightarrow q$
$\underline{q \rightarrow r}$
$\therefore p \rightarrow r$

2. $p \vee q$
$\underline{\sim p}$
$\therefore q$

3. $p \wedge q$
$\underline{\sim p}$
$\therefore q$

4. $p \rightarrow q$
$\underline{\sim q}$
$\therefore \sim p$

5. $p \rightarrow q$
$\underline{\sim p}$
$\therefore \sim q$

6. $p \rightarrow q$
$\underline{q \wedge r}$
$\therefore p \vee r$

7. $p \leftrightarrow q$
$\underline{q}$
$\therefore p$

8. $p \wedge q$
$\underline{\sim p \rightarrow \sim q}$
$\therefore p \wedge \sim q$

9. $p \rightarrow q$
$\underline{q \rightarrow p}$
$\therefore p \leftrightarrow q$

10. $p \rightarrow \sim q$
$\underline{p \veebar q}$
$\therefore \sim q$

11. $p \leftrightarrow q$
$\underline{q \leftrightarrow r}$
$\therefore p \leftrightarrow r$

12. $p \rightarrow q$
$\underline{q \leftrightarrow r}$
$\therefore p \wedge r$

13. $p \veebar r$
$\underline{q \wedge r}$
$\therefore p \rightarrow r$

14. $p \leftrightarrow q$
$q \vee r$
$\underline{\sim r}$
$\therefore p \rightarrow \sim r$

15. $p \leftrightarrow q$
$q \vee r$
$\underline{\sim p}$
$\therefore \sim p \rightarrow \sim r$

16. $p \rightarrow q$
$r \rightarrow q$
$\underline{p \wedge q}$
$\therefore p \vee r$

In Exercises 17–22, represent the argument symbolically, and determine whether it is a valid argument.

17. If Carla studies, then she passes her exams.

Carla did not study.

Therefore, Carla did not pass her exams.

18. If Tony is wealthy, he is either intelligent or a good businessman.

Tony is intelligent and he is not a good businessman.

Therefore, Tony is not wealthy.

19. Steve will attend the matinee and/or the evening show.

If Steve doesn't go to the matinee show, then he will not go to the evening show.

Therefore, Steve will attend the matinee show.

20. If Mary wins the race, then Stacy loses the race.

Neither Mary nor Linda won the race.

Therefore, Stacy won the race.

21. If mortgage rates go up, then housing prices will go up.

If housing prices go up, more people will rent houses.

More people are renting houses.

Therefore, mortgage rates went up.

22. If taxes are cut, then retail sales increase.

If retail sales increase, then the unemployment rate will decrease.

If the unemployment rate decreases, then the incumbent will win the election.

Therefore, if taxes are not cut, the incumbent will not win the election.

23. Show that the following argument is valid.

If George prepares gourmet food, then he is a good cook.

If Brenda does not prepare gourmet food, then Sarah buys fast food.

Sarah does not buy fast food.

Therefore, George does not prepare gourmet food, and Brenda does not prepare gourmet food.

24. What conclusion can be drawn from the following statements?

His date is pretty, or she is tall and skinny.

If his date is tall, then she is a brunette.

His date is not a brunette.

25. Show that modus tollens is a valid form of argument.

A.6   Applications of Logic to Switching Networks

In this section, we see how the principles of logic can be used in the design and analysis of switching networks. A **switching network** is an arrangement of wires and switches connecting two terminals. These networks are used extensively in digital computers.

A switch may be open or closed. If a switch is closed, current will flow through the wire. If it is open, no current will flow through the wire. Because a switch has exactly two states, it can be represented by a proposition p that is true if the switch is closed and false if the switch is open.

Now let's consider a circuit with two switches p and q. If the circuit is constructed as shown in Figure 1, the switches p and q are said to be **in series**.

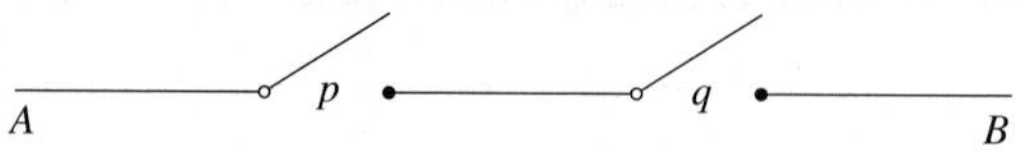

FIGURE 1
Two switches connected in series

For such a network, current will flow from A to B if both p and q are closed, but no current will flow if one or more of the switches is open. Thinking of p and q as propositions, we have the truth table shown in Table 19. (Recall that T corresponds to the situation in which the switch is closed.) From the truth table, we see that two switches p and q connected in series are analogous to the conjunction $p \wedge q$ of the two propositions p and q.

If a circuit is constructed as shown in Figure 2, the switches p and q are said to be connected **in parallel**.

TABLE 19		
p	q	
T	T	T
T	F	F
F	T	F
F	F	F

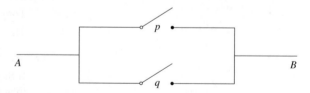

FIGURE 2
Two switches connected in parallel

For such a network, current will flow from A to B if and only if one or more of the switches p or q is closed. Once again, thinking of p and q as propositions, we have the truth table shown in Table 20. From the truth table, we conclude that two switches p and q connected in parallel are analogous to the inclusive disjunction $p \vee q$ of the two propositions p and q.

TABLE 20		
p	q	
T	T	T
T	F	T
F	T	T
F	F	F

EXAMPLE 1 Find a logic statement that represents the network shown in Figure 3. By constructing the truth table for this logic statement, determine the conditions under which current will flow from A to B in the network.

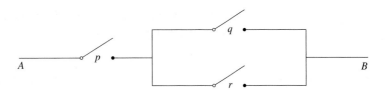

FIGURE 3
We want to determine when the current
will flow from A to B.

Solution   The required logic statement is $p \wedge (q \vee r)$. Next, we construct the truth table for the logic statement $p \wedge (q \vee r)$ (Table 21).

TABLE 21

p	q	r	$q \vee r$	$p \wedge (q \vee r)$
T	T	T	T	T
T	T	F	T	T
T	F	T	T	T
T	F	F	F	F
F	T	T	T	F
F	T	F	T	F
F	F	T	T	F
F	F	F	F	F

From the truth table, we conclude that current will flow from A to B if and only if one of the following conditions is satisfied:

1. p, q, and r are all closed.
2. p and q are closed, but r is open.
3. p and r are closed, but q is open.

In other words, current will flow from A to B if and only if p is closed and either q or r or both q and r are closed. ◼

Before looking at some additional examples, let's remark that $\sim p$ represents a switch that is open when p is closed and vice versa. Furthermore, a circuit that is always closed is represented by a tautology, $p \vee \sim p$, whereas a circuit that is always open is represented by a contradiction, $p \wedge \sim p$. (Why?)

EXAMPLE 2 Given the logic statement $(p \vee q) \wedge (r \vee s \vee \sim t)$, draw the corresponding network.

Solution   Recalling that the disjunction $p \vee q$ of the propositions p and q represents two switches p and q connected in parallel and the conjunction $p \wedge q$ represents two switches connected in series, we obtain the following network (Figure 4).

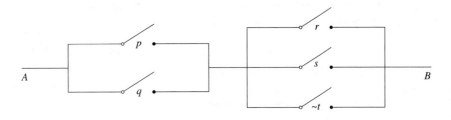

FIGURE 4
The network that corresponds to the logic
statement
$(p \vee q) \wedge (r \vee s \vee \sim t)$

When used in conjunction with the laws of logic, the theory of networks developed so far is a useful tool in network analysis. In particular, network analysis enables us to find equivalent, and often simpler, networks, as the following example shows.

EXAMPLE 3 Find a logic statement representing the network shown in Figure 5. Also, find a simpler but equivalent network.

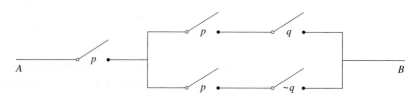

FIGURE 5
We want to find the logic statement that corresponds to the network shown in the figure.

Solution The logic statement corresponding to the given network is $p \wedge [(p \wedge q) \vee (p \wedge \sim q)]$. Next, using the rules of logic to simplify this statement, we obtain

$$p \wedge [(p \wedge q) \vee (p \wedge \sim q)] \Leftrightarrow p \wedge [p \wedge (q \vee \sim q)] \qquad \text{Distributive law}$$
$$\Leftrightarrow p \wedge p \qquad \text{Tautology}$$
$$\Leftrightarrow p$$

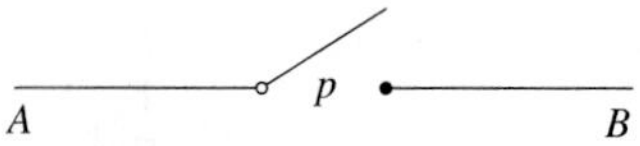

Thus, the network shown in Figure 6 is equivalent to the one shown in Figure 5. ∎

FIGURE 6
The network is equivalent to the one shown in Figure 5.

A.6 Exercises

In Exercises 1–5, find a logic statement corresponding to the network. Determine the conditions under which current will flow from A to B.

1.

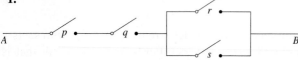

2.

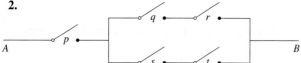

3.

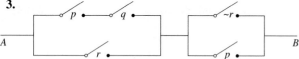

4.

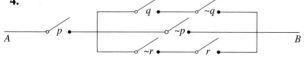

5.

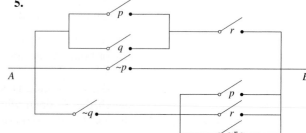

In Exercises 6–11, draw the network corresponding to the logic statement.

6. $p \vee (q \wedge r)$ **7.** $(p \wedge q) \wedge r$

8. $[p \vee (q \wedge r)] \wedge \sim q$

9. $(p \vee q) \vee [r \wedge (\sim r \vee \sim p)]$

10. $(\sim p \vee q) \wedge (p \vee \sim q)$

11. $(p \wedge q) \vee [(r \vee \sim q) \wedge (s \vee \sim p)]$

In Exercises 12–15, find a logic statement corresponding to the network. Then find a simpler but equivalent logic statement.

12.

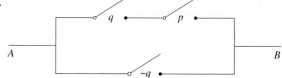

13.

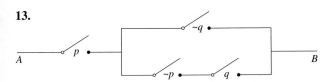

14.

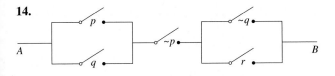

15.

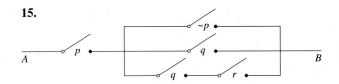

16. A hallway light is to be operated by two switches, one located at the bottom of the staircase and the other located at the top of the staircase. Design a suitable network.

Hint: Let p and q be the switches. Construct a truth table for the associated propositions.

THE SYSTEM OF REAL NUMBERS

In this appendix, we briefly review the **system of real numbers**. This system consists of a set of objects called real numbers together with two operations, addition and multiplication, that enable us to combine two or more real numbers to obtain other real numbers. These operations are subject to certain rules that we will state after first recalling the set of real numbers.

The set of real numbers may be constructed from the set of **natural** (also called **counting**) **numbers**

$$N = \{1, 2, 3, \ldots\}$$

by adjoining other objects (numbers) to it. Thus, the set

$$W = \{0, 1, 2, 3, \ldots\}$$

obtained by adjoining the single number 0 to N is called the set of **whole numbers**. By adjoining *negatives* of the numbers 1, 2, 3, . . . to the set W of whole numbers, we obtain the set of **integers**

$$I = \{\ldots, -3, -2, -1, 0, 1, 2, 3, \ldots\}$$

Next, consider the set

$$Q = \left\{ \frac{a}{b} \,\middle|\, a \text{ and } b \text{ are integers with } b \neq 0 \right\}$$

Now, the set I of integers is contained in the set Q of **rational numbers**. To see this, observe that each integer may be written in the form a/b with $b = 1$, thus qualifying as a member of the set Q. The converse, however, is false, for the rational numbers (fractions) such as

$$\frac{1}{2}, \quad \frac{23}{25}, \quad \text{and so on}$$

are clearly not integers.

The sets N, W, I, and Q constructed thus far have the relationship

$$N \subset W \subset I \subset Q$$

That is, N is a proper subset of W, W is a proper subset of I, and I is a proper subset of Q.

Finally, consider the set Ir of all real numbers that cannot be expressed in the form a/b, where a, b are integers ($b \neq 0$). The members of this set, called the set of **irrational numbers**, include $\sqrt{2}$, $\sqrt{3}$, π, and so on. The set

$$R = Q \cup Ir$$

which is the set of all rational and irrational numbers, is called the set of all **real numbers** (Figure 1).

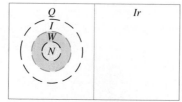

Q = Rationals
I = Integers
W = Whole numbers
N = Natural numbers
Ir = Irrationals

FIGURE 1
The set of all real numbers consists of the set of rational numbers and the set of irrational numbers.

Note the following important representation of real numbers: Every real number has a decimal representation; a rational number has a representation as a terminating or repeating decimal. For example, $\frac{1}{40} = 0.025$, and

$$\frac{1}{7} = 0.142857142857142857\ldots$$

Note that the block of integers 142857 repeats.

On the other hand, the irrational number $\sqrt{2}$ has a representation as a nonrepeating decimal. Thus,

$$\sqrt{2} = 1.41421\ldots$$

As was mentioned earlier, any two real numbers may be combined to obtain another real number. The operation of *addition*, written $+$, enables us to combine any two numbers a and b to obtain their sum, denoted by $a + b$. Another operation, called *multiplication* and written $\cdot$, enables us to combine any two real numbers a and b to form their product, denoted by $a \cdot b$ or, more simply, ab. These two operations are subjected to the following rules of operation: Given any three real numbers a, b, and c, we have

I. Under addition

  1. $a + b = b + a$ — Commutative law of addition

  2. $a + (b + c) = (a + b) + c$ — Associative law of addition

  3. $a + 0 = a$ — Identity law of addition

  4. $a + (-a) = 0$ — Inverse law of addition

II. Under multiplication

  1. $ab = ba$ — Commutative law of multiplication

  2. $a(bc) = (ab)c$ — Associative law of multiplication

  3. $a \cdot 1 = a$ — Identity law of multiplication

  4. $a(1/a) = 1 \qquad (a \neq 0)$ — Inverse law of multiplication

III. Under addition and multiplication

  1. $a(b + c) = ab + ac$ — Distributive law for multiplication with respect to addition

APPENDIX C
REVIEW OF LOGARITHMS

Logarithms

You are already familiar with exponential equations of the form

$$b^y = x \qquad (b > 0, b \neq 1)$$

where the variable x is expressed in terms of a real number b and a variable y. But what about solving this same equation for y? You may recall from your study of algebra that the number y is called the **logarithm of x to the base b** and is denoted by $\log_b x$. It is the power to which the base b must be raised to obtain the number x.

Logarithm of x to the Base b, $b > 0, b \neq 1$

$$y = \log_b x \quad \text{if and only if} \quad x = b^y \qquad (x > 0)$$

⚠ Observe that the logarithm $\log_b x$ is defined only for positive values of x.

EXAMPLE 1

a. $\log_{10} 100 = 2$ since $100 = 10^2$
b. $\log_5 125 = 3$ since $125 = 5^3$
c. $\log_3 \dfrac{1}{27} = -3$ since $\dfrac{1}{27} = \dfrac{1}{3^3} = 3^{-3}$
d. $\log_{20} 20 = 1$ since $20 = 20^1$

■

EXAMPLE 2 Solve each of the following equations for x.

a. $\log_3 x = 4$ b. $\log_{16} 4 = x$ c. $\log_x 8 = 3$

Solution

a. By definition, $\log_3 x = 4$ implies $x = 3^4 = 81$.
b. $\log_{16} 4 = x$ is equivalent to $4 = 16^x = (4^2)^x = 4^{2x}$, or $4^1 = 4^{2x}$, from which we deduce that

$$2x = 1 \qquad b^m = b^n \Rightarrow m = n$$

$$x = \frac{1}{2}$$

c. Referring once again to the definition, we see that the equation $\log_x 8 = 3$ is equivalent to

$$8 = 2^3 = x^3$$

$$x = 2 \qquad a^m = b^m \Rightarrow a = b$$

■

The two widely used systems of logarithms are the system of **common logarithms,** which uses the number 10 as the base, and the system of **natural logarithms,** which uses the irrational number $e = 2.71828\ldots$ as the base. Also, it is standard practice to write **log** for $\log_{10}$ and **ln** for $\log_e$.

Logarithmic Notation

$$\log x = \log_{10} x \qquad \text{Common logarithm}$$

$$\ln x = \log_e x \qquad \text{Natural logarithm}$$

The system of natural logarithms is widely used in theoretical work. Using natural logarithms rather than logarithms to other bases often leads to simpler expressions.

Laws of Logarithms

Computations involving logarithms are facilitated by the following **laws of logarithms.**

> Laws of Logarithms
>
> If m and n are positive numbers and $b > 0$, $b \neq 1$, then
>
> **1.** $\log_b mn = \log_b m + \log_b n$
>
> **2.** $\log_b \dfrac{m}{n} = \log_b m - \log_b n$
>
> **3.** $\log_b m^r = r \log_b m$ for any real number r
> **4.** $\log_b 1 = 0$
> **5.** $\log_b b = 1$

⚠ Do not confuse the expression $\log m/n$ (Law 2) with the expression $\log m/\log n$. For example,

$$\log \frac{100}{10} = \log 100 - \log 10 = 2 - 1 = 1 \neq \frac{\log 100}{\log 10} = \frac{2}{1} = 2$$

The following examples illustrate the properties of logarithms.

EXAMPLE 3

a. $\log(2 \cdot 3) = \log 2 + \log 3$ **b.** $\ln \dfrac{5}{3} = \ln 5 - \ln 3$

c. $\log \sqrt{7} = \log 7^{1/2} = \dfrac{1}{2} \log 7$ **d.** $\log_5 1 = 0$

e. $\log_{45} 45 = 1$

EXAMPLE 4 Given that $\log 2 \approx 0.3010$, $\log 3 \approx 0.4771$, and $\log 5 \approx 0.6990$, use the laws of logarithms to find

a. $\log 15$ **b.** $\log 7.5$ **c.** $\log 81$

Solution

a. Note that $15 = 3 \cdot 5$, so by Law 1 for logarithms,

$$\begin{aligned}
\log 15 &= \log 3 \cdot 5 \\
&= \log 3 + \log 5 \\
&\approx 0.4771 + 0.6990 \\
&= 1.1761
\end{aligned}$$

b. Observing that $7.5 = 15/2 = (3 \cdot 5)/2$, we apply Laws 1 and 2, obtaining

$$\begin{aligned}
\log 7.5 &= \log \frac{(3)(5)}{2} \\
&= \log 3 + \log 5 - \log 2 \\
&\approx 0.4771 + 0.6990 - 0.3010 \\
&= 0.8751
\end{aligned}$$

c. Since $81 = 3^4$, we apply Law 3 to obtain

$$\begin{aligned}
\log 81 &= \log 3^4 \\
&= 4 \log 3 \\
&\approx 4(0.4771) \\
&= 1.9084
\end{aligned}$$

Examples 5 and 6 illustrate how the properties of logarithms are used to solve equations.

EXAMPLE 5 Solve $\log_3(x + 1) - \log_3(x - 1) = 1$ for x.

Solution   Using the properties of logarithms, we obtain

$$\log_3(x + 1) - \log_3(x - 1) = 1$$

$$\log_3 \frac{x + 1}{x - 1} = 1 \qquad \text{Law 2}$$

$$\frac{x + 1}{x - 1} = 3^1 = 3 \qquad \text{Definition of logarithms}$$

So

$$\begin{aligned}
x + 1 &= 3(x - 1) \\
x + 1 &= 3x - 3 \\
4 &= 2x \\
x &= 2 \qquad \text{Remember to check to see whether the} \\
&\qquad\qquad \text{original equation holds true for } x = 2.
\end{aligned}$$

EXAMPLE 6 Solve $\log x + \log(2x - 1) = \log 6$.

Solution   We have

$$\log x + \log(2x - 1) = \log 6$$

$$\log x + \log(2x - 1) - \log 6 = 0$$

$$\log\left[\frac{x(2x - 1)}{6}\right] = 0 \qquad \text{Laws 1 and 2}$$

$$\frac{x(2x - 1)}{6} = 10^0 = 1 \qquad \text{Definition of logarithms}$$

So

$$\begin{aligned}
x(2x - 1) &= 6 \\
2x^2 - x - 6 &= 0 \\
(2x + 3)(x - 2) &= 0
\end{aligned}$$

$$x = -\frac{3}{2} \quad \text{or} \quad 2$$

Since the domain of $\log(2x - 1)$ is the interval $(\frac{1}{2}, \infty)$ (because $2x - 1$ must be positive), we reject the root $-\frac{3}{2}$ of the quadratic equation and conclude that the solution of the given equation is $x = 2$.

Note   Using the fact that $\log a = \log b$ if and only if $a = b$, we can also solve the equation of Example 6 in the following manner:

$$\begin{aligned}
\log x + \log(2x - 1) &= \log 6 \\
\log x(2x - 1) &= \log 6 \\
x(2x - 1) &= 6
\end{aligned}$$

The rest of the solution is the same as that in Example 6.

Exercises

In Exercises 1–6, express each equation in logarithmic form.

1. $2^6 = 64$

2. $3^5 = 243$

3. $3^{-2} = \dfrac{1}{9}$

4. $5^{-3} = \dfrac{1}{125}$

5. $32^{3/5} = 8$

6. $81^{3/4} = 27$

In Exercises 7–10, use the facts that $\log 3 \approx 0.4771$ and $\log 4 \approx 0.6021$ to find the value of each logarithm.

7. $\log 12$

8. $\log \dfrac{3}{4}$

9. $\log 16$

10. $\log \sqrt{3}$

In Exercises 11–14, write the expression as the logarithm of a single quantity.

11. $2 \ln a + 3 \ln b$

12. $\dfrac{1}{2} \ln x + 2 \ln y - 3 \ln z$

13. $\ln 3 + \dfrac{1}{2} \ln x + \ln y - \dfrac{1}{3} \ln z$

14. $\ln 2 + \dfrac{1}{2} \ln(x + 1) - 2 \ln(1 + \sqrt{x})$

In Exercises 15–22, use the laws of logarithms to solve the equation.

15. $\log_2 x = 3$

16. $\log_2 8 = x$

17. $\log_x 10^3 = 3$

18. $\log_x \dfrac{1}{16} = -2$

19. $\log_2(2x + 5) = 3$

20. $\log_4(5x - 4) = 2$

21. $\log_5(2x + 1) - \log_5(x - 2) = 1$

22. $\log(x + 7) - \log(x - 2) = 1$

In Exercises 23–30, use logarithms to solve the equation for t.

23. $e^{0.4t} = 8$

24. $\dfrac{1}{3} e^{-3t} = 0.9$

25. $5e^{-2t} = 6$

26. $4e^{t-1} = 4$

27. $2e^{-0.2t} - 4 = 6$

28. $12 - e^{0.4t} = 3$

29. $\dfrac{50}{1 + 4e^{0.2t}} = 20$

30. $\dfrac{200}{1 + 3e^{-0.3t}} = 100$

TABLES

TABLE 1

Binomial Probabilities

							p					
n	x	**0.05**	**0.1**	**0.2**	**0.3**	**0.4**	**0.5**	**0.6**	**0.7**	**0.8**	**0.9**	**0.95**
2	0	0.902	0.810	0.640	0.490	0.360	0.250	0.160	0.090	0.040	0.010	0.002
	1	0.095	0.180	0.320	0.420	0.480	0.500	0.480	0.420	0.320	0.180	0.095
	2	0.002	0.010	0.040	0.090	0.160	0.250	0.360	0.490	0.640	0.810	0.902
3	0	0.857	0.729	0.512	0.343	0.216	0.125	0.064	0.027	0.008	0.001	
	1	0.135	0.243	0.384	0.441	0.432	0.375	0.288	0.189	0.096	0.027	0.007
	2	0.007	0.027	0.096	0.189	0.288	0.375	0.432	0.441	0.384	0.243	0.135
	3		0.001	0.008	0.027	0.064	0.125	0.216	0.343	0.512	0.729	0.857
4	0	0.815	0.656	0.410	0.240	0.130	0.062	0.026	0.008	0.002		
	1	0.171	0.292	0.410	0.412	0.346	0.250	0.154	0.076	0.026	0.004	
	2	0.014	0.049	0.154	0.265	0.346	0.375	0.346	0.265	0.154	0.049	0.014
	3		0.004	0.026	0.076	0.154	0.250	0.346	0.412	0.410	0.292	0.171
	4			0.002	0.008	0.026	0.062	0.130	0.240	0.410	0.656	0.815
5	0	0.774	0.590	0.328	0.168	0.078	0.031	0.010	0.002			
	1	0.204	0.328	0.410	0.360	0.259	0.156	0.077	0.028	0.006		
	2	0.021	0.073	0.205	0.309	0.346	0.312	0.230	0.132	0.051	0.008	0.001
	3	0.001	0.008	0.051	0.132	0.230	0.312	0.346	0.309	0.205	0.073	0.021
	4			0.006	0.028	0.077	0.156	0.259	0.360	0.410	0.328	0.204
	5				0.002	0.010	0.031	0.078	0.168	0.328	0.590	0.774
6	0	0.735	0.531	0.262	0.118	0.047	0.016	0.004	0.001			
	1	0.232	0.354	0.393	0.303	0.187	0.094	0.037	0.010	0.002		
	2	0.031	0.098	0.246	0.324	0.311	0.234	0.138	0.060	0.015	0.001	
	3	0.002	0.015	0.082	0.185	0.276	0.312	0.276	0.185	0.082	0.015	0.002
	4		0.001	0.015	0.060	0.138	0.234	0.311	0.324	0.246	0.098	0.031
	5			0.002	0.010	0.037	0.094	0.187	0.303	0.393	0.354	0.232
	6				0.001	0.004	0.016	0.047	0.118	0.262	0.531	0.735
7	0	0.698	0.478	0.210	0.082	0.028	0.008	0.002				
	1	0.257	0.372	0.367	0.247	0.131	0.055	0.017	0.004			
	2	0.041	0.124	0.275	0.318	0.261	0.164	0.077	0.025	0.004		
	3	0.004	0.023	0.115	0.227	0.290	0.273	0.194	0.097	0.029	0.003	
	4		0.003	0.029	0.097	0.194	0.273	0.290	0.227	0.115	0.023	0.004
	5			0.004	0.025	0.077	0.164	0.261	0.318	0.275	0.124	0.041
	6				0.004	0.017	0.055	0.131	0.247	0.367	0.372	0.257
	7					0.002	0.008	0.028	0.082	0.210	0.478	0.698
8	0	0.663	0.430	0.168	0.058	0.017	0.004	0.001				
	1	0.279	0.383	0.336	0.198	0.090	0.031	0.008	0.001			
	2	0.051	0.149	0.294	0.296	0.209	0.109	0.041	0.010	0.001		
	3	0.005	0.033	0.147	0.254	0.279	0.219	0.124	0.047	0.009		
	4		0.005	0.046	0.136	0.232	0.273	0.232	0.136	0.046	0.005	
	5			0.009	0.047	0.124	0.219	0.279	0.254	0.147	0.033	0.005
	6			0.001	0.010	0.041	0.109	0.209	0.296	0.294	0.149	0.051
	7				0.001	0.008	0.031	0.090	0.198	0.336	0.383	0.279
	8					0.001	0.004	0.017	0.058	0.168	0.430	0.663

TABLE 1 (*continued*)

Binomial Probabilities

							p					
n	x	0.05	0.1	0.2	0.3	0.4	0.5	0.6	0.7	0.8	0.9	0.95
9	0	0.630	0.387	0.134	0.040	0.010	0.002					
	1	0.299	0.387	0.302	0.156	0.060	0.018	0.004				
	2	0.063	0.172	0.302	0.267	0.161	0.070	0.021	0.004			
	3	0.008	0.045	0.176	0.267	0.251	0.164	0.074	0.021	0.003		
	4	0.001	0.007	0.066	0.172	0.251	0.246	0.167	0.074	0.017	0.001	
	5		0.001	0.017	0.074	0.167	0.246	0.251	0.172	0.066	0.007	0.001
	6			0.003	0.021	0.074	0.164	0.251	0.267	0.176	0.045	0.008
	7				0.004	0.021	0.070	0.161	0.267	0.302	0.172	0.063
	8					0.004	0.018	0.060	0.156	0.302	0.387	0.299
	9						0.002	0.010	0.040	0.134	0.387	0.630
10	0	0.599	0.349	0.107	0.028	0.006	0.001					
	1	0.315	0.387	0.268	0.121	0.040	0.010	0.002				
	2	0.075	0.194	0.302	0.233	0.121	0.044	0.011	0.001			
	3	0.010	0.057	0.201	0.267	0.215	0.117	0.042	0.009	0.001		
	4	0.001	0.011	0.088	0.200	0.251	0.205	0.111	0.037	0.006		
	5		0.001	0.026	0.103	0.201	0.246	0.201	0.103	0.026	0.001	
	6			0.006	0.037	0.111	0.205	0.251	0.200	0.088	0.011	0.001
	7			0.001	0.009	0.042	0.117	0.215	0.267	0.201	0.057	0.010
	8				0.001	0.011	0.044	0.121	0.233	0.302	0.194	0.075
	9					0.002	0.010	0.040	0.121	0.268	0.387	0.315
	10						0.001	0.006	0.028	0.107	0.349	0.599
11	0	0.569	0.314	0.086	0.020	0.004						
	1	0.329	0.384	0.236	0.093	0.027	0.005	0.001				
	2	0.087	0.213	0.295	0.200	0.089	0.027	0.005	0.001			
	3	0.014	0.071	0.221	0.257	0.177	0.081	0.023	0.004			
	4	0.001	0.016	0.111	0.220	0.236	0.161	0.070	0.017	0.002		
	5		0.002	0.039	0.132	0.221	0.226	0.147	0.057	0.010		
	6			0.010	0.057	0.147	0.226	0.221	0.132	0.039	0.002	
	7			0.002	0.017	0.070	0.161	0.236	0.220	0.111	0.016	0.001
	8				0.004	0.023	0.081	0.177	0.257	0.221	0.071	0.014
	9				0.001	0.005	0.027	0.089	0.200	0.295	0.213	0.087
	10					0.001	0.005	0.027	0.093	0.236	0.384	0.329
	11							0.004	0.020	0.086	0.314	0.569
12	0	0.540	0.282	0.069	0.014	0.002						
	1	0.341	0.377	0.206	0.071	0.017	0.003					
	2	0.099	0.230	0.283	0.168	0.064	0.016	0.002				
	3	0.017	0.085	0.236	0.240	0.142	0.054	0.012	0.001			
	4	0.002	0.021	0.133	0.231	0.213	0.121	0.042	0.008	0.001		
	5		0.004	0.053	0.158	0.227	0.193	0.101	0.029	0.003		
	6			0.016	0.079	0.177	0.226	0.177	0.079	0.016		
	7			0.003	0.029	0.101	0.193	0.227	0.158	0.053	0.004	
	8			0.001	0.008	0.042	0.121	0.213	0.231	0.133	0.021	0.002
	9				0.001	0.012	0.054	0.142	0.240	0.236	0.085	0.017
	10					0.002	0.016	0.064	0.168	0.283	0.230	0.099
	11						0.003	0.017	0.071	0.206	0.377	0.341
	12							0.002	0.014	0.069	0.282	0.540

TABLE 1 (*continued*)

Binomial Probabilities

							p					
n	x	**0.05**	**0.1**	**0.2**	**0.3**	**0.4**	**0.5**	**0.6**	**0.7**	**0.8**	**0.9**	**0.95**
13	0	0.513	0.254	0.055	0.010	0.001						
	1	0.351	0.367	0.179	0.054	0.011	0.002					
	2	0.111	0.245	0.268	0.139	0.045	0.010	0.001				
	3	0.021	0.100	0.246	0.218	0.111	0.035	0.006	0.001			
	4	0.003	0.028	0.154	0.234	0.184	0.087	0.024	0.003			
	5		0.006	0.069	0.180	0.221	0.157	0.066	0.014	0.001		
	6		0.001	0.023	0.103	0.197	0.209	0.131	0.044	0.006		
	7			0.006	0.044	0.131	0.209	0.197	0.103	0.023	0.001	
	8			0.001	0.014	0.066	0.157	0.221	0.180	0.069	0.006	
	9				0.003	0.024	0.087	0.184	0.234	0.154	0.028	0.003
	10				0.001	0.006	0.035	0.111	0.218	0.246	0.100	0.021
	11					0.001	0.010	0.045	0.139	0.268	0.245	0.111
	12						0.002	0.011	0.054	0.179	0.367	0.351
	13							0.001	0.010	0.055	0.254	0.513
14	0	0.488	0.229	0.044	0.007	0.001						
	1	0.359	0.356	0.154	0.041	0.007	0.001					
	2	0.123	0.257	0.250	0.113	0.032	0.006	0.001				
	3	0.026	0.114	0.250	0.194	0.085	0.022	0.003				
	4	0.004	0.035	0.172	0.229	0.155	0.061	0.014	0.001			
	5		0.008	0.086	0.196	0.207	0.122	0.041	0.007			
	6		0.001	0.032	0.126	0.207	0.183	0.092	0.023	0.002		
	7			0.009	0.062	0.157	0.209	0.157	0.062	0.009		
	8			0.002	0.023	0.092	0.183	0.207	0.126	0.032	0.001	
	9				0.007	0.041	0.122	0.207	0.196	0.086	0.008	
	10				0.001	0.014	0.061	0.155	0.229	0.172	0.035	0.004
	11					0.003	0.022	0.085	0.194	0.250	0.114	0.026
	12					0.001	0.006	0.032	0.113	0.250	0.257	0.123
	13						0.001	0.007	0.041	0.154	0.356	0.359
	14							0.001	0.007	0.044	0.229	0.488
15	0	0.463	0.206	0.035	0.005							
	1	0.366	0.343	0.132	0.031	0.005						
	2	0.135	0.267	0.231	0.092	0.022	0.003					
	3	0.031	0.129	0.250	0.170	0.063	0.014	0.002				
	4	0.005	0.043	0.188	0.219	0.127	0.042	0.007	0.001			
	5	0.001	0.010	0.103	0.206	0.186	0.092	0.024	0.003			
	6		0.002	0.043	0.147	0.207	0.153	0.061	0.012	0.001		
	7			0.014	0.081	0.177	0.196	0.118	0.035	0.003		
	8			0.003	0.035	0.118	0.196	0.177	0.081	0.014		
	9			0.001	0.012	0.061	0.153	0.207	0.147	0.043	0.002	
	10				0.003	0.024	0.092	0.186	0.206	0.103	0.010	0.001
	11				0.001	0.007	0.042	0.127	0.219	0.188	0.043	0.005
	12					0.002	0.014	0.063	0.170	0.250	0.129	0.031
	13						0.003	0.022	0.092	0.231	0.267	0.135
	14							0.005	0.031	0.132	0.343	0.366
	15								0.005	0.035	0.206	0.463

TABLE 2

The Standard Normal Distribution

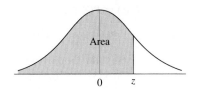

Area

0   z

$$F_z(z) = P(Z \le z)$$

z	0.00	0.01	0.02	0.03	0.04	0.05	0.06	0.07	0.08	0.09
−3.4	0.0003	0.0003	0.0003	0.0003	0.0003	0.0003	0.0003	0.0003	0.0003	0.0002
−3.3	0.0005	0.0005	0.0005	0.0004	0.0004	0.0004	0.0004	0.0004	0.0004	0.0003
−3.2	0.0007	0.0007	0.0006	0.0006	0.0006	0.0006	0.0006	0.0005	0.0005	0.0005
−3.1	0.0010	0.0009	0.0009	0.0009	0.0008	0.0008	0.0008	0.0008	0.0007	0.0007
−3.0	0.0013	0.0013	0.0013	0.0012	0.0012	0.0011	0.0011	0.0011	0.0010	0.0010
−2.9	0.0019	0.0018	0.0017	0.0017	0.0016	0.0016	0.0015	0.0015	0.0014	0.0014
−2.8	0.0026	0.0025	0.0024	0.0023	0.0023	0.0022	0.0021	0.0021	0.0020	0.0019
−2.7	0.0035	0.0034	0.0033	0.0032	0.0031	0.0030	0.0029	0.0028	0.0027	0.0026
−2.6	0.0047	0.0045	0.0044	0.0043	0.0041	0.0040	0.0039	0.0038	0.0037	0.0036
−2.5	0.0062	0.0060	0.0059	0.0057	0.0055	0.0054	0.0052	0.0051	0.0049	0.0048
−2.4	0.0082	0.0080	0.0078	0.0075	0.0073	0.0071	0.0069	0.0068	0.0066	0.0064
−2.3	0.0107	0.0104	0.0102	0.0099	0.0096	0.0094	0.0091	0.0089	0.0087	0.0084
−2.2	0.0139	0.0136	0.0132	0.0129	0.0125	0.0122	0.0119	0.0116	0.0113	0.0110
−2.1	0.0179	0.0174	0.0170	0.0166	0.0162	0.0158	0.0154	0.0150	0.0146	0.0143
−2.0	0.0228	0.0222	0.0217	0.0212	0.0207	0.0202	0.0197	0.0192	0.0188	0.0183
−1.9	0.0287	0.0281	0.0274	0.0268	0.0262	0.0256	0.0250	0.0244	0.0239	0.0233
−1.8	0.0359	0.0352	0.0344	0.0336	0.0329	0.0322	0.0314	0.0307	0.0301	0.0294
−1.7	0.0446	0.0436	0.0427	0.0418	0.0409	0.0401	0.0392	0.0384	0.0375	0.0367
−1.6	0.0548	0.0537	0.0526	0.0516	0.0505	0.0495	0.0485	0.0475	0.0465	0.0455
−1.5	0.0668	0.0655	0.0643	0.0630	0.0618	0.0606	0.0594	0.0582	0.0571	0.0559
−1.4	0.0808	0.0793	0.0778	0.0764	0.0749	0.0735	0.0722	0.0708	0.0694	0.0681
−1.3	0.0968	0.0951	0.0934	0.0918	0.0901	0.0885	0.0869	0.0853	0.0838	0.0823
−1.2	0.1151	0.1131	0.1112	0.1093	0.1075	0.1056	0.1038	0.1020	0.1003	0.0985
−1.1	0.1357	0.1335	0.1314	0.1292	0.1271	0.1251	0.1230	0.1210	0.1190	0.1170
−1.0	0.1587	0.1562	0.1539	0.1515	0.1492	0.1469	0.1446	0.1423	0.1401	0.1379
−0.9	0.1841	0.1814	0.1788	0.1762	0.1736	0.1711	0.1685	0.1660	0.1635	0.1611
−0.8	0.2119	0.2090	0.2061	0.2033	0.2005	0.1977	0.1949	0.1922	0.1894	0.1867
−0.7	0.2420	0.2389	0.2358	0.2327	0.2296	0.2266	0.2236	0.2206	0.2177	0.2148
−0.6	0.2743	0.2709	0.2676	0.2643	0.2611	0.2578	0.2546	0.2514	0.2483	0.2451
−0.5	0.3085	0.3050	0.3015	0.2981	0.2946	0.2912	0.2877	0.2843	0.2810	0.2776
−0.4	0.3446	0.3409	0.3372	0.3336	0.3300	0.3264	0.3228	0.3192	0.3156	0.3121
−0.3	0.3821	0.3783	0.3745	0.3707	0.3669	0.3632	0.3594	0.3557	0.3520	0.3483
−0.2	0.4207	0.4168	0.4129	0.4090	0.4052	0.4013	0.3974	0.3936	0.3897	0.3859
−0.1	0.4602	0.4562	0.4522	0.4483	0.4443	0.4404	0.4364	0.4325	0.4286	0.4247
−0.0	0.5000	0.4960	0.4920	0.4880	0.4840	0.4801	0.4761	0.4721	0.4681	0.4641

TABLE 2 (*continued*)

The Standard Normal Distribution

$$F_z(z) = P(Z \leq z)$$

z	0.00	0.01	0.02	0.03	0.04	0.05	0.06	0.07	0.08	0.09
0.0	0.5000	0.5040	0.5080	0.5120	0.5160	0.5199	0.5239	0.5279	0.5319	0.5359
0.1	0.5398	0.5438	0.5478	0.5517	0.5557	0.5596	0.5636	0.5675	0.5714	0.5753
0.2	0.5793	0.5832	0.5871	0.5910	0.5948	0.5987	0.6026	0.6064	0.6103	0.6141
0.3	0.6179	0.6217	0.6255	0.6293	0.6331	0.6368	0.6406	0.6443	0.6480	0.6517
0.4	0.6554	0.6591	0.6628	0.6664	0.6700	0.6736	0.6772	0.6808	0.6844	0.6879
0.5	0.6915	0.6950	0.6985	0.7019	0.7054	0.7088	0.7123	0.7157	0.7190	0.7224
0.6	0.7257	0.7291	0.7324	0.7357	0.7389	0.7422	0.7454	0.7486	0.7517	0.7549
0.7	0.7580	0.7611	0.7642	0.7673	0.7704	0.7734	0.7764	0.7794	0.7823	0.7852
0.8	0.7881	0.7910	0.7939	0.7967	0.7995	0.8023	0.8051	0.8078	0.8106	0.8133
0.9	0.8159	0.8186	0.8212	0.8238	0.8264	0.8289	0.8315	0.8340	0.8365	0.8389
1.0	0.8413	0.8438	0.8461	0.8485	0.8508	0.8531	0.8554	0.8577	0.8599	0.8621
1.1	0.8643	0.8665	0.8686	0.8708	0.8729	0.8749	0.8770	0.8790	0.8810	0.8830
1.2	0.8849	0.8869	0.8888	0.8907	0.8925	0.8944	0.8962	0.8980	0.8997	0.9015
1.3	0.9032	0.9049	0.9066	0.9082	0.9099	0.9115	0.9131	0.9147	0.9162	0.9177
1.4	0.9192	0.9207	0.9222	0.9236	0.9251	0.9265	0.9278	0.9292	0.9306	0.9319
1.5	0.9332	0.9345	0.9357	0.9370	0.9382	0.9394	0.9406	0.9418	0.9429	0.9441
1.6	0.9452	0.9463	0.9474	0.9484	0.9495	0.9505	0.9515	0.9525	0.9535	0.9545
1.7	0.9554	0.9564	0.9573	0.9582	0.9591	0.9599	0.9608	0.9616	0.9625	0.9633
1.8	0.9641	0.9649	0.9656	0.9664	0.9671	0.9678	0.9686	0.9693	0.9699	0.9706
1.9	0.9713	0.9719	0.9726	0.9732	0.9738	0.9744	0.9750	0.9756	0.9761	0.9767
2:0	0.9772	0.9778	0.9783	0.9788	0.9793	0.9798	0.9803	0.9808	0.9812	0.9817
2.1	0.9821	0.9826	0.9830	0.9834	0.9838	0.9842	0.9846	0.9850	0.9854	0.9857
2.2	0.9861	0.9864	0.9868	0.9871	0.9875	0.9878	0.9881	0.9884	0.9887	0.9890
2.3	0.9893	0.9896	0.9898	0.9901	0.9904	0.9906	0.9909	0.9911	0.9913	0.9916
2.4	0.9918	0.9920	0.9922	0.9925	0.9927	0.9929	0.9931	0.9932	0.9934	0.9936
2.5	0.9938	0.9940	0.9951	0.9943	0.9945	0.9946	0.9948	0.9949	0.9951	0.9952
2.6	0.9953	0.9955	0.9956	0.9957	0.9959	0.9960	0.9961	0.9962	0.9963	0.9964
2.7	0.9965	0.9966	0.9967	0.9968	0.9969	0.9970	0.9971	0.9972	0.9973	0.9974
2.8	0.9974	0.9975	0.9976	0.9977	0.9977	0.9978	0.9979	0.9979	0.9980	0.9981
2.9	0.9981	0.9982	0.9982	0.9983	0.9984	0.9984	0.9985	0.9985	0.9986	0.9986
3.0	0.9987	0.9987	0.9987	0.9988	0.9988	0.9989	0.9989	0.9989	0.9990	0.9990
3.1	0.9990	0.9991	0.9991	0.9991	0.9992	0.9992	0.9992	0.9992	0.9993	0.9993
3.2	0.9993	0.9993	0.9994	0.9994	0.9994	0.9994	0.9994	0.9995	0.9995	0.9995
3.3	0.9995	0.9995	0.9995	0.9996	0.9996	0.9996	0.9996	0.9996	0.9996	0.9997
3.4	0.9997	0.9997	0.9997	0.9997	0.9997	0.9997	0.9997	0.9997	0.9997	0.9998

Answers to Odd-Numbered Exercises

CHAPTER 1

Exercises 1.1, page 6

1. $(3, 3)$; Quadrant I   3. $(2, -2)$; Quadrant IV

5. $(-4, -6)$; Quadrant III   7. A

9. E, F, and G 11. F

13–19. See the following figure.

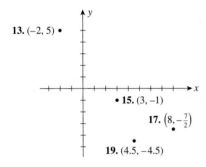

13. $(-2, 5)$ •

• 15. $(3, -1)$

17. $\left(8, -\frac{7}{2}\right)$

19. $(4.5, -4.5)$

21. 5   23. $\sqrt{61}$ 25. $(-8, -6)$ and $(8, -6)$

29. $(x - 2)^2 + (y + 3)^2 = 25$

31. $x^2 + y^2 = 25$

33. $(x - 2)^2 + (y + 3)^2 = 34$ 35. 3400 mi

37. Route 1   39. Model C

41. **a.** $d = 10\sqrt{13}\, t$ **b.** 72.11 mi

43. **a.** $\sqrt{16,000,000 + x^2}$ ft   **b.** 20,396 ft

45. True

47. **b.** $\left(\frac{1}{2}, -\frac{3}{2}\right)$

Exercises 1.2, page 18

1. $\frac{1}{2}$ 3. Not defined   5. 5   7. $\frac{5}{6}$

9. $\dfrac{d - b}{c - a}$ $(a \neq c)$ 11. **a.** 4   **b.** -8

13. Parallel   15. Perpendicular

17. $a = -5$ 19. $y = -3$

21. (e)   23. (a)   25. (f)   27. $y = 2x - 10$

29. $y = 2$ 31. $y = 3x - 2$ 33. $y = x + 1$

35. $y = 3x + 4$ 37. $y = 5$

39. $y = \frac{1}{2}x$; $m = \frac{1}{2}$; $b = 0$

41. $y = \frac{2}{3}x - 3$; $m = \frac{2}{3}$; $b = -3$

43. $y = -\frac{1}{2}x + \frac{7}{2}$; $m = -\frac{1}{2}$; $b = \frac{7}{2}$

45. $y = \frac{1}{2}x + 3$ 47. $y = \frac{4}{3}x + \frac{4}{3}$ 49. $y = -6$ 51. $y = b$

53. $y = \frac{2}{3}x - \frac{2}{3}$ 55. $k = 8$

57.

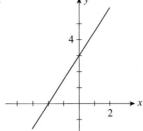

59.

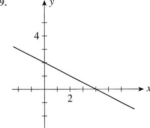

61.

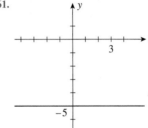

65. $y = -2x - 4$

67. $y = \frac{1}{8}x - \frac{1}{2}$

69. Yes

71. **a.**

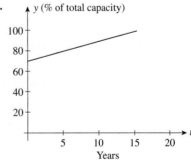

b. 1.9467; 70.082

c. The capacity utilization has been increasing by 1.9467% each year since 1990 when it stood at 70.082%.

d. In the first half of 2005

73. **a.** $y = 0.55x$ **b.** 2000

75. 84.8%

77. a and **b.**

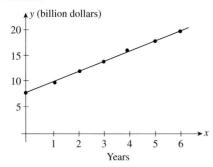

c. $y = 1.82x + 7.9$
d. $17 billion; same

79. a and **b.**

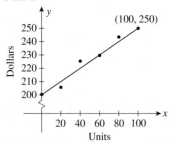

c. $y = \frac{1}{2}x + 200$
d. $227

81. a and **b.**

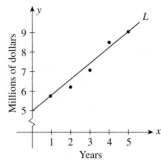

c. $y = 0.8x + 5$
d. $12.2 million

83. a. A family of parallel lines having slope m
    b. A family of straight lines that pass through the point $(0, b)$

85. False

87. True

89. True

Using Technology Exercises 1.2, page 26

Graphing Utility

1.

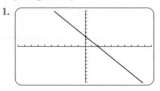

3.

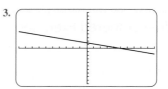

5. a.

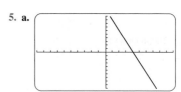

b.

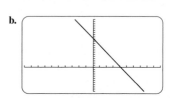

7. a.

b.

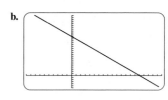

9.

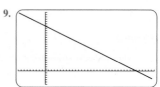

11.

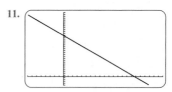

Excel

1.

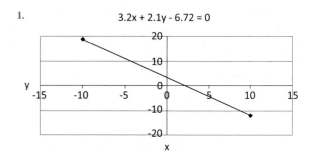

$3.2x + 2.1y - 6.72 = 0$

3.

1.6x + 5.1y = 8.16

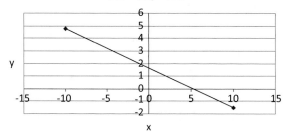

5.

12.1x + 4.1y = 49.61

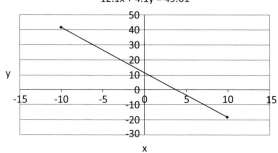

7.

20x + 16y = 300

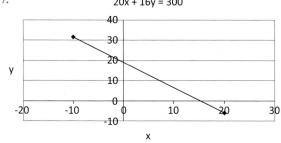

9.

20x + 30y = 600

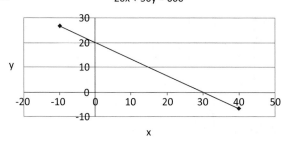

11.

22.4x + 16.1y - 352 = 0

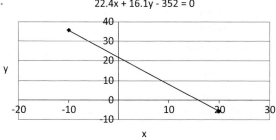

Exercises 1.3, page 33

1. Yes; $y = -\frac{2}{3}x + 2$ **3.** Yes; $y = \frac{1}{2}x + 2$

5. Yes; $y = \frac{1}{2}x + \frac{9}{4}$ **7.** No   **9.** No

11. a. $C(x) = 8x + 40,000$
   b. $R(x) = 12x$
   c. $P(x) = 4x - 40,000$
   d. Loss of $8000; profit of $8000

13. $m = -1; b = 2$

15. $900,000; $800,000

17. $6 billion; $43.5 billion; $81 billion

19. a. $y = 1.053x$ **b.** $1074.06

21. $C(x) = 0.6x + 12,100; R(x) = 1.15x;$
   $P(x) = 0.55x - 12,100$

23. a. $12,000/year   **b.** $V = 60,000 - 12,000t$

   c.

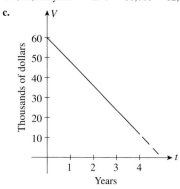

   d. $24,000

25. $900,000; $800,000

27. a. $m = a/1.7; b = 0$ **b.** 117.65 mg

29. $f(t) = 6.5t + 20 \ (0 \le t \le 8)$; 72 million

31. a. $F = \frac{9}{5}C + 32$ **b.** 68°F   **c.** 21.1°C

33. a.   **b.** 3000

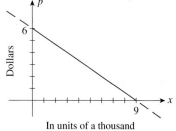

35. a.   **b.** 10,000

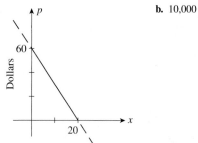

37. $p = -\frac{3}{40}x + 130$; $130; 1733   **39.** 2500 units

41. a.

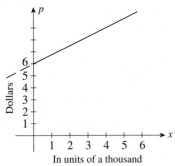

In units of a thousand

b. 2667 units

c.

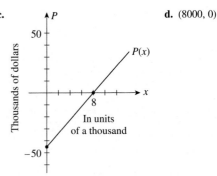

In units of a thousand

d. (8000, 0)

43. a.

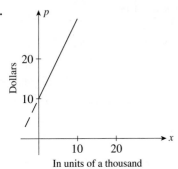

In units of a thousand

b. 2000 units

13. 9259 units; $83,331

15. a. $C_1(x) = 18,000 + 15x$
$C_2(x) = 15,000 + 20x$

b.

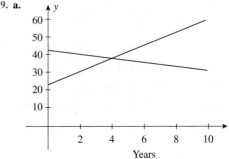

45. $p = \frac{1}{2}x + 40$ (x is measured in units of a thousand)

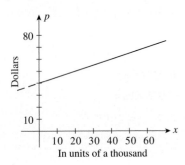

In units of a thousand

60,000 units

47. False

Using Technology Exercises 1.3, page 39

1. 2.2875   3. 2.880952381   5. 7.2851648352

7. 2.4680851064

Exercises 1.4, page 46

1. (2, 10)   3. $(4, \frac{2}{3})$ 5. (−4, −6)

7. 1000 units; $15,000

9. 600 units; $240

11. a.

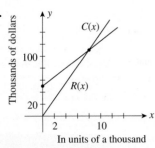

In units of a thousand

b. 8000 units; $112,000

c. Machine II; machine II; machine I
d. ($1500); $1500; $4750

17. Middle of 2003

19. a.

y axis with values 60, 50, 40, 30, 20, 10; t axis with values 2, 4, 6, 8, 10; Years

b. Feb. 2005

21. 8000 units; $9   **23.** 2000 units; $18

25. a. $p = -0.08x + 725$
b. $p = 0.09x + 300$
c. 2500 DVD players; $525

27. 300 fax machines; $600

29. a. $\dfrac{b - d}{c - a}; \dfrac{bc - ad}{c - a}$

b. If c is increased, x gets smaller and p gets larger.
c. If b is decreased, x decreases and p decreases.

31. True

33. a. $m_1 = m_2$ and $b_2 \neq b_1$
b. $m_1 \neq m_2$
c. $m_1 = m_2$ and $b_1 = b_2$

Using Technology Exercises 1.4, page 50

1. (0.6, 6.2)   3. (3.8261, 0.1304)

5. (386.9091, 145.3939)

7. a.

b. (3548, 27,997)

c.

    x-intercept: 3548

9. a. $C_1(x) = 34 + 0.18x; C_2(x) = 28 + 0.22x$

b.   **c.** (150, 61)

d. If the distance driven is less than or equal to 150 mi, rent from Acme Truck Leasing; if the distance driven is more than 150 mi, rent from Ace Truck Leasing.

11. a. $p = -\frac{1}{10}x + 284; p = \frac{1}{60}x + 60$

b.   (1920, 92)

c. 1920/week; $92/radio

Exercises 1.5, page 56

1. a. $y = 2.3x + 1.5$

b.

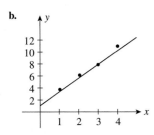

3. a. $y = -0.77x + 5.74$

b.

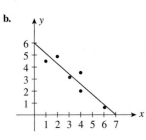

5. a. $y = 1.2x + 2$

b.

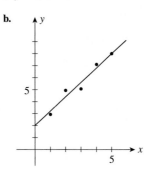

7. a. $y = 0.34x - 0.9$

b.

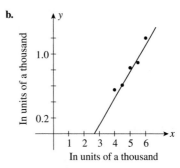

c. 1276 applications

9. a. $y = -2.8x + 440$

b.   **c.** 420

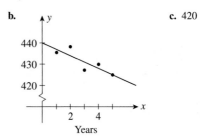

11. a. $y = 2.8x + 17.6$ **b.** $40,000,000

13. a. $y = 7.25x + 60.21$ **b.** $139.96 billion   **c.** $7.25 billion/year

15. a. $y = 25.6x + 74$ **b.** 304 million

17. a. $y = 0.058t + 1.38$ **b.** $58 billion/year   **c.** $1.96 trillion

19. a. $y = 0.305x + 1.41$ **b.** $0.305 billion/year   **c.** $3.24 billion

21. a. $y = 0.4x + 5.22$ **b.** $0.4 billion/year

23. a. $y = 3.87x + 82.94$ **b.** $117,770

25. a. $y = 0.09x + 15.90$ **b.** 19.50 years   **c.** 18.6 years

27. $y = 0.23x + 1.16$ **b.** 2.8 billion

29. False   **31.** True

Using Technology Exercises 1.5, page 62

1. $y = 2.3596x + 3.8639$

3. $y = -1.1948x + 3.5525$

5. a. $y = 1.03x + 2.33$ **b.** $10.57 billion

7. a. $y = 13.321x + 72.571$ **b.** 192 million tons

9. a. $y = 14.43x + 212.1$ **b.** 247 trillion cu ft

Chapter 1 Concept Review Questions, page 64

1. ordered; abscissa (x-coordinate); ordinate (y-coordinate)

2. a. x-; y-;   **b.** third

3. $\sqrt{(c - a)^2 + (d - b)^2}$

4. $(x - a)^2 + (y - b)^2 = r^2$

5. a. $\dfrac{y_2 - y_1}{x_2 - x_1}$ **b.** undefined   **c.** 0   **d.** positive

6. $m_1 = m_2$; $m_1 = -\dfrac{1}{m_2}$

7. a. $y - y_1 = m(x - x_1)$; point-slope
    b. $y = mx + b$; slope-intercept

8. a. $Ax + By + C = 0$ (A, B, not both zero)   **b.** $-\dfrac{a}{b}$

9. $mx + b$

10. a. price; demanded; demand
    b. price; supplied; supply

11. break-even   **12.** demand; supply

Chapter 1 Review Exercises, page 64

1. 5   **2.** 5   **3.** 5   **4.** 2

5. $x = -2$ **6.** $y = 4$

7. $x + 10y - 38 = 0$ **8.** $y = -\frac{4}{5}x + \frac{12}{5}$

9. $5x - 2y + 18 = 0$ **10.** $y = \frac{3}{4}x + \frac{11}{2}$

11. $y = -\frac{1}{2}x - 3$ **12.** $\frac{3}{5}$; $-\frac{6}{5}$

13. $3x + 4y - 18 = 0$

14. $y = -\frac{3}{5}x + \frac{12}{5}$ **15.** $3x + 2y + 14 = 0$

16.

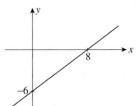

17.

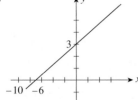

18. 60,000   **19. a.** $f(x) = x + 2.4$ **b.** $5.4 million

21. b. 117 mg   **22. a.** $200,000/year   **b.** $4,000,000

23. a. $22,500/year   **b.** $V = -22,500t + 300,000$

24. a. $6x + 30,000$ **b.** $10x$ **c.** $4x - 30,000$
    d. ($6,000); $2000; $18,000

25. $p = -0.05x + 200$

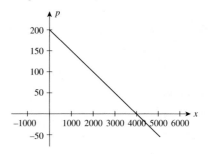

26. $p = \frac{1}{36}x + \frac{400}{9}$ **27.** $(2, -3)$ **28.** $(6, \frac{21}{2})$

29. $(2500, 50,000)$ **30.** 6000; $22

31. a. $y = 0.25x$ **b.** 1600   **32.** 600; $80

33. a. $y = 1.9x + 27$ **b.** $38.4/hr

34. a. $y = 0.059x + 19.5$ **b.** 21.9 years   **c.** 21.3 years

Chapter 1 Before Moving On, page 66

1. $\sqrt{34}$

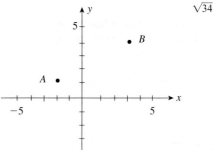

2. $y = 3x - 8$ **3.** Yes

4. a. $15   **b.** $22,000   **c.** $18

5. $(1, \frac{4}{3})$ **6.** After 5 years

CHAPTER 2
Exercises 2.1, page 73

1. Unique solution; $(2, 1)$ **3.** No solution

5. Unique solution; $(3, 2)$

7. Infinitely many solutions; $\left(t, \frac{2}{5}t - 2\right)$; t, a parameter

9. Unique solution; $(1, -2)$

11. No solution   **13.** Unique solution; $\left(\frac{1}{2}, \frac{1}{2}\right)$

15. Infinitely many solutions; $\left(2t + \frac{2}{3}, t\right)$ **17.** $k = -2$

19. $\begin{aligned} x + \quad y &= \quad 500 \\ 42x + 30y &= 18,600 \end{aligned}$ **21.** $\begin{aligned} x + \quad y &= 100 \\ 5x + 6y &= 560 \end{aligned}$

23. $\begin{aligned} x + \quad y &= 1000 \\ 0.5x + 1.5y &= 1300 \end{aligned}$

25. $\begin{aligned} 0.06x + 0.08y + 0.12z &= 21,600 \\ z &= 2x \\ 0.12z &= 0.08y \end{aligned}$

27. $18x + 20y + 24z = 26,400$
$4x + 4y + 3z = 4,900$
$5x + 4y + 6z = 6,200$

29. $18,000x + 27,000y + 36,000z = 2,250,000$
$x = 2y$
$x + y + z = 100$

31. $10x + 6y + 8z = 100$
$10x + 12y + 6z = 100$
$5x + 4y + 12z = 100$

33. True

Exercises 2.2, page 86

1. $\begin{bmatrix} 2 & -3 & | & 7 \\ 3 & 1 & | & 4 \end{bmatrix}$

3. $\begin{bmatrix} 0 & -1 & 2 & | & 6 \\ 2 & 2 & -8 & | & 7 \\ 0 & 3 & 4 & | & 0 \end{bmatrix}$

5. $3x + 2y = -4$
$x - y = 5$

7. $x + 3y + 2z = 4$
$ 2x = 5$
$3x - 3y + 2z = 6$

9. Yes   **11.** No   **13.** Yes   **15.** No   **17.** No

19. $\begin{bmatrix} 1 & 2 & | & 4 \\ 0 & -5 & | & -10 \end{bmatrix}$ **21.** $\begin{bmatrix} 1 & -2 & | & -3 \\ 0 & 16 & | & 20 \end{bmatrix}$

23. $\begin{bmatrix} 1 & 2 & 3 & | & 6 \\ 0 & -1 & -5 & | & -7 \\ 0 & -7 & -7 & | & -14 \end{bmatrix}$

25. $\begin{bmatrix} -6 & -11 & 0 & | & -5 \\ 2 & 4 & 1 & | & 3 \\ 1 & -2 & 0 & | & -10 \end{bmatrix}$

27. $\begin{bmatrix} 3 & 9 & | & 6 \\ 2 & 1 & | & 4 \end{bmatrix} \xrightarrow{\frac{1}{3}R_1} \begin{bmatrix} 1 & 3 & | & 2 \\ 2 & 1 & | & 4 \end{bmatrix}$

$\xrightarrow{R_2 - 2R_1} \begin{bmatrix} 1 & 3 & | & 2 \\ 0 & -5 & | & 0 \end{bmatrix} \xrightarrow{-\frac{1}{5}R_2}$

$\begin{bmatrix} 1 & 3 & | & 2 \\ 0 & 1 & | & 0 \end{bmatrix} \xrightarrow{R_1 - 3R_2} \begin{bmatrix} 1 & 0 & | & 2 \\ 0 & 1 & | & 0 \end{bmatrix}$

29. $\begin{bmatrix} 1 & 3 & 1 & | & 3 \\ 3 & 8 & 3 & | & 7 \\ 2 & -3 & 1 & | & -10 \end{bmatrix} \begin{array}{l} \xrightarrow{R_2 - 3R_1} \\ \xrightarrow{R_3 - 2R_1} \end{array}$

$\begin{bmatrix} 1 & 3 & 1 & | & 3 \\ 0 & -1 & 0 & | & -2 \\ 0 & -9 & -1 & | & -16 \end{bmatrix} \xrightarrow{-R_2}$

$\begin{bmatrix} 1 & 3 & 1 & | & 3 \\ 0 & 1 & 0 & | & 2 \\ 0 & -9 & -1 & | & -16 \end{bmatrix} \begin{array}{l} \xrightarrow{R_1 - 3R_2} \\ \xrightarrow{R_3 + 9R_2} \end{array}$

$\begin{bmatrix} 1 & 0 & 1 & | & -3 \\ 0 & 1 & 0 & | & 2 \\ 0 & 0 & -1 & | & 2 \end{bmatrix} \begin{array}{l} \xrightarrow{R_1 + R_3} \\ \xrightarrow{-R_3} \end{array}$

$\begin{bmatrix} 1 & 0 & 0 & | & -1 \\ 0 & 1 & 0 & | & 2 \\ 0 & 0 & 1 & | & -2 \end{bmatrix}$

31. $(2, 0)$ **33.** $(-1, 2, -2)$ **35.** $(2, 1)$

37. $(4, -2)$ **39.** $(-1, 2)$ **41.** $\left(\frac{1}{2}, \frac{3}{2}\right)$

43. $\left(\frac{1}{2}, \frac{1}{4}\right)$ **45.** $\left(\frac{7}{9}, -\frac{1}{9}, -\frac{2}{3}\right)$ **47.** $(19, -7, -15)$

49. $(3, 0, 2)$ **51.** $(1, -2, 1)$

53. $(-20, -28, 13)$ **55.** $(4, -1, 3)$

57. 300 acres of corn, 200 acres of wheat

59. In 100 lb of blended coffee, use 40 lb of the $5/lb coffee and 60 lb of the $6/lb coffee.

61. 200 children and 800 adults

63. $40,000 in a savings account, $120,000 in mutual funds, $80,000 in bonds

65. 400 bags of grade A fertilizer; 600 bags of grade B fertilizer; 300 bags of grade C fertilizer

67. 60 compact, 30 intermediate-size, and 10 full-size cars

69. 4 oz of Food I, 2 oz of Food II, 6 oz of Food III

71. 240 front orchestra seats, 560 rear orchestra seats, 200 front balcony seats

73. 7 days in London, 4 days in Paris, and 3 days in Rome

75. False

Using Technology Exercises 2.2, page 91

1. $x_1 = 3; x_2 = 1; x_3 = -1; x_4 = 2$

3. $x_1 = 5; x_2 = 4; x_3 = -3; x_4 = -4$

5. $x_1 = 1; x_2 = -1; x_3 = 2; x_4 = 0; x_5 = 3$

Exercises 2.3, page 98

1. a. One solution   **b.** $(3, -1, 2)$

3. a. One solution   **b.** $(2, 4)$

5. a. Infinitely many solutions
b. $(4 - t, -2, t)$; t, a parameter

7. a. No solution

9. a. Infinitely many solutions
b. $(2, -1, 2 - t, t)$; t, a parameter

11. a. Infinitely many solutions
b. $(2 - 3s, 1 + s, s, t)$; s, t, parameters

13. $(2, 1)$ **15.** No solution   **17.** $(1, -1)$

19. $(2 + 2t, t)$; t, a parameter   **21.** $(4 + t, -3 - t, t)$

23. $\left(\frac{4}{3} - \frac{2}{3}t, t\right)$; t, a parameter   **25.** No solution

27. $\left(-1, \frac{17}{7}, \frac{23}{7}\right)$

29. $\left(1 - \frac{1}{4}s + \frac{1}{4}t, s, t\right)$; s, t, parameters

31. No solution   **33.** $(2, -1, 4)$

35. $x = 20 + z$, $y = 40 - 2z$; 25 compact cars, 30 mid-sized cars, and 5 full-sized cars; 30 compact cars, 20 mid-sized cars, and 10 full-sized cars

39. $10,000 in money-market account, $60,000 in stocks, and $30,000 in bonds; $20,000 in money-market account, $70,000 in stocks, and $10,000 in bonds

41. a.
$$\begin{aligned} x_1 \quad\quad\quad + x_6 \quad\quad &= 1700 \\ x_1 - x_2 \quad\quad\quad + x_7 &= 700 \\ x_2 - x_3 \quad\quad\quad\quad &= 300 \\ - x_3 + x_4 \quad\quad\quad &= 400 \\ - x_4 + x_5 \quad + x_7 &= 700 \\ x_5 + x_6 \quad\quad &= 1800 \end{aligned}$$

b. $(1700 - s, 1000 - s + t, 700 - s + t, 1100 - s + t, 1800 - s, s, t)$; (900, 1000, 700, 1100, 1000, 800, 800); (1000, 1100, 800, 1200, 1100, 700, 700)

c. x_6 must have at least 300 cars/hr.

43. $k = -36$; $(4 + \frac{2}{3}y - \frac{4}{3}z, y, z)$ **45.** False

Using Technology Exercises 2.3, page 102

1. $(1 + t, 2 + t, t)$; t, a parameter

3. $(-\frac{17}{7} + \frac{6}{7}t, 3 - t, -\frac{18}{7} + \frac{1}{7}t, t)$; t, a parameter

5. No solution

Exercises 2.4, page 109

1. 4×4; 4×3; 1×5; 4×1 **3.** 2; 3; 8

5. D; $D^T = [1 \quad 3 \quad -2 \quad 0]$ **7.** 3×2; 3×2; 3×3; 3×3

9. $\begin{bmatrix} 1 & 6 \\ 6 & -1 \\ 2 & 2 \end{bmatrix}$ **11.** $\begin{bmatrix} 1 & 1 & -4 \\ -1 & -8 & 1 \\ 6 & 3 & 1 \end{bmatrix}$

13. $\begin{bmatrix} 3 & 5 & 9 \\ 4 & 10 & 13 \end{bmatrix}$ **15.** $\begin{bmatrix} 3 & -4 & -16 \\ 17 & -4 & 16 \end{bmatrix}$

17. $\begin{bmatrix} -1.9 & 3.0 & -0.6 \\ 6.0 & 9.6 & 1.2 \end{bmatrix}$

19. $\begin{bmatrix} \frac{7}{2} & 3 & -1 & \frac{10}{3} \\ -\frac{19}{6} & \frac{2}{3} & -\frac{17}{2} & \frac{23}{3} \\ \frac{29}{3} & \frac{17}{6} & -1 & -2 \end{bmatrix}$

21. $u = 3$, $x = \frac{5}{2}$, $y = 7$, and $z = 2$

23. $x = 2$, $y = 2$, $z = -\frac{7}{3}$, and $u = 15$

31. $\begin{bmatrix} 3 \\ 2 \\ -1 \\ 5 \end{bmatrix}$ **33.** $\begin{bmatrix} 1 & 3 & 0 \\ -1 & 4 & 1 \\ 2 & 2 & 0 \end{bmatrix}$

35. $\begin{bmatrix} 220 & 215 & 210 & 205 \\ 220 & 210 & 200 & 195 \\ 215 & 205 & 195 & 190 \end{bmatrix}$ **37.** $B = \begin{bmatrix} 350.2 & 370.8 & 391.4 \\ 422.3 & 442.9 & 453.2 \\ 638.6 & 679.8 & 721 \end{bmatrix}$

39. a. $D = \begin{bmatrix} 2960 & 1510 & 1150 \\ 1100 & 550 & 490 \\ 1230 & 590 & 470 \end{bmatrix}$

b. $E = \begin{bmatrix} 3256 & 1661 & 1265 \\ 1210 & 605 & 539 \\ 1353 & 649 & 517 \end{bmatrix}$

41.
$$\begin{array}{c} \quad\quad 2000 \quad 2001 \quad 2002 \\ \begin{array}{c} \text{MA} \\ \text{U.S.} \end{array} \begin{bmatrix} 6.88 & 7.05 & 7.18 \\ 4.13 & 4.09 & 4.06 \end{bmatrix} \end{array}$$

43.
$$\begin{array}{c} \quad\quad\; \text{White} \quad \text{Black} \quad \text{Hispanic} \\ \begin{array}{c} \text{Women} \\ \text{Men} \end{array} \begin{bmatrix} 81 & 76.1 & 82.2 \\ 76 & 69.9 & 75.9 \end{bmatrix} \end{array}$$

$$\begin{array}{c} \quad\quad\quad\;\; \text{Women} \quad \text{Men} \\ \begin{array}{c} \text{White} \\ \text{Black} \\ \text{Hispanic} \end{array} \begin{bmatrix} 81 & 76 \\ 76.1 & 69.9 \\ 82.2 & 75.9 \end{bmatrix} \end{array}$$

45. True   **47.** False

Using Technology Exercises 2.4, page 115

1. $\begin{bmatrix} 15 & 38.75 & -67.5 & 33.75 \\ 51.25 & 40 & 52.5 & -38.75 \\ 21.25 & 35 & -65 & 105 \end{bmatrix}$

3. $\begin{bmatrix} -5 & 6.3 & -6.8 & 3.9 \\ 1 & 0.5 & 5.4 & -4.8 \\ 0.5 & 4.2 & -3.5 & 5.6 \end{bmatrix}$

5. $\begin{bmatrix} 16.44 & -3.65 & -3.66 & 0.63 \\ 12.77 & 10.64 & 2.58 & 0.05 \\ 5.09 & 0.28 & -10.84 & 17.64 \end{bmatrix}$

7. $\begin{bmatrix} 22.2 & -0.3 & -12 & 4.5 \\ 21.6 & 17.7 & 9 & -4.2 \\ 8.7 & 4.2 & -20.7 & 33.6 \end{bmatrix}$

Exercises 2.5, page 122

1. 2×5; not defined   **3.** 1×1; 7×7

5. $n = s$; $m = t$ **7.** $\begin{bmatrix} -1 \\ 3 \end{bmatrix}$

9. $\begin{bmatrix} 9 \\ -10 \end{bmatrix}$ **11.** $\begin{bmatrix} 4 & -2 \\ 9 & 13 \end{bmatrix}$

13. $\begin{bmatrix} 2 & 9 \\ 5 & 16 \end{bmatrix}$ **15.** $\begin{bmatrix} 0.57 & 1.93 \\ 0.64 & 1.76 \end{bmatrix}$

17. $\begin{bmatrix} 6 & -3 & 0 \\ -2 & 1 & -8 \\ 4 & -4 & 9 \end{bmatrix}$ **19.** $\begin{bmatrix} 5 & 1 & -3 \\ 1 & 7 & -3 \end{bmatrix}$

21. $\begin{bmatrix} -4 & -20 & 4 \\ 4 & 12 & 0 \\ 12 & 32 & 20 \end{bmatrix}$ **23.** $\begin{bmatrix} 4 & -3 & 2 \\ 7 & 1 & -5 \end{bmatrix}$

27. $AB = \begin{bmatrix} 10 & 7 \\ 22 & 15 \end{bmatrix}$; $BA = \begin{bmatrix} 5 & 8 \\ 13 & 20 \end{bmatrix}$

31. $A = \begin{bmatrix} -2 & -1 \\ 5 & 2 \end{bmatrix}$ **33. b.** No   **35. a.** $A^T = \begin{bmatrix} 2 & 5 \\ 4 & -6 \end{bmatrix}$

37. $AX = B$, where $A = \begin{bmatrix} 2 & -3 \\ 3 & -4 \end{bmatrix}$, $X = \begin{bmatrix} x \\ y \end{bmatrix}$,

and $B = \begin{bmatrix} 7 \\ 8 \end{bmatrix}$

39. $AX = B$, where $A = \begin{bmatrix} 2 & -3 & 4 \\ 0 & 2 & -3 \\ 1 & -1 & 2 \end{bmatrix}$, $X = \begin{bmatrix} x \\ y \\ z \end{bmatrix}$,

and $B = \begin{bmatrix} 6 \\ 7 \\ 4 \end{bmatrix}$

41. $AX = B$, where $A = \begin{bmatrix} -1 & 1 & 1 \\ 2 & -1 & -1 \\ -3 & 2 & 4 \end{bmatrix}$, $X = \begin{bmatrix} x_1 \\ x_2 \\ x_3 \end{bmatrix}$,

and $B = \begin{bmatrix} 0 \\ 2 \\ 4 \end{bmatrix}$

43. **a.** $AB = \begin{bmatrix} 51{,}400 \\ 54{,}200 \end{bmatrix}$

b. The first entry shows that William's total stock holdings are $51,400; the second shows that Michael's stock holdings are $54,200.

45. **a.**

	N krones	S krones	D krones	R rubles
$A = $ Kaitlin	82	68	62	1200
Emma	64	74	44	1600

b. $B = \begin{bmatrix} 0.1651 \\ 0.1462 \\ 0.1811 \\ 0.0387 \end{bmatrix} \begin{matrix} N \\ S \\ D \\ R \end{matrix}$ **c.** Kaitlin: $81.15; Emma: $91.27

47. **a.** $\begin{bmatrix} 90 & 125 & 210 & 55 \end{bmatrix}$; the entries give the respective total number of Model I, II, III, and IV houses built in the three states.

b. $\begin{bmatrix} 300 \\ 120 \\ 60 \end{bmatrix}$; the entries give the respective total number of Model I, II,

III, and IV houses built in all three states.

49. $B = \begin{bmatrix} 4 \\ 6 \\ 8 \end{bmatrix}$; $AB = \begin{bmatrix} 1960 \\ 3180 \\ 2510 \\ 3300 \end{bmatrix}$; $10,950

51.

	Dem	Rep	Ind
$BA = $	41,000	35,000	14,000

53. $AB = \begin{bmatrix} 1575 & 1590 & 1560 & 975 \\ 410 & 405 & 415 & 270 \\ 215 & 205 & 225 & 155 \end{bmatrix}$

55. $[277.60]$; it represents Cindy's long-distance bill for phone calls to London, Tokyo, and Hong Kong.

57. **a.** $\begin{bmatrix} 8800 \\ 3380 \\ 1020 \end{bmatrix}$ **b.** $\begin{bmatrix} 8800 \\ 3380 \\ 1020 \end{bmatrix}$ **c.** $\begin{bmatrix} 17{,}600 \\ 6{,}760 \\ 2{,}040 \end{bmatrix}$

59. False   61. True

Using Technology Exercises 2.5, page 129

1. $\begin{bmatrix} 18.66 & 15.2 & -12 \\ 24.48 & 41.88 & 89.82 \\ 15.39 & 7.16 & -1.25 \end{bmatrix}$

3. $\begin{bmatrix} 20.09 & 20.61 & -1.3 \\ 44.42 & 71.6 & 64.89 \\ 20.97 & 7.17 & -60.65 \end{bmatrix}$

5. $\begin{bmatrix} 32.89 & 13.63 & -57.17 \\ -12.85 & -8.37 & 256.92 \\ 13.48 & 14.29 & 181.64 \end{bmatrix}$

7. $\begin{bmatrix} 128.59 & 123.08 & -32.50 \\ 246.73 & 403.12 & 481.52 \\ 125.06 & 47.01 & -264.81 \end{bmatrix}$

9. $\begin{bmatrix} 87 & 68 & 110 & 82 \\ 119 & 176 & 221 & 143 \\ 51 & 128 & 142 & 94 \\ 28 & 174 & 174 & 112 \end{bmatrix}$

$\begin{bmatrix} 113 & 117 & 72 & 101 & 90 \\ 72 & 85 & 36 & 72 & 76 \\ 81 & 69 & 76 & 87 & 30 \\ 133 & 157 & 56 & 121 & 146 \\ 154 & 157 & 94 & 127 & 122 \end{bmatrix}$

11. $\begin{bmatrix} 170 & 18.1 & 133.1 & -106.3 & 341.3 \\ 349 & 226.5 & 324.1 & 164 & 506.4 \\ 245.2 & 157.7 & 231.5 & 125.5 & 312.9 \\ 310 & 245.2 & 291 & 274.3 & 354.2 \end{bmatrix}$

Exercises 2.6, page 137

5. $\begin{bmatrix} 3 & -5 \\ -1 & 2 \end{bmatrix}$ 7. Does not exist

9. $\begin{bmatrix} 2 & -11 & -3 \\ 1 & -6 & -2 \\ 0 & -1 & 0 \end{bmatrix}$ 11. Does not exist

13. $\begin{bmatrix} -\frac{13}{10} & \frac{7}{5} & \frac{1}{2} \\ \frac{2}{5} & -\frac{1}{5} & 0 \\ -\frac{7}{10} & \frac{3}{5} & \frac{1}{2} \end{bmatrix}$

15. $\begin{bmatrix} 3 & 4 & -6 & 1 \\ -2 & -3 & 5 & -1 \\ -4 & -4 & 7 & -1 \\ -4 & -5 & 8 & -1 \end{bmatrix}$

17. **a.** $A = \begin{bmatrix} 2 & 5 \\ 1 & 3 \end{bmatrix}$; $X = \begin{bmatrix} x \\ y \end{bmatrix}$; $B = \begin{bmatrix} 3 \\ 2 \end{bmatrix}$

b. $x = -1$; $y = 1$

19. **a.** $A = \begin{bmatrix} 2 & -3 & -4 \\ 0 & 0 & -1 \\ 1 & -2 & 1 \end{bmatrix}$; $X = \begin{bmatrix} x \\ y \\ z \end{bmatrix}$; $B = \begin{bmatrix} 4 \\ 3 \\ -8 \end{bmatrix}$

b. $x = -1$; $y = 2$; $z = -3$

21. **a.** $A = \begin{bmatrix} 1 & 4 & -1 \\ 2 & 3 & -2 \\ -1 & 2 & 3 \end{bmatrix}$; $X = \begin{bmatrix} x \\ y \\ z \end{bmatrix}$; $B = \begin{bmatrix} 3 \\ 1 \\ 7 \end{bmatrix}$

b. $x = 1$; $y = 1$; $z = 2$

23. a. $A = \begin{bmatrix} 1 & 1 & -1 & 1 \\ 2 & 1 & 1 & 0 \\ 2 & 1 & 0 & 1 \\ 2 & -1 & -1 & 3 \end{bmatrix}$; $X = \begin{bmatrix} x_1 \\ x_2 \\ x_3 \\ x_4 \end{bmatrix}$; $B = \begin{bmatrix} 6 \\ 4 \\ 7 \\ 9 \end{bmatrix}$

b. $x_1 = 1$; $x_2 = 2$; $x_3 = 0$; $x_4 = 3$

25. b. (i) $x = 4.8$ and $y = 4.6$ **(ii)** $x = 0.4$ and $y = 1.8$

27. b. (i) $x = -1$; $y = 3$; $z = 2$
  (ii) $x = 1$; $y = 8$; $z = -12$

29. b. (i) $x = -\frac{2}{17}$; $y = -\frac{10}{17}$; $z = -\frac{60}{17}$
  (ii) $x = 1$; $y = 0$; $z = -5$

31. b. (i) $x_1 = 1$; $x_2 = -4$; $x_3 = 5$; $x_4 = -1$
  (ii) $x_1 = 12$; $x_2 = -24$; $x_3 = 21$; $x_4 = -7$

33. a. $A^{-1} = \begin{bmatrix} -\frac{5}{2} & -\frac{3}{2} \\ 2 & 1 \end{bmatrix}$

35. a. $ABC = \begin{bmatrix} 4 & 10 \\ 2 & 3 \end{bmatrix}$; $A^{-1} = \begin{bmatrix} 3 & -5 \\ 1 & -2 \end{bmatrix}$;

  $B^{-1} = \begin{bmatrix} 1 & -3 \\ -1 & 4 \end{bmatrix}$; $C^{-1} = \begin{bmatrix} \frac{1}{8} & -\frac{3}{8} \\ \frac{1}{4} & \frac{1}{4} \end{bmatrix}$

37. $\begin{bmatrix} \frac{5}{7} & \frac{3}{7} \\ -\frac{3}{7} & \frac{8}{7} \end{bmatrix}$

39. a. 3214; 3929 **b.** 4286; 3571 **c.** 3929; 5357

41. a. 400 acres of soybeans; 300 acres of corn; 300 acres of wheat
  b. 500 acres of soybeans; 400 acres of corn; 300 acres of wheat

43. a. \$80,000 in high-risk stocks; \$20,000 in medium-risk stocks; \$100,000 in low-risk stocks
  b. \$88,000 in high-risk stocks; \$22,000 in medium-risk stocks; \$110,000 in low-risk stocks
  c. \$56,000 in high-risk stocks; \$64,000 in medium-risk stocks; \$120,000 in low-risk stocks

45. All values of k except $k = \frac{3}{2}$; $\dfrac{1}{3 - 2k} \begin{bmatrix} 3 & -2 \\ -k & 1 \end{bmatrix}$

47. A^{-1} exists provided $ad \neq 0$; every entry along the main diagonal is not equal to zero.

49. True **51.** True

Using Technology Exercises 2.6, page 143

1. $\begin{bmatrix} 0.36 & 0.04 & -0.36 \\ 0.06 & 0.05 & 0.20 \\ -0.19 & 0.10 & 0.09 \end{bmatrix}$

3. $\begin{bmatrix} 0.01 & -0.09 & 0.31 & -0.11 \\ -0.25 & 0.58 & -0.15 & -0.02 \\ 0.86 & -0.42 & 0.07 & -0.37 \\ -0.27 & 0.01 & -0.05 & 0.31 \end{bmatrix}$

5. $\begin{bmatrix} 0.30 & 0.85 & -0.10 & -0.77 & -0.11 \\ -0.21 & 0.10 & 0.01 & -0.26 & 0.21 \\ 0.03 & -0.16 & 0.12 & -0.01 & 0.03 \\ -0.14 & -0.46 & 0.13 & 0.71 & -0.05 \\ 0.10 & -0.05 & -0.10 & -0.03 & 0.11 \end{bmatrix}$

7. $x = 1.2$; $y = 3.6$; $z = 2.7$

9. $x_1 = 2.50$; $x_2 = -0.88$; $x_3 = 0.70$; $x_4 = 0.51$

Exercises 2.7, page 149

1. a. \$10 million **b.** \$160 million
  c. Agricultural; manufacturing and transportation

3. $x = 23.75$ and $y = 21.25$

5. $x = 42.85$ and $y = 57.14$

9. a. \$318.2 million worth of agricultural products and \$336.4 million worth of manufactured goods
  b. \$198.2 million worth of agricultural products and \$196.4 million worth of manufactured goods

11. a. \$443.75 million, \$381.25 million, and \$281.25 million worth of agricultural products, manufactured goods, and transportation, respectively
  b. \$243.75 million, \$281.25 million, and \$221.25 million worth of agricultural products, manufactured goods, and transportation, respectively

13. \$45 million and \$75 million

15. \$34.4 million, \$33 million, and \$21.6 million

Using Technology Exercises 2.7, page 153

1. The final outputs of the first, second, third, and fourth industries are 602.62, 502.30, 572.57, and 523.46 million dollars, respectively.

3. The final outputs of the first, second, third, and fourth industries are 143.06, 132.98, 188.59, and 125.53 million dollars, respectively.

Chapter 2 Concept Review Questions, page 154

1. a. one; many; no **b.** one; many; no **2.** equations

3. $R_i \leftrightarrow R_j$; cR_i; $R_i + aR_j$; solution

4. a. unique **b.** no; infinitely many; unique

5. size; entries **6.** size; corresponding

7. $m \times n$; $n \times m$; a_{ji} **8.** cA; c

9. a. columns; rows **b.** $m \times p$

10. a. $A(BC)$; $AB + AC$ **b.** $n \times r$

11. $A^{-1}A$; AA^{-1}; singular **12.** $A^{-1}B$

Chapter 2 Review Exercises, page 154

1. $\begin{bmatrix} 2 & 2 \\ -1 & 4 \\ 3 & 3 \end{bmatrix}$ **2.** $\begin{bmatrix} -2 & 0 \\ -2 & 6 \end{bmatrix}$ **3.** $[-6 \quad -2]$ **4.** $\begin{bmatrix} 17 \\ 13 \end{bmatrix}$

5. $x = 2$; $y = 3$; $z = 1$; $w = 3$ **6.** $x = 2$; $y = -2$

7. $a = 3$; $b = 4$; $c = -2$; $d = 2$; $e = -3$

8. $x = -1$; $y = -2$; $z = 1$

9. $\begin{bmatrix} 8 & 9 & 11 \\ -10 & -1 & 3 \\ 11 & 12 & 10 \end{bmatrix}$ **10.** $\begin{bmatrix} -1 & 7 & -3 \\ -2 & 5 & 11 \\ 10 & -8 & 2 \end{bmatrix}$

11. $\begin{bmatrix} 6 & 18 & 6 \\ -12 & 6 & 18 \\ 24 & 0 & 12 \end{bmatrix}$ 12. $\begin{bmatrix} -10 & 10 & -18 \\ 4 & 14 & 26 \\ 16 & -32 & -4 \end{bmatrix}$

13. $\begin{bmatrix} -11 & -16 & -15 \\ -4 & -2 & -10 \\ -6 & 14 & 2 \end{bmatrix}$ 14. $\begin{bmatrix} 5 & 20 & 19 \\ -2 & 20 & 8 \\ 26 & 10 & 30 \end{bmatrix}$

15. $\begin{bmatrix} -3 & 17 & 8 \\ -2 & 56 & 27 \\ 74 & 78 & 116 \end{bmatrix}$ 16. $\begin{bmatrix} \frac{3}{2} & -2 & -5 \\ \frac{11}{2} & -1 & 11 \\ \frac{7}{2} & -3 & 0 \end{bmatrix}$

17. $x = 1$; $y = -1$ 18. $x = -1$; $y = 3$

19. $x = 1$; $y = 2$; $z = 3$

20. $(2, 2t - 5, t)$; t, a parameter   21. No solution

22. $x = 1$; $y = -1$; $z = 2$; $w = 2$

23. $x = 1$; $y = 0$; $z = 1$ 24. $x = 2$; $y = -1$; $z = 3$

25. $\begin{bmatrix} \frac{2}{5} & -\frac{1}{5} \\ -\frac{1}{5} & \frac{3}{5} \end{bmatrix}$ 26. $\begin{bmatrix} \frac{3}{4} & -\frac{1}{2} \\ -\frac{1}{8} & \frac{1}{4} \end{bmatrix}$

27. $\begin{bmatrix} -1 & 2 \\ 1 & -\frac{3}{2} \end{bmatrix}$ 28. $\begin{bmatrix} \frac{1}{4} & \frac{1}{2} \\ \frac{1}{8} & -\frac{1}{4} \end{bmatrix}$

29. $\begin{bmatrix} \frac{5}{4} & \frac{1}{4} & -\frac{7}{4} \\ -\frac{1}{4} & -\frac{1}{4} & \frac{3}{4} \\ -\frac{3}{4} & \frac{1}{4} & \frac{5}{4} \end{bmatrix}$ 30. $\begin{bmatrix} -\frac{1}{4} & \frac{1}{2} & -\frac{1}{4} \\ \frac{7}{8} & -\frac{3}{4} & -\frac{5}{8} \\ -\frac{1}{8} & \frac{1}{4} & \frac{3}{8} \end{bmatrix}$

31. $\begin{bmatrix} -\frac{1}{5} & \frac{2}{5} & 0 \\ \frac{2}{3} & -\frac{1}{3} & \frac{1}{3} \\ -\frac{1}{30} & \frac{1}{15} & -\frac{1}{6} \end{bmatrix}$ 32. $\begin{bmatrix} 0 & -\frac{1}{5} & \frac{2}{5} \\ -2 & 1 & 1 \\ -1 & \frac{1}{5} & \frac{3}{5} \end{bmatrix}$

33. $\begin{bmatrix} \frac{3}{2} & 1 \\ -\frac{7}{2} & -1 \end{bmatrix}$ 34. $\begin{bmatrix} \frac{11}{24} & -\frac{7}{8} \\ -\frac{1}{12} & \frac{1}{4} \end{bmatrix}$

35. $\begin{bmatrix} \frac{2}{5} & -\frac{3}{5} \\ \frac{1}{5} & \frac{1}{5} \end{bmatrix}$ 36. $\begin{bmatrix} \frac{4}{7} & -\frac{3}{7} \\ -\frac{3}{7} & \frac{4}{7} \end{bmatrix}$

37. $A^{-1} = \begin{bmatrix} \frac{2}{7} & \frac{3}{7} \\ \frac{1}{7} & -\frac{2}{7} \end{bmatrix}$; $x = -1$; $y = -2$

38. $A^{-1} = \begin{bmatrix} \frac{2}{5} & \frac{3}{10} \\ -\frac{1}{5} & \frac{1}{10} \end{bmatrix}$; $x = 2$; $y = 1$

39. $A^{-1} = \begin{bmatrix} 1 & -\frac{2}{5} & \frac{4}{5} \\ -1 & 1 & -1 \\ -\frac{1}{2} & \frac{3}{5} & -\frac{7}{10} \end{bmatrix}$; $x = 1$; $y = 2$; $z = 4$

40. $A^{-1} = \begin{bmatrix} 0 & \frac{1}{7} & \frac{2}{7} \\ -1 & -\frac{4}{7} & \frac{6}{7} \\ -\frac{1}{2} & -\frac{1}{7} & \frac{1}{2} \end{bmatrix}$; $x = 3$; $y = -1$; $z = 2$

41. $9274, $8628, and $11,366

42. $2,300,000; $2,450,000; an increase of $150,000

43. a. $A = \begin{bmatrix} 800 & 1200 & 400 & 1500 \\ 600 & 1400 & 600 & 2000 \end{bmatrix}$ b. $B = \begin{bmatrix} 50.26 \\ 31.00 \\ 103.07 \\ 38.67 \end{bmatrix}$

b. William: $176,641; Michael: $212,738

44. a. $A =$

	IBM	Google	Boeing	GM	
	800	500	1200	1500	Olivia
	500	600	2000	800	Max

;

$B =$

	IBM	Google	Boeing	GM	
	900	600	1000	1200	Olivia
	700	500	2100	900	Max

b. $C =$

	IBM	Google	Boeing	GM	
	100	100	-200	-300	Olivia
	200	-100	100	100	Max

45. 30 of each type

46. Houston: 100,000 gallons; Tulsa: 600,000 gallons

47. a. $30 million   b. $75 million   c. agricultural; manufacturing

48. $31.18 million, $31.79 million, and $36.31 million worth of the first, second, and third industry, respectively

49. a. $145.86 million worth of agricultural products; $111.28 million worth of manufactured goods
    b. $45.86 million worth of agricultural products and $31.28 million worth of manufactured goods

Chapter 2 Before Moving On, page 156

1. $\left(\frac{2}{3}, -\frac{2}{3}, \frac{5}{3}\right)$

2. a. $(2, -3, 1)$ b. No solution   c. $(2, 1 - 3t, t)$, t, a parameter
   d. $(0, 0, 0, 0)$ e. $(2 + t, 3 - 2t, t)$, t, a parameter

3. a. $(-1, 2)$ b. $\left(\frac{4}{7}, -\frac{5}{7} + 2t, t\right)$, t, a parameter

4. a. $\begin{bmatrix} 3 & 1 & 4 \\ 5 & -2 & 6 \end{bmatrix}$ b. $\begin{bmatrix} 14 & 3 & 7 \\ 14 & 5 & 1 \end{bmatrix}$ c. $\begin{bmatrix} 0 & 5 & 3 \\ 4 & -1 & -11 \end{bmatrix}$

5. $\begin{bmatrix} 3 & -2 & -5 \\ -3 & 2 & 6 \\ -1 & 1 & 2 \end{bmatrix}$ 6. $(1, -1, 2)$

CHAPTER 3

Exercises 3.1, page 165

1.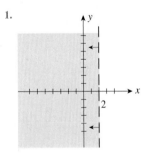

3.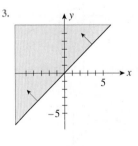

5.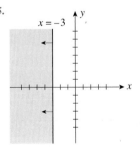

7.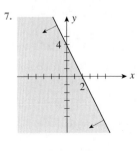

9.

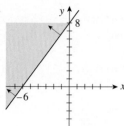

11. $x \geq 1$; $x \leq 5$; $y \geq 2$; $y \leq 4$

13. $2x - y \geq 2$; $5x + 7y \geq 35$; $x \leq 4$

15. $x - y \geq -10$; $7x + 4y \leq 140$; $x + 3y \geq 30$

17. $x + y \geq 7$; $x \geq 2$; $y \geq 3$; $y \leq 7$

19.

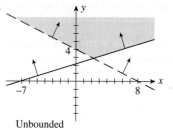

Unbounded

21.

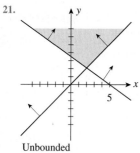

Unbounded

23.

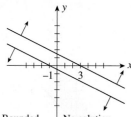

Bounded   No solution

25.

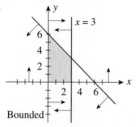

Bounded

27.

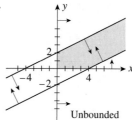

Unbounded

29.

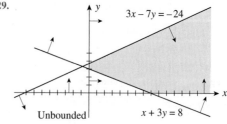

Unbounded $x + 3y = 8$

31.

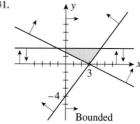

Bounded

33.

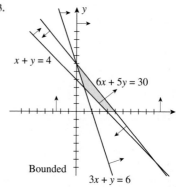

Bounded $3x + y = 6$

35.

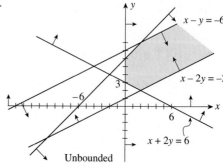

Unbounded

37. False   **39.** True

Exercises 3.2, page 172

1. Maximize $P = 3x + 4y$
   subject to $6x + 9y \leq 300$
   $5x + 4y \leq 180$
   $x \geq 0, y \geq 0$

3. Maximize $P = 2x + 1.5y$
   subject to $3x + 4y \leq 1000$
   $6x + 3y \leq 1200$
   $x \geq 0, y \geq 0$

5. Maximize $P = 45x + 20y$
   subject to $40x + 16y \leq 3200$
   $3x + 4y \leq 520$
   $x \geq 0, y \geq 0$

7. Maximize $P = 0.1x + 0.12y$
   subject to $x + y \leq 20$
   $x - 4y \geq 0$
   $x \geq 0, y \geq 0$

9. Maximize $P = 50x + 40y$
   subject to $\frac{1}{200}x + \frac{1}{200}y \leq 1$
   $\frac{1}{100}x + \frac{1}{300}y \leq 1$
   $x \geq 0, y \geq 0$

11. Minimize $C = 14{,}000x + 16{,}000y$
    subject to $50x + 75y \geq 650$
    $3000x + 1000y \geq 18{,}000$
    $x \geq 0, y \geq 0$

13. Minimize $C = 300x + 500y$
    subject to $x + y \geq 10$
    $x \leq 5$
    $y \leq 10$
    $y \geq 6$
    $x \geq 0$

15. Minimize $C = 2x + 5y$
    subject to $30x + 25y \geq 400$
    $x + 0.5y \geq 10$
    $2x + 5y \geq 40$
    $x \geq 0, y \geq 0$

17. Minimize $C = 1000x + 800y$
    subject to $70{,}000x + 10{,}000y \geq 2{,}000{,}000$
    $40{,}000x + 20{,}000y \geq 1{,}400{,}000$
    $20{,}000x + 40{,}000y \geq 1{,}000{,}000$
    $x \geq 0, y \geq 0$

19. Maximize $P = 0.1x + 0.15y + 0.2z$
    subject to $x + y + z \leq 2{,}000{,}000$
    $-2x - 2y + 8z \leq 0$
    $-6x + 4y + 4z \leq 0$
    $-10x + 6y + 6z \leq 0$
    $x \geq 0, y \geq 0, z \geq 0$

21. Maximize $P = 18x + 12y + 15z$
    subject to $2x + y + 2z \leq 900$
    $3x + y + 2z \leq 1080$
    $2x + 2y + z \leq 840$
    $x \geq 0, y \geq 0, z \geq 0$

23. Maximize $P = 26x + 28y + 24z$
    subject to $\frac{5}{4}x + \frac{3}{2}y + \frac{3}{2}z \leq 310$
    $x + y + \frac{3}{4}z \leq 205$
    $x + y + \frac{1}{2}z \leq 190$
    $x \geq 0, y \geq 0, z \geq 0$

25. Minimize $C = 60x_1 + 60x_2 + 80x_3 + 80x_4 + 70x_5 + 50x_6$
    subject to $x_1 + x_2 + x_3 \leq 300$
    $x_4 + x_5 + x_6 \leq 250$
    $x_1 + x_4 \geq 200$
    $x_2 + x_5 \geq 150$
    $x_3 + x_6 \geq 200$
    $x_1 \geq 0, x_2 \geq 0, \ldots, x_6 \geq 0$

27. Maximize $P = x + 0.8y + 0.9z$
    subject to $8x + 4z \leq 16{,}000$
    $8x + 12y + 8z \leq 24{,}000$
    $4y + 4z \leq 5000$
    $z \leq 800$
    $x \geq 0, y \geq 0, z \geq 0$

29. False

Exercises 3.3, page 183

1. Max: 35; min: 5   3. No max. value; min: 27

5. Max: 44; min: 15   7. $x = 0$; $y = 6$; $P = 18$

9. Any point (x, y) lying on the line segment joining $\left(\frac{5}{2}, 0\right)$ and $(1, 3)$; $P = 5$

11. $x = 0$; $y = 8$; $P = 64$

13. $x = 0$; $y = 4$; $P = 12$

15. $x = 2$; $y = 1$; $C = 10$

17. Any point (x, y) lying on the line segment joining $(20, 10)$ and $(40, 0)$; $C = 120$

19. $x = 14$; $y = 3$; $C = 58$

21. $x = 3$; $y = 3$; $C = 75$

23. $x = 15$; $y = 17.5$; $P = 115$

25. $x = 10$; $y = 38$; $P = 134$

27. Max: $x = 6$; $y = \frac{33}{2}$; $P = 258$
    Min: $x = 15$; $y = 3$; $P = 186$

29. 20 Product A, 20 Product B; $140

31. 120 model A, 160 model B; $480

33. 40 tables; 100 chairs; $3800

35. $16 million in homeowner loans, $4 million in auto loans; $2.08 million

37. 50 fully assembled units, 150 kits; $8500

39. Saddle Mine: 4 days; Horseshoe Mine: 6 days; $152,000

41. Reservoir: 4 million gallons; pipeline: 6 million gallons; $4200

43. Infinitely many solutions; 10 oz of Food A and 4 oz of Food B or 20 oz of Food A and 0 oz of Food B, etc., with a minimum value of 40 mg of cholesterol

45. 30 in Newspaper I, 10 in Newspaper II; $38,000

47. 80 from I to A, 20 from I to B, 0 from II to A, 50 from II to B

49. $22,500 in growth stocks and $7500 in speculative stocks; maximum return; $5250

51. 750 urban, 750 suburban; $10,950

53. False   55. **a.** True   **b.** True

59. a.

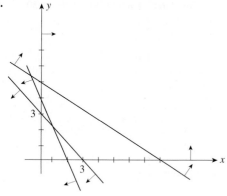

b. No solution

Exercises 3.4, page 198

1. c. $216

3. a. Between 750 and 1425
b. It cannot be decreased by more than 60 units.

5. a. $x = 3$; $y = 2$; $P = 17$ **b.** $\frac{8}{3} \le c \le 8$
c. $8 \le b \le 24$ **d.** $\frac{5}{4}$
e. Both constraints are binding.

7. a. $x = 4$; $y = 0$; $C = 8$ **b.** $0 \le c \le \frac{5}{2}$
c. $b \ge 3$ **d.** 2
e. Constraint 1 is binding; constraint 2 is nonbinding.

9. a. $x = 3$; $y = 5$; $P = 27$ **b.** $2 \le c \le 5$
c. $21 \le b \le 33$ **d.** $\frac{2}{3}$
e. The first two constraints are binding; the third is nonbinding.

11. a. 20 units of each product   **b.** $\frac{8}{3} \le c \le 5$
c. $216 \le b \le 405$ **d.** $\frac{8}{21}$

13. a. Operate Saddle Mine for 4 days, Horseshoe Mine for 6 days
b. $10{,}666\frac{2}{3} \le c \le 48{,}000$ **c.** $300 \le b \le 1350$
d. $194.29

15. a. Produce 60 of each; maximum profit of $1320
b. $8\frac{1}{3} \le c \le 15$ **c.** $1100 \le b \le 1633\frac{1}{3}$
d. $0.55
e. Constraints 1 and 2 are binding; constraint 3 is not.

17. a. 120 model A and 160 model B grates; maximum profit of $480
b. $1.125 \le c \le 3$ **c.** $600 \le b \le 1100$
d. $0.20
e. Constraints 1 and 2 are binding; constraint 3 is nonbinding.

Chapter 3 Concept Review Questions, page 201

1. a. half-plane; line   **b.** $ax + by \le c$; $ax + by = c$

2. a. points; each   **b.** bounded; enclosed

3. objective function; maximized; minimized; linear; inequalities

4. a. corner point   **b.** line

5. parameters; optimal

6. resource; amount; value; improved; increased

Chapter 3 Review Exercises, page 202

1. Max: 18—any point (x, y) lying on the line segment joining $(0, 6)$ and $(3, 4)$; min: 0

2. Max: 27—any point (x, y) lying on the line segment joining $(3, 5)$ and $(6, 1)$; min: 7

3. $x = 0$, $y = 4$; $P = 20$

4. $x = 0$, $y = 12$; $P = 36$

5. $x = 3$, $y = 4$; $C = 26$

6. $x = 1.25$, $y = 1.5$; $C = 9.75$

7. $x = 3$, $y = 10$; $P = 29$

8. $x = 8$, $y = 0$; $P = 48$

9. $x = 20$, $y = 0$; $C = 40$

10. $x = 2$, $y = 4$; $C = 14$

11. $x = 2$, $y = 6$; $C = 14$

12. Max: $x = \frac{100}{11}$, $y = \frac{210}{11}$; $Q = \frac{1140}{11}$; min: $x = 0$, $y = 10$; $Q = 40$

13. Max: $x = 22$, $y = 0$; $Q = 22$; min: $x = 3$, $y = \frac{5}{2}$; $Q = \frac{11}{2}$

14. Max: $x = 12$, $y = 6$; $Q = 54$; min: $x = 4$, $y = 0$; $Q = 8$

15. $40,000 in each company; $13,600

16. 60 model A satellite radios; 60 model B satellite radios; $1320

17. 93 model A, 180 model B; $456

18. 600 to Warehouse I and 400 to Warehouse II; $11,200

Chapter 3 Before Moving On, page 203

1. a.

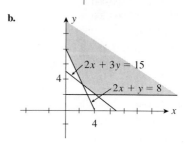

b.

2. Min: $C = -7$; max: $P = 76$

3. Max: $x = 0$, $y = \frac{24}{7}$; $P = \frac{72}{7}$

4. Min: $x = 0$, $y = 10$; $C = 10$

5. a. Max: $x = 4$, $y = 6$; $P = 26$ **b.** Between 1.5 and 4.5
c. Between 8 and 24   **d.** 1.25
e. Constraints 1 and 2 are binding.

CHAPTER 4

Exercises 4.1, page 221

1. a. It is already in standard form.

b.

x	y	u	v	P	Constant
1	4	1	0	0	12
1	3	0	1	0	10
−2	−4	0	0	1	0

3. a. Maximize $P = 2x + 3y$
subject to $x + y \le 10$
$x + 2y \le 12$
$2x + y \le 12$
$x \ge 0, y \ge 0$

b.

x	y	u	v	w	P	Constant
1	1	1	0	0	0	10
1	2	0	1	0	0	12
2	1	0	0	1	0	12
−2	−3	0	0	0	1	0

5. a. Maximize $P = x + 3y + 4z$
subject to $x + 2y + z \le 40$
$x + y + z \le 30$
$x \ge 0, y \ge 0, z \ge 0$

b.

x	y	z	u	v	P	Constant
1	2	1	1	0	0	40
1	1	1	0	1	0	30
−1	−3	−4	0	0	1	0

7. In final form; $x = \frac{30}{7}, y = \frac{20}{7}, u = 0, v = 0; P = \frac{220}{7}$

9. Not in final form; pivot element is $\frac{1}{2}$, lying in the first row, second column.

11. In final form; $x = \frac{1}{3}, y = 0, z = \frac{13}{3}, u = 0, v = 6, w = 0$; $P = 17$

13. Not in final form; pivot element is 1, lying in the third row, second column.

15. In final form; $x = 30, y = 10, z = 0, u = 0, v = 0; P = 60$; $x = 30, y = 0, z = 0, u = 10, v = 0; P = 60$; among others

17. $x = 0, y = 4, u = 0, v = 1; P = 16$

19. $x = 6, y = 3, u = 0, v = 0; P = 96$

21. $x = 6, y = 6, u = 0, v = 0, w = 0; P = 60$

23. $x = 0, y = 4, z = 4, u = 0, v = 0; P = 36$

25. $x = 0, y = 3, z = 0, u = 90, v = 0, w = 75; P = 12$

27. $x = 15, y = 3, z = 0, u = 2, v = 0, w = 0; P = 78$

29. $x = \frac{5}{4}, y = \frac{15}{2}, z = 0, u = 0, v = \frac{15}{4}, w = 0; P = 90$

31. $x = 2, y = 1, z = 1, u = 0, v = 0, w = 0; P = 87$

35. No model A, 2500 model B; $100,000

37. 65 acres of Crop A, 80 acres of Crop B; $25,750; yes; 5 acres of land

39. $62,500 in the money market fund, $125,000 in the international equity fund, $62,500 in the growth-and-income fund; $25,625

41. 180 units of Product A, 140 units of Product B, and 200 units of Product C; $7920; no

43. 22 min of morning advertising time, 3 min of evening advertising time

45. 80 units of model A, 80 units of model B, and 60 units of model C; maximum profit: $5760; no

47. 9000 bottles of Formula I, 7833 bottles of Formula II, 6000 bottles of Formula III; maximum profit: $4986.60; Yes, ingredients for 4167 bottles of Formula II

49. Project A: $800,000, project B: $800,000, and project C: $400,000; $280,000

51. False   **53.** True

Using Technology Exercises 4.1, page 231

1. $x = 1.2, y = 0, z = 1.6, w = 0; P = 8.8$

3. $x = 1.6, y = 0, z = 0, w = 3.6; P = 12.4$

Exercises 4.2, page 241

1. $x = 4, y = 0; C = -8$

3. $x = 4, y = 3; C = -18$

5. $x = 0, y = 13, z = 18, w = 14; C = -111$

7. $x = \frac{5}{4}, y = \frac{1}{4}, u = 2, v = 3;\ C = P = 13$

9. $x = 5, y = 10, z = 0, u = 1, v = 2; C = P = 80$

11. Maximize $P = 4u + 6v$
subject to $u + 3v \le 2$
$2u + 2v \le 5$; $x = 4, y = 0; C = 8$
$u \ge 0, v \ge 0$

13. Maximize $P = 60u + 40v + 30w$
subject to $6u + 2v + w \le 6$
$u + v + w \le 4$; $x = 10, y = 20; C = 140$
$u \ge 0, v \ge 0, w \ge 0$

15. Maximize $P = 10u + 20v$
subject to $20u + v \le 200$
$10u + v \le 150$; $x = 0, y = 0, z = 10; C = 1200$
$u + 2v \le 120$
$u \ge 0, v \ge 0$

17. Maximize $P = 10u + 24v + 16w$
subject to $u + 2v + w \le 6$
$2u + v + w \le 8$; $x = 8, y = 0, z = 8; C = 80$
$2u + v + w \le 4$
$u \ge 0, v \ge 0, w \ge 0$

19. Maximize $P = 6u + 2v + 4w$
subject to $2u + 6v \le 30$
$4u + 6w \le 12$; $x = \frac{1}{3}, y = \frac{4}{3}, z = 0; C = 26$
$3u + v + 2w \le 20$
$u \ge 0, v \ge 0, w \ge 0$

21. 2 type A vessels; 3 type B vessels; $250,000

23. 30 in Newspaper I; 10 in Newspaper II; $38,000

25. 8 oz of orange juice; 6 oz of pink grapefruit juice; 178 calories

27. True

Using Technology Exercises 4.2, page 248

1. $x = 1.333333, y = 3.333333, z = 0$; and $C = 4.66667$

3. $x = 0.9524, y = 4.2857, z = 0; C = 6.0952$

5. **a.** $x = 3, y = 2, P = 17$ **b.** $\frac{8}{3} \leq c_1 \leq 8; \frac{3}{2} \leq c_2 \leq \frac{9}{2}$
 c. $8 \leq b_1 \leq 24; 4 \leq b_2 \leq 12$ **d.** $\frac{5}{4}; \frac{1}{4}$
 e. Both constraints are binding.

7. **a.** $x = 4, y = 0, C = 8$ **b.** $0 \leq c_1 \leq \frac{5}{2}; 4 \leq c_2 < \infty$
 c. $3 \leq b_1 < \infty; -\infty < b_2 \leq 4$ **d.** 2; 0
 e. First constraint binding; second constraint non-binding

Exercises 4.3, page 258

1. Maximize $\quad P = -C = -2x + 3y$
 subject to $\quad -3x - 5y \leq -20$
 $\quad\quad\quad\quad\quad 3x + y \leq 16$
 $\quad\quad\quad\quad\quad -2x + y \leq 1$
 $\quad\quad\quad\quad\quad x \geq 0, y \geq 0$

3. Maximize $\quad P = -C = -5x - 10y - z$
 subject to $\quad -2x - y - z \leq -4$
 $\quad\quad\quad\quad\quad -x - 2y - 2z \leq -2$
 $\quad\quad\quad\quad\quad 2x + 4y + 3z \leq 12$
 $\quad\quad\quad\quad\quad x \geq 0, y \geq 0, z \geq 0$

5. $x = 5, y = 2; P = 9$

7. $x = 4, y = 0; C = -8$

9. $x = 4, y = \frac{2}{3}; P = \frac{20}{3}$

11. $x = 3, y = 2; P = 7$

13. $x = 24, y = 0, z = 0; P = 120$

15. $x = 0, y = 17, z = 1; C = -33$

17. $x = \frac{46}{7}, y = 0, z = \frac{50}{7}; P = \frac{142}{7}$

19. $x = 0, y = 0, z = 10; P = 30$

21. 80 acres of Crop A, 68 acres of Crop B

23. $50 million worth of home loans, $10 million worth of commercial-development loans; $4.6 million

25. 0 units of Product A, 280 units of Product B, 280 units of Product C; $7560

27. 10 oz of Food A, 4 oz of Food B, 40 mg of cholesterol; infinitely many other solutions

Chapter 4 Concept Review Questions, page 261

1. maximized; nonnegative; less than; equal to

2. equations; slack variables; $-c_1x_1 - c_2x_2 - \cdots - c_nx_n + P = 0$; below; augmented

3. minimized; nonnegative; greater than; equal to

4. dual; objective; optimal value

Chapter 4 Review Exercises, page 262

1. $x = 3, y = 4, u = 0, v = 0; P = 25$

2. $x = 3, y = 6, u = 4, v = 0, w = 0; P = 36$

3. $x = \frac{11}{3}, y = 4, u = \frac{7}{3}, v = 0, w = 0; P = 19$

4. $x = 8, y = 4, u = 2, v = 0, w = 0; P = 52$

5. $x = \frac{56}{5}, y = \frac{2}{5}, z = 0, u = 0, v = 0; P = \frac{118}{5}$

6. $x = 0, y = \frac{11}{3}, z = \frac{25}{6}, u = \frac{37}{6}, v = 0, w = 0; P = \frac{119}{6}$

7. $x = 2, y = 2, u = 0, v = 0; C = -22$

8. $x = 0, y = 4, z = 0, u = 20, v = 0, w = 20; C = -12$

9. Primal problem: $x = 2, y = 1; C = 9$; dual problem: $u = \frac{3}{10}, v = \frac{11}{10}$; $P = 9$

10. Maximize $\quad P = 14u + 21v + 12w$
 subject to $\quad u + 4v - 3w \leq 2$
 $\quad\quad\quad\quad\quad 2u + v - 2w \leq 4$
 $\quad\quad\quad\quad\quad u + 2v + 5w \leq 3$
 $\quad\quad\quad\quad\quad u \geq 0, v \geq 0, w \geq 0$

11. $x = \frac{3}{2}, y = 1; C = \frac{13}{2}$

12. $x = \frac{32}{11}, y = \frac{36}{11}; C = \frac{104}{11}$

13. $x = \frac{3}{4}, y = 0, z = \frac{7}{4}; C = 60$

14. $x = 0, y = 2, z = 0; C = 4$

15. $x = 45, y = 0, u = 0, v = 35; P = 135$

16. $x = 4, y = 4, u = 2, v = 0, w = 0; C = 20$

17. $x = 5, y = 2, u = 0, v = 0; P = 16$

18. $x = 20, y = 25, z = 0, u = 0, v = 30, w = 10; C = -160$

19. Saddle Mine: 4 days; Horseshoe Mine: 6 days; $152,000

20. $70,000 in blue-chip stocks; $0 in growth stocks; $30,000 in speculative stocks; maximum return: $13,000

21. 0 unit of Product A, 30 units of Product B, 0 unit of Product C; $P = $180

22. $50,000 in stocks, $100,000 in bonds, $50,000 in money market funds; $P = $21,500

Chapter 4 Before Moving On, page 263

1.

x	y	z	u	v	w	P	Constant
2	①	−1	1	0	0	0	3
1	−2	3	0	1	0	0	1
3	2	4	0	0	1	0	17
−1	−2	3	0	0	0	1	0

2. $x = 2, y = 0, z = 11, u = 2, v = 0, w = 0; P = 28$

3. $x = 6, y = 2; u = 0, v = 0; P = 34$ 4. $x = 3, y = 0; C = 3$

5. $x = 10, y = 0; P = 20$

CHAPTER 5

Exercises 5.1, page 278

1. $80; $580 3. $836 5. $1000 7. 146 days

9. 10%/year 11. $1718.19 13. $4974.47

15. $27,566.93 17. $261,751.04 19. $214,986.69

21. $10\frac{1}{4}$%/year 23. 8.3%/year 25. $29,227.61

27. $30,255.95 29. $6885.64 31. 24%/year

33. $123,600 35. 5%/year 37. 2.39%/year 39. $852.21

41. $255,256 43. $2.58 million 45. $22,163.75 47. $26,267.49

49. **a.** $34,626.88 **b.** $33,886.16 **c.** $33,506.76

51. Acme Mutual Fund 53. $23,329.48 55. $5994.86

57. $339.79 billion 59. Investment A

61. $33,885.14; $33,565.38   **63.** $80,000e^{(\sqrt{t}/2 - 0.09t)}$; $151,718

67. 4.2%   **69.** 5.83%   **71.** True   **73.** True

75. 2.2 years   **77.** 7.7 years   **79.** 6.08%/year   **81.** 2.06 years

Using Technology Exercises 5.1, page 284

1. $5872.78   **3.** $475.49   **5.** 8.95%/year

7. 10.20%/year   **9.** $29,743.30   **11.** $53,303.25

Exercises 5.2, page 291

1. $15,937.42   **3.** $54,759.35   **5.** $37,965.57

7. $137,209.97   **9.** $28,733.19   **11.** $15,558.61

13. $15,011.29   **15.** $109,658.91   **17.** $455.70

19. $44,526.45   **21.** Karen   **23.** $9850.12   **25.** $608.54

27. Between $383,242 and $469,053

29. Between $307,014 and $373,768   **31.** $17,887.62

33. $70,814.38   **35.** False

Using Technology Exercises 5.2, page 296

1. $59,622.15   **3.** $8453.59   **5.** $35,607.23

7. $13,828.60

Exercises 5.3, page 304

1. $14,902.95   **3.** $444.24   **5.** $622.13

7. $731.79   **9.** $1491.19   **11.** $516.76

13. $172.95   **15.** $1957.36   **17.** $3450.87

19. $16,274.54   **21. a.** $212.27   **b.** $1316.36; $438.79

23. a. $484.01; $380.44   **b.** $2424.36; $3261.12

25. $1761.03; $41,833; $59,461; $124,853   **27.** $60,982.31

29. $3135.48   **31.** $242.23   **33.** $199.07

35. $2090.41; $4280.21   **37.** $1,111.63   **39.** $24,639.53

41. $33,835.20   **43.** $212.77   **45.** $167,341.33

47. $1957.80; $257,135.23

49. a. $1681.71   **b.** $194,282.67   **c.** $1260.11   **d.** $421.60

51. $1000.92   **53.** $71,799   **55.** $640,569.40

Using Technology Exercises 5.3, page 310

1. $628.02   **3.** $1685.47   **5.** $1960.96

7. $894.12   **9.** $18,288.92

Exercises 5.4, page 317

1. 30   **3.** $-\frac{9}{2}$ **5.** $-3, 8, 19, 30, 41$ **7.** $x + 6y$

9. 795   **11.** 792   **13.** 550

15. a. 275   **b.** -280 **17.** At the beginning of the 37th week

19. $15.80   **21. b.** $800   **23.** GP; 256; 508   **25.** Not a GP

27. GP; 1/3; $364\frac{1}{3}$ **29.** 3; 0   **31.** 293,866

33. $56,284   **35.** Annual raise of 8%/year

37. a. $20,113.57   **b.** $87,537.38   **39.** $25,165.82

41. $39,321.60; $110,678.40   **43.** True

Chapter 5 Concept Review Questions, page 319

1. a. original; $P(1 + rt)$ **b.** interest; $P(1 + i)^n$; $A(1 + i)^{-n}$

2. simple; one; nominal; m; $\left(1 + \dfrac{r}{m}\right)^m - 1$

3. annuity; ordinary annuity; simple annuity.

4. a. $R\left[\dfrac{(1 + i)^n - 1}{i}\right]$ **b.** $R\left[\dfrac{1 - (1 + i)^{-n}}{i}\right]$

5. $\dfrac{Pi}{1 - (1 + i)^{-n}}$ **6.** future; $\dfrac{iS}{(1 + i)^n - 1}$

7. constant d; $a + (n - 1)d$; $\dfrac{n}{2}[2a + (n - 1)d]$

8. constant r; ar^{n-1}; $\dfrac{a(1 - r^n)}{1 - r}$

Chapter 5 Review Exercises, page 320

1. a. $7320.50   **b.** $7387.28   **c.** $7422.53
d. $7446.77

2. a. $19,859.95   **b.** $20,018.07   **c.** $20,100.14
d. $20,156.03

3. a. 12%   **b.** 12.36%   **c.** 12.5509%   **d.** 12.6825%

4. a. 11.5%   **b.** 11.8306%   **c.** 12.0055%   **d.** 12.1259%

5. $30,000.29   **6.** $39,999.95   **7.** $5557.68

8. $23,221.71   **9.** $7861.70   **10.** $173,804.43

11. $694.49   **12.** $318.93   **13.** $332.73   **14.** $208.44

15. 7.442%   **16.** 10.034%   **17.** $80,000

18. $2,592,702; $8,612,002   **19.** $5,491,922   **20.** $2982.73

21. $15,000   **22.** $5000   **23.** 7.6%   **24.** $218.64

25. $73,178.41   **26.** $13,026.89   **27.** $2000

28. a. $965.55   **b.** $227,598   **c.** $42,684

29. a. $1217.12   **b.** $99,081.60   **c.** $91,367

30. $19,573.56   **31.** $4727.67   **32.** $205.09; 20.27%/year

33. $2203.83

Chapter 5 Before Moving On, page 321

1. $2540.47   **2.** 6.18%/year   **3.** $569,565.47   **4.** $1213.28

5. $35.13   **6. a.** 210   **b.** 127.5

CHAPTER 6

Exercises 6.1, page 330

1. $\{x \mid x$ is a gold medalist in the 2010 Winter Olympic Games$\}$

3. $\{x \mid x$ is an integer greater than 2 and less than 8$\}$

5. $\{2, 3, 4, 5, 6\}$ 7. $\{-2\}$

9. **a.** True   **b.** False   11. **a.** False   **b.** False

13. True   15. **a.** True   **b.** False

17. **a.** and **b.**

19. **a.** $\varnothing, \{1\}, \{2\}, \{1, 2\}$
    b. $\varnothing, \{1\}, \{2\}, \{3\}, \{1, 2\}, \{1, 3\}, \{2, 3\}, \{1, 2, 3\}$
    c. $\varnothing, \{1\}, \{2\}, \{3\}, \{4\}, \{1, 2\}, \{1, 3\}, \{1, 4\}, \{2, 3\}, \{2, 4\}, \{3, 4\},$
    $\{1, 2, 3\}, \{1, 2, 4\}, \{1, 3, 4\}, \{2, 3, 4\}, \{1, 2, 3, 4\}$

21. $\{1, 2, 3, 4, 6, 8, 10\}$

23. $\{$Jill, John, Jack, Susan, Sharon$\}$

25. **a.**

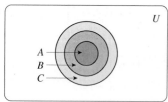

b.

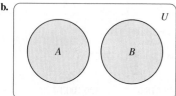

c.

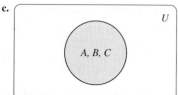

27. **a.**

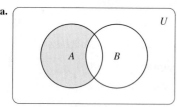

b.

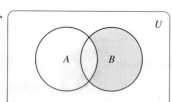

29. **a.**

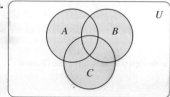

b.

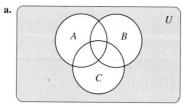

31. **a.**

b.

33. **a.** $\{2, 4, 6, 8, 10\}$ **b.** $\{1, 2, 4, 5, 6, 8, 9, 10\}$
    c. $\{1, 2, 3, 4, 5, 6, 7, 8, 9, 10\}$

35. **a.** $C = \{1, 2, 4, 5, 8, 9\}$ **b.** $\varnothing$ **c.** $\{1, 2, 3, 4, 5, 6, 7, 8, 9, 10\}$

37. **a.** Not disjoint   **b.** Disjoint

39. **a.** The set of all employees at Universal Life Insurance who do not drink tea
    b. The set of all employees at Universal Life Insurance who do not drink coffee

41. **a.** The set of all employees at Universal Life Insurance who drink tea but not coffee
    b. The set of all employees at Universal Life Insurance who drink coffee but not tea

43. **a.** The set of all employees in a hospital who are not doctors
    b. The set of all employees in a hospital who are not nurses

45. **a.** The set of all employees in a hospital who are female doctors
    b. The set of all employees in a hospital who are both doctors and administrators

47. **a.** $D \cap F$ **b.** $R \cap F^c \cap L^c$

49. **a.** B^c **b.** $A \cap B$ **c.** $A \cap B \cap C^c$

51. **a.** $A \cap B \cap C$; the set of tourists who have taken the underground, a cab, and a bus over a 1-week period in London
    b. $A \cap C$; the set of tourists who have taken the underground and a bus over a 1-week period in London
    c. B^c; the set of tourists who have not taken a cab over a 1-week period in London

53.

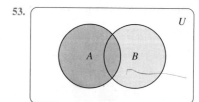

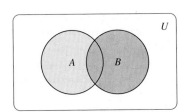

55.

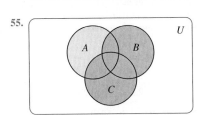

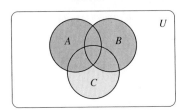

57.

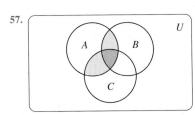

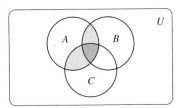

61. a. x, y, v, r, w, u **b.** v, r

63. a. s, t, y **b.** t, z, w, x, s **65.** $A \subset C$

67. False   **69.** True   **71.** True   **73.** True   **75.** True

Exercises 6.2, page 336

3. a. 4   **b.** 5   **c.** 7   **d.** 2

7. 20

9. a. 15   **b.** 30   **c.** 15   **d.** 12   **e.** 50   **f.** 20

11. a. 140   **b.** 100   **c.** 60

13. 13   **15.** 0   **17.** 13   **19.** 61

21. a. 106   **b.** 64   **c.** 38   **d.** 14

23. a. 182   **b.** 118   **c.** 56   **d.** 18   **25.** 30

27. a. 16   **b.** 31   **c.** 4   **d.** 21   **e.** 11

29. a. 64   **b.** 10   **31. a.** 36   **b.** 36   **33.** 5

35. a. 62   **b.** 33   **c.** 25   **d.** 38

37. a. 108   **b.** 15   **c.** 45   **d.** 12

39. a. 22   **b.** 80

41. True   **43.** True

Exercises 6.3, page 343

1. 12   **3.** 64   **5.** 24

7. 24   **9.** 60   **11.** 1 billion   **13.** 64   **15.** 5^{50}

17. 400   **19.** 9990

21. a. 17,576,000   **b.** 17,576,000

23. 1024; 59,049   **25.** 2730

27. 217   **29.** True

Exercises 6.4, page 354

1. 360   **3.** 10   **5.** 120

7. 20   **9.** n **11.** 1

13. 35   **15.** 1   **17.** 84

19. $\dfrac{n(n-1)}{2}$ **21.** $\dfrac{n!}{2}$

23. Permutation   **25.** Combination

27. Permutation   **29.** Combination

31. $P(4, 4) = 24$ **33.** $P(4, 4) = 24$

35. $P(9, 9) = 362{,}880$ **37.** $C(12, 3) = 220$

39. 151,200   **41.** 2520

43. 20   **45.** $C(12, 3) = 220$

47. $C(100, 3) = 161{,}700$ **49.** $P(6, 6) = 720$

51. $P(12, 6) = 665{,}280$

53. a. $P(10, 10) = 3{,}628{,}800$
  b. $P(3, 3)P(4, 4)P(3, 3)P(3, 3) = 5184$

55. a. $P(20, 20) = 20!$
  b. $P(5, 5)P[(4, 4)]^5 = 5!(4!)^5 = 955{,}514{,}880$

57. a. $P(12, 9) = 79{,}833{,}600$
  b. $C(12, 9) = 220$ **c.** $C(12, 9) \cdot C(3, 2) = 660$

59. $2\{C(2, 2) + [C(3, 2) - C(2, 2)]\} = 6$

61. $C(3,3)[C(8, 6) + C(8, 7) + C(8, 8)] = 37$

63. a. $C(12, 3) = 220$ **b.** $C(11, 2) = 55$
  c. $C(5, 1)C(7, 2) + C(5, 2)C(7, 1) + C(5, 3) = 185$

65. $P(7, 3) + C(7, 2)P(3, 2) = 336$

67. $C(5, 1)C(3, 1)C(6, 2)[C(4, 1) + C(3, 1)] = 1575$

69. $10C(4, 1) = 40$

71. $C(4, 1)C(13, 5) - 40 = 5108$

73. $13C(4, 3) \cdot 12C(4, 2) = 3744$

75. $C(6, 2) = 15$

77. $C(12, 6) + C(12, 7) + C(12, 8) + C(12, 9) +$
  $C(12, 10) + C(12, 11) + C(12, 12) = 2510$

79. $4! = 24$ **83.** True   **85.** True

Using Technology Exercises 6.4, page 359

1. $1.307674368 \times 10^{12}$ 3. $2.56094948229 \times 10^{16}$

5. 674,274,182,400   7. 133,784,560

9. 4,656,960

11. 658,337,004,000

Chapter 6 Concept Review Questions, page 360

1. set; elements; set   2. equal   3. subset

4. **a.** no   **b.** all   5. union; intersection

6. complement   7. $A^c \cap B^c \cap C^c$

8. permutation; combination

Chapter 6 Review Exercises, page 360

1. {3}   2. {A, E, H, L, S, T}

3. {4, 6, 8, 10}   4. {-4}   5. Yes

6. Yes   7. Yes   8. No

9.
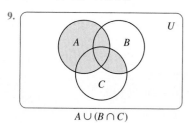
$A \cup (B \cap C)$

10.
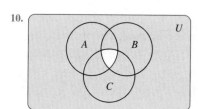
$(A \cap B \cap C)^c$

11.
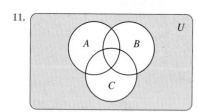
$A^c \cap B^c \cap C^c$

12.
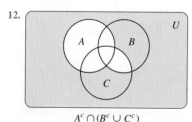
$A^c \cap (B^c \cup C^c)$

17. The set of all participants in a consumer-behavior survey who both avoided buying a product because it is not recyclable and boycotted a company's products because of its record on the environment.

18. The set of all participants in a consumer-behavior survey who avoided buying a product because it is not recyclable and/or voluntarily recycled their garbage.

19. The set of all participants in a consumer-behavior survey who both did not use cloth diapers rather than disposable diapers and voluntarily recycled their garbage.

20. The set of all participants in a consumer-behavior survey who did not boycott a company's products because of its record on the environment and/or did not voluntarily recycle their garbage.

21. 150   22. 230   23. 270   24. 30   25. 70   26. 200

27. 190   28. 181,440   29. 120   30. 8400   31. None

32. **a.** 446   **b.** 377   **c.** 34   33. 720   34. 20   35. 144

36. **a.** 720   **b.** 480   37. **a.** 50,400   **b.** 5040

38. **a.** 60   **b.** 125   39. 108   40. 30   41. 80

42. **a.** 1287   **b.** 288   43. 720   44. 1050

45. **a.** 2704   **b.** 2652

46. **a.** 5040   **b.** 3600

47. **a.** 487,635   **b.** 550   **c.** 341,055

48. **a.** 1365   **b.** 1155

49. **a.** 720   **b.** 72   **c.** 48   50. **a.** 495   **b.** 210   **c.** 420

Chapter 6 Before Moving On, page 362

1. **a.** {d, f, g}   **b.** {b, c, d, e, f, g}   **c.** {b, c, e}

2. 3   3. 15   4. 264   5. 200

CHAPTER 7

Exercises 7.1, page 369

1. {a, b, d, f}; {a}   3. {b, c, e}; {a}   5. No   7. S

9. $\varnothing$ 11. Yes   13. Yes   15. $E \cup F$ 17. G^c

19. $(E \cup F \cup G)^c$

21. **a.** {(2, 1), (3, 1), (4, 1), (5, 1), (6, 1), (3, 2), (4, 2), (5, 2), (6, 2), (4, 3), (5, 3), (6, 3), (5, 4), (6, 4), (6, 5)}
    b. {(1, 2), (2, 4), (3, 6)}

23. $\varnothing$, {a}, {b}, {c}, {a, b}, {a, c}, {b, c}, S

25. **a.** $S = $ {B, R}   **b.** $\varnothing$, {B}, {R}, S

27. **a.** $S = $ {(H, 1), (H, 2), (H, 3), (H, 4), (H, 5), (H, 6), (T, 1), (T, 2), (T, 3), (T, 4), (T, 5), (T, 6)}
    b. {(H, 2), (H, 4), (H, 6)}

29. **a.** No   **b.** No

31. $S = $ {$ddd, ddn, dnd, ndd, dnn, ndn, nnd, nnn$}

33. **a.** $S = $ {$bbbb, bbbg, bbgb, bbgg, bgbb, bgbg, bggb, bggg, gbbb, gbbg, gbgb, gbgg, ggbb, ggbg, gggb, gggg$}
    b. $E = $ {$bbbg, bbgb, bgbb, gbbb$}
    c. $F = $ {$bbbg, bbgg, bgbg, bggg, gbbg, gbgg, ggbg, gggg$}
    d. $G = $ {$gbbg, gbgg, ggbg, gggg$}

35. **a.** {ABC, ABD, ABE, ACD, ACE, ADE, BCD, BCE, BDE, CDE}
    b. 6   **c.** 3   **d.** 6

37. **a.** E^c **b.** $E^c \cap F^c$ **c.** $E \cup F$
    d. $(E \cap F^c) \cup (E^c \cap F)$

39. a. $\{t \mid t > 0\}$ **b.** $\{t \mid 0 < t \le 2\}$ **c.** $\{t \mid t > 2\}$

41. a. $S = \{0, 1, 2, 3, \ldots, 10\}$ **b.** $E = \{0, 1, 2, 3\}$
c. $F = \{5, 6, 7, 8, 9, 10\}$

43. a. $S = \{0, 1, 2, \ldots, 20\}$
b. $E = \{0, 1, 2, \ldots, 9\}$ **c.** $F = \{20\}$

49. False

Exercises 7.2, page 377

1. $\{(H, H)\}, \{(H, T)\}, \{(T, H)\}, \{(T, T)\}$

3. $\{(D, m)\}, \{(D, f)\}, \{(R, m)\}, \{(R, f)\}, \{(I, m)\}, \{(I, f)\}$

5. $\{(1, i)\}, \{(1, d)\}, \{(1, s)\}, \{(2, i)\}, \{(2, d)\}, \{(2, s)\}, \ldots,$
$\{(5, i)\}, \{(5, d)\}, \{(5, s)\}$

7. $\{(A, Rh^+)\}, \{(A, Rh^-)\}, \{(B, Rh^+)\}, \{(B, Rh^-)\},$
$\{(AB, Rh^+)\}, \{(AB, Rh^-)\}, \{(O, Rh^+)\}, \{(O, Rh^-)\}$

9.

Grade	A	B	C	D	F
Probability	.10	.25	.45	.15	.05

11.

Answer	Falling behind	Staying even	Increasing faster	Don't know
Probability	.40	.44	.12	.04

13. .69

15.

Number of Days	0	1	2	3	4	5	6	7
Probability	.05	.06	.09	.15	.11	.20	.17	.17

17.

Event	A	B	C	D	E
Probability	.026	.199	.570	.193	.012

19. a. $S = \{(0 < x \le 200), (200 < x \le 400),$
$(400 < x \le 600), (600 < x \le 800),$
$(800 < x \le 1000), (x > 1000)\}$

b.

Cars, x	Probability
$0 < x \le 200$	.075
$200 < x \le 400$	.1
$400 < x \le 600$	.175
$600 < x \le 800$	.35
$800 < x \le 1000$	.225
$x > 1000$	.075

21. .469

23. a. .856   **b.** .144   **25.** .46

27. a. $\frac{1}{4}$ **b.** $\frac{1}{2}$ **c.** $\frac{1}{13}$ **29.** $\frac{3}{8}$

31. a. 0.4   **b.** 0.1   **c.** 0.4

33. a. .633   **b.** .276   **35. a.** .35   **b.** .33

37. .530   **39. a.** .4   **b.** .23

41. a. .448   **b.** .255   **43.** .783

45. There are six ways of obtaining a sum of 7.

47. No   **49. a.** $\frac{1}{6}$ **b.** $\frac{5}{6}$ **c.** 1   **51.** True

Exercises 7.3, page 386

1. $\frac{1}{2}$ **3.** $\frac{1}{36}$ **5.** $\frac{1}{9}$ **7.** $\frac{1}{52}$

9. $\frac{3}{13}$ **11.** $\frac{12}{13}$ **13.** .002; .998

15. $P(a) + P(b) + P(c) \ne 1$

17. Since the five events are not mutually exclusive, Property 3 cannot be used; that is, he could win more than one purse.

19. The two events are not mutually exclusive; hence, the probability of the given event is $\frac{1}{6} + \frac{1}{6} - \frac{1}{36} = \frac{11}{36}$.

21. $E^C \cap F^C = \{e\} \ne \varnothing$

23. $P[(G \cup C^c)] \ne 1 - P(G) - P(C)$; he has not considered the case in which a customer buys both glasses and contact lenses.

25. a. 0   **b.** .7   **c.** .8   **d.** .3

27. a. $\frac{1}{2}, \frac{3}{8}$ **b.** $\frac{1}{2}, \frac{5}{8}$ **c.** $\frac{1}{8}$ **d.** $\frac{3}{4}$ **29. a.** .41   **b.** .48   **31.** .332

33. a. .24   **b.** .46   **35. a.** .16   **b.** .38   **c.** .22

37. a. .41   **b.** .518   **39. a.** .52   **b.** .34

41. a. .439   **b.** .385   **43. b.** .52   **c.** .859

45. a. .90   **b.** .40   **c.** .40

47. a. .6   **b.** .332   **c.** .232   **d.** .6

51. True   **53.** False

Exercises 7.4, page 396

1. $\frac{1}{32}$ **3.** $\frac{31}{32}$

5. $P(E) = 13C(4, 2)/C(52, 2) \approx .059$

7. $C(26, 2)/C(52, 2) \approx .245$

9. $[C(3, 2)C(5, 2)]/C(8, 4) = 3/7$

11. $[C(5, 3)C(3, 1)]/C(8, 4) = 3/7$ **13.** $C(3, 2)/8 = 3/8$

15. 1/8   **17.** $C(10, 6)/2^{10} \approx .205$

19. a. $C(4, 2)/C(24, 2) \approx .022$
b. $1 - C(20, 2)/C(24, 2) \approx .312$

21. a. $C(6, 2)/C(80, 2) \approx .005$
b. $1 - C(74, 2)/C(80, 2) \approx .145$

23. a. .12; $C(98, 10)/C(100, 12) \approx .013$
b. .15; .015

25. $[C(12, 8)C(8, 2) + C(12, 9)C(8, 1) + C(12, 10)]/C(20, 10) \approx .085$

27. a. $\frac{3}{5}$ **b.** $C(3, 1)/C(5, 3) = .3$ **c.** $1 - C(3, 3)/C(5, 3) = .9$

29. $\frac{1}{729}$ **31.** .0001   **33.** .1   **35.** $40/C(52, 5) \approx .0000154$

37. $[4C(13, 5) - 40]/C(52, 5) \approx .00197$

39. $[13C(4, 3) \cdot 12C(4, 2)]/C(52, 5) \approx .00144$

41. a. .618   **b.** .059   **43.** .030

Exercises 7.5, page 408

1. a. .4   **b.** .33   **3.** .3   **5.** Independent

7. Independent   **9. a.** .24   **b.** .76   **c.** .4   **d.** .24

11. a. .5   **b.** .4   **c.** .2   **d.** .35   **e.** No   **f.** No

13. a. .4   **b.** .3   **c.** .12   **d.** .30   **e.** Yes   **f.** Yes

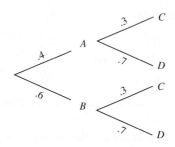

15. **a.** $\frac{1}{12}$ **b.** $\frac{1}{36}$ **c.** $\frac{1}{6}$ **d.** $\frac{1}{6}$ **e.** No

17. $\frac{4}{11}$ **19.** Independent   **21.** Not independent   **23.** .1875

25. **a.** $\frac{4}{9}$ **b.** $\frac{4}{9}$ **27. a.** $\frac{1}{21}$ **b.** $\frac{1}{3}$ **29.** .48   **31.** .06

33. $\frac{1}{7}$ **35. a.**

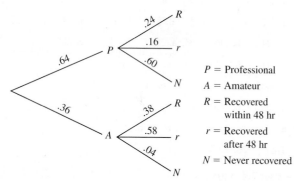

$P = $ Professional
$A = $ Amateur
$R = $ Recovered within 48 hr
$r = $ Recovered after 48 hr
$N = $ Never recovered

   b. .24   **c.** .3984

37. **a.** .16   **b.** .424   **c.** .1696

39. **a.** .092   **b.** .008

41. **a.** .28; .39; .18; .643; .292   **b.** Not independent

43. Not independent   **45.** .0000068   **47. a.** $\frac{7}{10}$ **b.** $\frac{1}{5}$

49. 3   **53.** 1   **57.** True   **59.** True

Exercises 7.6, page 416

1.

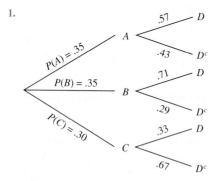

3. **a.** .45   **b.** .2222   **5. a.** .48   **b.** .33

7. **a.** .08   **b.** .15   **c.** .348

9. **a.** $\frac{1}{12}$ **b.** $\frac{1}{4}$ **c.** $\frac{1}{18}$ **d.** $\frac{3}{14}$

11.

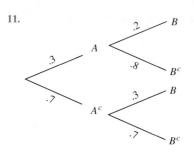

a. .27   **b.** .22   **c.** .73   **d.** .33

13. $\frac{4}{17}$ **15.** $\frac{4}{51}$

17.

$$\frac{2}{5} \quad W \quad \frac{4}{9} \quad W$$
$$\frac{5}{9} \quad B$$
$$\frac{3}{5} \quad B \quad \frac{1}{3} \quad W$$
$$\frac{2}{3} \quad B$$

19. $\frac{9}{17}$ **21.** .422   **23. a.** $\frac{3}{4}$ **b.** $\frac{2}{9}$ **25.** .125   **27.** .407

29. **a.** .543   **b.** .545   **c.** .455   **31.** .377

33. **a.** .297   **b.** .10   **35.** .856   **37. a.** .57   **b.** .691

39. .647   **41.** .172   **43.** .301

45. **a.** .763   **b.** .276   **c.** .724

47. **a.** .4906   **b.** .62   **c.** .186   **49.** .028   **51.** .012

Chapter 7 Concept Review Questions, page 423

1. experiment; sample; space; event   **2.** $\varnothing$ **3.** uniform; $\frac{1}{n}$

4. conditional   **5.** independent   **6.** a posteriori probability

Chapter 7 Review Exercises, page 423

1. **a.** 0   **b.** .6   **c.** .6   **d.** .4   **e.** 1

2. **a.** .35   **b.** .65   **c.** .05

3. **a.** .53   **b.** .35   **c.** .82   **d.** .18

4. **a.** .49   **b.** .39   **c.** .48

5. $\frac{2}{7}$ **6. a.** .019   **b.** .981   **7.** .364   **8.** No   **9.** .5

10. .18   **11.** .25   **12.** .06   **13.** .49   **14.** .37

15. **a.** $\frac{7}{8}$ **b.** $\frac{7}{8}$ **c.** No   **16. a.** .284   **b.** .984

17. .150   **18.** $\frac{2}{15}$ **19.** $\frac{1}{24}$ **20.** $\frac{1}{52}$ **21.** .00018

22. .00995   **23.** .245   **24.** .510   **25.** .245

26.

Figures Produced (in dozens)	30	31	32	33	34	35	36
Probability	.125	0	.1875	.25	.1875	.125	.125

27.

Income, $	0–24,999	25,000–49,999	50,000–74,999	75,000–99,999
Probability	.287	.293	.195	.102

Income, $	100,000–124,999	125,000–149,999	150,000–199,999	200,000 or more
Probability	.052	.025	.022	.024

28. a. .54   **b.** .72   **29. a.** .79   **b.** .59

30. a. $\frac{3}{8}$ **b.** $\frac{1}{2}$ **c.** $\frac{1}{4}$ **31. a.** .757   **b.** .243

32. a. .56   **b.** .4   **33.** .5   **34.** .457   **35.** .368

36. a. .68   **b.** .053   **37.** .32   **38.** .619

39. .180   **40. a.** .513   **b.** .390

Chapter 7 Before Moving On, page 426

1. $\frac{5}{12}$ **2.** $\frac{4}{13}$ **3. a.** .9   **b.** .3   **4.** .72   **5.** .308

CHAPTER 8

Exercises 8.1, page 434

1. a. See part (b).

b.

Outcome	GGG	GGR	GRG	RGG
Value	3	2	2	2

Outcome	GRR	RGR	RRG	RRR
Value	1	1	1	0

c. {GGG}

3. Any positive integer   **5.** $\frac{1}{6}$

7. Any positive integer; infinite discrete

9. $x \geq 0$; continuous

11. Any positive integer; infinite discrete

13. No. The probability assigned to a value of the random variable X cannot be negative.

15. No. The sum of the probabilities exceed 1.

17. $a = 0.2$

19. a. .20   **b.** .60   **c.** .30   **d.** 1   **e.** .40   **f.** 0

21.

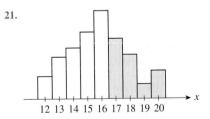

23. a.

x	1	2	3	4	5	6
$P(X = x)$	$\frac{1}{6}$	$\frac{1}{6}$	$\frac{1}{6}$	$\frac{1}{6}$	$\frac{1}{6}$	$\frac{1}{6}$

y	1	2	3	4	5	6
$P(Y = y)$	$\frac{1}{6}$	$\frac{1}{6}$	$\frac{1}{6}$	$\frac{1}{6}$	$\frac{1}{6}$	$\frac{1}{6}$

b.

x + y	2	3	4	5	6	7
$P(X + Y = x + y)$	$\frac{1}{36}$	$\frac{2}{36}$	$\frac{3}{36}$	$\frac{4}{36}$	$\frac{5}{36}$	$\frac{6}{36}$

x + y	8	9	10	11	12
$P(X + Y = x + y)$	$\frac{5}{36}$	$\frac{4}{36}$	$\frac{3}{36}$	$\frac{2}{36}$	$\frac{1}{36}$

25. a.

x	0	1	2	3	4
$P(X = x)$	.017	.067	.033	.117	.233

x	5	6	7	8	9	10
$P(X = x)$	.133	.167	.100	.050	.067	.017

b.

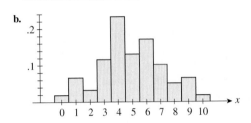

c. .217

27. a.

x	1	2	3	4	5
$P(X = x)$	.007	.029	.021	.079	.164

x	6	7	8	9	10
$P(X = x)$	.15	.20	.207	.114	.029

b. .70

29. True

Using Technology Exercises 8.1, page 439

Graphing Utility

1.

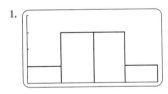

3.

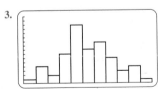

Excel

1.

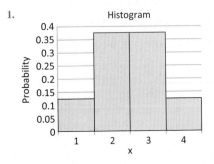

3.

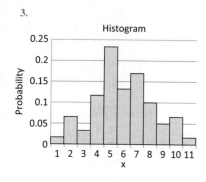

Histogram

Exercises 8.2, page 448

1. a. 2.6

b.

x	0	1	2	3	4	
$P(X = x)$	0	.1	.4	.3	.2	; 2.6

3. 0.86   **5.** $78.50   **7.** 0.91

9. 0.12   **11.** 1.73   **13.** 4.16%

15. $-39¢$ **17.** $100   **19.** $118,800

21. City B **23.** Company B **25.** 2.86%

27. $-5.3¢$ **29.** $-2.7¢$ **31.** 2 to 3; 3 to 2

33. .4   **35.** $\frac{7}{12}$ **37.** $\frac{5}{14}$

41. a. Mean: 74; mode: 85; median: 80   **b.** Mode

43. 3; close   **45.** 16; 16; 16   **47.** True

Exercises 8.3, page 458

1. $\mu = 2$, Var$(X) = 1$, $\sigma = 1$

3. $\mu = 0$, Var$(X) = 1$, $\sigma = 1$

5. $\mu = 518$, Var$(X) = 1891$, $\sigma \approx 43.5$

7. Figure (a)   **9.** 1.56

11. $\mu = 4.5$, Var$(X) = 5.25$

13. a. Let X = the annual birthrate during the years 1997–2006.

b.

x	13.9	14.0	14.1	14.2	14.5	14.6	14.7
$P(X = x)$	.1	.2	.2	.1	.2	.1	.1

c. $\mu = 14.26$, Var$(X) = 0.0744$, $\sigma \approx 0.2728$

15. a. Mutual Fund A: $\mu = \$620$, Var$(X) = 267,600$;
Mutual Fund B: $\mu = \$520$, Var$(X) = 137,600$
b. Mutual Fund A
c. Mutual Fund B

17. 1

19. $\mu = \$439,600$; Var$(X) = 1,443,840,000$; $\sigma \approx \$37,998$

21. 95.3%; 0.5%   **23.** 34.95; 5.94   **25.** -25.5%; 9.23

27. 21.59%; 5.20   **29.** 9.6%; 1.64   **31.** 94.56%; 19.94

33. 1607; 182   **35.** 3.324; 0.4497

37. a. At least .75
b. At least .96

39. 7   **41.** At least $\frac{7}{16}$

43. At least $\frac{15}{16}$ **45.** True

Using Technology Exercises 8.3, page 464

1. a.

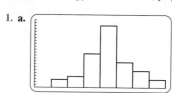

b. $\mu = 4$,
$\sigma \approx 1.40$

3. a.

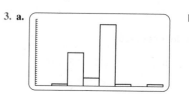

b. $\mu = 17.34$,
$\sigma \approx 1.11$

5. a. Let X denote the random variable that gives the weight of a carton of sugar.

b.

x	4.96	4.97	4.98	4.99	5.00	5.01
$P(X = x)$	$\frac{3}{30}$	$\frac{4}{30}$	$\frac{4}{30}$	$\frac{1}{30}$	$\frac{1}{30}$	$\frac{5}{30}$

x	5.02	5.03	5.04	5.05	5.06
$P(X = x)$	$\frac{3}{30}$	$\frac{3}{30}$	$\frac{4}{30}$	$\frac{1}{30}$	$\frac{1}{30}$

c. $\mu \approx 5.00$; $\sigma \approx 0.03$

7. a.

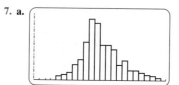

b. 65.875; 1.73

Exercises 8.4, page 472

1. Yes

3. No. There are more than two outcomes to each trial.

5. No. The probability of an accident on a clear day is not the same as the probability of an accident on a rainy day.

7. .296   **9.** .051   **11.** .132

13. .656   **15.** .004   **17.** .116

19. a. $P(X = 0) \approx .078$; $P(X = 1) \approx .259$;
$P(X = 2) \approx .346$; $P(X = 3) \approx .230$;
$P(X = 4) \approx .077$; $P(X = 5) \approx .010$

b.

x	0	1	2	3	4	5
$P(X = x)$	.078	.259	.346	.230	.077	.010

c. $\mu = 2$; $\sigma \approx 1.1$

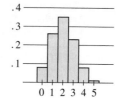

21. No. The probability that at most 1 is defective is
$P(X = 0) + P(X = 1) = .74$.

23. .165   25. .0002

27. **a.** .633   **b.** .367   29. **a.** .0329   **b.** .329

31. **a.** .273   **b.** .650   33. **a.** .817   **b.** .999

35. **a.** .075   **b.** .012   37. **a.** 0.35; 3.5%

39. **a.** .122   **b.** .358

41. .349   43. At least 7 times   45. $\mu = 375$; $\sigma \approx 9.68$

47. False   49. False

Exercises 8.5, page 482

1. .9265   3. .0401   5. .8657

7. **a.** 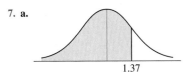   **b.** .9147

9. **a.** 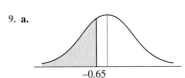   **b.** .2578

11. **a.**    **b.** .8944

13. **a.** 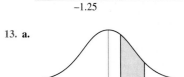   **b.** .2266

15. **a.** 1.23   **b.** −0.81   17. **a.** 1.9   **b.** −1.9

19. **a.** .9772   **b.** .9192   **c.** .7333

Exercises 8.6, page 490

1. **a.** .2206   **b.** .2206   **c.** .2960

3. **a.** .0228   **b.** .0228   **c.** .4772   **d.** .7258

5. **a.** .0038   **b.** .0918   **c.** .4082   **d.** .2514

7. .6247   9. 0.62%   11. A: 80; B: 73; C: 62; D: 54

13. **a.** .4207   **b.** .4254   **c.** .0125

15. **a.** .2877   **b.** .0008   **c.** .7287

17. .9265   19. .8686

21. **a.** .0037   **b.** The drug is effective.   23. 2142

Chapter 8 Concept Review Questions, page 493

1. random   2. finite; infinite; continuous   3. sum; .75

4. **a.** $\dfrac{P(E)}{P(E^C)}$ **b.** $\dfrac{a}{a+b}$

5. $p_1(x_1 - \mu)^2 + p_2(x_2 - \mu)^2 + \cdots + p_n(x_n - \mu)^2$; $\sqrt{\text{Var}(X)}$

6. fixed; two; same; independent

7. continuous; probability density function; set

8. normal; large; 0; 1

Chapter 8 Review Exercises, page 493

1. **a.** {WWW, BWW, WBW, WWB, BBW, BWB, WBB, BBB}

b.

Outcome	WWW	BWW	WBW	WWB
Value of X	0	1	1	1

Outcome	BBW	BWB	WBB	BBB
Value of X	2	2	2	3

c.

x	0	1	2	3
$P(X = x)$	$\frac{1}{35}$	$\frac{12}{35}$	$\frac{18}{35}$	$\frac{4}{35}$

d.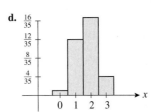

2. $100

3. **a.** .8   **b.** $\mu = 2.7$; $\sigma \approx 1.42$

4. **a.**

x	0	1	2	3	4
$P(X = x)$	.1296	.3456	.3456	.1536	.0256

b. $\mu = 1.6$; $\text{Var}(X) = 0.96$; $\sigma \approx 0.9798$

5. .6915

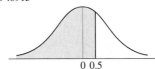

6. .2266

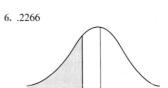

7. .4649

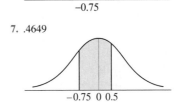

8. .4082

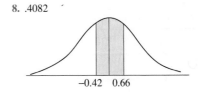

9. 2.42   10. −1.05   11. −2.03   12. 1.42   13. .6915

14. .8413   15. .2417   16. .7333   17. 41.3 mph

18. $12,000   19. .2646; .9163   20. 15.87%   21. At least .75

22. €26.76 billion; €1.6317 billion   23. $\mu = 27.87$; $\sigma = 6.41$

24. .677   25. $\mu = 120$; $\sigma \approx 10.1$ 26. 0.6%

27. **a.** .246   **b.** .901   28. **a.** .050   **b.** .995

29. .9738   30. .9997

Chapter 8 Before Moving On, page 494

1.

x	−3	−2	0	1	2	3
$P(X = x)$	.05	.1	.25	.3	.2	.1

2. **a.** .8   **b.** .92

3. 0.44; 4.0064; 2.0016

4. **a.** .2401; .4116; .2646; .0756; .0081   **b.** 1.2; .917

5. **a.** .9772   **b.** .9772   **c.** .9544

6. **a.** .0222   **b.** .6085   **c.** .0222

CHAPTER 9

Exercises 9.1, page 504

1. Yes   3. Yes   5. No   7. Yes   9. No

11. **a.** Given that the outcome state 1 has occurred, the conditional probability that the outcome state 1 will occur is .3.

b. .7   **c.** $\begin{bmatrix} .48 \\ .52 \end{bmatrix}$

13. $TX_0 = \begin{bmatrix} .4 \\ .6 \end{bmatrix}$;

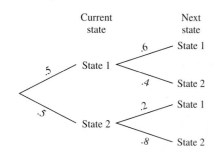

15. $X_2 = \begin{bmatrix} .576 \\ .424 \end{bmatrix}$ 17. $X_2 = \begin{bmatrix} \frac{5}{16} \\ \frac{27}{64} \\ \frac{17}{64} \end{bmatrix}$

19. **a.**

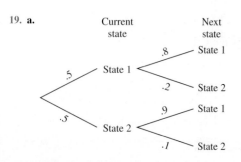

b. $T = \begin{array}{c} \\ L \\ R \end{array} \begin{array}{cc} L & R \\ \begin{bmatrix} .8 & .9 \\ .2 & .1 \end{bmatrix} \end{array}$ **c.** $X_0 = \begin{array}{c} L \\ R \end{array} \begin{bmatrix} .5 \\ .5 \end{bmatrix}$ **d.** .85

21. **a.** Vote is evenly split.   **b.** Democrat

23. After one year: 78.8% in the city and 21.2% in the suburbs. After two years: 77.7% in the city and 22.3% in the suburbs.

25. University: 37%, Campus: 35%, Book Mart: 28%; University: 34.5%, Campus: 31.35%, Book Mart: 34.15%

27. Business: 36.0%, humanities: 23.8%, education: 15.0%, natural sciences and others: 25.1%

29. False

Using Technology Exercises 9.1, page 508

1. $X_5 = \begin{bmatrix} .204489 \\ .131869 \\ .261028 \\ .186814 \\ .215800 \end{bmatrix}$

3. Manufacturer A will have 23.95% of the market share, Manufacturer B will have 49.71% of the market share, and Manufacturer C will have 26.34% of the market share.

Exercises 9.2, page 514

1. Regular   3. Not regular   5. Regular

7. Not regular   9. $\begin{bmatrix} \frac{3}{11} \\ \frac{8}{11} \end{bmatrix}$ 11. $\begin{bmatrix} \frac{2}{7} \\ \frac{5}{7} \end{bmatrix}$

13. $\begin{bmatrix} \frac{3}{13} \\ \frac{8}{13} \\ \frac{2}{13} \end{bmatrix}$ 15. $\begin{bmatrix} \frac{3}{19} \\ \frac{8}{19} \\ \frac{8}{19} \end{bmatrix}$ 17. 81.8%

19. 40.8% one wage earner and 59.2% two wage earners; 30% one wage earner and 70% two wage earners

21. 72.5% in single-family homes and 27.5% in condominiums; 70% in single-family homes and 30% in condominiums

23. **a.** 31.7% ABC, 37.35% CBS, 30.95% NBC
b. $33\frac{1}{3}$% ABC, $33\frac{1}{3}$% CBS, $33\frac{1}{3}$% NBC

25. 25% red, 50% pink, 25% white   27. False

Using Technology Exercises 9.2, page 518

1. $X_5 = \begin{bmatrix} .2045 \\ .1319 \\ .2610 \\ .1868 \\ .2158 \end{bmatrix}$

Exercises 9.3, page 524

1. Yes   3. Yes   5. Yes   7. Yes

9. $\begin{bmatrix} 1 & .4 \\ 0 & .6 \end{bmatrix}$, $R = [.6]$, and $S = [.4]$

11. $\begin{bmatrix} 1 & .4 & .5 \\ 0 & .4 & .5 \\ 0 & .2 & 0 \end{bmatrix}$, $R = \begin{bmatrix} .4 & .5 \\ .2 & 0 \end{bmatrix}$, and $S = \begin{bmatrix} .4 & .5 \end{bmatrix}$, or

$\begin{bmatrix} 1 & .5 & .4 \\ 0 & 0 & .2 \\ 0 & .5 & .4 \end{bmatrix}$, $R = \begin{bmatrix} 0 & .2 \\ .5 & .4 \end{bmatrix}$, and $S = \begin{bmatrix} .5 & .4 \end{bmatrix}$

13. $\begin{bmatrix} 1 & 0 & .2 & .4 \\ 0 & 1 & .3 & 0 \\ 0 & 0 & .3 & .2 \\ 0 & 0 & .2 & .4 \end{bmatrix}$,

$R = \begin{bmatrix} .3 & .2 \\ .2 & .4 \end{bmatrix}$ and $S = \begin{bmatrix} .2 & .4 \\ .3 & 0 \end{bmatrix}$, or

$\begin{bmatrix} 1 & 0 & .4 & .2 \\ 0 & 1 & 0 & .3 \\ 0 & 0 & .4 & .2 \\ 0 & 0 & .2 & .3 \end{bmatrix}$,

$R = \begin{bmatrix} .4 & .2 \\ .2 & .3 \end{bmatrix}$, $S = \begin{bmatrix} .4 & .2 \\ 0 & .3 \end{bmatrix}$, and so forth

15. $\begin{bmatrix} 1 & 1 \\ 0 & 0 \end{bmatrix}$ 17. $\begin{bmatrix} 1 & 1 & 1 \\ 0 & 0 & 0 \\ 0 & 0 & 0 \end{bmatrix}$

19. $\begin{bmatrix} 1 & 0 & 1 & 1 \\ 0 & 1 & 0 & 0 \\ 0 & 0 & 0 & 0 \\ 0 & 0 & 0 & 0 \end{bmatrix}$ 21. $\begin{bmatrix} 1 & 0 & \frac{1}{2} & \frac{1}{2} \\ 0 & 1 & \frac{1}{2} & \frac{1}{2} \\ 0 & 0 & 0 & 0 \\ 0 & 0 & 0 & 0 \end{bmatrix}$

23. $\begin{bmatrix} 1 & 0 & 0 & \frac{7}{22} & \frac{3}{11} \\ 0 & 1 & 0 & \frac{5}{22} & \frac{9}{22} \\ 0 & 0 & 1 & \frac{5}{11} & \frac{7}{22} \\ 0 & 0 & 0 & 0 & 0 \\ 0 & 0 & 0 & 0 & 0 \end{bmatrix}$

25. **a.** $\begin{array}{c} \\ B \\ D \end{array} \begin{array}{cc} B & D \\ \end{array}$ $\begin{bmatrix} 1 & .2 \\ 0 & .8 \end{bmatrix}$, $R = \begin{bmatrix} .8 \end{bmatrix}$, and $S = \begin{bmatrix} .2 \end{bmatrix}$

b. $\begin{bmatrix} 1 & 1 \\ 0 & 0 \end{bmatrix}$; eventually, only broadband Internet service will be used.

27. .25; .50; .75

29. **a.** $\begin{array}{cccc} & D & G & 1 & 2 \end{array}$
$\begin{array}{c} D \\ G \\ 1 \\ 2 \end{array} \begin{bmatrix} 1 & 0 & .25 & .1 \\ 0 & 1 & 0 & .9 \\ 0 & 0 & 0 & 0 \\ 0 & 0 & .75 & 0 \end{bmatrix}$

b. $\begin{bmatrix} 1 & 0 & .325 & .1 \\ 0 & 1 & .675 & .9 \\ 0 & 0 & 0 & 0 \\ 0 & 0 & 0 & 0 \end{bmatrix}$

c. .675

31. False

Exercises 9.4, page 534

1. *R*: row 1; *C*: column 2   3. *R*: row 1; *C*: column 1

5. *R*: row 1 or row 3; *C*: column 3

7. *R*: row 1 or row 3; *C*: column 2

9. Strictly determined;
   a. 2   **b.** *R*: row 1; *C*: column 1
   c. 2   **d.** Favors row player

11. Strictly determined;
   a. 1   **b.** *R*: row 1; *C*: column 1
   c. 1   **d.** Favors row player

13. Strictly determined;
   a. 1   **b.** *R*: row 1; *C*: column 1
   c. 1   **d.** Favors row player

15. Not strictly determined   17. Not strictly determined

19. **a.** $\begin{bmatrix} 2 & -3 & 4 \\ -3 & 4 & -5 \\ 4 & -5 & 6 \end{bmatrix}$

   b. Robin: row 1; Cathy: column 1 or column 2
   c. Not strictly determined
   d. Not strictly determined

21. **a.**

	Economy	
	Good	Recess.
Mgmt. Expand	200,000	120,000
Not exp.	50,000	150,000

   b. Yes

23. **a.**

	Charley		
	Raises	Holds	Lowers
Roland Raises	3	−1	−3
Holds	2	0	−2
Lowers	5	2	1

25. True

Exercises 9.5, page 544

1. $\dfrac{3}{10}$ 3. $\dfrac{5}{12}$ 5. 0.16

7. **a.** 1   **b.** −2   **c.** 0

   d. −.3; (a) is most advantageous

9. **a.** 1   **b.** −.35   **c.** The first pair of strategies

11. $P = \begin{bmatrix} \frac{1}{4} & \frac{3}{4} \end{bmatrix}$, $Q = \begin{bmatrix} \frac{1}{2} \\ \frac{1}{2} \end{bmatrix}$, and $E = 2.5$; favors row player

13. $P = \begin{bmatrix} \frac{4}{7} & \frac{3}{7} \end{bmatrix}$, $Q = \begin{bmatrix} \frac{5}{7} \\ \frac{2}{7} \end{bmatrix}$, and $E = -\frac{1}{7}$; favors column player

15. $P = \begin{bmatrix} \frac{1}{2} & \frac{1}{2} \end{bmatrix}$, $Q = \begin{bmatrix} \frac{1}{4} \\ \frac{3}{4} \end{bmatrix}$, and $E = -5$; favors column player

17. **a.** $P = \begin{bmatrix} \frac{1}{3} & \frac{2}{3} \end{bmatrix}$ and $Q = \begin{bmatrix} \frac{1}{3} \\ \frac{2}{3} \end{bmatrix}$

   b. $E = 0$; no

19. **a.** $5714 in hotel stock; $34,286 in brewery stock
   b. $4857

21. a.

$$\begin{array}{c} & \text{C} \\ & \begin{array}{cc} \text{N} & \text{F} \end{array} \\ \text{R} \quad \begin{array}{c} \text{N} \\ \text{F} \end{array} & \begin{bmatrix} .48 & .65 \\ .50 & .45 \end{bmatrix} \end{array}$$

C = Carlton; R = Russell
N = local newspaper; F = flier

b. Russell's strategy: $P \approx [.23 \quad .77]$

Carlton's strategy: $Q \approx \begin{bmatrix} .91 \\ .09 \end{bmatrix}$

Chapter 9 Concept Review Questions, page 547

1. probabilities; preceding   2. state; state

3. transition   4. $n \times n$; nonnegative; 1

5. Distribution; steady-state

6. Regular; columns; equal; positive; $TX = X$; elements; 1

7. absorbing; leave; steps

8. **a.** zero-sum   **b.** maximin; minimax   9. optimal

10. saddle point; maximin; row; saddle; minimax; column; saddle

Chapter 9 Review Exercises, page 548

1. Not regular   2. Regular

3. Regular   4. Not regular

5. $\begin{bmatrix} .3675 \\ .36 \\ .2725 \end{bmatrix}$ 6. $\begin{bmatrix} .1915 \\ .4215 \\ .387 \end{bmatrix}$

7. Yes   8. No   9. No   10. Yes

11. $\begin{bmatrix} \frac{3}{7} & \frac{3}{7} \\ \frac{4}{7} & \frac{4}{7} \end{bmatrix}$ 12. $\begin{bmatrix} \frac{4}{9} & \frac{4}{9} \\ \frac{5}{9} & \frac{5}{9} \end{bmatrix}$

13. $\begin{bmatrix} .457 & .457 & .457 \\ .200 & .200 & .200 \\ .343 & .343 & .343 \end{bmatrix}$ 14. $\begin{bmatrix} .323 & .323 & .323 \\ .290 & .290 & .290 \\ .387 & .387 & .387 \end{bmatrix}$

15. a.

$$\begin{array}{c} & \begin{array}{ccc} \text{A} & \text{U} & \text{N} \end{array} \\ \begin{array}{c} \text{A} \\ \text{U} \\ \text{N} \end{array} & \begin{bmatrix} .85 & 0 & .10 \\ .10 & .95 & .05 \\ .05 & .05 & .85 \end{bmatrix} \end{array}$$

A = Agriculture
U = Urban
N = Nonagricultural

b. $\begin{array}{c} \text{A} \\ \text{U} \\ \text{N} \end{array} \begin{bmatrix} .50 \\ .15 \\ .35 \end{bmatrix}$ **c.** $\begin{array}{c} \text{A} \\ \text{U} \\ \text{N} \end{array} \begin{bmatrix} .424 \\ .262 \\ .314 \end{bmatrix}$

16. 12.5% large cars, 30.36% intermediate cars, 57.14% small cars

17. Strictly determined; R: row 3; C: column 1; value is 4.

18. Strictly determined; R: row 1; C: column 2; value is 0.

19. Strictly determined; R: row 1; C: column 1; value is 1.

20. Not strictly determined

21. $-\frac{1}{4}$ 22. $\frac{10}{9}$ 23. 2   24. 1.04

25. $P = [\frac{1}{2} \quad \frac{1}{2}]$, $Q = \begin{bmatrix} \frac{5}{6} \\ \frac{1}{6} \end{bmatrix}$, and $E = \frac{1}{2}$; favors row player

26. $P = [\frac{1}{2} \quad \frac{1}{2}]$, $Q = \begin{bmatrix} \frac{13}{22} \\ \frac{9}{22} \end{bmatrix}$, and $E = -\frac{1}{2}$, favors column player

27. $P = [\frac{1}{10} \quad \frac{9}{10}]$, $Q = \begin{bmatrix} \frac{4}{5} \\ \frac{1}{5} \end{bmatrix}$, and $E = 1.2$; favors row player

28. $P = [\frac{4}{5} \quad \frac{1}{5}]$, $Q = \begin{bmatrix} \frac{2}{5} \\ \frac{3}{5} \end{bmatrix}$, and $E = 10.8$; favors row player

29. a. $\begin{bmatrix} .5 & .7 \\ .4 & .5 \end{bmatrix}$ **b.** $7

30. 25% compact models; 75% subcompact models

Chapter 9 Before Moving On, page 549

1. $\begin{bmatrix} .366 \\ .634 \end{bmatrix}$ 2. $\begin{bmatrix} \frac{3}{11} \\ \frac{8}{11} \end{bmatrix}$ 3. $\begin{bmatrix} 1 & 1 & 1 \\ 0 & 0 & 0 \\ 0 & 0 & 0 \end{bmatrix}$

4. **a.** -1 **b.** R: row 1; C; column 3   **c.** -1; column player

5. **a.** 3 units   **b.** 1.22 units

6. **a.** $P = [\frac{2}{3} \quad \frac{1}{3}]$, $Q = \begin{bmatrix} \frac{1}{6} \\ \frac{5}{6} \end{bmatrix}$ **b.** $\frac{4}{3}$; row player

APPENDIX A

Exercises A.1, page 555

1. Yes   3. Yes   5. No

7. Yes   9. Yes   11. No

13. No   15. Negation   17. Conjunction

19. Conjunction

21. New orders for manufactured goods did not fall last month.

23. Drinking during pregnancy does not affect both the size and weight of babies.

25. The commuter airline industry is not now undergoing a shakeup.

27. **a.** Domestic car sales increased over the past year, or foreign car sales decreased over the past year, or both.
    b. Domestic car sales increased over the past year, and foreign car sales decreased over the past year.
    c. Either domestic car sales increased over the past year or foreign car sales decreased over the past year.
    d. Domestic car sales did not increase over the past year.
    e. Domestic car sales did not increase over the past year, or foreign car sales decreased over the past year, or both.
    f. Domestic car sales did not increase over the past year, or foreign car sales did not decrease over the past year, or both.

29. **a.** Either the doctor recommended surgery to treat Sam's hyperthyroidism or the doctor recommended radioactive iodine to treat Sam's hyperthyroidism.
    b. The doctor recommended surgery to treat Sam's hyperthyroidism, or the doctor recommended radioactive iodine to treat Sam's hyperthyroidism, or both.

31. **a.** $p \wedge q$ **b.** $p \veebar q$ **c.** $\sim p \wedge \sim q$ **d.** $\sim(\sim q)$

33. **a.** Both the popularity of prime-time soaps and the popularity of prime-time situation comedies did not increase this year.
    b. The popularity of prime-time soaps did not increase this year, or the popularity of prime-time detective shows decreased this year, or both.
    c. The popularity of prime-time detective shows decreased this year, or the popularity of prime-time situation comedies did not increase this year, or both.

d. Either the popularity of prime-time soaps did not increase this year or the popularity of prime-time situation comedies did not increase this year.

Exercises A.2, page 558

1.

p	q	$\sim q$	$p \vee \sim q$
T	T	F	T
T	F	T	T
F	T	F	F
F	F	T	T

3.

p	$\sim p$	$\sim(\sim p)$
T	F	T
F	T	F

5.

p	$\sim p$	$p \vee \sim p$
T	F	T
F	T	T

7.

p	q	$\sim p$	$p \vee q$	$\sim p \wedge (p \vee q)$
T	T	F	T	F
T	F	F	T	F
F	T	T	T	T
F	F	T	F	F

9.

p	q	$\sim q$	$p \vee q$	$p \wedge \sim q$	$(p \vee q) \wedge (p \wedge \sim q)$
T	T	F	T	F	F
T	F	T	T	T	T
F	T	F	T	F	F
F	F	T	F	F	F

11.

p	q	$p \vee q$	$\sim(p \vee q)$	$(p \vee q) \wedge \sim(p \vee q)$
T	T	T	F	F
T	F	T	F	F
F	T	T	F	F
F	F	F	T	F

13.

p	q	r	$p \vee q$	$p \vee r$	$(p \vee q) \wedge (p \vee r)$
T	T	T	T	T	T
T	T	F	T	T	T
T	F	T	T	T	T
T	F	F	T	T	T
F	T	T	T	T	T
F	T	F	T	F	F
F	F	T	F	T	F
F	F	F	F	F	F

15.

p	q	r	$p \wedge q$	$\sim r$	$(p \wedge q) \vee \sim r$
T	T	T	T	F	T
T	T	F	T	T	T
T	F	T	F	F	F
T	F	F	F	T	T
F	T	T	F	F	F
F	T	F	F	T	T
F	F	T	F	F	F
F	F	F	F	T	T

17.

p	q	r	$\sim q$	$p \wedge \sim q$	$p \wedge r$	$(p \wedge \sim q) \vee (p \wedge r)$
T	T	T	F	F	T	T
T	T	F	F	F	F	F
T	F	T	T	T	T	T
T	F	F	T	T	F	T
F	T	T	F	F	F	F
F	T	F	F	F	F	F
F	F	T	T	F	F	F
F	F	F	T	F	F	F

19. 16 rows

Exercises A.3, page 562

1. $\sim q \to p$; $q \to \sim p$; $\sim p \to q$

3. $p \to q$; $\sim p \to \sim q$; $\sim q \to \sim p$

5. Conditional: If it is snowing, then the temperature is below freezing. Biconditional: It is snowing if and only if the temperature is below freezing.

7. Conditional: If the company's union and management reach a settlement, then the workers do not strike. Biconditional: The company's union and management will reach a settlement if and only if the workers do not strike.

9. False   **11.** False

13. It is false when I do not buy the house after the owner lowers the selling price.

15.

p	q	$p \to q$	$\sim(p \to q)$
T	T	T	F
T	F	F	T
F	T	T	F
F	F	T	F

17.

p	q	$p \to q$	$\sim(p \to q)$	$\sim(p \to q) \wedge p$
T	T	T	F	F
T	F	F	T	T
F	T	T	F	F
F	F	T	F	F

19.

p	q	$\sim p$	$\sim q$	$p \to \sim q$	$(p \to \sim q) \underline{\vee} \sim p$
T	T	F	F	F	F
T	F	F	T	T	T
F	T	T	F	T	F
F	F	T	T	T	F

21.

p	q	$\sim p$	$\sim q$	$p \to q$	$\sim q \to \sim p$	$(p \to q) \leftrightarrow (\sim q \to \sim p)$
T	T	F	F	T	T	T
T	F	F	T	F	F	T
F	T	T	F	T	T	T
F	F	T	T	T	T	T

23.

p	q	$p \wedge q$	$p \vee q$	$(p \wedge q) \to (p \vee q)$
T	T	T	T	T
T	F	F	T	T
F	T	F	T	T
F	F	F	F	T

25.

p	q	r	$p \vee q$	$\sim r$	$(p \vee q) \to \sim r$
T	T	T	T	F	F
T	T	F	T	T	T
T	F	T	T	F	F
T	F	F	T	T	T
F	T	T	T	F	F
F	F	T	T	F	T
F	F	F	F	T	T

27.

p	q	r	$q \vee r$	$p \to (q \vee r)$
T	T	T	T	T
T	T	F	T	T
T	F	T	T	T
T	F	F	F	F
F	T	T	T	T
F	T	F	T	T
F	F	T	T	T
F	F	F	F	T

29. Logically equivalent

31. Logically equivalent

33. Not logically equivalent

35. Not logically equivalent

37. **a.** $p \to \sim q$　　**b.** $\sim p \to q$　　**c.** $\sim q \leftrightarrow p$

d. $p \to \sim q$　　**e.** $p \leftrightarrow \sim q$

Exercises A.4, page 566

1.

p	p	$p \wedge p$
T	T	T
F	F	F

3.

p	q	r	$p \wedge q$
T	T	T	T
T	T	F	T
T	F	T	F
T	F	F	F
F	T	T	F
F	T	F	F
F	F	T	F
F	F	F	F

$(p \wedge q) \wedge r$	$q \wedge r$	$p \wedge (q \wedge r)$
T	T	T
F	F	F
F	F	F
F	F	F
F	T	F
F	F	F
F	F	F
F	F	F

5.

p	q	$p \wedge q$	$q \wedge p$
T	T	T	T
T	F	F	F
F	T	F	F
F	F	F	F

7.

p	q	r	$q \wedge r$	$p \vee (q \wedge r)$
T	T	T	T	T
T	T	F	F	T
T	F	T	F	T
T	F	F	F	T
F	T	T	T	T
F	T	F	F	F
F	F	T	F	F
F	F	F	F	F

$p \vee q$	$p \vee r$	$(p \vee q) \wedge (p \vee r)$
T	T	T
T	T	T
T	T	T
T	T	T
T	F	F
F	T	F
F	F	F

9. Tautology　　**11.** Tautology　　**13.** Tautology

15. Tautology　　**17.** Neither

19. $\sim(p \wedge q)$: The candidate does not oppose changes in the Social Security system, or the candidate does not support immigration reform.

$\sim(p \vee q)$: The candidate does not oppose changes in the Social Security system, and the candidate does not support immigration reform.

21. $[p \wedge (q \vee \sim q) \vee (p \wedge q)]$
$\Leftrightarrow p \wedge t \vee (p \wedge q)]$　　By Law 11
$\Leftrightarrow p \vee (p \wedge q)$　　By Law 14

23. $(p \wedge \sim q) \vee (p \wedge \sim r)$
$\Leftrightarrow p \wedge (\sim q \vee \sim r)$　　By Law 7

25. $(p \wedge \sim(q \wedge r)$
$\Leftrightarrow p \wedge (\sim q \vee \sim r)$　　By Law 10
$\Leftrightarrow (p \wedge \sim q) \vee (p \wedge \sim r)$　　By Law 7

Exercises A.5, page 571

1. Valid　　**3.** Valid　　**5.** Invalid　　**7.** Valid

9. Valid　　**11.** Valid　　**13.** Valid　　**15.** Invalid

17. $p \to q$; invalid　　　**19.** $p \vee q$; valid
　　$\sim p$　　　　　　　　　　$\sim p \to \sim q$
　　$\therefore \sim q$　　　　　　　　　$\therefore p$

21. $p \to q$; invalid
　　$q \to r$
　　r
　　$\therefore p$

Exercises A.6, page 574

1. $p \wedge q \wedge (r \vee s)$

3. $[(p \wedge q) \vee r] \wedge (\sim r \vee p)$

5. $[(p \vee q) \wedge r] \vee (\sim p) \vee [\sim q \wedge (p \vee r \vee \sim r)]$

7.

9.

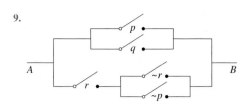

11.

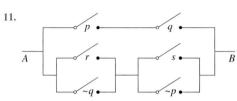

13. $p \wedge [\sim q \vee (\sim p \wedge q)]; p \wedge \sim q$

15. $p \wedge [\sim p \vee q \vee (q \wedge r)]; p \wedge q$

APPENDIX C

Exercises, page 585

1. $\log_2 64 = 6$ 3. $\log_3 \frac{1}{9} = -2$ 5. $\log_{32} 8 = \frac{3}{5}$

7. 1.0792   9. 1.2042   11. $\ln a^2 b^3$

13. $\ln \dfrac{3\sqrt{x}\, y}{\sqrt[3]{z}}$ 15. $x = 8$ 17. $x = 10$

19. $x = \frac{3}{2}$ 21. $x = \frac{11}{3}$ 23. 5.1986

25. -0.0912 27. -8.0472 29. -4.9041

INDEX

Appendix E

"Suppose you are walking where there is no regular path, as long as everything goes smoothly, you do not have to think about your walking. Suddenly you find a ditch in your way. You think you will jump it (plan); but to make sure, you survey it with your eyes (observation), and you find it is pretty wide and that the bank is slippery (data). You then wonder if the ditch may not be narrower somewhere else (idea), and you look up and down the stream (observation) to see how matters stand (test of ideas by observation). You do not find any good place and so are thrown back upon forming a new plan. You discover a log (fact, again). You ask yourself whether you could not haul that to the ditch and get it across the ditch to use as a bridge (idea, again). So you get the log and manage to put it in place and walk across (test and confirmation by overt action)." (Dewey, 1939)

FIVE POINTS FOR GOOD PROBLEM SOLVING

1. **Positive Attitude**—Idea that problems can be solved through careful, persistent analysis. Poor problem solvers express the opinion "either you know the answer or you don't and if you don't you might as well give up.

2. **Concern for Accuracy**—Understand the facts and relationships fully. Reread the problem several times.

3. **Breaking the Problem into Parts**—Break into smaller steps. Start at a point where you can make some sense of it and proceed.

4. **Avoid Wild Guessing**—Avoid jumping to conclusions without going through the necessary steps to make sure the conclusions are accurate.

5. **Activeness in Problem Solving**—Good problem solvers do more things as they try to understand and answer difficult questions. Examples: Mental pictures, real diagrams, viewing the problem or terms with familiar experiences and concrete examples, ask questions, "talk to themselves" to clarify thoughts.

PROBLEM-SOLVING SKILLS

The following chart gives the steps necessary that one needs to take to successfully solve a problem in mathematics. Under each step are some subskills or strategies that need to be developed.

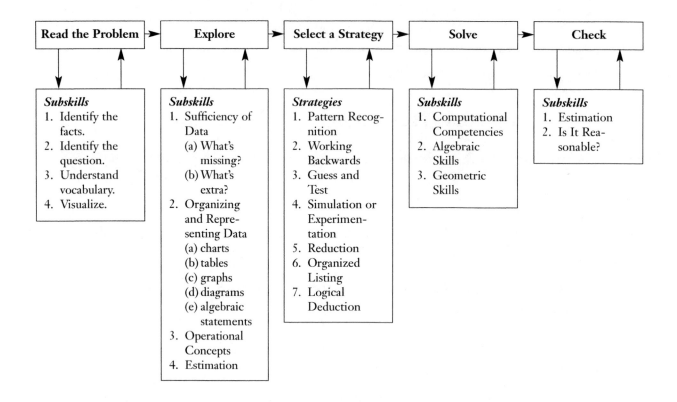

Subskills
1. Identify the facts.
2. Identify the question.
3. Understand vocabulary.
4. Visualize.

Subskills
1. Sufficiency of Data
   (a) What's missing?
   (b) What's extra?
2. Organizing and Representing Data
   (a) charts
   (b) tables
   (c) graphs
   (d) diagrams
   (e) algebraic statements
3. Operational Concepts
4. Estimation

Strategies
1. Pattern Recognition
2. Working Backwards
3. Guess and Test
4. Simulation or Experimentation
5. Reduction
6. Organized Listing
7. Logical Deduction

Subskills
1. Computational Competencies
2. Algebraic Skills
3. Geometric Skills

Subskills
1. Estimation
2. Is It Reasonable?

From: *A Sourcebook for Teaching Problem Solving* by Stephen Krulik and Jesse A. Rudnick

BECOMING MATH LEARNERS

Beginnings of a Math Course
1. Ask and record, instructor's office hours and phone numbers.
2. Join a study group that meets regularly.
3. Find all the resources on campus that will support the learner in the math class; use the Academic Support Center, other students, and the instructor as sources of information.
4. Search our math books in the library that relate to the math course you are taking.

In the Classroom
1. Attend every class.
2. Read ahead so that you have an idea of what the instructor will be teaching in class.
3. Keep up with the instructor in class, writing only important things in your notes.
4. Ask questions.
5. Do the "Making Connections" strategy at the end of class.

Doing Assignments
1. Read the text, nothing new terms and studying the examples.
2. Read your class notes and jot down any questions.
3. When you get "stuck" on a problem:
   a. Don't give up.
   b. Use all your resources.
   c. Work through a similar example.
   d. Ask your instructor, a classmate, or find some other resource before the next class.

Taking a Math Test

Pre:
- Follow the suggestions given above.
- Be sure you have been able to do each assignment.
- Reverse the time factor. Give yourself a little less time at home than you would have in the exam.
- Compile a set of index cards. Use the concepts you listed in the "Making Connections" strategy. They can act as "Cue Cards" by writing a formula definition, or a problem on the front and the answer on the back. Be sure to number the cards and then mix them up to test yourself.

During:
- Write something as soon as you get the test, such as definition, formula, or rule.
- Survey the test and budget your time. Begin the test working on problems with which you are secure. Remember, you do not need to work the test in the order that the problems appear.
- If you begin to tense up, practice some relaxation exercises such as forgetting the test for a few moments and thinking of a pleasant experience. This is not a waste of time; but it puts you back in control of the test-taking situation.

Post: Analyze the test.
         Did the content of the test come from:
         1. Class notes
         2. Assignments
         3. Textbook
         Did your errors come from:
         1. Carelessness
         2. Unknown material
         This will help you to prepare for the next exam.

TIPS ON USING YOUR MATH TEXTBOOK

Your math textbook is a very valuable tool. Used wisely, it can help you build strong mathematical skills. Here are some suggestions of things you can do that will help you get the maximum benefit out of your book:

1. **Skim.** Each time your instructor assigns you a new section of material, begin your study by skimming through that section in your book to get a feel for what is being presented.

2. **Read.** Then read the section slowly, concentrating on understanding the material.

3. **Reread.** Reread the section one or more times until you have mastered it.

4. **List Questions.** As you read, make a list of questions about things that are not clear to you. If you seek assistance from a teacher or tutor, having a list of specific trouble items will greatly aid that person in knowing how to help you.

5. **Use Cards.** On 3" x 5" cards record new terms and definitions, formulas, points emphasized in the text, sample problems, and anything that you find difficult and need to work on more. You may want to put on cards one example for each type of problem that you study. Regular review of the cards will aid your mastery of the material. The cards can be reviewed during your odd moments of time such as while you are waiting for a class to begin. Reviewing the cards in an excellent way to prepare for a quiz or an exam.

6. **Work Sample Problems.** Work through sample problems for yourself. Simply reading them will not give you the depth of comprehension that actually doing them will.

7. **Work Exercise Problems.** Work through the exercise problems. When you have finished the problems, check your answers against those which the book provides. This will give you feedback on whether you are doing the problems correctly. Avoid looking at the answers until you have finished the problems. If you have a problem you can't solve, work it out as much as you can, then look up the correct answer. The answer may give you a clue as to what is missing in your problem-solving process. Attempt to rework the problem, making whatever changes are necessary. Work problems until you understand them.

8. **Read Ahead.** Read ahead in your text. Become familiar with each section of material before your teacher presents it in class. By doing this, it will be easier for your to follow your teacher's instruction. You will also be prepared to ask questions which might not arise until you start to do your homework.

9. **Know Your Text.** Review the table of contents and thumb through your text to find out what's in it. Many texts include a glossary and/or tables of numbers which may be very useful to you.

STUDY QUESTIONS

Below are some questions that you may use when you complete your homework assignment. Too often students "do" the problems, get the correct answers and don't stop to see where the concepts fit with other concepts previously learned. The following questions should help in encouraging this type of thinking.

1. What are the different kinds of problems and how can they be recognized? Is it the format of the problem or the directions which will indicate the specific technique to be used?

2. How are these different problems related? (Or are they?)

3. What other versions are possible for this type of problem? How can this problem be restated?

4. What are the different ways in which the directions can be worded and still mean the same thing?

5. What changes in the wording of the directions indicate different procedures?

6. Is there only one method to work this type of problem or are several techniques applicable? If several techniques are appropriate, how does one choose which to use? (Or does it matter?)

7. What means (if any) are available to check your answer other than reworking the problem in the same way?

8. How are the problems from this section/chapter different from the problems of previous sections/chapters?

9. How are the problems from this section/chapter like the problems of previous sections/chapters?

*Remember: The most important part of doing your assignments is to have a better idea of the **process**, not the answers.*

Taken from *Studying Mathematics* by Hudspeth & Hirsch

STUDY STRATEGIES

Directions: Check (✔) if you tried strategy and circle how helpful you found it. Note courses for which you use the strategy.

	Helpful?	
	Yes	No

I. Time Management

   A. Use daily "To Do" lists

	Yes	No
1. Prioritize. Do "high priority" items.	—	—
2. Be specific with study tasks.	—	—
3. Set realistic goals.	—	—
4. Cross off completed tasks.	—	—

   B. Keep a present work and recreation schedule.

	Yes	No
1. Keep track of what you do for one week.	—	—
2. Outline blocks of class time.	—	—
3. Be specific with study times.	—	—
4. Be specific with free time.	—	—
5. Evaluate schedule.	—	—
— Add up study times for each subject.	—	—
— Block off times you could have used for study.	—	—
— Check balance in schedule.	—	—
6. Set up proposed schedule.	—	—
— Set aside regular study hours.	—	—
— Plan at least one hour blocks of study time.	—	—
— Reward yourself for study efforts.	—	—
— Schedule study periods before and after class.	—	—
— Work on difficult subjects when you are alert.	—	—
— Keep schedule flexible. You may need to revise it.	—	—

   C. Use a calendar for long-range planning.

	Yes	No
1. Put all exams and quizzes on calendar.	—	—
2. Include deadlines for assignments	—	—
3. Include social functions, meetings, etc.	—	—
4. Use the "Swiss Cheese Method" to organize reviews.	—	—
— List specific tasks to complete (on back to calendar).	—	—
— Put these tasks on calendar.	—	—
— Alternate subjects.	—	—

II. Textbook Reading (SQ3R)

A. Survey
1. Read title, introduction. ___ ___
2. Read headings, subheadings. Think about relationships. ___ ___
3. Read first sentences of paragraphs. ___ ___
4. Read italicized words. ___ ___
5. Look at pictures, charts, graphs. ___ ___
6. Read summary. ___ ___
7. Read end-of-chapter questions. ___ ___

B. Question
1. Use headings and subheadings to make up questions. ___ ___
— Use newspaper questions: Who? What? Where? When? Why? How? How much? ___ ___
— A large section may require more than one question. ___ ___
— Give yourself the license to change your question if you think of a better one. ___ ___
2. If there are no headings, use topic sentences of paragraphs to formulate questions. ___ ___

C. Read to answer your questions. Do not underline. Yet. ___ ___

D. Recite
1. Test yourself on the material. ___ ___
2. Answer the questions of review main ideas in Sections. ___ ___

E. Review
1. Put it all together. ___ ___
2. Try to recall main ideas or answers to questions. ___ ___
3. Reread sections if necessary. ___ ___
4. Underline or highlight important points and support. ___ ___

III. Notetaking

A. Before the lecture
1. Read text material for background or preview material. ___ ___
2. Check course outline. ___ ___
3. Know terminology. ___ ___
4. Use outside materials for support. ___ ___
5. Review previous notes. ___ ___
6. Discuss material with othes. ___ ___

B. During the lecture
1. Sit near instructor   —— ——
2. Listen attentively   —— ——
3. Record notes as follows:
 — Date (top of page).   —— ——
 — Topic (top of page).   —— ——
 — Write certain items exactly (quotes, definitions, formulas).   —— ——
 — Use own words.   —— ——
 — Be selective. Use key words and phrases.   —— ——
 — Use abbreviations.   —— ——
 — Include examples.   —— ——
 — Organize notes (indentation and spacing).   —— ——

C. After the lecture
1. Edit notes within 24 hours after class.   —— ——
 — Make corrections.   —— ——
 — Fill in gaps (details, examples, etc.).   —— ——
 — Add cue words or phrases   —— ——
 — Predict test questions from main points.   —— ——
 — Summarize lecture in a sentence or two.   —— ——
2. Recite from notes, using cue phrases.   —— ——
3. Coordinate notes with text.   —— ——

IV. Other Study Suggestions

A. Use cue cards (3" × 5" or 4" × 6")
1. Put part of information on front of card.   —— ——
2. Put remainder of information on back.   —— ——
3. Use for definitions, dates, vocabulary, formulas.   —— ——
4. Can divide packs according to those you know/don't know.   —— ——
5. Can use cards effectively in short blocks of time.   —— ——

B. Use the "Summary Sheet System." Condense the material.
1. Use for material that is interrelated or connected/that needs to be learned as a whole.   —— ——
 — Theories/principles   —— ——
 — Causes/effects   —— ——
 — Pros and cons   —— ——
 — Summaries   —— ——
 — Groups of related facts.   —— ——
2. Select information to be learned.   —— ——
3. Outline information. Group important points that relate to each topic.   —— ——
4. Test yourself on material. Use recall cues (marginal phrases or headings in outline).   —— ——

C. Study with someone
1. Review material first (text, notes, cards, summary sheets). ___ ___
2. Predict test questions.
    — Make note of formulas, definitions, examples. ___ ___
    — Text (headings, subheadings, summaries, end-of-chapter questions. ___ ___
    — Clues from instructor/TA. ___ ___
    — Clues from past quizzes, exams. ___ ___
    — Clues from other students. ___ ___
    — Study guides. ___ ___
3. Test each other. ___ ___
4. Fill in gaps for each other. ___ ___

D. Get tutoring
1. Clarify questions, gaps, problems. ___ ___
2. Focus on what is important. ___ ___

E. Review old exams, quizzes
1. Check strengths. ___ ___
2. Check for patterns of errors. ___ ___
3. Analyze kinds of questions on test (broad, detailed, etc.). ___ ___

F. Put yourself in a testing situation. Practice like you will be tested.
1. Go over each type of problem. ___ ___
2. Do many problems. ___ ___
3. After predicting test questions for essay exam, set up mini-outlines for answering questions. Key word system is helpful. Organization is the key. ___ ___
4. Predict multiple-choice questions and answer them. ___ ___

G. Use techniques for effective memorization.
1. Organize material into meaningful sections or categories. ___ ___
    — Know the big picture (major ideas). ___ ___
    — Fit details into framework. ___ ___
2. Intend to remember. Attitude is crucial to effective memorization. ___ ___
3. Recite. Test yourself repeatedly on the material. ___ ___

HYPERGEOMETRIC RANDOM VARIABLES

Another type of random variable is the hypergeometric random variable. Following is an example.

Example: An office supply store receives a shipment of 20 chairs from a manufacturer. Each chair is in a box containing chair parts which the customer is expected to assemble. The store has had problems before with this manufacturer not including all the parts for each chair. The store manager asks an employee to open up 5 of the boxes to check whether all the parts are there. If two or more boxes are missing parts, the store will send the shipment back. If 6 of the 20 boxes in the shipment are missing parts, what is the probability the store will send the shipment back?

We have seen this type of problem earlier, in Example 3 on page 84, sec 2.4 exercises 9–12 and 18–22.

We let the random variable X be the number of boxes the employee opens which have missing parts. So the problem is asking for $P(X \geq 2)$. The random variable X above is an example of a hypergeometric random variable.

We can find $P(X = 3)$ for example by noting that since there are 6 bad boxes and 14 good boxes in the shipment, there are $C(6,3)$ ways of choosing 3 bad boxes and $C(14,2)$ ways of choosing 2 good boxes. So just as in Example 3 on page 84 we see

$$P(X = 3) = C(6,3) \cdot C(14,2) / C(20,5) \approx .1174$$

To find $P(X \geq 2) = P(X = 2) + P(X = 3) + P(X = 4) + P(X = 5)$, it is an easier computation to find $P(X < 2) = P(X = 0) + P(X = 1)$. So we compute

$$P(X = 0) = C(6,0) \cdot C(14,5)/C(20,5) \approx .1291$$

$$P(X = 1) = C(6,1) \cdot C(14,4)/C(20,5) \approx .3874$$

So $P(X \geq 2) = 1 - .1291 - .3874 = .4835$ and the probability the shipment will be returned is .4835.

Hypergeometric Experiment: Here is the general form of a hypergeometric random variable. Suppose there is a population of r objects of which g are "good" and b are "bad". (So $r = g + b$.) Suppose you choose n of the objects without replacement. Let the hypergeometric random variable X be the number of objects you chose which were "bad." Then

$$P(X = k) = C(b,k) \cdot C(g,n - k)/C(r,n)$$

Of course it is not necessary that the objects actually be good or bad, just that they are divided into two types. For example they could be boys and girls, or red marbles and green marbles, or Democrats and Republicans, or whatever. But often hypergeometric random variables occur when you are sampling to find defects so often the two types are literally good and bad.

Mean and variance of a hypergeometric random variable: It is possible to calculate the mean and variance of a hypergeometric random variable by the following formulae:

$$\mu, = E(X) = nb/r$$
$$\text{Var}(X) = (r - n)nbg/(r^2(r - 1))$$

Bionomial approximation: It is worth comparjng the. hypergeometric random variable to a similar binomial random variable. Suppose there is a population of r objects of which g are "good" and b are "bad." (So $r = g + b$.) Suppose you choose n of the objects with replacement. If Y is the number of "bad" objects chosen, then Y is a binomial random variable and $P(Y = k) = C(n,k)p^k q^{n-k}$ where $p = b/r$ and $q = g/r$. The only difference between Y and X is that the hypergeometric random variable X involved choosing without replacement and the binomial Y involved choosing with replacement. As a practical matter, if the population r is much bigger than the sample size n then the binomial random variable Y will be a reasonably good approximation of X. This was exploited in some of the problems: in section 8 of Tan.

Example: For example let us look again at Example 5 in section 8 of Tan. This involved sampling 20 solar cells from a large production run and finding the probability that 2 or fewer were defective. Since the production run was large, it was reasonable to solve the problem by assuming the number of defectives was a binomial random variable. The answers obtained were slightly inaccurate but the error was insignificant. But if the production run were smaller, say just 100 cells of which 5 were defective it would be better to use a hypergeometric random variable. Redoing this problem for a production run of only 100 cells of which 5 are defective we see that:

$$P(X = 0) = C(5,0) \cdot C(95,5)/C(100,5) \approx .3193$$
$$P(X = 1) = C(5,1) \cdot C(95,4)/C(100,5) \approx .4201$$
$$P(X = 2) = C(5,2) \cdot C(95,3)/C(100,5) \approx .2073$$

and so $P(X \le 2) \approx .3193 + .4201 + .2073 = 0.9467$. This compares with the answer .9246 obtained in 8 of Tan using the binomial approximation.

Winning at Blackjack: This difference between the hypergeometric and binomial random variable has been exploited to make a (rather complicated) system for beating the house playing the game of blackjack. The game of blackjack, as with many card games, is a card game where players are dealt cards from a deck. When the deck is exhausted the deck is reshuffled and cards are dealt from the reshuffled deck. Since cards are not replaced after dealing each hand, the dealt cards form a sample without replacement. However 1 casinos figure their odds for blackjack by using the binomial approximation, erroneously believing that they have set the odds so that they will always make money in the long run. But if a gambler uses a complicated system which exploits the difference between the hypergeometric and binomial random variables, his expected winnings are positive and he can expect to win money in the long run. For example if half the deck is dealt out but only one quarter of the aces have been dealt, the player knows that aces are more likely to be dealt in ensuing hands and can adjust his strategy accordingly. Don't get any ideas of quitting school and making a living playing blackjack though. Your expected winnings are small and if the casino. suspects you are using such a system you may be visited by a large person who requests you do your gambling elsewhere.

This is only the beginning: It is worth pointing out a bit of unreality in the problems we present here. The problems all assume the number b of bad objects is known. In reality, of course, you would not actually know this number b unless you sampled all r objects in the population, which is usually not feasible to do. For example, the customers of the office supply store might prefer to purchase an unopened box because they might suspect an opened box was returned for some reason. Also, the employees have more productive things to do than opening every single box of every single shipment and checking to see if it is okay.

In reality you most likely want to take the results of your small sample and use them to estimate the value of b. This is in effect what the store manager was doing. She figured that if there were 2 or more defectives in the sample of 5, then there were probably lots of defectives in the whole batch, enough to make it worthwhile to refuse the shipment. Using statistics it is possible to answer such questions as given that X = 2, what is the probability $b \geq 5$? This is beyond the scope of this course, but the ideas we present here are a prerequisite for finding the answer.

Self-Check Problems:
1. A bag with 15 jellybeans contains 3 Licorice flavored jelly beans. You pick 5 jellybeans from the bag at random and eat them.
   a) What is the expected number of licorice jellybeans you eat?
   b) What is the probability you eat less than 2 licorice jellybeans?
2. A shipment of 100 scooters contains 10 defective scooters. You test six scooters. Let X be the number of defective scooters you find. Find the mean, variance and, standard deviation of X.

Exercises
1. A box of a, dozen eggs contains two rotten eggs. You make a cake using three eggs from the box. Let X be the number of rotten eggs you use in your cake. Find the probability distribution for X and draw a histogram for X. Find the expected value and standard deviation of X.
2. Redo problems 36, 37, and 38 of section 8 using hype~geometric random variables. In 36a, 37, and 38 assume 2 of the 20 are defective, in 36b assume 1 of the 20 is defective.
3. Eighteen uncounted punch card ballots from a recent election are discovered under an election official's couch. Six of them have a dimpled chad. A reporter gets to sneak a peek at three of the ballots. Let X be the number of ballots with dimpled chads the reporter sees. Compute the probability distribution of X. What is the expected value of X? What is the standard deviation of X?
4. A six person committee is chosen at random from a class with 12 boys and 9 girls. What is the probability that there are 2 boys and 4 girls on the committee?
5. A bunch of grapes contains 60 grapes, of which 4 are rotten. You eat 6 of the grapes at random. Let X be the number of rotten grapes you eat.
   a) Find $P(X > 0)$ and $P(X \leq 4)$.
   b) Find the expected value, variance, and standard deviation of X.
6. The border patrol of a certain country randomly searches cars coming into the country for smuggled goods.
   a) In one hour, fifty cars pass a border checkpoint, ten of these cars are. smuggling goods and the border patrol selects five cars for a thorough search. What is the probability that two or more smuggler's cars are searched?
   b) The head border patrol officer at one checkpoint thinks for some reason that smugglers tend to drive flashy red convertibles. So he orders his officers to only select flashy red convertibles

for a search. In one hour, fifty cars pass the checkpoint, ten of these cars are smugglers, twelve are flashy red convertibles, and six smugglers are not driving flashy red convertibles. The border patrol selects five flashy red convertibles for a thorough search. What is the probability that two or more smuggler's cars are searched?

7. You are dealt 5 cards from a standard 52 card deck with 4 aces. Let X be the number of aces in your hand.

   a) What is $P(X \le 2)$?

   b) What is the probability your hand contains two or fewer aces?

   c) What is the' expected number of aces in your hand?

   d) Suppose you know that four other players have no aces in the hands they were dealt. What is the probability your hand contains two or fewer aces?

Answers to Self-Check Problems:

1. Let the random variable X be the number of licorice jellybeans you eat. Then X is hypergeometric random variable and

$$E(X) = 5 \cdot 3/15 = 1$$

so you expect to eat an average of one licorice jellybean.

$$P(X \le 2) = P(X = 0) + P(X = 1)$$
$$= C(3,0) \cdot C(12,5)/C(15,5) + C(3,1) \cdot C(12,4)/C(15,5)$$

$$\frac{3!}{0! \cdot 3!} \frac{12!}{5! \cdot 7!} \frac{5! \cdot 10!}{15!} + \frac{3!}{1! \cdot 2!} \frac{12!}{4! \cdot 8!} \frac{5! \cdot 10!}{15!}$$

$$= \frac{3!}{3!} \frac{5!}{5!} \frac{10!}{7!} \frac{12!}{15!} + \frac{3!}{2!} \frac{5!}{4!} \frac{10!}{8!} \frac{12!}{15!}$$

$$= \frac{10 \cdot 9 \cdot 8}{15 \cdot 14 \cdot 13} + \frac{3 \cdot 5 \cdot 10 \cdot 9}{15 \cdot 14 \cdot 13}$$

$$= \frac{720}{2730} + \frac{1350}{2730} = \frac{2070}{2730} \approx .7582$$

$$E(X) = 6 \cdot 10/100 = .6$$
$$\text{Var}(X) = (100 - 6) \cdot 6 \cdot 10 \cdot 90/(100 \cdot 100 \cdot 99) \approx .5127$$
$$(X) = \sqrt{\text{Var}(X)} = \sqrt{.5127} \approx .7160$$

EMPIRICAL PROBABILITIES—
AN INTRODUCTION TO STATISTICS
MATH III NOTES

Often in the news you will read such statements as 64% of the people believe such and such or 55% of the voting age population support some candidate. These are not exact figures, but they are estimates obtained by polling some segment of the population. They are examples of empirical probabilities (see section 7.2 of Tan). If someone asks 200 voters which candidate they prefer and 110 prefer Senator Small, then you figure the probability anyone will vote for Senator Small is 110/200 or 55%. But because of random variations this 55% might not be correct.

Example: Suppose 60% of the voting age population of a state prefer Senator Small in the next election. You ask 200 randomly chosen voting age people in the state which candidate they prefer. What is the probability that 55% or fewer of the people you ask support Senator Small?

Let the random variable X be the number of people you ask who support Senator Small. Let the random variable Y be the proportion of the people you ask who support Senator Small. Then $Y = X/200$. Now X is a binomial random variable which we may approximate by the normal random variable

$$X \approx 200(.6) + \sqrt{200(.6)(.4)}\, Z = 120 + 6.928Z$$

But then Y is also approximately a normal random variable

$$Y = X/200 \approx \frac{120 + 6.928Z}{200} = .6 + .03464Z$$

So

$$P(Y < .55) \approx P(.6 + .03464Z < .55)$$
$$= P(.03464Z < .55 - .6)$$
$$= P(Z < \frac{.55 - .6}{.03464})$$
$$= P(Z < -1.44) = .0749$$

So there is about a 7.5% chance your poll will claim 55% or fewer voters support the Senator.

In general then, suppose you do n trials of a binomial experiment with probability of success p. Let the random variable Y be the proportion of successes. Then

$$Y \approx \frac{np + \sqrt{npq}\, Z}{n} = p + \sqrt{\frac{pq}{n}}\, Z$$

So Y is approximately a normal random variable with mean p and standard deviation $\sqrt{pq/n}$.

The problem with the above election example is that our calculations involved the actual probability of success $p = .6$. In real life, you would not know this. If you did, there would be no need to poll the voters. So if you want to get some idea of how accurate your empirical probability is we must do more.

For example, suppose you have a coin and wish to estimate the probability it will come up heads when tossed. You can test this by flipping it a large number of times and seeing how often it comes up heads. But your results ate subject to random variation. How many times must you flip the coin to be reasonably sure your empirical probability of getting heads is close to the actual probability?

Suppose you toss the coin n times and it comes up heads h of those n times. Then your empirical probability of getting heads is h/n. This is most likely different from the actual probability p of getting heads. Let the random variable Y be your empirical probability, $Y = h/n$. Then the probability that Y is within .01 of the actual probability p is

$$P(p - .01 < Y < p + .01)$$

We saw above that Y is very nearly a normal random variable with mean p and standard deviation $\sqrt{pq/n}$. So we may approximate Y by the normal random variable.

Consequently we have

$$P(p - .01 < Y < p + .01) \approx P(p - .01 < p + \sqrt{pq/n}\, Z < p + .01)$$

$$= P(-.01 < \sqrt{pq/n}\, Z < .01)$$

$$= P\left(\frac{-.01}{\sqrt{pq/n}} < Z < \frac{.01}{\sqrt{pq/n}}\right)$$

If we want to be 95% certain that our empirical probability y is within .01 of p then we want

$$P(p - .01 < Y < p + .01) \geq .95$$

which means that

$$P\left(\frac{-.01}{\sqrt{pq/n}} < Z < \frac{.01}{\sqrt{pq/n}}\right) \geq .95$$

Just as in Example 2c on page 180 of Tan, we get

$$2P\left(Z < \frac{.01}{\sqrt{pq/n}}\right) - 1 \geq .95$$

and so

$$P\left(Z < \frac{.01}{\sqrt{pq/n}}\right) \geq (.95 + 1)/2 = .975$$

Looking up the table of the normal distribution we see that this is true if

$$\frac{.01}{\sqrt{pq/n}} \geq 1.96$$

Multiplying by $\sqrt{pq/n}$ we get

$$.01 \geq 1.96 \sqrt{pq/n}$$

Squaring both sides we get

$$(.01)^2 \geq (1.96)^2 pq/n$$

We can now solve for n,

$$n \geq (1.96)^2 pq/(.01)^2$$

We do not know what pq is, but it can be shown that $pq \leq .25$ no matter what p and $q = 1 - p$ are [†]. Consequently we may take

$$n \geq (1.96)^2(.25)/(.01)^2 = 9604$$

So if you flip the coin 9604 or more times you can be 95% certain that your empirical probability of getting heads is within .01 of the actual probability.

---

† To see this, let $r = p - .05$. Then $p = .5 + r$ and $q = .5 - r$. So $pq = (.5 + r)(.5 - r) = .25 - r^2$. Since $r^2 \geq 0$ we know that $pq \leq .25$.

Example: Look at Table 2 in section 7.2 of Tan. In 10,000 flips there were 5,034 heads which gives an empirical probability $Y = .5034$. So after these 10,000 coin flips you are 95% sure that the probability p of coming up heads is somewhere between .4934 and .5134. Table 2.2 also shows data for more coin flips. Flipping the coin more times increases either the certainty or the accuracy of the empirical probability, or a little bit of both if you wish.

Here is the procedure you can use to solve problems like this. Suppose you have a binomial experiment, but you do not know the probability p of success. How many trials should you perform so that the empirical probability is within d of p with certainty r? Do the following steps:

1. Using the table of normal distribution, find z so that

$$P(Z < z) = (r + 1)/2$$

2. Take the number trials to be at least

$$\frac{z^2}{4d^2}$$

You may round the number of trials up a little bit to be on the safe side and so your answer does not seem to imply more precision than it actually gives. So while $\frac{z^2}{4d^2} = 9604$ in the coin flip example, a good answer would be that you should do 10,000 coin flips.

Example: You wish to determine, with 95% certainty, the probability p that a coin will come up heads. You will accept an error for p of up to .005. How many times should you toss the coin? In this example) $r = .95$ and $d = .005$. So we first find z so $P(Z < z) = (.95 + 1)/2 = .975$. We find $z = 1.96$. So we should do at least $\frac{1.96^2}{4(.005)^2} = 38416$ coin tosses. You could round this up to 40,000. If your results were as in Table 2.2, you would get an empirical probability of .5008 and you would then be 95% certain that the true probability is between .4958 and .5058.

Exercises
1. None of the 120 students in a psychology class know the answer to a multiple-choice question on their final exam. They all guess by randomly choosing one of the four answers. What is the probability that more than 30% of the students guess the correct answer?
2. Suppose 10% of the raisin bran boxes coming off the assembly line have fewer than 10 raisins in them. If you sample 150 boxes, what is the probability that less than 12% have fewer than 10 raisins.
3. How many times should you toss a six-sided die to estimate the probability it comes up six? You want to be 95% sure that your answer is accurate to within .001.
4. Senator Small wants to determine his popularity with his constituents. He asks you to find out, with an error of .04, what proportion of his constituents approve of the job he is doing. How many constituents must you poll to be 80% sure of your answer?
5. The treasury department wants to find out the proportion of quarters in circulation in your city dated before 1990. You estimate this by getting rolls of quarters from the local bank and deter-

mining what proportion of them are dated before 1990. How many quarters should you examine to be 99% sure your answer is accurate to within .01?

6. A biologist catches 100 trout from a lake, marks their fins and then throws them back alive. Now she wants to determine the probability p that a trout in the lake has a marked fin. She does this by catching n trout, noting whether their fins are marked. If m have marked fines, she figures p is about m/n. How many fish n should she catch to be 90% certain that the empirical probability m/n is within .03 of p? (Note, this is a way she can estimate the population of trout in the lake since the number of trout in the lake is $100/p$.)